ALFRED BENZON SYMPOSIUM 13

Specific Eukaryotic Genes

SPECIFIC EUKARYOTIC GENES

STRUCTURAL ORGANIZATION AND FUNCTION

Proceedings of the Alfred Benzon Symposium 13 held at the premises of the Royal Danish Academy of Sciences and Letters, Copenhagen 16–20 August 1978

EDITED BY

JAN ENGBERG
HANS KLENOW
VAGN LEICK

Published by
Munksgaard, Copenhagen

Distributed in Japan by
Nankodo, Tokyo

SCANDINAVIAN UNIVERSITY BOOKS
DENMARK MUNKSGAARD *Copenhagen*
NORWAY UNIVERSITETSFORLAGET *Oslo, Bergen, Tromsø*
SWEDEN ESSELTE STUDIUM *Stockholm, Gothenburg, Lund*

Printed in Denmark by P.J.Schmidts Bogtrykkeri, Vojens
ISBN 87-16-2905-4
ISSN 0105-3639

Published simultaneously in Japan by
Nankodo Company Ltd.

Contents

List of Participants

P. ANDERSSON
Center for Cancer Research
Massachusetts Institute of Technology
77, Massachusetts Avenue
Cambridge, Massachusetts 02139
U.S.A.

S. ARTAVANIS-TSAKONAS
Department of Cell Biology
Biozentrum der Universität Basel
Klingenbergstrasse 70
CH-4056 Basel
Switzerland

M. BIRNSTIEL
Institut für Molekularbiologie II
   der Universität Zürich
Winterthurerstrasse 266A
CH-8057 Zürich
Switzerland

P. BORST
Universiteit van Amsterdam
Jan Swammerdam Instituut
Eerste Constantijn Huygenstraat 20
Amsterdam
Holland

R. BRAUN
Universität Bern
Institut für allgemeine Mikrobiologie
Altenbergrain 21
CH-3013 Bern
Switzerland

F. H. C. CRICK
MRC Laboratory of Molecular Biology
University Postgraduate Med. School
Hills Road, Cambridge CB2 2OH
England

D. CUMMINGS
Microbiologic Department
University of Colorado Medical Center
4200 East 9th Avenue
Denver, Colorado 80220
U.S.A.

B. DANEHOLT
Karolinska Institutet
Department of Histology
S-10401 Stockholm 60
Sweden

I. B. DAWID
Laboratory of Biochemistry
National Cancer Institute
Bethesda, Maryland 20014
U.S.A.

J. ENGBERG
Biochemical Institute B
Panum-Institute
3c, Blegdamsvej
DK-2200 Copenhagen N
Denmark

R. A. FLAVELL
Laboratorium voor Biochemie
Jan Swammerdam Instituut
Eerste Constantijn Huygenstraat 20
Amsterdam
Holland

S. FREDERIKSEN
Biochemical Institute B
Panum-Institute
3c, Blegdamsvej
DK-2200 Copenhagen N
Denmark

J. G. GALL
Yale University
Department of Biology
Kline Biology Tower
New Haven, Connecticut 06520
U.S.A.

H. M. GOODMAN
University of California
School of Medicine
Department of Biochemistry and Biophysics
San Francisco, California 94143
U.S.A.

D. H. HAYES
Institut de Biologie Physico-Chimique
Fondation Edmond de Rotschild
13, rue Pierre et Marie Curie
F-75005 Paris
France

P. HELLUNG-LARSEN
Biochemical Institute B
Panum-Institute
3c, Blegdamsvej
DK-2200 Copenhagen N
Denmark

J. HESS THAYSEN
Department of Medicine P
Rigshospitalet
9, Blegdamsvej
DK-2100 Copenhagen Ø
Denmark

D. S. HOGNESS
Stanford University Medical Center
Department of Biochemistry
Stanford, California 94305
U.S.A.

W. JELINEK
The Rockefeller University
1230, York Avenue
New York, N.Y. 10021
U.S.A.

H. KLENOW
Biochemical Institute B
Panum-Institute
3c, Blegdamsvej
DK-2200 Copenhagen N
Denmark

V. LEICK
Biochemical Institute B
Panum-Institute
3c, Blegdamsvej
DK-2200 Copenhagen N
Denmark

A. LIMA-DE-FARIA
Institute of Molecular Cytogenetics
University of Lund
Tornavägen 13
S-223 63 Lund
Sweden

T. MANIATIS
California Institute of Technology
Division of Biology
Pasadena, California 91125
U.S.A.

B. A. NEWTON
University of Cambridge
The Molteno Institute of Biology and
    Parasitology
Downing Street
Cambridge CB2 3EE
England

M. L. PARDUE
Massachusetts Institute of Technology
Department of Biology
77, Massachusetts Avenue
Cambridge, Massachusetts 02139
U.S.A.

J. PAUL
The Beatson Institute for Cancer Research
Wolfson Laboratory for Molecular Pathology
Garscube Estate
Glasgow G61
Scotland

R. E. PEARLMAN
York University
Department of Biology
4700 Keele Street
Downsview, Ontario M3J 1P3
Canada

P. PLESNER
Carlsberg Laboratorium
Department of Chemistry
10, Gamle Carlsbergvej
DK-2500 Valby
Denmark

D. M. PRESCOTT
University of Colorado at Boulder
Department of Molecular, Cellular and
  Developmental Biology
Boulder, Colorado 80309
U.S.A.

J. RETÉL
Vrije Universiteit
Biochemisch Laboratorium
De Boelelaan 1085
Amsterdam, Buitenveldert
Holland

A. RICH
Department of Biology
Massachusetts Institute of Technology
Cambridge, Massachusetts 02139
U.S.A.

W. SHAFFNER
Institut für Molekularbiologie II der
  Universität Zürich
Winterthurerstrasse 266A
CH-8057 Zürich
Switzerland

V. SORSA
Department of Genetics
University of Helsinki
SF-Helsinki
Finland

I. TAMM
The Rockefeller University
1230, York Avenue
New York, N.Y. 10021
U.S.A.

S. TONEGAWA
Basel Institute for Immunology
487 Grenzacherstrasse
CH-4005 Basel 5
Switzerland

C. WEISSMANN
Universität Zürich
Institut für Molekularbiologie
CH-8093 Zürich, Hönggerberg
Switzerland

O. WESTERGAARD
Institute of Molecular Biology
Århus University
DK-8000 Århus C
Denmark

Preface

The genomes of smaller prokaryotes and viruses have been analyzed in great detail and in a few cases the complete nucleotide sequence is known. The complexity of the genome of most eukaryotes is several orders of magnitude larger than that of prokaryotic organisms. It is therefore not surprising that our knowledge of the organization of the genes in the eukaryotic genome until recently has been very modest. Nevertheless, considerable insight into this area has lately been gained. This is true not only at the microscopic and electron microscopic level, but it has even been possible to analyze well-defined DNA fragments harboring specific genetic information down to the level of the base sequence. As a consequence, several unexpected properties that specify the eukaryotic genome have already been revealed and it seems possible that physical mapping of genes might find an application in the study of human genetic diseases. The organizers of the thirteenth Alfred Benzon Symposium felt, therefore, that it would be of great value at this stage to bring together experts in this rapidly developing field to discuss the most recent developments.

It was a great pleasure, indeed, that so many distinguished scientists were willing to participate in this Symposium in such an active and inspiring way.

Jan Engberg, Hans Klenow and Vagn Leick

I. Structural Organization of the Transcriptional Unit in Chromosomes

Aspects of Chromatin Structure

F. H. C. Crick

In this short introduction I do not propose to make a detailed review of the present state of our knowledge of chromatin and chromosome structure. At this present moment the picture is too confused and too incomplete, so that any attempt at an elaborate summary would soon be out of date. Instead I will try to give a bird's-eye view of some aspects of the topic and indicate some of the general problems which face us. Certain matters, such as chromosome banding, heterochromatin and polytene chromosomes I will omit altogether. Nor shall I say anything about *E. coli*, SV40 or histone modification.

DOES 3D STRUCTURE MATTER?

First I must say what I mean by structure. There are two possible meanings. It could refer to 1D structure and in particular to the base sequence of the DNA, or alternatively to 3D structure, such as the position in space of the atoms in a core nucleosome. I shall use the word "structure" here in the latter sense.

This brings us to our first general question: How much does the 3D structure matter? We would all agree that for many purposes the DNA sequence alone must be decisive. The precise "translation" of a stretch of DNA into the amino acid sequence of the corresponding protein, by means of the genetic code, is unlikely to depend to any considerable extent on its 3D structure in the chromosome. But whether the control of such a gene – to be more specific, the *rate* at which it is transcribed – depends in part on its 3D structure is less clear. All we know at the moment is that some chromatin exists in an "active" state (shown by its increased susceptibility to DNase I digestion) as first discovered by Weintraub & Groudine (1976) and that genes being transcribed in a particular

Salk Institute for Biological Studies, P.O. Box 1809, San Diego, California, U.S.A. 92112.

SPECIFIC EUKARYOTIC GENES, Alfred Benzon Symposium 13, Munksgaard 1979

tissue appear to be in this state. But which is cause and which is effect our experiments do not yet tell us, though they may before too long. Nor do we know the precise extent of a region of active chromatin. Is it the whole of a domain? (This term is discussed below.) Or is it usually only part of a domain, or even a part of two adjacent domains?

WHAT IS 3D STRUCTURE FOR?

In fact we would do well to pause and ask, why does DNA in eukaryotes need to be folded into a 3D structure at all? The primary reason is plain. To go through the elaborate dance of mitosis the DNA needs to be packaged. The degree of packaging achieved is indeed remarkable. The length of a mammalian metaphase chromosome is only about one ten thousandth of the length of its DNA.

It is also possible that in interphase the spread of these immensely long DNA molecules may need to be restrained to some extent. But we must beware of over-simple answers. Once Nature has invented a useful gadget, or discovered a useful process, she tends to make further use of it, to develop it and embroider it. This, at bottom, is the reason why it is so difficult to guess *all* the uses to which this packaging may be put, a packaging which at its simplest level – that of the core nucleosome – is far more regular and universal than was suspected 5 or 6 years ago.

THE STRUCTURE OF THE CORE NUCLEOSOME

The postulated structure of a core nucleosome (or "platysome") is now too well known to require more than a brief description. Most core particles are assumed to consist of two each of the four common histones together with some 140 base pairs of DNA wound fairly tightly on the "outside" of the particle. The DNA is believed, on the basis of rather little evidence, to follow a fairly shallow helical path. Its estimated length (defined as the length of DNA which is resistant to a brief digestion by micrococcal DNase) has risen, as the result of recalibration, from about 140 base pairs to nearer 146 (Kornberg *et al.*, in manuscript). These core particles appear the same, or very similar, in all eukaryotes. The DNA between these core particles varies in length, both between species and also between different tissues of the same individual. The fifth histone, Hl, is widely believed to be especially associated with these parts of the DNA.

There is no convincing evidence that the "phase" of the DNA on the nucleosome is always strictly determined, though it is possible that nucleosome positions may not be completely random. This line of thinking has so far not proved to be very rewarding experimentally.

The detailed structure of the isolated core nucleosome is likely to be discovered, to a reasonable resolution (5Å?) by studies on the x-ray diffraction of the crystals (Finch *et al.* 1977, Finch *et al.* 1978) perhaps not this year but within the next 2 or 3 years, given a little luck. This prospect has tended to inhibit somewhat further studies by other methods. I will not linger over recent developments because though important to the specialist they do not appear to have wider implications. We know now, for example, that the mean position of DNase I attack is not exactly at every tenth base pair, as we once thought, but at a slightly larger spacing. Cuts spaced "80" apart are, on average, nearer 83 apart, for example. Exactly what this implies about the way the DNA is wound on the nucleosome is likely to be a matter of opinion (Kornberg *et al.*, in manuscript).

HIGHER ORDER COILING

There has been a rather marked absence of progress in our understanding of how the DNA is coiled between the core nucleosomes, notwithstanding brave attempts (Worcel & Benyajati 1977) to guess the answer. Nor do we know exactly how the next level of coiling take place, to give the "250Å" fiber, nor whether a "perfect" 250Å fiber is ever possible. That is, whether the apparent irregularity so frequently observed is an experimental artefact or whether, more likely, it is a necessary condition for the formation of higher orders of coiling. There is now much unpublished exploratory work on various nonhistone proteins and on their roles in the structure but there are no signs yet of simple answers emerging.

DOMAINS

The only approaches which are giving us a tantalizing glimpse of the higher order folding is the work on domains. This has various aspects. Domains have been detected in several ways, as regions of supercoiling (Cook & Brazell 1975 Benyajati & Worcel 1976) as regions defined by enzymatic excision of intact chromatin (Igo-Kemenes & Zachan 1978) and as lengths of DNA seen attached to the "scaffolding" of the chromosome. This latter work, pioneered by Laemmli

(Adolph *et al.* 1977 Paulson & Laemmli 1977) is the most striking. If all the histones and much of the nonhistone protein are removed by 2M NaCl only a few proteins remain. These hold what is left of the chromosome in some structure whose length is not unlike that of a metaphase chromosome but which has enormously long loops of DNA attached to the scaffolding.

Whether domains, which appear to vary considerably in size from one loop to another (their average length being, in the very roundest terms, about 50,000 base pairs), are the same entities being revealed by the three different techniques has yet to be firmly established. Nor do we have a clear idea of how their average size varies between widely different species, such as yeast, *Drosophila* and man, to say nothing of the mud puppy and the lily. Progress in this area, however, is likely to be rapid, if only because the scaffolding, although strictly speaking an artefact, is relatively easy to study and hopefully may reveal some fairly simple basic plan for these higher levels of organization. But how exactly the DNA is held in these loops and how the exact positions of the roots of these loops are determined – is 4-stranded DNA (Johnson & Morgan 1978) involved, for example? – has yet to be discovered.

CONCLUSION

The ultimate solutions to the twin problems of gene control and DNA packaging are likely to be complex. The complications we already find in prokaryotes (for example, the control systems in phage λ) should warn us against oversimple answers. We can at least hope that there will be *some* underlying generalizations for certain aspects of these problems. Which aspects are indeed based on a simple plan and which are best viewed as baroque elaboration (or even rococo decoration) has yet to be revealed to us. Theoretical approaches to these problems have not, so far, proved very rewarding and at the moment we can only hope that by a wide variety of experimental attacks we shall eventually stumble on the generalizations the subject so badly needs.

REFERENCES

There are three good general references which review much of the previous work on chromatin. The first is the exhaustive, not to say exhausting, volume of the 1977 Cold Spring Harbor meeting (Volume 42) which although not available at the moment of writing is expected shortly. The second is the Royal Society

Discussion on "Structure of eukaryotic chromosomes and chromatin" (edited by H. G. Callan & A. Klug) published as an issue of *Phil. Trans. Roy. Soc. London* (1978) *B283*, No 997, pages 231–416 (this issue can be bought separately from the Royal Society, 6 Carlton House Terrace, London SW1Y 5AG, U. K.). The third is a review article by Gary Felsenfeld, entitled "Chromatin", *Nature* (1978) *271*, 115–122.

REFERENCES

Adolph, K.W., Cheng, S.M. & Laemmli, U.K. (1977) Role of nonhistone proteins in metaphase cromosome structure. *Cell 12*, 805–816.

Benyajati, C. & Worcel, A. (1976) Isolation, characterization, and structure of the folded interphase genome of Drosophila melanogaster. *Cell 9*, 343–407.

Cook, P.R. & Brazell, I.A. (1975) Supercoils in human DNA. *J. Cell Sci.19*, 261–279.

Finch, J.T., Lutter, L.C., Rhodes, D., Brown, R.S., Rushton, B., Levitt, M. & Klug, A. (1977) Structure of nucleosome core particles of chromatin. *Nature 269*, 29–36.

Finch, J.T., Lutter, L.C., Brown, R.S. Rhodes, D., Rushton, B. & Klug, A. (1978) X-ray and electron microscope studies on the nucleosome structure. *FEBS Symposium,* Dresden. In press.

Igo-Kemenes, T. & Zachau, H. G. (1978) Domains in chromatin structure. In: the *Cold Spring Harbor* volume referred to above.

Johnson, D. & Morgan, A.R. (1978) Unique structures formed by pyrimidine DNAs which may be four-stranded. *Proc. Nat. Acad. Sci. U.S.A. 75*, 1637–1641.

Paulson, J.R. & Laemmli, U.K. (1977) The structure of histone-depleted metaphase chromosomes. *Cell 12*, 817–828.

Weintraub, H. & Groudine, M. (1976) Chromosome subunits in active genes have an altered conformation. *Science 193*, 848–856.

Worcel, A. & Benyajati, C. (1977) Higher order coiling of DNA in chromatin. *Cell 12*, 83–100.

DISCUSSION

PAUL: I wonder if you would give us your personel assessment of the evidence for nucleosomes in actively transcribed chromatin?

CRICK: This is a difficult subject. As I understand it, if you look at a gene which is being transcribed extremely rapidly, as some of the ribosomal ones are, it is difficult to convince oneself that there are nucleosomes there. The technical problem, as you know, is that an RNA polymerase molecule has the same size as the nucleosome, and therefore it is not always easy to make the distinction. On the other hand there are claims, none of which are very compelling, that when a gene is being transcribed rather slowly, there are nucleosomes in between the polymerases.

PAUL: One can see the topological problem involved in transcribing DNA associated with nucleosomes. Can you envisage a mechanism which would permit it?

CRICK: I am very reluctant to guess how this can occur. Of course there is a report I have heard that you can transcribe onto RNA at the same time as DNA polymerase is going along. I am not sure I believe this story.

RICH: What do you think the evidence is on the movement of a nucleosome as it has been pushed, so to speak, by a polymerase? Roughly speaking, the histones could come off, perhaps detach entirely, and reassemble. Some people think the nucleosome proteins might shuffle along.

CRICK: I would rather doubt that myself, but there is a very real problem here. I do not know what the solution is. I do not feel there is anything on theoretical grounds you can say, except that there must be some change if the rough picture we have of the nucleosome has any validity. We have a reasonable hope of getting the structure of the static nucleosome within 2 or 3 years, given a bit of luck. That may be very revealing and suggest new ideas.

WEISSMANN: Is it fair to say, though, that histones do not come off during transcription?

CRICK: I am not sure the definitive experiment was ever done. The question really is the one Alex Rich asked – can they slide? There is an experiment designed in which you had the nucleosomes on a cold piece of DNA and you joined it to a hot bit of DNA and then you tried to see if they could slide along onto the hot bit. I don't know if that was ever done. I am not terribly much in favor of sliding, unless we can see a neat way of doing it.

WEISSMANN: But there is no conceptional difficulty, because after all the polymerase could travel around the nucleosome.

CRICK: No. Here is a conceptional difficulty. The diameter of the nucleosome is roughly the diameter of the polymerase. It is difficult to see how the polymerase can get underneath the DNA.

DAWID: A further complication, at least in my mind, is that not just the RNA polymerase has to go there, which is big, but often a very long tail of RNA goes along with it, as in electron micrographs showing 10 μm RNA fibrils attached to the DNA.

CRICK: Yes, I do agree, we must not forget them, but once you got the RNA spinning off and going onto particles, this may not be a severe problem. If you look at the rate at which things of that size diffuse, it is enormously fast.

WESTERGAARD: Do you think that there is any correlation between replicons and domains and do you find variation in domains in the same manner as you find variations in replicons? In slowly growing *Tetrahymena* we find for instance very well-defined replicons of 50,000 base pairs (Westergaard *et al.* 1978) which is of the same size as those domains you spoke about.

CRICK: The answer is, we do not know. I have to confess I don't know what the best estimate for a replicon size is. I think it varies.

HOGNESS: Certainly the replicon size in *Drosophila* can be much less than 50,000 base pairs, it is of the order of 8,000 base pairs, and there seems to be a repeating pattern of about 3,400 bases in the very rapidly replicating nuclei.

Westergaard, O. *et al.* (1978) *Eur. J. Biochem.* 86, 255.

CRICK: I suppose if I were pressed I would have to say that we don't know the domain size and this 50,000 is very rough.

Prediction of Gene Location and Classification of Genes According to the Chromosome Field

A. Lima-de-Faria

Chromomeres vary in size and number from tissue to tissue within one and the same organism. Similarly the gene is a poorly defined unit as it has now become evident that it is a split structure in which the components may not even be

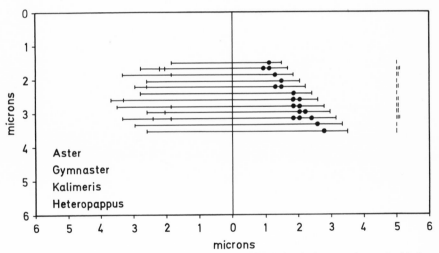

Fig. 1. Location of the genes for 28S and 18S ribosomal RNA (nucleolus organizer region) in four genera of the family *Compositae: Aster, Gymnaster, Kalimeris* and *Heteropappus*. Twenty-one metaphase chromosomes are represented. All centromeres are located on the vertical line at 0 microns. The arms having a nucleolus (black circles) are located to the right. The arms of the same chromosomes without the nucleolus are to the left of the centromere line. All the telomeres of the nucleolar arms are located at an angle of 45^0 to the kinetochore (or centromere) axis.

Institute of Molecular Cytogenetics, University of Lund, Lund, Sweden.

SPECIFIC EUKARYOTIC GENES, Alfred Benzon Symposium 13, Munksgaard 1979

LIMA-DE-FARIA

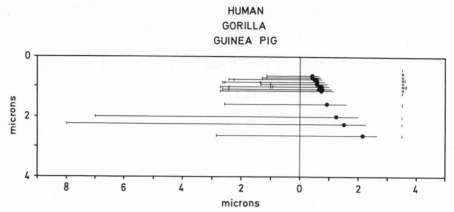

Fig. 2. Location of the genes for 28S and 18S ribosomal RNA (black circles) in three species of mammals: human, gorilla and guinea pig, 21 chromosomes are represented.

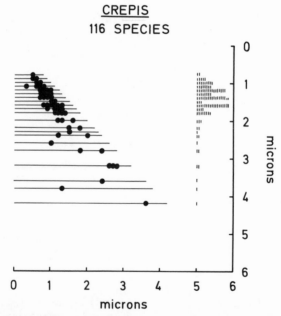

Fig. 3. Location of 28S and 18S ribosomal RNA genes (nucleolus organizer region) in 116 species of Crepis (black circles). Only the chromosome arms having a nucleolus are represented. All centromeres are located at the left extremity of each arm (at 0 microns). All telomeres are at the right extremity and are located at an angle of 45° to the centromere axis. The distribution of the ribosomal genes forms a straight line, only three values deviating from this distribution. This is less than 3%. The deviating values are attributed to recently formed inversions or translocations, the genes not yet having had time to find their natural territory.

located in the same chromosome. The only genetic unit that is well defined is the chromosome, since it has sharp physical limits imposed by the location of telomeres and centromeres (when the latter are terminal).

The current view of the chromosome is that it is a chaotic structure in which genes, mutations and structural rearrangements occur at random (e.g. White 1973). In opposition to this view I have proposed the concept of the chromosome field (Lima-de-Faria 1954, 1976a). The concept is based on experimental and

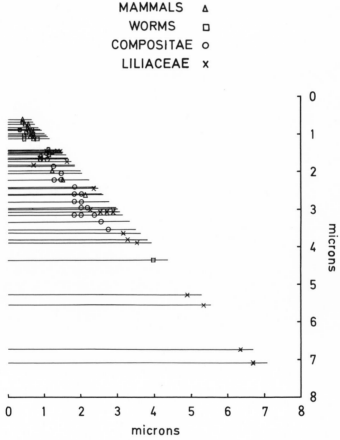

Fig. 4. Distribution of 28S and 18S ribosomal RNA genes in species of mammals, worms, *Compositae* and *Liliaceae* (plants). Only chromosome arms with a nucleolus are represented. The ribosomal genes are distributed along a straight line and at a constant distance from the telomeres irrespective of: (1) species, (2) phylum and (3) chromosome arm length. Ribosomal genes are telons since their territory is near the telomeres.

MAGNOLIA PUMILA

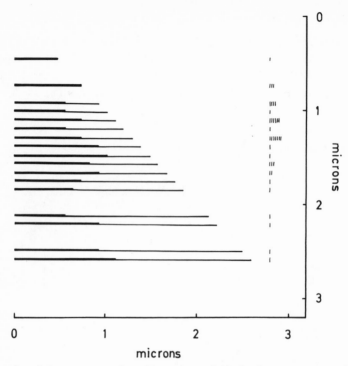

Fig. 5. Location of chromomere gradients (heterochromatin) in the chromosome arms of *Magnolia pumila* (thick black lines). Thirty-six arms are represented. The chromomere gradients always start at the centromere. The same distribution has been found in over 70 plant species (cf. Lima-de-Faria 1976e). Chromomere gradients are centrons since they always appear on both sides of the centromere.

structural evidence which shows that the chromosome is a highly organized element. The chromosome appears to be a hierarchic structure in which centromeres and telomeres are the main organizers. Each gene has an optimal position within the centromere-telomere field. This position is called the gene territory. It is postulated that the gene has sensors that recognize messages from the centromere and the telomere regions.

The location of the genes for 28S and 18S ribosomal RNA (the nucleolus organizer region) has now been checked in more than 100 species from algae to humans (including worms, higher plants and various mammals) and has been found to be wholly dependent on the centromere-telomere relationship (Figs. 1–4). The distribution of these genes is so regular that it can be predicted by means of a straight-line equation (Lima-de-Faria 1973).

Other genes also have distributions in the centromere-telomere field which are the same in widely different organisms, but which differ from ribosomal genes (Lima-de-Faria 1976b, c, d, e). Such a specific gene territory allows us to classify genes as centrons, medons and telons according to whether they happen to have their territory near the centromeres, in the median regions of the arms or near the telomeres, respectively (Fig. 10).

The DNA sequences which form the chromomere gradients are located on both sides of the centromeres. These sequences are typical centrons (Fig. 5). They have so far been found in over 70 species of plants.

The chiasmata localized near the centromeres in *Allium* and other plant and animal species are also centrons (Fig. 6). The regions of delayed separation in B

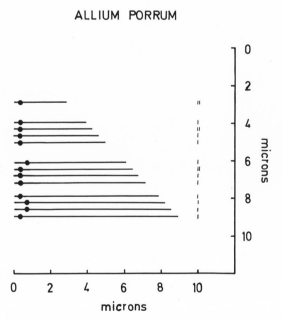

ALLIUM PORRUM

Fig. 6. Location of chiasmata in the chromosome arms of *Allium porrum* (black circles). Sixteen arms are represented. This distribution close to the centromere has been found n several other species of plants and animals including *Fritillaria* and *Mecostethus*. The chiasmata of these species are centrons since their territory is in the close vicinity of the centromere.

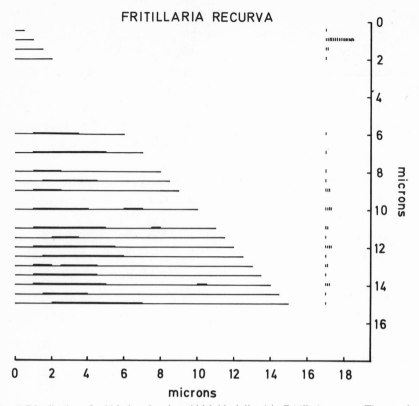

Fig. 7. Distribution of cold-induced regions (thick black lines) in *Fritillaria recurva*. These regions have a similar location in other plant species such as *Trillium*. Their main distribution is in the median regions of the chromosome arms. Genes with this type of territory are called medons.

chromosomes of plants have a location very close to the centromere. They are also centrons.

DNA sequences with their territory located in the median regions of the arms (medons) are the cold-induced regions of *Trillium* and *Fritillaria* (Fig. 7). Other medons are the regions of human chromosomes which exhibit structural changes after UV and chemical treatment (Fig. 8).

Typical examples of telons are the genes for 28S and 18S ribosomal RNA as they are located near the telomeres. The "knobs" (large chromomeres) of maize and many other plant species that are located at the telomeres, or in their immediate vicinity, are also telons (Fig. 9).

Structural rearrangements can also be classified according to their relation to the field. They may maintain the order previously established or they may disturb it. Rearrangements can be classified accordingly as conservative, discordant, disruptive, destructive and incompatible (Figs. 11–15). The rearrangements that least disturb the field are those that most often occur under natural conditions such as the Robertsonian translocations which involve whole arms and thus do not alter the centromere-telomere relationship.

The concept of the chromosome field allows us to make predictions

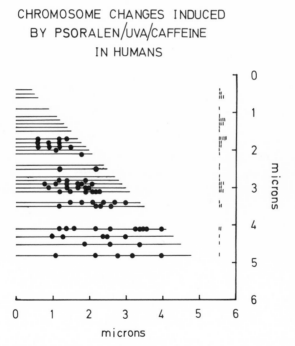

CHROMOSOME CHANGES INDUCED
BY PSORALEN/UVA/CAFFEINE
IN HUMANS

Fig. 8. Location of chromosome changes (black circles) induced by Psoralen, ultraviolet light and caffeine (human chromosomes). Based on the data of Waksvik *et al.* (1977). The territory of these chromosome segments is mainly in the median regions of the chromosome arms and are thus classified as medons.

SOLANUM   LYCOPERSICUM

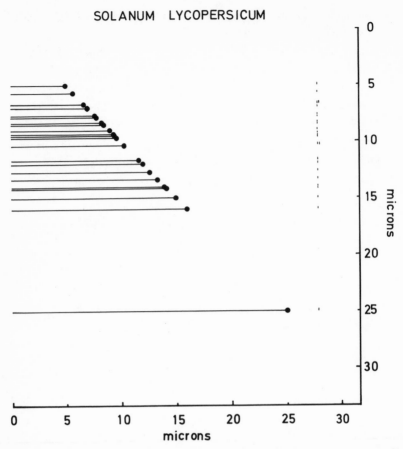

Fig. 9. Location of "knobs" (black circles) in *Solanum lycopersicum*. "Knobs" are groups of large chromomeres. The terminal location of knobs is characteristic of many plant species. For this reason these DNA segments are classified as telons.

concerning gene location and gene behavior which are difficult to conceive in terms of a chaotic view of the chromosome.

CLASSIFICATION OF GENES AND PROPERTIES
ACCORDING TO THEIR LOCATION
IN THE CHROMOSOME FIELD

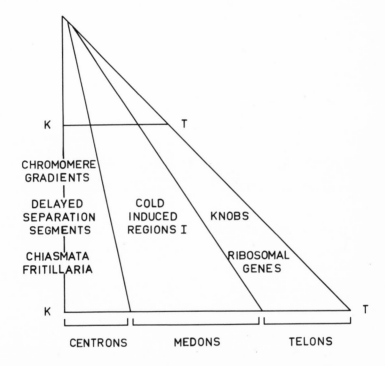

Fig. 10. Classification of genes and chromosome properties according to their territory in the chromosome field. The fact that each gene has a specific territory allows us to classify the different DNA sequences of the chromosome as centrons, medons and telons according to whether they happen to have their territory near the centromeres, in the median regions of the arms or near the telomeres, respectively.

Some examples of these types of genes are shown in the figure. K=Kinetochore or centromere, T=Telomere.

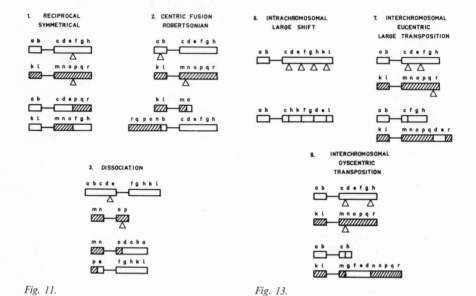

Fig. 11.

Fig. 13.

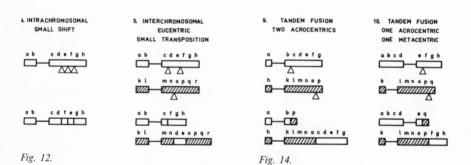

Fig. 12.

Fig. 14.

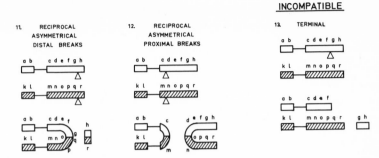

Fig. 15.

Figs. 11–15. Classification of translocations according to the chromosome field. Structural rearrangements can be classified according to their relation to the field. They may maintain the order previously established or they may disturb it. Translocations, inversions, duplications and deletions can accordingly be classified as conservative, discordant, disruptive, destructive and incompatible. There is experimental evidence that those classified as incompatible do not occur in nature or appear very seldom. The rearrangements which are conservative, i.e. which preserve the field, happen to be those that are commonest in natural populations.

REFERENCES

Lima-de-Faria, A. (1954) Chromosome gradient and chromosome field in *Agapanthus. Chromosoma 6,* 330–370.

Lima-de-Faria, A. (1973) Equations defining the position of ribosomal cistrons in the eukaryotic chromosome. *Nature New. Biol. 241,* 136–139.

Lima-de-Faria, A. (1976a) The chromosome field. I. Prediction of the location of ribosomal cistrons. *Hereditas 83,* 1–22.

Lima-de-Faria, A. (1976b) The chromosome field. II. The location of "knobs" in relation to telomeres. *Hereditas 83,* 23–34.

Lima-de-Faria, A. (1976c) The chromosome field. III. The regularity of distribution of cold-induced regions. *Hereditas 83,* 139–152.

Lima-de-Faria, A. (1976d) The chromosome field. IV. The distribution of non-disjunction, chiasmata and other properties. *Hereditas 83,* 175–190.

Lima-de-Faria, A. (1976e) The chromosome field. V. The distribution of chromomere gradients in relation to kinetochore and telomeres. *Hereditas 84,* 19–34.

Waksvik, H., Brøgger, A. & Stene, J. (1977) Psoralen /UVA treatment and chromosomes. I. Aberrations and sister chromatid exchange in human lymphocytes *in vitro* and synergism with caffeine. *Hum. Genet. 38,* 195–207.

White, M. J. D. (1973) *Animal Cytology and Evolution*, 3rd ed. pp. 1–961. University Press, Cambridge.

DISCUSSION

PARDUE: Don't you think that there is a possibility that the ribosomal genes are very close to the telomeres, not so much for sensing reasons but because there might be a lot of crossing-over between the nucleolar organizers on non-homologous chromosomes? Uneven numbers would result in exchange of the material distal to the nucleolus organizer. Perhaps the distance of the nucleolus organizer from the telemere is limited to those parts of the chromosome which can be shuffled around without damage.

LIMA-DE-FARIA: Very little is known about crossing-over in the nucleolar organizing region. Moreover, crossing-over cannot easily explain the ordered position of the ribosomal genes, since it could be equally invoked to explain the opposite condition, i.e. a variable position of these genes.

PARDUE: It is very clear that in many species the ribosomal genes are telomeric, and I think you probably overlook a lot of ribosomal genes that are even more telomeric in other species. The ones you have seen are mostly the ones that are far enough in so that the secondary constriction becomes evident. And when you start looking with molecular probes for ribosomal genes there are even more telomeric ones. But there is still no evidence to eliminate a gene balance explanation such as I mentioned.

LIMA-DE-FARIA: We have looked very carefully for the presence of ribosomal genes which are strictly telomeric, but we have found very few instances of such a situation, less than one per 100 species.

PARDUE: Certainly the satellite sequences, for example, can be found other places in other species.

LIMA-DE-FARIA: Yes, there are exceptions, as we already pointed out in our previous papers, and these exceptions are very valuable. We know also that the exceptions to the rule are more common in animals than in plants. The field shows that the chromosome has a rigid organization, but at the same time it must have a certain degree of freedom, otherwise it would not evolve. The ribosomal genes must move along the chromosome by rearrangements but there is a mechanism that puts them back at a specific position.

CRICK: It seems to me you have produced a number of facts which require some explanation. One is that heterochromatin, although it can be elsewhere, tends to be near the centromere. The other is that the ribosomal genes tend to be near the telomere. But to deduce from that, that the gene has senses that recognize messages from the centromere and the telemere regions, is going beyond the evidence that you have produced. I agree with Dr. Pardue that it is much more likely to be due to the effects of crossing-over, and separating things – whole business of evolution and disruption – and not due to any interaction between different parts of the chromosome. All we have to assume is that for some reason the heterochromatin is preferentially near the centromere.

LIMA-DE-FARIA: The experimental evidence for interaction between different chromosome regions is quite extensive. I will mention only a few cases. Rhoades (1952) has shown in maize that the presence of an heterochromatic distal region of chromosome 10 results in neo-centromere activity at the telomeres of other chromosomes of the complement. Delayed separation in B-chromosomes can be manifested only when the centromere and the telomeres of the same or other chromosomes are present. If the centromere or telomere are removed, this region (which is in the middle of the arms) does not function (Roman 1950, Müntzing & Lima-de-Faria 1952, Ward 1972). Baker (1971) has shown by means of inversions in *Drosophila* that centromeric heterochromatin influences the expression of ribosomal genes.

Recently Miklos & Nankivell (1976) have demonstrated by biochemical methods that the DNA satellites located in telomeres were active in controlling crossing-over at regions located in other segments of the arms. The examples could be multiplied.

Rhoades, M. M. (1952) Preferential segregation in maize. In *Heterosis* (Ed. J. W. Gowen), The Iowa State College Press, pp. 66–80.

Roman, H. (1950) Factors affecting mitotic nondisjunction in maize. *Genetics* 35, 132.

Müntzing, A. & Lima-de-Faria, A. (1952) Pachytene analysis of a deficient accessory chromosome in rye. *Hereditas* 38, 1–10.

Ward, E. (1972) Effects of various segments of the B chromosome on recombination and nondisjunction. *Maize Genetics Coop. News Letter* 46, 53–59.

Baker, W. K. (1971) Evidence for position-effect suppression of the ribosomal RNA cistrons in *Drosophila melanogaster*. *Proc. Nat. Acad. Sci.* 68, 2472–2476.

Miklos, G. L. G. & Nankivell, R. N. (1976) Telomeric satellite DNA functions in regulating recombination. *Chromosoma* 56, 143–167.

CRICK: I am familiar with the position effects in *Drosophila* and I have worried about them for a number of years. Although the data have been reasonably well presented, in molecular terms the explanations are rather feeble. In fact, nobody has shown that position effect variegation which is not inactivation of the gene due to deletion, e.g. I am not willing to accept position effect variegation as some extraordinarily subtle effect of chromosome structure as a whole.

LIMA-DE-FARIA: Position effects are among the best established phenomena of genetics. It has been shown recently that they exert an effect at the level of DNA replication and transcription (Ananiev & Gvozdev 1974).

GALL: An obvious exception to the subterminal localization of the nucleolus organizer is provided by *Drosophila melanogaster*. Have you compiled the positions in a variety of *Drosophila* species, and does *Drosophila* as a whole agree with your model?

LIMA-DE-FARIA: We are just starting to do that. First you look for the rule, then you look for the exceptions. In each rule the exceptions usually indicate the presence of a secondary phenomenon that it superimposed and which should be carefully investigated.

BIRNSTIEL: Could I just pose a question to Francis Crick? Would you then accept as likely the alternative that genes are arranged on the chromosomes at random?

CRICK: No, I would not accept that, because it is not true. But the fact is that the genes are the primary things and the arrangement of them is a second order effect, in my view.

LIMA-DE-FARIA: This is a statement which has no experimental support and as such deserves no comment. I find it valuable that it is included in the discussion.

Ananiev, E. V & Gvozdev, V. A. (1974) Changed pattern of transcription and replication in polytene chromosomes of *Drosophila melanogaster* resulting from eu-heterochromatin rearrangement. *Chromosoma* 45, 173–191.

The Transcription Unit in Balbiani Ring 2 and Its Relation to the Chromomeric Subdivision of the Polytene Chromosome

B. Daneholt, S. T. Case, J. Derksen, M. M. Lamb, L. G. Nelson & L. Wieslander

Polytene chromosomes have for many years been a model system for analysis of chromosome structure and chromosome function in interphase cells. By cytological means Beermann (1964) noted that transcriptive activity often takes place at defined regions corresponding to single chromosome bands, and he proposed that a band (on the chromatid level, a chromomere) might be equivalent to a transcription unit. Applying both electron microscopic and biochemical methods we have further investigated the problem of how the structure of polytene chromosomes is related to transcription units and transcriptive activity. Our attention has been focussed on one particular chromosome puff, Balbiani ring 2 (BR 2) on chromosome IV in the salivary glands of the dipteran *Chironomus tentans*. The transcription product in BR 2, 75 S RNA, has been characterized and its fate studied in some detail (for review, see Case & Daneholt 1977). It has been shown that 75 S RNA is transferred from BR 2 via nuclear sap into cytoplasm, where it constitutes a major, nonribosomal RNA species. Moreover, most of the cytoplasmic 75 S RNA is present in polysomes. It is therefore likely that the giant puff BR 2 represents an active gene synthesizing an abundant messenger RNA. This conclusion is in good agreement with cytogenetic data reported by Beermann (1961) and Grossbach (1973), which suggest that BRs in *Chironomus* salivary glands are coupled to the production of salivary polypeptides, the predominant product of these cells. In order to relate the 75 S RNA transcription unit in BR 2 to chromosome structure and to describe the events taking place upon activation of the 75 S RNA gene, we

Department of Medical Cell Genetics and Department of Histology, Karolinska Institutet, S-10401 Stockholm 60, Sweden.

SPECIFIC EUKARYOTIC GENES, Alfred Benzon Symposium 13, Munksgaard 1979

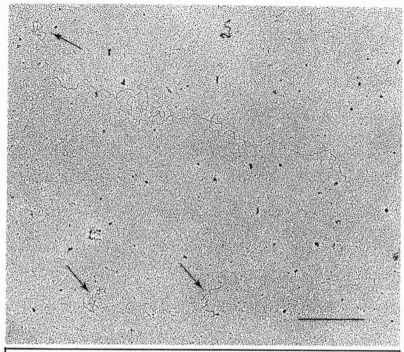

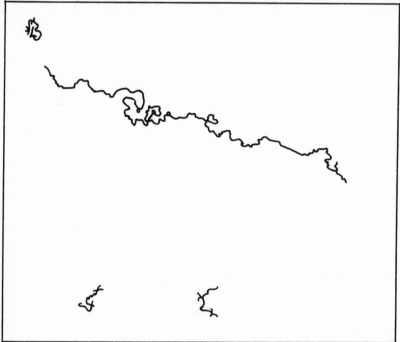

have further characterized the 75 S RNA transcription unit in its active and in its inactive state.

THE SIZE OF THE 75 S RNA TRANSCRIPTION UNIT

The population of growing RNA molecules in BR 2 as well as mature 75 S RNA has been possible to analyze by biochemical methods (for review, see Daneholt 1975). It has been demonstrated that the primary transcript in BR 2 is approximately of the same size as the cytoplasmic 75 S RNA, which implies that the size of 75 S RNA reflects the size of the 75 S RNA transcription unit itself. Using denaturing gels, Case & Daneholt (1978) could estimate that the size of 75 S RNA is in the range of 12–14 million daltons. Moreover, 75 S RNA was also purified and spread for electron microscopy along with 28 S RNA molecules which served as internal standards. The 28 S RNA molecules exhibited the characteristic pattern of hairpin loops (e.g. Wellauer & Dawid 1973), while the considerably longer 75 S RNA molecules did not display any reproducible secondary structures (Fig. 1). The length of the 75 S RNA molecules suggested a molecular weight for 75 S RNA of 12.3 million daltons. As this result agreed with the range obtained by electrophoretic analysis, we accepted the figure of 12.3 million daltons, or 37 kilo bases (kb), as an estimate of the size of 75 S RNA, and hence of the 75 S RNA transcription unit itself.

VISUALIZATION OF ACTIVE 75 S RNA TRANSCRIPTION UNITS

Electron microscopic analysis of active transcription units in BRs on chromosome IV has recently been carried out by Lamb & Daneholt (1978) essentially following the Miller procedure (Miller & Bakken 1972). Salivary glands were isolated, treated in a nonionic detergent solution and pipetted through a small opening. Single chromosomes were then released into the solution, and for each analysis, one fourth chromosome was transferred to a low ionic strength medium at pH 9. The chromosome was allowed to expand, then sedimented

Fig. 1. Electron micrograph of 75 S RNA and 28 S RNA molecules. 75 S RNA from *Chironomus tentans* and 28 S RNA from HeLa cells were eluted from agarose gels, mixed and spread for electron microscopy by a urea-formamide method. The 28 S RNA molecules were included as length standards and could be recognized because of their secondary structures. The arrows indicate the position of the 28 S RNA molecules. The bar represents 1 μm. For experimental details, consult Case & Daneholt (1978).

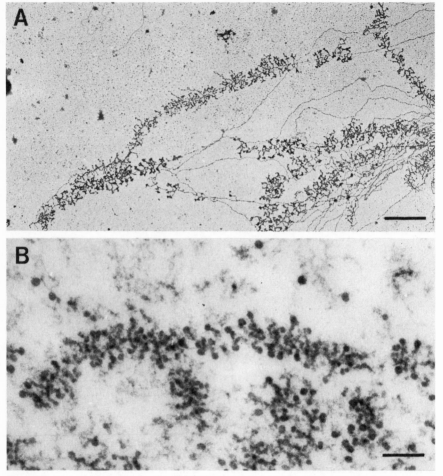

Fig. 2. Electron micrographs of active 75 S RNA transcription units as spread by the Miller method (A) and as observed *in situ* by conventional electron microscopy (B). Nuclear sap granules, presumably of BR origin, can be seen in the upper half of B. The bar in panel A corresponds to 1 μm and in B to 0.2 μm. For further information, see Lamb & Daneholt (1978).

onto a grid and analyzed in the electron microscope. We observed a network of beaded chromosome fibers as well as several putative transcription units (Fig. 2A). Each unit displayed the characteristic features of a gene active in transcription, i.e. a lateral fiber gradient corresponding to the growing ribonucleoprotein (RNP) fibers, and a densely staining granule at the base of each lateral fiber corresponding to an RNA polymerase (e.g. Miller *et al.* 1970). Since the synthesis of 75 S RNA comprises more than 85% of the RNA synthesis on chromosome IV (Daneholt *et al.* 1969, unpublished data), it can be expected that most of the transcription units in our spreads are of the 75 S RNA type. The by far most prevalent transcription unit was determined to be about 7.7 μm in length. This value falls within the predicted range for a 75 S RNA transcription unit, if it is assumed that the 75 S RNA unit exhibits a similar DNA compaction as other nonribosomal genes (DNA compaction 1.1–1.9; for examples, see Laird *et al.* 1976, McKnight *et al.* 1978). Moreover, the lateral fibers were densely spaced (averaging 123 fibers per unit, or about one fiber per 300 nucleotide pairs). Such a high fiber density is to be expected from a 75 S RNA transcription unit producing abundant mRNA. We therefore conclude that the long units we record are likely to represent the 75 S RNA transcription units.

The description of the active 75 S RNA transcription unit by the Miller method has also enabled us to identify the active units *in situ* (Lamb & Daneholt 1978). It has earlier been observed in sectioned material (Beermann & Bahr 1954, Stevens & Swift 1966, Vasquez-Nin & Bernhard 1971, Daneholt 1975) that BRs contain characteristic lampbrush loop structures consisting of a deoxyribonucleoprotein axis and RNP granules attached to this axis by RNP stalks (Fig. 2B). When electron micrographs of the sectioned BRs are compared with those of the spread genes, it appears likely that the lampbrush loop structures represent segments of active 75 S RNA transcription units (Fig. 2A and B). It should also be noted that the extended RNP fibers seen in spread preparations are not observed *in situ*. It seems as if the growing RNP fibers are packed into granular structures along with transcription. The completed and released products are presumably the abundant nuclear sap RNP granules, which correspond in size and stainability to the largest stalked granules in BRs (about 500 Å in diameter) (Fig. 2B).

The Miller spreads also give us some information on the arrangement of the active 75 S RNA transcription units in a Balbiani ring. Due to the polytene nature of the chromosomes, the active units appear clustered (Fig. 2A). There is, however, no evidence for a tandem arrangement of the active 75 S RNA genes within a BR. We could not detect an adjacent 75 S RNA unit in spite of the circumstance that in favorable cases the chromosome fiber preceding or following the unit, was possible to analyze for a distance corresponding to two to three transcription units. Furthermore, the average number of active 75 S RNA units per chromosome fiber in a BR has been estimated. The amount of RNA per transcription unit was calculated from the number of lateral fibers (123 per unit) and the size of primary transcript (37 kb). Knowing the amount of RNA per BR 2 (10.8 pg according to Edström *et al.* 1978), we could then establish that there are about 8500 active units in BR 2, which is about the number of chromatids in a salivary gland cell in *Chironomus tentans* (Daneholt & Edström 1967). The most straightforward interpretation of our data is therefore that there is only one active 75 S RNA transcription unit per chromatid in BR 2.

THE TRANSCRIPTION PROCESS IN BR 2

The electron micrographs of the active 75 S RNA transcription units indicate that there are no segments of the unit that consistently lack RNA polymerases with associated RNP fibers. This suggests that the RNA polymerases traverse the transcription unit from the initiation to the termination site. Whether or not the polymerases are also transcriptionally active over the whole unit is difficult to decide. It has not been feasible to establish a strict length gradient of the lateral fibers, although a gradient is indicated. Stronger evidence for a continuous transcription can be derived from electrophoretic analysis of BR 2 RNA. When newly synthesized RNA was studied in agarose gels under conditions minimizing degradation, a smooth distribution of radioactivity up to the peak at 75 S was observed (Fig. 1 in Daneholt *et al.* 1978a). Several lines of evidence suggest that this population of RNA molecules represents the molecules *in statu nascendi* in BR 2 (for discussion, see Daneholt 1975). The gradual increase in activity with no peaks smaller than 75 S RNA (except for 4–5 S RNA) suggests a continuous transcription along the unit. If the polymerases had passed selected segments of the unit without adding nucleotides to the growing molecules, some RNA sizes would be relatively more frequent than others. It can therefore be concluded that the RNA polymerases are probably not only traversing the whole unit but are also synthetically active along the whole unit. It should also be added that there is no evidence for staggered RNA polymerases on the unit, suggesting that the polymerases move along the unit with about the same rate.

On the basis of the available biochemical and electron microscopic information one can now better characterize the transcription process in BR 2. Based on the average number of fibers per unit (123) and the transcription time (20 min at 18°C according to Egyházi 1976), we can estimate that about 6 RNA polymerases start per minute at each transcription unit. Furthermore, knowing the length of the unit (37 kb) and the transcription time we can also state that the RNA polymerases move along the unit with a rate of 31 nucleotides per second

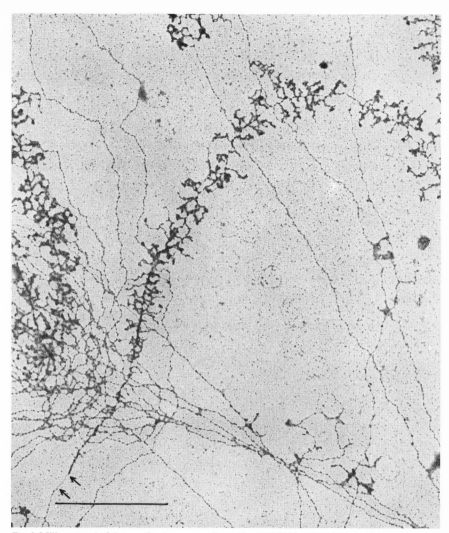

Fig. 3. Miller spread of the proximal segment of an active 75 S RNA transcription unit. A nonbeaded segment proximal to the first RNA polymerase has been demarcated in the figure by two arrows. The bar equals 1 μm.

at 18°C. This knowledge of the transcription process in the BR 2 system makes it feasible to begin studying regulation of transcription. In this context, it is of particular importance that the RNA synthesis at this unit can be selectively and reversibly changed by treatment of the larvae with galactose (Beermann 1973, Nelson *et al.* 1978). At different levels of RNA production, the distribution of the

RNA polymerases, the length and distribution of the RNP fibers and the transcription time should be investigated at the 75 S RNA unit with the methods applied above. Hopefully, it should then be possible to investigate the mechanisms involved in regulation of RNA synthesis on the chromosomal level (initiation, pretermination, posttranscriptional degradation, etc.).

THE PROPERTIES OF THE CHROMOSOME FIBER WITHIN AND OUTSIDE THE ACTIVE TRANSCRIPTION UNIT

The transcriptionally inactive chromatin is regularly beaded (Fig. 2A) as noted earlier in other chromatin preparations spread according to Miller (e.g. Laird *et al.* 1976). The beaded structure probably reflects the nucleosomal organization of the fiber. However, the chromosome fiber within the active unit displays fewer beads than adjacent inactive chromatin. Instead long stretches of the fiber appear smooth and nonbeaded which has also been observed in highly active lampbrush loops of amphibian oocytes (Franke *et al.* 1976). The chromosome fiber is evidently changed in the transcribed region but the nature of this change is not known (for discussion, see e.g. Lilley 1978). It is of particular interest that there is also a short nonbeaded segment proximal to the first polymerase (Fig. 3). When the start of RNA synthesis was determined from the length of the growing RNP fibers according to Laird *et al.* (1976), it was found that the synthesis begins at about the position of the first polymerase and that the smooth region proximal to this polymerase is probably not transcribed. The significance of this smooth segment can only be a matter of speculation. One possibility might be that a fiber segment, in this particular case somewhat longer than the actual transcription unit, is changed upon inactivation in an event preceding the start of transcription. Such a phenomenon would be analogous to what has recently been demonstrated for the ribosomal genes in *Oncopeltus* (Foe 1978). In this context it is interesting to recall the observation by Berendes (1968), that specific chromosome puffs can be induced also in the absence of RNA synthesis, suggesting that uncoiling of the chromosome fiber is not dependent on RNA synthesis.

THE INACTIVE TRANSCRIPTION UNIT AND ITS RELATION TO CHROMOSOME STRUCTURE

When the transcriptive activity in the BR 2 region is suppressed by galactose according to Beermann (1973), the giant puff regresses and a defined chromosome banding pattern can be discerned (Daneholt *et al.* 1978b). The

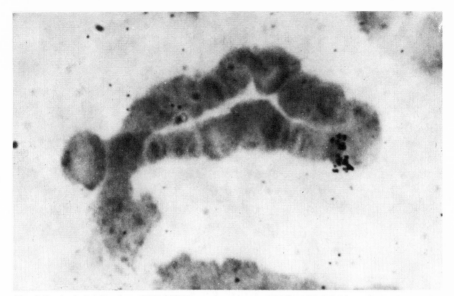

Fig. 4. In situ hybridization of BR 2 RNA to chromosome IV from Malpighian tubules. The grains are restricted to a narrow region in segment 3B of chromosome IV. For further information, see Derksen *et al.* (1978).

banding pattern of the BR 2 region of salivary glands was then found to be similar to the pattern of the corresponding region in Malpighian tubules in which no or very little transcriptive activity takes place in this region. By *in situ* hybridization it can be shown that the sequences complementary to BR 2 RNA are confined to a small region in the 3 B segment of chromosome IV (Fig. 4). In a series of experiments it was recently established that this region corresponds to a single band in the 3 B segment (Derksen *et al.* 1978). Using microspectro-photometric methods Derksen *et al.* (1978) could also determine the amount of DNA in the BR 2 band relative to that of the whole chromosome set (0.205%). Since late or nonreplicating DNA constitutes a negligible part of *Chironomus tentans* DNA (beermann 1962), it was possible to estimate from the obtained percent figure and the haploid DNA amount (0.25 pg) that a BR 2 chromomere contains 470 kb of DNA. This amount of DNA is considerably larger than the amount needed to accomodate one 75 S RNA transcription unit. We are therefore left with several possibilities for the structure of the BR 2 chromomere. There might be more than one 75 S RNA transcription unit, although only one is likely to be active. There might also be transcription units other than the 75 S

RNA unit. The crucial question therefore remains, namely whether or not there is a more than one functional unit in the BR 2 chromomere.

SUMMARY (Fig. 5)

1. In its *inactive state,* the BR 2 75 S RNA transcription unit, 37 kb in length, resides in a single chromomere, the BR 2 chromomere. The DNA content of the BR 2 chromomere has been determined to be 470 kb, which implies that the BR 2

BR 2 chromomere

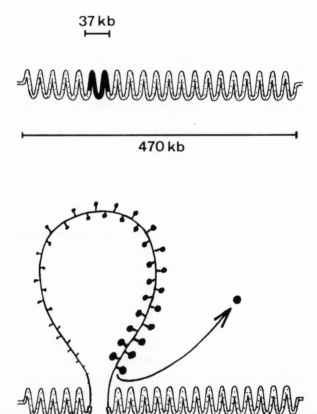

Fig. 5. Schematic presentation of the 75 S RNA transcription unit in its inactive and active state, as well as its relation to the BR 2 chromomere. Upon activation the chromosome fiber is unfolded into a loop and transcription takes place along the loop. The product of the 75 S RNA transcription unit is an RNP granule, 500 Å in diameter.

chromomere contains considerably more DNA than required for just one 75 S RNA transcription unit. It is not clear whether there are one, two or more 75 S RNA transcription units within the BR 2 chromomere, nor whether the chromomere harbors transcription units other than the 75 S RNA unit.

2. When *active*, the 75 S RNA transcription unit exhibits densely spaced RNA polymerases carrying ribonucleoprotein fibers *in statu nascendi* (about one fiber per 300 nucleotide pairs). Within the cell, the active unit forms a loop, and along the loop the growing ribonucleoprotein fibers are packed into stalked granules. The completed and released transcription products appear as ribonucleoprotein granules. There is no evidence for a tandem arrangement of active 75 S RNA transcription units and most likely, there is only one active unit per chromatid in BR 2.

ACKNOWLEDGMENTS

We are indebted to Miss Eva Mårtenzon, Miss Jeanette Nilsson and Mrs. Sigrid Sahlén for technical assistance and to Mrs. Vivi Jacobson for typing the manuscript. The research was supported by the Swedish Cancer Society, Magnus Bergvalls Stiftelse and Karolinska Institutet (Reservationsanlaget). S.T.C. was a recipient of an N.I.H. National Research Service Award from the National Institute of General Medical Sciences, J. D. a recipient of an EMBO fellowship and M.M.L. a recipient of a postdoctoral fellowship from the American Cancer Society and a National Service Award from the National Institute of General Medical Sciences.

REFERENCES

Beermann, W. (1961) Ein Balbiani-Ring als Locus einer Speicheldrüsen-Mutation. *Chromosoma* 12, 1–25.

Beermann, W. (1962) Riesenchromosomen. In: *Protoplasmatologia*, vol. 6B, pp. 1–165. Springer-Verlag, Vienna.

Beermann, W. (1964) Structure and function of interphase chromosomes. In: *Genetics Today*, pp. 375–384. Pergamon Press, Oxford.

Beermann, W. (1973) Directed changes in the pattern of Balbiani ring puffing in *Chironomus*: effects of a sugar treatment. *Chromosoma* 41, 297–326.

Beermann, W. & Bahr, G. F. (1954) The submicroscopic structure of the Balbiani ring. *Exptl. Cell Res.* 6, 195–201.

Berendes, H. D. (1968) Factors involved in the expression of gene activity in polytene chromosomes. *Chromosoma* 24, 418–437.

Case, S. T. & Daneholt, B. (1977) Cellular and molecular aspects of genetic expression in *Chironomus* salivary glands. In: *Biochemistry of Cell Differentiation II*, vol. 15, ed. Paul, J., pp. 45–77. University Park Press, Baltimore.

Case, S. T. & Daneholt, B. (1978) The size of the transcription unit in Balbiani ring 2 of *Chironomus tentans* as derived from analysis of the primary transcript and 75 S RNA. *J. Mol. Biol.* 124, 223–241.

Daneholt, B. (1975) Transcription in polytene chromosomes. *Cell* 4, 1–9.

Daneholt, B. & Edström, J.-E. (1967) The content of deoxyribonucleic acid in individual polytene chromosomes of *Chironomus tentans*. *Cytogenetics* 6, 350–356.

Daneholt, B., Edström, J.-E., Egyházi, E., Lambert, B. & Ringborg, U. (1969) RNA synthesis in a Balbiani ring in *Chironomus tentans* salivary gland cells. *Chromosoma* 28, 418–429.

Daneholt, B., Case, S. T., Lamb, M. M., Nelson, L. G. & Wieslander, L. (1978a) The 75 S RNA transcription unit in Balbiani ring 2 and its relation to chromosome structure. *Phil. Trans. R. Soc. Lond.* B 283, 383–389.

Daneholt, B., Case, S T., Derksen, J., Lamb, M. M., Nelson, L. G. & Wieslander, L. (1978b) The size and chromosomal location of the 75 S RNA transcription unit in Balbiani ring 2. *Cold Spring Harb. Symp. Quant. Biol.* 42, 867–876.

Derksen, J., Wieslander, L., van der Ploeg, M. & Daneholt, B. (1978) Identification of the Balbiani ring 2 chromomere and determination of its DNA content. In preparation.

Edström, J.-E., Lindgren, S., Lönn, U. & Rydlander, L. (1978) Balbiani ring RNA content and half-life in nucleus and cytoplasm of *Chironomus tentans* salivary gland cells. *Chromosoma* 66, 33–44.

Egyházi, E. (1976) Quantitation of turnover and export to the cytoplasm of hnRNA transcribed in the Balbiani rings. *Cell* 7, 507–515.

Foe, V. E. (1978) Modulation of ribosomal RNA synthesis in *Oncopeltus fasciatus*: an electron microscope study of the relationship between changes in chromatin structure and transcriptional activity. *Cold Spring Harb. Symp. Quant. Biol.* 42, 723–740.

Franke, W. W., Scheer, U., Trendelenburg, M. F., Spring, H. & Zentgraf, H. (1976) Absence of nucleosomes in transcriptionally active chromatin. *Cytobiologie* 13, 401–434.

Grossbach, U. (1973) Chromosome puffs and gene expression in polytene cells. *Cold Spring Harb. Symp. Quant. Biol.* 38, 619–627.

Laird, C. D., Wilkinson, L. E., Foe, V. E. & Chooi, W. Y. (1976) Analysis of chromatin associated fiber arrays. *Chromosoma* 58, 169–190.

Lamb, M. M. & Daneholt, B. (1978) Characterization of active transcription units in Balbiani rings of *Chironomus tentans*. In preparation.

Lilley, D. M. J. (1978) Active chromatin structure. *Cell Biol. Int. Reports* 2, 1–10.

McKnight, S. L., Bustin, M. & Miller, Jr., O. L. (1978) Electron microscopic analysis of chromosome metabolism in the *Drosophila melanogaster* embryo. *Cold. Spring Harb. Symp. Quant. Biol.* 42, 741–754.

Miller, Jr., O. L. & Bakken, A. H. (1972) Morphological studies of transcription. *Acta Endocrin.* 168, 155–177.

Miller, O. L., Jr., Beatty, B. R., Hamkalo, B. A. & Thomas, C. A., Jr. (1970) Electron microscopic visualization of transcription. *Cold Spring Harb. Symp. Quant. Biol.* 35, 505–512.

Nelson, L. G., Derksen, J., Lamb, M. M., Wieslander, L. & Daneholt, B. (1978) Suppression of transcription in Balbiani ring 2 and the effect on chromosome structure. In: *FEBS 11th Meeting Copenhagen 1977*, vol. 43 Symp. A 2, ed. Clark, B. F. C., Klenow, H. & Zeuthen, J., pp. 279–286. Pergamon Press, Oxford.

Stevens, B. J. & Swift, H. (1966) RNA transport from nucleus to cytoplasm in *Chironomus* salivary glands. *J. Cell Biol.* 31, 55–77.

Vasquez-Nin, G. & Bernhard, W. (1971) Comparative ultrastructural study of perichromatin and Balbiani ring granules. *J. Ultrastruct. Res.* 36, 842–861.

Wellauer, P. K. & Dawid, I. B. (1973) Secondary structure maps of ribosomal RNA and its precursors as determined by electron microscopy. *Cold Spring Harb. Symp. Quant. Biol.* 38, 525–535.

DISCUSSION

PAUL: You have not undertaken a $c_o t$ analysis to try to estimate whether there is more than one copy of the gene?

DANEHOLT: Lars Wieslander (in preparation) has carried out a $c_o t$ analysis with BR 2 RNA. He obtained a biphasic curve, showing that about half of the RNA corresponds to a repetition above 1,000, and the other half to less than 10. He also ran saturation experiments with iodinated 75 S RNA containing sequences hybridizing in situ to both BR 1 and BR 2. The saturation level corresponds to about five 75 S RNA transcription units. Since the distribution of the units in between BR 1 and BR 2 is not known, it is concluded that the number of units in BR 2 is likely to be in the range of one to four.

PAUL: May I ask you one other question about the relationship between the nuclear 75 S RNA and cytoplasmic RNA in view of all the evidence in favor of processing of Hn RNA?

DANEHOLT: We can say that when we compare the size of 75 S RNA in BR 2 and cytoplasmic 75 S RNA by electrophoresis under denaturing conditions, we do not record a change in size. But when analyzing these very large molecules by this method, we would probably not detect a size difference of 1,000 bases, or maybe even of as many as 5,000 bases.

HOGNESS: What is the length of the apparently new region in front of the Christmas tree?

DANEHOLT: It amounts to 0.18 μm, which we have estimated to correspond to about 800 base pairs of DNA.

MAALØE: How do you make the estimate of the time it takes to transcribe the "Christmas tree" structure?

DANEHOLT: Two methods have been used to estimate the transcription time for 75 S RNA in BR 2. First, we can determine the time it takes to reach saturation of labeling in Br 2 RNA. In principle, this time represents the sum of transcription and storage time. Since the electrophoretic analysis of BR 2 RNA after different labeling times suggests that there is no storage of the completed product in BR 2, the recorded time to reach saturation corresponds to the transcription time. The other approach (Egyhazi 1975) to determine the transcription time is to add the RNA synthesis inhibitor DRB and to establish the time it takes for all the growing molecules to be completed and released from the template.

MANIATIS: What is the evidence that the bare region is not transcribed?

DANEHOLT: The RNA polemerases are closely spaced on the transcription unit. If the non-beaded segment proximal to the transcription unit were transcribed, we would expect to see an average of 2–3 polymerases on the segment.

MANIATIS: Can you rule out the possibility of differential rates of elongation through that area so that the probability of seeing polymerase molecules is low?

DANEHOLT: We cannot rule out such a possibility but then we have to deal with two quite different elongation rates on the same transcription unit. Furthermore, our analysis of the length of the growing RNP fibers suggested that the start of RNA synthesis takes place at about the position of the first polymerase, and that the non-beaded segment proximal to this polymerase is probably not transcribed.

MANIATIS: Does the 800 bp measurement assume a mass per unit length of bare DNA?

DANEHOLT: No. The chromosome fiber in the smooth region is not likely to be bare. It is thicker than you expect from a naked DNA molecule and has about the same diameter as the largely non-beaded fiber within the transcription unit.

GALL: But the 800 bp was gotten by using data from the transcribed region?

DANEHOLT: Yes, we have assumed a similar DNA compaction in the transcription unit and in the non-beaded segment proximal to the unit.

Egyhazi, E. (1975) Inhibition of Balbiani ring RNA synthesis at the initiation level. *Proc. Nat. Acad. Sci.* 72, 947–950.

SORSA: Could it be possible that this starting region is in an interband?

DANEHOLT: That we cannot rule out. The *in situ* hybridization experiments with Malpighian tubule chromosomes suggest that at least most of the sequences complementary to BR 2 RNA are present in the BR 2 band, but the experiments do not permit us to make a more definite statement as to the location of the transcription unit(s) within the band.

GALL: In your *in situ* hybrid you showed a rather condenced band. If you looked at a partially puffed region you could perhaps tell whether hybridization is at the ends or in the middle of the Balbiani ring. Have you tried to do that?

DANEHOLT: No, we have not carried out such an experiment, although it should be perfectly feasible to hybridize BR 2 RNA to, e.g. BRs whose activity has been almost completely suppressed by galactose. When we hybridize BR 2 RNA to Malpighian tubules the grains are distributed over the entire BR 2 band, and we have found no evidence for an asymmetric distribution. But as you suggest, it is possible that in a slightly puffed Br 2 region, different segments of the BR 2 band are more separated from each other, providing an improved resolution in an *in situ* experiment.

Electron Microscopic Localization and Ultrastructure of Certain Gene Loci in Salivary Gland Chromosomes of *Drosophila melanogaster*

Veikko Sorsa

INTRODUCTION

The polytene salivary gland chromosomes of *Drosophila melanogaster* have been the object of thousands of cytological investigations since Painter (1933) realized their cytogenetical importance. The actual "gene numbers game" started with the creation of the reference maps for the salivary gland chromosome bands (Bridges 1935), and with the first estimations of the total number of genes in the X chromosome of *Drosophila melanogaster* by Alikhanian (1937). At that time the structure of genes was unknown and it was quite natural that genes were connected to the existence of interphase chromomeres forming the bands in polytene chromosomes (Muller & Prokofyeva 1935). However, the essential questions concerning the exact number and location of genes remained unanswered. A most difficult task was to find methods to testify that the number of genes is really the same or even approximates the number of bands, and that the genes are actually located in the bands.

Successful experimental attacks on the gene number problem were made rather recently by Hochman (1971) and Judd *et al.* (1972) both showing an evident correlation between the numbers of recognizable gene loci and bands in given chromosome regions. But also the exact number of bands has proven to be a quite perplexing question.

An imposing starting point for the "band numbers game" on the salivary gland chromosomes of *Drosophila melanogaster* was given by the revised

Department of Genetics, University of Helsinki, Finland.

SPECIFIC EUKARYOTIC GENES, Alfred Benzon Symposium 13, Munksgaard 1979

reference maps of Bridges (1938, 1939, 1941, 1942). Unfortunately, later cytologists have encountered serious difficulties in finding all the bands, especially small bands and doublets which were depicted in the revised chromosome maps. Suspicions have arisen that many of those bands may not even exist (cf. Lefevre 1976). However, a careful electron microscopic analysis recently carried out on two distal divisions 21 and 22 of the chromosome arm 2L (Saura & Sorsa, in press) indicates that the number of recognizable bands found in good electron micrographs can be 30–40% higher than depicted in the revised reference map of 2L (Bridges 1942).

The question of the exact location of genes in the salivary gland chromosomes has turned out to be extremely complicated. The ribosomal RNA genes (cf. Wimber & Steffensen 1970) and some other repetitive genes (cf. Pardue et al. 1977) have been localized rather exactly at the light microscopic level by means of hybridization autoradiography. Transcriptionally active loci in polytene chromosomes can be marked and counted by using the uridine labeling at the synthetic phase (see e.g. Ananiev & Barsky 1978). Many active regions can be recognized from the puffing pattern of the salivary gland chromosomes (cf. Becker 1959, Ashburner 1967, 1969, Sorsa & Pfeifer 1972). Certain genes which are known to be active in the salivary gland cells have been localized by using the mutants with different or absent signs of activity (Korge 1977).

Also many gene loci which are inactive in salivary gland chromosomes have been localized rather accurately by means of chromosomal rearrangements (cf Lefevre & Wilkins 1966, Lefevre & Green 1972, Welshons 1974). The exact localization of a given gene into a certain chromomere or interchromomere fibril is, however, a very laborious task and needs a great deal of careful cytogenetic investigation, because the smallest deletions, which are usually the most useful ones, are near the resolution limit of the light microscopes (cf. Sorsa et al. 1973, Sorsa 1974).

The classical hypothesis of the chromomeric location of genes is strongly supported by the observations on the giant lampbrush chromosomes of Amphibia. Both the experimental and visual evidence show that the transcriptional activity appears in chromosomeric loops of the meiotic prophase chromosomes (cf. Gall & Callan 1962, Miller et al. 1970). Several observations on the puffed bands of the polytene chromosomes (cf. Sorsa 1969), and particularly the size of transcription products as well as the estimated length of repetitive genes (cf. Edström 1974) also support the chromomeric location of transcriptionally active units.

The distribution of uridine labeling at the salivary gland chromosomes, on the other hand, has brought forth another hypothesis, according to which the active genes may be located between the bands in the interband fibrils (Fujita & Takamoto 1963, Beermann 1965). Both of these hypotheses have found their advocates and theorizers (cf. Crick 1971, Paul 1972, Speiser 1975, Sorsa 1975). Quite recently, some light microscopic results of uridine autoradiography have been interpreted as evidence for the transcriptional activity in the interbands, and thus an indication of the possible location of genes between the bands (cf. Zhimulev & Belyaeva 1975). On the other hand, convincing contradictory results and interpretations of similar uridine labeling experiments have been published later by Ananiev & Barsky (1978).

Skaer (1977) published an electron microscopic study on polytene chromosomes *Drosophila melanogaster* showing RNP granules which were interpreted as products of interband transcription. Unfortunately, the electron micrographs, from which it is impossible to identify at least those bands depicted in the light microscopic maps of Bridges, can not be taken seriously. Furthermore, the large size of RNP granules contradicts the shortness of interband fibrils. The first results of the electron microscopic uridine autoradiography on the salivary gland chromosomes of *Drosophila melanogaster* are promising, although the location of the labeling is rather obscure (cf. Kerkis *et al.* 1977).

Jamrich *et al.* (1977) have localized the RNA polymerase B both into the puffs and interband regions of the salivary gland chromosomes of Drosophila by using antibody markers. Due to the poor resolution of light microscopy the exact interband location of polymerases is more a question of interpretation, since the polymerases found on the outside of large puffs may be located in small puffed bands. If, however, the interband location holds true, it may be explained as an indication of promoter type of function for the interchromomeric DNA rather than a site of active genes.

It seems now that the actual "bottle neck" of all cytogenetic studies on the polytene chromosomes is a lack of necessary microscopic resolution in the observations. During the last decade we have developed and used the squash thin-sectioning method for the electron microscopic localization of genes and the mapping of salivary gland chromosomes of *Drosophila melanogaster*. Details of procedural phases of the method have been described previously (cf. Sorsa & Sorsa 1967). Aceto methanol (AM) fixation has been used for mapping of the salivary gland chromosomes; the formaldehyde ringer (FAR) fixation has been mainly used for demonstrating the transcription products at the salivary gland chromosomes. In this report I should like to introduce some results of the electron microscopic localization of transcriptionally active sites and their ultrastructure in salivary gland chromosomes of *Drosophila melanogaster.* Also

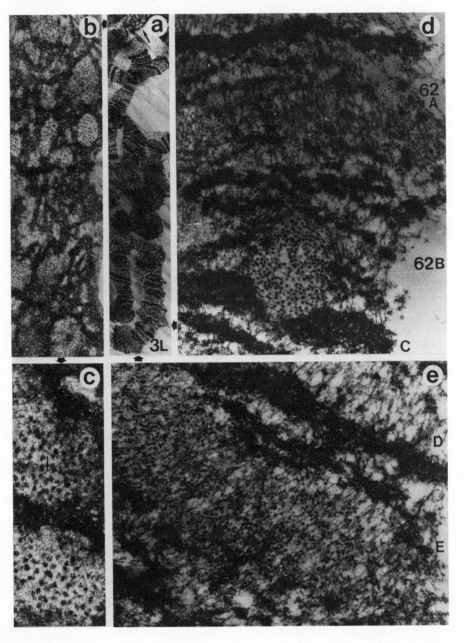

some results of the electron microscopic studies on white locus will be briefly discussed, and an EM analysis of the banding pattern in the zeste-white interval will be presented.

ELECTRON MICROSCOPIC STUDIES ON THE ACTIVE GENE LOCI

The puffing pattern in the salivary gland chromosomes of *Drosophila melanogaster* was comprehensively clarified at the light microscopic level by the extensive studies of Becker (1959) and Ashburner (1967, 1969). In his investigation Ashburner followed the development and disappearance of altogether 103 puffed regions recognizable by means of the light microscopy. The highest numbers of puffs were found in both arms of the third chromosome: 23 puffs in 3L and in 3R, 18 puffs were found in both arms of the second chromosome (Ashburner 1967), and 21 puffed regions were found in the X chromosome (Ashburner 1969). Despite careful research no puffs were found in the fourth chromosome. Sorsa & Pfeifer (1972) analyzed the variability of the puffing pattern in larvae of the same physiological age from different *Drosophila melanogaster* strains. In the 0-hour prepupae they were able to register puffing activity in altogether 121 sites at the salivary gland chromosomes of a wild stock.

The uridine autoradiography has always revealed labeling also outside the actual puffs along the whole chromosome complement. Electron microscopy has shown that besides the light microscopic puffs there exists a large number of puffed small bands (Sorsa 1969), which may explain the results obtained in the labeling experiments. Already very tentative counts of the sites, which seem to express signs of transcriptional activity in FAR-fixed chromosomes indicate that there are three to five active regions per each Bridges' division, also in the fourth chromosome. This means that there are several hundred of active gene loci at one time in the whole salivary gland chromosome complement. (Figs. 1, 2).

Fig. 1. Electron micrographs of salivary gland chromosomes of *Drosophila melanogaster* showing transcriptional activity in chromocenter and in chromosome arms. a. General view of thin-sectioned polytene chromosomes. The chromocenter (arrow) and the division 62 from 3L are depicted with higher magnifications in b–e. b. Chromocentric heterochromatin with large amount of RNP granules. c. Part of b showing the granules and thin fibrils (arrow). d–e. Subdivisions 62 A–E of the chromosome arm 3L showing two active puffs in 62A and 62E as well as a great amount of RNP granules synthesized during short activity period of the heavy band 62C 1–2, and then encased into the polytene chromosome during the rapid regression period. Magnifications ca. x 2000 in fig. a, ca. x 25,000 in b, and ca. x 50,000 in c–e.

Quite recently Ananiev & Barsky (1978) reported their results from the uridine-labeling experiments on the distal divisions of the X chromosomes, which were stretched by means of micromanipulation. One of the most interesting facts revealed by this study is the clear labeling of certain compact

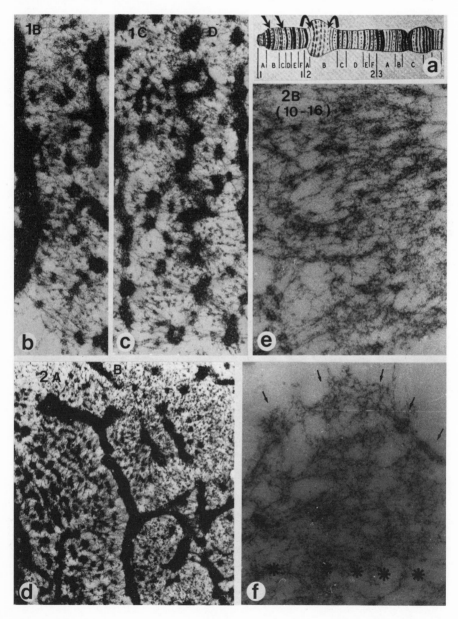

bands which do not show any puffing and which have never been reported to be found in the puffed stage. Similar labeling on the unpuffed bands was observed by Pelling (1959) in the salivary gland chromosomes of Chironomus.

Electron microscopy of these regions obviously explains the labeling of compact bands. Actually there are numerous prominent bands in the salivary gland chromosomes around which can be recognized signs of transcription similar to the ones in the normal puffs (Fig. 2 b,c). These bands show controlled moderate activity, or only parts of chromomeric fibrils are looped out from these otherwise compact and inactive bands for the transcription of only certain genes. Many of these bands are fractionated into smaller pieces, and in the Bridges' maps they are usually depicted with dotted lines.

The pufflike appearance of the more or less total transcription usually exists in rather small bands. For instance, the small band region of 2B (9–16) at the X chromosome seems to open for transcription more totally than the region of heavier bands at 2B 1–5 (Fig. 2). In the traditional puffs of *Drosophila melanogaster* the chromomeres and also the puff products, the RNP granules are of rather small size, only about 100–200 Å in diameter. Considerably taller granules exist in certain heavy bands, which do not have the appearance of actual puffing, or else they go through their puffing stage very rapidly (Fig. 1 d).

The large size of RNP granules may point to exceptionally long transcripts, which may be copies of tandemly repeated sequences (cf. Edström 1974). The similar large size of RNP granules is also very typical for the heterochromatic regions in the chromocenter of salivary gland cells in *Drosophila melanogaster* (cf. Lakhotia & Jacob 1974). Thin sections of the chromocenter of FAR-fixed cells show vacuolelike spaces in the chromatin containing large amounts of these granules (Fig. 1). The granules seem to form rows as if they were attached to some fibrils, resembling polysomal attachment of ribosomes during translation. The size of these chromatin granules is much larger, 300 Å in diameter,

---

Fig. 2. Electron micrographs of the sites of transcriptional activity at the distal divisions of the X chromosome. a. Part of Bridges' reference map (1935) for the X chromosome. The unpuffed active regions (b and c) are marked with straight arrows, and the puffed regions (d–e) are marked with bent arrows on the map. b and c. Transcription in the unpuffed bands of the subdivisions 1B and 1C–D. d. FAR-fixed puff of the subdivision 2B showing an abundance of puff granules. e. AM-fixed small band region (10–16) of the subdivision 2B. Bands are difficult to identify because most chromomeres are puffed. f. Part of the puff in AM-fixed chromosome showing that several subsequent chromomeres are uncoiled (arrows). Proposed banding is marked with asterisks. Magnifications ca. x 60,000 in all micrographs.

resembling the Balbiani ring granules in Chironomus (cf. Beermann & Bahr 1954).

Unfortunately, very few products are known of those obviously several hundreds of gene loci which are active in the salivary gland chromosomes. The saliva proteins are compounds which are known to be synthesized in the salivary gland cells. The saliva protein gene 4 has been recently localized by Korge (1977) into the puff which appears at the small band area 3C 11–12 according to Bridges' (1938) revised map of the X chromosome. Electron microscopy of this region shows typically puffed small chromosomeres. Because of the unsynchronized activation and puffing, or of a complete lack of transcription, there exist some groups of chromatids in the middle sections of polytenized X chromosome, which are not involved in puffing. In the electron micrographs these unpuffed chromatid groups seem to contain at least four subsequent chromomeres, which means that four narow bands should exist in the map of this region.

Histone genes of *Drosophila melanogaster* have been localized by Pardue *et al.* (1977) by using the histone messenger for hybridization autoradiography. In light micrographs the label is almost exactly above the band complex 39DE at the proximal end of 2L chromosome. In electron micrographs this region is usually more or less puffed. By studying the partly puffed chromosomes it can be observed that the activation of this proposed histone gene locus is initiated at the small bands 39D 3–5, or during the regression of active genes these bands are closed last. During maximum activity, however, also the neighboring larger bands 39D2 and possibly part of 39E1 are also involved in the puffing of this region. The transcription products of this proposed histone messenger locus are obviously very small. At least no particlelike products, which are typical for many other puffs in Drosophila, can be recognized in the electron micrographs.

The other well-known repetitive locus in *Drosophila melanogaster,* the 5S RNA genes, have also been localized by hybridization autoradiography. In this case the label appears on the heavy band complex 56F at the chromosome 2R (Wimber & Steffensen 1970). Electron microscopy of this region shows that the band complex 56F is usually almost completely closed and the only marks of transcriptional activity with typical RNP granules are found in the puff at the neighboring subdivision 56E. In some preparations, however, the first bands of subdivision 56F seem to be fused into the puff 56E (Sorsa 1973). This indicates that all the transcriptional activity needed for producing necessary 5S RNA in the salivary gland cells may be confined to a small fraction of the whole gene supply, which consists of approximately 200,000 copies of 5S RNA genes in the polytene chromosomes of *Drosophila melanogaster* (Tartof & Perry 1970). The strongest labeling at the borderline of subdivisions 56E and F often revealed by the hybridization autoradiography (Steffensen, personal communication) may be explained by the transcriptional activity of this region.

ELECTRON MICROSCOPIC STUDIES ON THE INACTIVE GENE LOCI
The refinement of cytogenetic methods in gene localization studies has practically extended to the resolution limit of the light microscopes. Thin sectioning of squashed salivary gland chromosomes offers a way to make EM preparations which are highly comparable to normal LM preparations. This method was originally developed in Berkeley for studying the synaptonemal complexes in fern chromosomes. Ten years ago this method was applied to gene localization studies on *Drosophila melanogaster,* and it was used for instance in the cytogenetic localization of the white gene (cf. Sorsa *et al.* 1973).

The essential role of normal white$^+$ loci in the expression of zeste mutation in the eye color of *Drosophila melanogaster* was demonstrated for the first time by Gans (1953). She was able to show that duplication of white$^+$ locus reveals zeste phenotype also in males, which normally have red eyes although zeste is present in their X chromosome. Later Green (1959) and Judd (1961) were able to confine the zeste-enhancing segment to the right end of white$^+$ locus. Actually a duplication of w^{+R} behaves as an enhancer of zeste and, vice versa, a deletion of w^{-R} behaves as a suppressor of zeste. In accordance with these rules the triplication of w^{+R} sublocus produces zeste phenotype both in males and females.

Already the light microscopic investigation of salivary gland chromosomes enabled the demonstration of an increase in the size of doublet band 3C 2–3 in case of triplication, and consequently a decrease in size of this band in case of deletion of w^{+R}. Electron microscopy of triplication an deletion of w^{+R} clearly verifies these conclusions (Fig. 3). Both of these structural changes in band 3C 2–3 are so great that a considerable amount of other DNA than just of sublocus w^{+R} is obviously involved in these rearrangements. In any case the triplication and deletion of w^{+R} indisputably show that the right end of the white locus must be located in the chromomeric DNA.

How small is the amount of band material actually included in a normal white$^+$locus was clarified by the cytological investigation of an inversion named In (1) z^{+64b9}. This inversion was found by M.M. Green after irradiation of the triplication stock of w^{+R} in Tübingen. The small segment of band 3C2, which is hardly detectable in light micrographs (Fig. 3) still contains a complete white⁺locus with a normal regulation of zeste. Electron microscopic analysis of both ends of this inversion is capable of showing more details. The fragment of 3C2, which includes the w⁺ functions was found to be joined to a fragment of the inverted small band 12 B 9. The other part of 12B9 is obviously joined to the inverted main part of the doublet band 3C 2–3. This doublet also probably

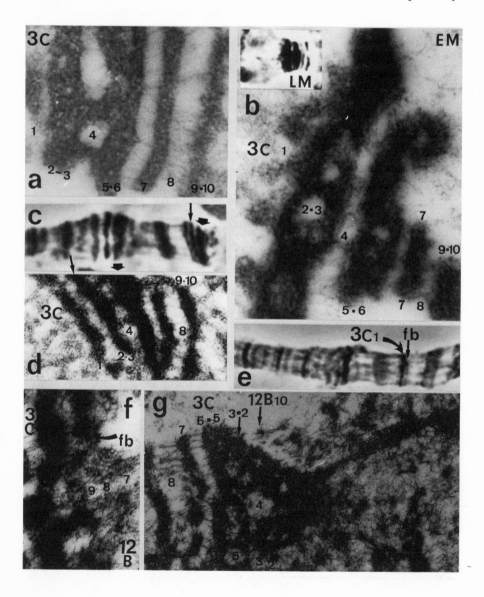

includes more or less totally the two rightmost subloci of w^{+R} of the original triplication, although they are not capable of enhancing zeste. The normal activity of the white$^+$ segment after the interband 3C 1–2 and the inactivity of the inverted w^{+R} segments indicate that the promotor and control segments of the white locus are at the left end, located next to the interband 3C 1–2 or partly in the interband area (Sorsa 1974, 1975).

Electron microscopic studies on normal white regions have not supported the speculations of an extra band existing between 3C1 and 3C2 and containing white locus (Judd 1976, Young & Judd 1978). This band may appear only in X chromosomes of special stocks carrying some structural changes in the doublet 3C 2–3. The location of the right side boundary of the white locus was tested by cytogenetical studies on several white$^+$ deficiencies created by M.M. Green by irradiating the inversion stock $z^{+\,64\,b\,9}$, white^{crimson} stocks and normal stocks with X rays. Results of light and electron microscopic analyses of irradiated X chromosomes are in full accordance with the hypothesis that white locus is included in the DNA of a narrow distal border of the band 3C2 in *Drosophila melanogaster* (Sorsa *et al.* 1973, Sorsa 1974, Green *et al.* unpublished results).

ELECTRON MICROSCOPIC ANALYSIS OF BANDING PATTERN IN ZESTE – WHITE REGION

According to cytogenetical analysis of mutable gene loci carried out by Judd *et al.* (1972), Kaufman *et al.* (1975), and Young & Judd (1978) in the zeste-white region of the X chromosome, a remarkable accordance between the numbers of identifiable gene loci and chromosome bands has been found. Later studies on the same region have actually revealed more gene loci than bands recognizable in light microscopy (Young & Judd 1978). Also the electron micrographs,

---

Fig. 3. Light and electron micrographs of the white region in the X chromosome of *Drosophila melanogaster.* a. Bands 3C 1–10 carrying normal white$^+$ locus. The doublets 3C 2–3 and 3C 5–6 are usually equal. b. Light micrograph (LM) and electron micrograph (EM) of 3C region with a triplication of white^{+R} show that the band doublet 3C 2–3 is very fat. c and d. Respectively in case of the deletion of white^{-R} the same band 3C 2–3 is very narrow, almost equal to band 3C1. e. Light micrograph and f–g. Electron micrographs of the white region in the inversion chromosome zeste$^{+\,64}$ $^{b\,9}$ show only a faint band (fb) at the site of 3C 2–3, which still includes a normal white$^+$ functions. g. The other end of inversion $z^{+\,64\,b\,9}$ at the subdivision 12B contains the main part of the band 3C 2–3. Late replicated material normally next to white locus shows ectopic pairing to heavy bands in 12E. Magnifications ca. x 30,000 in a, b and f, ca. x 25,000 in f, ca. x 20,000 in d, and ca. x 2000 in light micrographs.

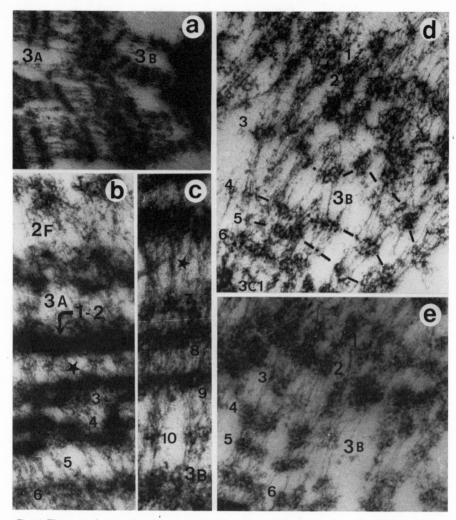

Fig. 4. Electron micrographs of zeste-white region of the X chromosome. a. General view of the subdivisions 3A and 3B. b–c. Higher mangifications of the regions 2F – 3B show that the doubleness of 3A 1–2 is not evident, but the single bands 3A 3 and 4 of the Bridges' map are actually doublets. Two small bands between 3A 1–2 and 3A 3 as well as between 3B 6 and 7 are not depicted in Bridges' revised map (1938) of the X chromosome. d–e. Electron micrographs of the subdivision 3B show that the bands 3B 1–2 may consist of several subsequent chromomeres. Thus the total number of bands in 3B may be higher than six. The actual white region is depicted in Fig. 3. Magnifications ca. x 20,000 in a, ca. x 50,000 in b, ca. x 60,000 in c, and about x 50,000 in d and e.

obviously depending on the preparation procedures, seem to show some variation in banding pattern (Berendes 1970). According to electron micrographs showing the maximum number of separable bands, 14 bands can be counted in the subdivision 3 A and at least six bands in the subdivision 3 B (Fig. 4).

CONCLUSIONS

EM analysis of transcriptional activity in the salivary gland chromosomes of *Drosophila melanogaster* indicates that there exist three to five simultaneously active sites per Bridges division, which means several hundred active regions in whole chromosome complement. Most of these sites are puffed small bands or transcriptionally active unpuffed bands, which are not recognizable with the light microscope. This explains the wide distribution of uridine labeling outside the actual puffs on the polytene chromosomes. Chromomeres seem to be always involved in active regions. The role of the interbands is obscure. Border segments of certain interbands seem to behave as "synaptic elements" aligning the parallel strands. Total number of bands found in the electron micrographs of the zeste-white region is 14 bands in subdivision 3A and at least six bands in subdivision 3B. All experiments for the localization of white gene have resulted in that the main part of DNA including the white$^+$ functions is located in a narrow distal border segment of the band 3C 2.

REFERENCES

Alikhanian, S.I. (1937) A study of the lethal mutations in the left end of the sex chromosome in *Drosophila melanogaster. Zool. Zh.* (Mosc.) 16, 247–279.

Ananiev, E.V. & Barsky, V.E. (1978) Localization of RNA synthesis sites in the 1B – 3C region of the *Drosophila melanogaster* X chromosome. *Chromosoma* 65, 359–371.

Ashburner, M. (1967) Patterns of puffing activity in the salivary gland chromosomes of *Drosophila*. I. Autosomal puffing patterns in a laboratory stock of *Drosophila melanogaster. Chromosoma* 21, 398–428.

Ashburner, M. (1969) Patterns of puffing activity in tha salivary gland chromosomes of *Drosophila*. II. The X chromosome puffing patterns of *D. melanogaster* and *D. simulans. Chromosoma* 27, 47–63.

Becker, H.J. (1959) Die Puffs der Speicheldrüsenchromosomen von *Drosophila melanogaster*. I. Beobachtungen zum Verhalten des Puffmusters im Normalstamm und bei zwei Mutanten, *giant* und *lethalgiant-larvae. Chromosoma* 10, 654–678.

Beermann, W. (1965) Operative Gliederung der Chromosomen. *Naturwiss.* 52, 365–375.

Beermann, W. & Bahr, G.F. (1954) The submicroscopic structure of the Balbiani ring. *Exp. Cell Res.* 6, 195–201.

Berendes, H.D. (1970) Polytene chromosome structure at the submicroscopic level. I. A map of region X, 1–4E of *Drosophila melanogaster. Chromosoma* 29, 118–130.

Bridges, C.B. (1935) Salivary chromosome maps with a key to the banding of the chromosomes of *Drosophila melanogaster. J. Hered.* 26, 60–64.

Bridges, C.B. (1938) A revised map of the salivary gland X chromosome of *Drosophila melanogaster*. *J. Hered.* 29, 11–13.

Bridges, C.B. & Bridges, P.N. (1939) A new map of the second chromosome. (A revised map of the right limb of the second chromosome of *Drosophila melanogaster) J. Hered.* 30, 475–476.

Bridges, P.N. (1941a) A revised map of the left limb of the third chromosome of *Drosophila melanogaster. J. Hered.* 32, 64–65.

Bridges, P.N. (1941b) A revision of the salivary gland chromosome 3R map of *Drosophila melanogaster. J. Hered.* 32, 299–300.

Bridges, P.N. (1942) A new map of the salivary gland 2L-chromosome of *Drosophila melanogaster J. Hered.* 33, 403–408.

Crick, F. (1971) General model for the chromosomes in higher organisms. *Nature* 234, 25–27.

Edström, J.-E. (1974) Polytene chromosomes in studies of gene expression. *The Cell Nucleus* Vol. III, pp. 293–332. Acad. Press, San Francisco.

Fujita, S. & Takamoto, K. (1963) Synthesis of messenger RNA on the polytene chromosomes of dipteran salivary gland. *Nature* 200, 494–495.

Gall, J.G. & Callan, H.G. (1962) H^3 uridine incorporation in lampbrush chromosomes. *Proc. Natl. Acad. Sci. U.S.A.* 48, 562–570.

Gans, M. (1953) Etude genetique et physiologique de mutant z de *Drosophila melanogaster. Bull, Biol. France Belg.* (Suppl.) 38, 1–90.

Green, M.M. (1959) Spatial and functional properties of pseudoalleles at the *white* locus in *Drosophila melanogaster. Hered.* 13, 302–315.

Hochman, B. (1971) Analysis of chromosome 4 in *Drosophila melanogaster.* II. Ethyl methanesulfonate induced lethals. *Genetics* 67, 235–252.

Jamrich, M., Greenleaf, A.L. & Bautz, E.K.F. (1977) Localization of RNA polymerase in the polytene chromosomes of *Drosophila melanogaster. Proc. Natl. Acad. Sci. U.S.A.* 74, 2079–2083.

Judd, B. (1961) Formation of duplication-deficiency products by asymmetrical exchange within a complex locus of *Drosophila melanogaster. Proc. Natl. Acad. Sci. U.S.A.* 47, 545–550.

Judd, B., Shen, M. W. & Kaufman, T. C. (1972) The anatomy and function of a segment of the X chromosome of *Drosophila melanogaster. Genetics* 71, 139–156.

Kaufman, T.C., Shannon, M.P., Shen, M.W. & Judd, B. (1975) A revision of the cytology and ontogeny of several deficiencies in the 3A 1–3C 6 region of the X chromosome of *Drosophila melanogaster. Genetics* 79, 265–282.

Kerkis, A.Ju., Zhimulev, I.F. & Belyaeva (1977) EM autoradiographic study of ^{3}H-uridine incorporation into *Drosophila melanogaster* salivary gland chromosomes. *Dros. Inf. Serv.* 52, 14–17.

Korge, G. (1977) Direct correlation between a chromosome puff and the synthesis of a larval saliva protein in *Drosophila melanogaster. Chromosoma* 62, 155–174.

Lakhotia, S.C. & Jacob, J. (1974) EM autoradiographic studies on polytene nuclei of *Drosophila melanogaster. Exp. Cell Res.* 86, 253–263.

Lefevre, G.,Jr. (1976) A photographic representation and interpretation of the polytene chromosomes of *Drosophila melanogaster* salivary glands. In: *Genetics and Biology of Drosophila* Vol. 1a. ed. Ashburner, M. & Novitski, E. pp. 31–66. Acad. Press, London.

Lefevre, G.,Jr. & Green, M.M. (1972) Genetic duplication in the *white-split* interval of the X chromosome in *Drosophila melanogaster. Chromosoma* 36, 391–412.

Lefevre, G.,Jr. & Wilkins, M.D. (1966) Cytogenetic studies on the *white* locus *Drosophila melanogaster. Genetics* 53, 175–187.

Miller, O.L., Beatty, B.R., Hamkalo, B.A. & Thomas, C.A.,Jr. (1970) Electron microscopic visualization of transcription. *Cold Spring Harb. Symp. Quant. Biol.* 35, 505–512.

Muller, H.J. & Prokofyeva, A.A. (1935) The individual gene in relation to the chromomere and the chromosome. *Proc. Natl. Acad. Sci. U.S.A.* 21, 16–26.

Painter, T.S. (1933) The morphology of the X chromosome in salivary glands of *Drosophila melanogaster* and a new type of chromosome map for this element. *Genetics* 19, 448–469.

Pardue, M.L., Kedes, L.H., Weinberg, E.S. & Birnstiel, M.L. (1977) Localization of sequences coding for histone messenger RNA in the chromosomes of *Drosophila melanogaster*. *Chromosoma* 63, 135–151.

Paul, J. (1972) General theory of chromosome structure and gene activation in eukaryotes. *Nature* 238, 444–446.

Pelling, C. (1959) Chromosomal synthesis of ribonucleic acid as shown by incorporation of uridin labelled with tritium. *Nature* 184, 655–656.

Saura, A.O. & Sorsa, V. (1978) Electron microscopic analysis of the banding pattern of the salivary gland chromosome 2L in *Drosophila melanogaster*. Divisions 21 and 22 – *Hereditas.* In press.

Skaer, R.J. (1977) Interband transcription in *Drosophila. J. Cell Sci.* 26, 251–266.

Sorsa, M. (1969) Ultrastructure of puffs in the proximal part of chromosome 3R in *Drosophila melanogaster. Ann. Acad. Sci. Fenn. Ser. a IV,* 150, 1–21.

Sorsa, M. & Pfeifer, S. (1972) Puffing pattern of 0-hour prepupae of *Drosophila melanogaster. Hereditas* 71, 119–130.

Sorsa, M. & Sorsa, V. (1967) Electron microscopic observations on interband fibrils in *Drosophila* salivary chromosomes. *Chromosoma* 22, 32–41.

Sorsa, V. (1973) Ultrastructure of the 5S RNA locus in the salivary gland chromosomes of *Drosophila melanogaster. Hereditas* 74, 297–301.

Sorsa, V. (1974) Organization of chromomeres. *Cold Spring Harbor Symp. Quant. Biol. 38,* 601–608.

Sorsa, V. (1975) A hypothesis for the origin and evolution of chromomere DNA. *Hereditas* 81, 77–84.

Sorsa, V., Green, M.M. & Beermann, W. (1973) Cytogenetic fine structure and chromosomal localization of the *white* gene in *Drosophila melanogaster. Nature New Biol.* 245, 34–37.

Speiser, C. (1974) Eine hypothese über die funktionelle Organization der Chromosomen höherer Organismen. *Theor. Appl. Gent.* 44, 97–99.

Tartof, K.D. & Perry, R.P. (1970) The 5S RNA genes of *Drosophila melanogaster. J. Mol. biol.* 51, 171–183.

Welshons, W.J. (1974) The cytogenetic analysis of a fractured gene in *Drosophila. Genetics* 76, 775–794.

Wimber, D. E. & Steffensen, D. M. (1970) Localization of 5S RNA genes on *Drosophila* chromosomes by RNA-DNA hybridization. *Science* 170, 639–641.

Young, M.W. & Judd, B.H. (1978) Nonessential sequences, genes and the polytene chromosome bands of *Drosophila melanogaster. Genetics* 88, 723–742.

Zhimulev, I.F. & Belyaeva, E.S. (1975) Proposals to the problem of structural and functional organization of polytene chromosomes. *Theor. Appl. Genet.* 45, 335–340.

DISCUSSION

HOGNESS: You said there were three to five transcription regions per division. Do you mean bands?

SORSA: I mean recognizable activity sites. In some cases there are many bands, in some cases there is only one band active. It means that in the whole chromosome complement there should be many hundreds of sites which are active at a moment. This is very similar to Bertil Daneholt's observations on Balbiani rings, because also in *Drosophila* many heavy bands which are active are producing very large granules, and small bands which are puffing are producing smaller particles.

PAUL: I wonder if you could repeat some of your ideas about the interband regions. The suggestion is of course that polymerases accumulate there. Do you have any evidence from your EM studies for polymerases in interbands?

SORSA: Unfortunately, I cannot localize polymerases just now. We are beginning some work in that direction to mark polymerases with antibodies. In all cases I have an impression that activity is beginning right at the end of the band. I agree with Dr. Daneholt that most of the band can be closed and only a short region of it may be open and produce some particles which are not known in this case.

SCHAFFNER: It appears to me that there is a conflict between your results indicating that transcription occurs in the polytene chromosome bands, and the ones reported by Jamrich *et al.* (1977) who say RNA polymerase II is present in interbands.

SORSA: Yes, but what are those interbands? Are they really recognizable with Bridges' map. Because, e.g. Jamrich *et al.* (1977) have called an "interband" a band group (21E–22A) which is including 10 bands. How could this be explained to be an interband? The preparations should be capable of demonstrating at least those bands drawn by Bridges 40 years ago.

Jamrich, M., Greenleaf, A. L. & Bautz, E. K. F. (1977) Localization of RNA polymerase in polytene chromosomes of *Drosophila melanogaster. Proc. Nat. Acad. Sci. USA* 74, 2079–2083.

CRICK: What would you estimate then as the total number of bands in the haploids sets of *Drosophila* in the way you defined it?

SORSA: It must be something like 5,000.

CRICK: But even if you allow for the fact that Bridges counted some bands twice, and left out a lot of bands, I would still think it would come to more than 5,000, more like 7,000.

SORSA: Maybe it can increase to 6–7,000. I have drawn the tentative EM-maps which are 40 meters long, but the EM analyses of chromosomes are not completely ready.

PAUL: Have you made a study of the effects of ribonuclease treatment on chromosomes, considering that RNA might have a role in the structure of the chromosome?

SORSA: I have not. But it should be done on the electron microscopic level. There are some earlier EM-studies on the distribution of RNA and on the effects of ribonuclease in the polytene chromosomes of *Chironomus* (e.g. Wolstenholme 1965, Lezzi 1965), and also of *Drosophila* (e.g. Wolstenholme 1966). These experiments show that the ribonuclease digestion does not cause any drastic breaks or other structural changes in the salivary gland chromosomes but DNase treatment is capable of breaking the interband fibrils.

Wolstenholme, D. R. (1965) *Chromosoma* 17, 219–229.
Lezzi, M. (1965) *Exp. Cell Res.* 39, 289–292.
Wolstenholme, D. R. (1966) *Genetics* 53, 357–360.

Heat Activated Genes of
Drosophila melanogaster

S. *Artavanis-Tsakonas*[1], P. *Schedl*[1], R. *Steward*[1] W. J. *Gehring*[1], M.-E. *Mirault*[2], L. *Moran*[2], M. *Goldschmidt-Clermont*[2], P. *Arrigo*[2], A. *Tissières*[2], & J. *Lis*[3]

THE HEAT SHOCK SYSTEM IN *DROSOPHILA MELANOGASTER*

In *D. melanogaster* it is possible to simultaneously activate a limited number of genes by either temperature elevation (heat shock) or with agents which interfere with respiratory metabolism. Such treatments induce a set of seven to nine specific puffs in the salvary gland chromosomes (Ritossa 1962, 1964, Ashburner 1970). These puffs have been shown to be sites of intense ^{3}H-uridine incorporation (Tissières *et al.* 1974) and RNA polymerase accumulation (Plagens *et al.* 1976) supporting the contention that puffing reflects active gene transcription (Beerman 1952, Pelling 1964).

Heat shock not only induces specific puffing in salivary gland chromosomes but also causes dramatic changes in the pattern of protein synthesis of *D. melanogaster* tissues and tissue culture cells (Tissières *et al.* 1974, McKenzie *et al.* 1975, Lewis *et al.* 1975), As shown in Fig. 1, most proteins made under normal growth conditions are either no longer synthesized or their synthesis is substantially reduced. Instead, seven to nine new polypeptides are produced. This change in the pattern of protein synthesis is correlated with a disaggregation of preexisting polysomes and the formation of new polysomes containing newly synthesized RNA species which are found to hybridize *in situ* to the heat-induced puff sites of the polytene chromosomes (Spradling *et al.* 1975, McKenzie *et al.* 1975). The newly synthesized RNAs can be isolated from polysomes and, as shown in Fig. 1, they direct the *in vitro* synthesis of the same polypeptides

[1] Biozentrum, University of Basel, Switzerland.
[2] Department of Molecular Biology, University of Geneva, Switzerland.
[3] Department of Biochemistry, Molecular and Cell Biology, Cornell University, Ithaca, N.Y. U.S.A.

SPECIFIC EUKARYOTIC GENES, Alfred Benzon Symposium 13, Munksgaard 1979

observed *in vivo*. The heat shock mRNAs can be fractionated into two distinct size classes: 12s and 20s. The 20s RNA contains at least three mRNA species coding, respectively, for the 68 k, 70 k, and 84 k heat shock polypeptides, while the 12s RNA directs the synthesis of the small heat shock proteins (Mirault *et al.* 1978).

This apparently coordinate expression of a small number of genes after heat shock in *D. melanogaster*, which seems to be controlled at both the transcriptional and translational level, provides a suitable system for the investigation of gene regulation in eukaryotes. In this paper we will describe the isolation and characterization of two chromosomal segments which contain structural genes for the 70 k heat shock-induced protein. We hope that detailed analysis of their structure will provide some insight into the mechanisms which control their expression.

Isolation of chromosomal segments complementary to heat shock RNA
We have established a collection of *D. melanogaster* hybrid clones (Artavanis-Tsakonas *et al.* 1977) which were constructed by inserting randomly sheared embryonic *D. melanogaster* DNA by the poly dA dT connector method (Lobban & Kaiser 1973) into the RI restriction site of the ampicillin-resistant plasmid RSF2124 (So *et al.* 1975). The colony hybridization procedure of Grunstein & Hogness (1975) permits the identification of clones in the collection which contain DNA sequences complementary to a specific radioactive probe. This procedure was used to screen about 11,000 independent hybrid clones with *in vitro*-labeled poly A^+ RNA isolated from large and small heat shock polysomes (Fig. 1). Of the clones identified by this procedure two hybrids, 56H8 and 132E3, were found to hybridize specifically to *in vivo* ^{3}H-uridine-labeled newly synthesized poly A^+ RNA isolated from heat shocked *Drosophila* tissue culture cells. In contrast, both plasmids showed limited hybridization to ^{3}H-labeled RNA obtained from non-heat shocked cells and hence are expected to contain *Drosophila* DNA sequences complementary to RNA species, the synthesis of which is induced by heat shock.

Identification of the heat shock mRNA species complementary to
the hybrid plasmids 56H8 and 132E3
When *in vivo*-labeled polysomal poly A^+RNA isolated from heat shock cells is

---

1 kb=1000 base pairs, 1 k=1 kilodalton.

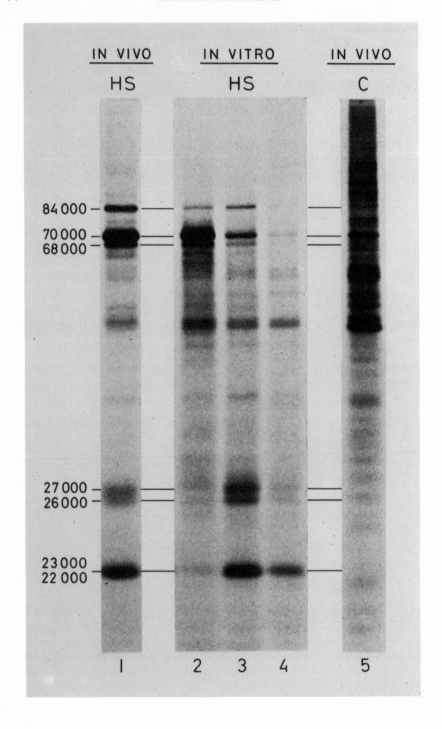

analyzed on sucrose gradients, a major 20s and a minor 12s peak are observed. Hybridization of this fractionated mRNA to excess 56H8 or 132E3 plasmid DNA immobilized on nitrocellulose filters shows that the RNA species complementary to both plasmids is restricted to the 20s fraction. This however does not identify the mRNA species complementary to either plasmid since *in vitro* translation studies show that the 20s peak is composed of at least three different mRNAs. On the other hand, as the major component of the 20s peak codes for the 70 k protein and nearly 40% of the input RNA counts hybridize to both plasmid DNAs, it might be expected that they contain sequences complementary to the 70 k protein mRNA. To test this suggestion further the two plasmids were used to arrest the *in vitro* translation of their complementary mRNA. Excess plasmid DNA was denatured and then hybridized to polysomal heat shock poly A$^+$ RNA. After hybridization, the mixture was translated *in vitro* and the products analyzed on polyacrylamid gels (Schedl *et al.* 1978). The result of such an experiment is shown in Fig. 2. It is evident that both plasmids specifically block the translation of the 70 k protein, indicating that the two cloned eukaryotic segments contain DNA sequences complementary to the mRNA coding for this protein.

Arrangement of the DNA sequences coding for the 70 k heat shock polypeptide
Since both 56H8 and 132E3 are complementary to the major 20s mRNA species, the two cloned *D. melanogaster* segments are expected to contain homologous sequences. On the other hand, a number of studies (Spradling *et al.* 1977, Ish-Horowicz *et al.* 1977, Henikoff & Meselson 1977) have suggested that there are multiple copies of the 70 k protein gene distributed at two distinct cytogenetic loci. Hence, the homologous sequences in 56H8 and 132E3 could be adjacent to regions which are quite different. In this case, any differences in sequence organization could reflect the different cytogenetic origin of the two cloned *D.*

Fig. 1. In vitro translation of polysomal poly A$^+$ RNA from heat-shocked cells. Polysomal poly A$^+$ RNA was prepared as previously described (Mirault *et al.* 1978) from a culture of cells growing at 25 °C, concentrated to about 2×10^7 cells/ml incubated for 75 min at 37 °C. This RNA was translated *in vitro* in the reticulocyte cell free system developed by Pelham & Jackson (1976). ^{35}S-methionine-labeled polypeptides were analyzed by SDS gel electrophoresis and revealed by fluorography (Laskey & Mills 1975). Lanes 2,3,4: polypeptides synthesized *in vitro* by poly A$^+$ RNA from large polysomes, small polysomes and monosomes respectively. Lanes 1 and 5 polypeptides labeled *in vivo* at 37 °C (heat shock) and 25 °C respectively. A larger amount of protein was loaded on lane 5 (2.5 times more than on lane 1) in order to reveal weakly labeled polypeptides.

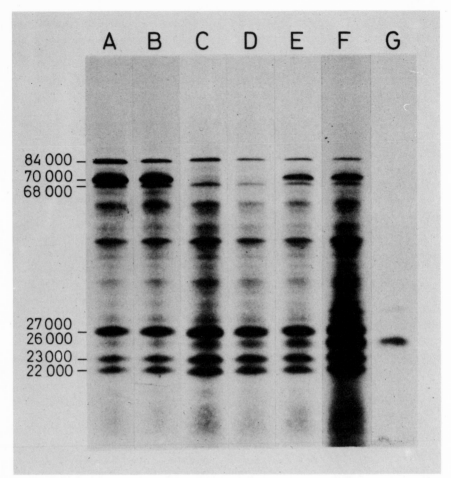

Fig. 2. Translation arrest of heat shock mRNA by plasmid DNA hybridization. Messenger RNA from heat-shocked cells was hybridized with an excess of fragmented plasmid DNA as described in the Experimental Procedures (Schedl *et al.* 1978). The mixture was translated *in vitro* in a reticulocyte lysate (Pelham & Jackson 1976). The ^{35}S-methionine-labeled translation products were separated by SDS-polyacrylamide gel electrophoresis and detected by fluorography.

Lane A, untreated RNA; B, mock hybridization in the absence of DNA; C, hybridization to 132E3 DNA; D, hybridization to 56H8 DNA; E, hybridization to 77E4 DNA. (This plasmid contains *Drosophila* sequences which hybridize to RNA labeled at 25°C but not to heat shock RNA); F, hybridization to IIF2 DNA. (This hybrid plasmid contains *Drosophila* rDNA sequences); G, endogeneous activity of the translation system. Exposures were adjusted in the figure to compensate for differences in sample activity. (A and B): 17 h; C), D), E) and F): 3 days; G): 6 days.

melanogaster segments, while similarities may indicate certain structural features which could prove important in understanding the regulation of gene expression in eukaryotes. For these reasons the arrangement of the *D. melanogaster* DNA sequences in the two plasmids was characterized in detail.

The position of restriction sites for a variety of different enzymes in 58H8 and 132E3 was detemined by comparing the fragments obtained in single and combined enzyme digests. The restriction maps deduced from these studies are shown in Fig. 3 (Moran *et al.* 1979). Two different approaches were used to confirm each restriction map. First, a number of restriction fragments were subcloned and their sequence organization was determined. Second, a variety of isolated restriction fragments were used as probes in cross hybridization experiments with appropriate digests of each plasmid.

Comparison of the restriction maps of 132E3 and 56H8 shows that the cloned DNA fragments are derived from nonoverlapping segments of the *D. melanogaster* genome. On the other hand, there are in both plasmids regions which have a similar distribution of restriction sites. This region is roughly defined, as is indicated in Fig. 3, by the closely spaced Xba Xho sites on the left, through the Bam HI site to the Sal site on the right. 56H8 has only a single copy of this region while 132E3 has two. Cross hybridization experiments show that the sequences

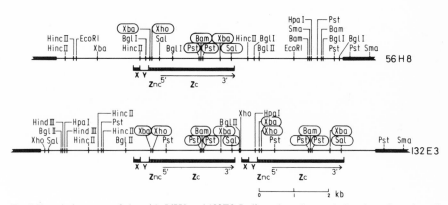

Fig. 3. Restriction maps of plasmids 56H8 and 132E3. Indicated are the restriction sites of a variety of different enzymes found in the eukaryotic DNA sequences (thin line) of the two hybrid plasmids 56H8 and 132E3. Heavily drawn lines at the two extremities of each map represent RRF2124 sequences.

In 132E3 two regions have similar distributions of restriction sites (encircled sites) while in 56H8 only one such region is found. Each of these common regions is composed of three distinct structural elements, x, y, z, which together define what we call the "common unit". z is subdivided into two segments, z_c and z_{nc}. z_c ("coding") is complementary to the 70 k protein mRNA while z_{nc}("noncoding") is not. x, z_{nc} and z are homologous in all three common units while y is not (for details see Moran *et al.* 1979, and Artavanis-Tsakonas *et al.* 1979).

in these three regions are homologous (Moran *et al.* 1979). Moreover, hybridization of a highly purified *in vitro*-labeled 70 k protein mRNA probe to restriction digests transferred to nitrocellulose filters (Southern 1975) shows that each of these common regions contain sequences complementary to the message (Artavanis-Tsakonas *et al.* 1979).

We have obtained a more accurate definition of both this homologous region and the mRNA coding sequences by detailed hybridization, heteroduplex and r-loop analysis (Moran *et al.* 1979, Artavanis-Tsakonas *et al.* 1979). These studies reveal that the three common regions have an intriguing arrangement of sequences (Fig. 3). Each region is composed of three distinct contiguous sequence elements, x, y, and z, which together define what we have termed the "common unit". The largest element, z, has a length of about 2.5 kb and is homologous in all three common units. Although the restriction analysis shows sequence variations in z, no interruption in homology within the three z elements has been detected. The coding sequences for the 70 k protein mRNA are located within z and subdivide it into two segments: a 2.15 kb DNA segment which is complementary to the 70 k protein mRNA and which we call z_c (z coding) and a 0.45 kb "noncoding" element, z_{nc}. Moreover, within the limits of detection of either the restriction or r-loop analysis, no evidence for DNA sequences complementary to the mRNA outside of z_c was obtained. These findings indicate that 56H8 and 132E3 contain one and two complete copies of the gene coding for the 70 k protein mRNA.

The second structural element of the common unit, y, is located to the left of z and has a length of 0.3 kb. Unlike z, the y element of 56H8 is not homologous to either of the 132E3 y elements. In addition, the two 132E3 y elements display some sequence divergence. Finally, the 0.18 kb long x element is located at the proximal end of the common unit. The sequences in x are complementary in all these repeats. However, while the x element of 56H8 and the first 132E3 repeats appear to be quite similar, the x element of the second 132E3 common unit has diverged considerably in nucleotide sequences. Since the direction of transcription of the 70 k protein mRNA is from left to right, as indicated in Fig. 3, the three sequence elements x, y, and z_{nc} are located to the left of the 5' end of the mature message. It is possible that one or more of these sequence elements, x, y or z_{nc}, may play a role in regulating the expression of the 70 k protein genes under different conditions, including heat shock. If this is the case, these elements, either alone or in combination, might be adjacent to other *D. melanogaster* genes and could provide a mechanism to coordinate the expression of a variety of

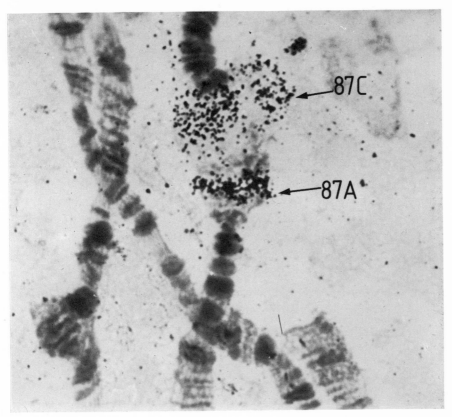

Fig. 4. Localization of the 70 k protein genes in the *D. melanogaster* genome. A 56H8 restriction fragment containing only sequences complementary to the mRNA (Sal-Sal within segments z, see Fig. 3) coding for the 70 k heat shock protein and hybridized *in situ* (Pardue & Gall 1975) to salivary gland chromosomes isolated from heat-shocked larvae in order to induce puffing (Schedl *et al.* 1978). Only the sites 87A and 87C are labeled with this probe.

different genes. In support of this hypothesis we find that the z_{nc} element is located very close to the 5′ end of another class of heat-induced genes which have been recently described by Lis *et al.* (1978). These same studies indicate that the 132E3 y element, or at least part of it, may also be present at the 5′ end of these genes while sequences corresponding to the 56H8 y and to the x elements are not found.

The arrangements of the 70 k protein genes in the D. melanogaster genome
In situ hybridization studies with heat shock polysomal mRNA led Spradling

et al. (1977) and Henikoff & Meselson (1978) to suggest that the DNA sequences complementary to the mRNA coding for the 70 k protein are located at the cytogenetic loci 87A and 87C. A more direct demonstration may be obtained by *in situ* hybridization of an isolated restriction fragment (essentially z_c) which contains only mRNA coding sequences (Artavanis-Tsakonas *et al.* 1979). The pattern of hybridization of such fragment to salivary gland chromosomes isolated from heat shocked larvae is shown in Fig. 4. Two distinct cytogenetic loci, corresponding to the heat-induced puffs, 87A and 87C, are labeled by this probe, while no other sites were found to hybridize (Artavanis-Tsakonas *et al.* 1979). Since 56H8 and 132E3 carry respectively one and two copies of a 70 k protein gene, there must be at least three such genes in the *D. melanogaster* genome. In fact, recent results indicate that there may be as many as five to ten copies (Mirault *et al.* 1979). On the basis of the grain counts observed at the two loci in *in situ* hybridization experiments, it is expected that the ratio of the number of genes at 87C to 87A is 1.6.

There are, however, clear differences in the arrangement of the 70 k protein genes. Restriction analysis (in collaboration with David Ish-Horowicz) of DNA from homozygous deficiencies which delete 87A or 87C demonstrates that the cloned DNA segment of 56H8 derives from 87A while the one of 132E3 comes from 87C.

Although it is not clear at present why there are 70 k protein genes at two sites, it is conceivable that genes at each locus are differentially expressed under various conditions. *In situ* localization of the nascent 70 k protein mRNA in heat shocked salivary gland chromosomes (Artavanis-Tsakonas *et al.* 1979) indicates, in agreement with the genetic analysis (Ish-Horowicz *et al.* 1977, Ish-Horowicz, personal communication), that both loci are transcriptionally active. This, however, does not imply that both loci are always simultaneously active under heat shock conditions. For example, they could be differentially expressed in various types of tissues under conditions other than heat shock. In this respect it may be of interest that 56H8 which derives from 87A has somewhat different 5' sequence elements from those of 132E3.

ACKNOWLEDGMENTS

This work was supported by grants from the Swiss National Science Foundation (to W. J. G. and A. T.). S. A. T. was supported by a long-term EMBO fellowship and the Swiss National Science Foundation (to W. J. G.). P. S. is a postdoctoral fellow of the Helen Hay Whitney Foundation, and supported by the Roche Research Foundation for Scientific Exchange and Biomedical Collaboration with Switzerland. We thank M. Schedl, G. Martin and M. Stempfel and J. Molliet for their assistance and Mr. O. Jenni for drawings and plates. We are grateful to Dr. R. J. Jackson for his advice and his gift of reticulocyte lysate, and to Dr. T. Bickle for the generous gift of some of the restriction enzymes.

REFERENCES

Artavanis-Tsakonas, S., Schedl, P., Steward, R. & Gehring, W. J. (1977) A collection of hybrid plamid clones corresponding to the entire *Drosophila melanogaster* genome. *Experientia* 33, 811.

Artavanis-Tsakonas, S., Scheld, P., Mirault, M.-E., Moran, L. & Lis, J. (1979) *Cell,* in press.

Ashburner, M. (1970) Patterns of puffing activity in the salivary gland chromosomes of *Drosophila.* V. Responses to environmental treatments. *Chromosoma* 31, 356–376.

Beerman, W. (1952) Ein Balbiani-Ring als Locus einer Speicheldrüsen-Mutation. *Chromosoma* 12, 1–25.

Grunstein, M. & Hogness, D. S. (1975) Colony hybridization: A method for the isolation of cloned DNAs that contain a specific gene. *Proc. Nat. Acad. Sci.* 72, 3961–3965.

Henikoff, S. & Meselson, M. (1977) Transcription at two heat shock loci in *Drosophila. Cell* 12, 441–451.

Ish-Horowicz, D., Holden, J. J. & Gehring, W. J. (1977) Deletions of two heat-activated loci in *Drosophila melanogaster* and their effects on heat-induced protein synthesis. *Cell* 12, 643–652.

Laskey, R. A. & Mills, A. D. (1975) Quantitative film detection of ^{3}H and ^{14}C in polyacrylamide gels by fluorography. *Eur. J. Biochem.* 56, 335–341.

Lewis, M., Helmsing, P. J. & Ashburner, M. (1975) Parallel changes in puffing activity and patterns of protein synthesis in salivary glands of *Drosophila. Proc. Nat. Acad. Sci.* 72, 3604–3608.

Lobban, P. E. & Kaiser, A. D. (1973) Enzymatic end-to-end joining of DNA molecules. *J. Mol. Biol.* 78, 453–471.

Lis, J. T., Prestidge, L. & Hogness, D. S. (1978) A novel arrangement of tandemly repeated genes at a major heat shock site in *Drosophila melanogaster. Cell* 14. In press.

McKenzie, S. L., Henikoff, S. & Meselson, M. (1975) Localization of RNA from heat-induced polysomes at puff sites in *Drosophila melanogaster. Proc. Nat. Acad. Sci.* 72, 1117–1121.

Mirault, M.-E., Goldschmidt-Clermont, M., Moran, L., Arriog, P. A. & Tissières, A. (1978) The effect of heat shock on gene expression in *Drosophila melanogaster. Cold Spring Harbor Symp. Quant. Biol.* 42. In press.

Mirault, M.-E., Moran, L., Schedl, P. & Artavanis-Tsakonas, S. (1979) In preparation.

Moran, L., Mirault, M.-E., Tissières, A., Schedl, P., Artavanis-Tsakonas, S. & Gehring, W. J. (1979) *Cell,* in press.

Pardue, M. L. & Gall, J. G. (1975) Nucleic acid hybridization to the DNA of cytological preparations. In: *Methods in Cell Biology,* vol. 10, 1–16.

Pelham, H. R. B. & Jackson, R. J. (1976) An efficient mRNA-dependent translation system from reticulocyte lysates. *Eur. J. Biochem.* 67, 247–256.

Pelling, C. (1964) Ribonukleinsäuresynthese der Riesenchromosomen. Autoradiographische Untersuchungen an *Chironomus Tentans. Chromosoma* 15, 17–122.

Plagens, U., Greenleaf, A. L. & Bautz, E. K. F. (1976) Distribution of RNA polymerase on *Drosophila* polytene chromosomes as stydied by indirect immunofluoroscence. *Chromosoma* 59, 157–165.

Ritossa, F. M. (1962) A new puffing pattern induced by temperature shock and DNP in *Drosophila*. *Experientia* 18, 571–573.

Ritossa, F. M. (1964) Experimental activation of specific loci in polytene chromosomes of *Drosophila. Exp, Cell Res.* 35, 601–607.

Schedl, P., Artavanis-Tsakonas, S., Steward, R., Gehring, W. J., Mirault, M.-E., Goldschmidt-Clermont, M., Moran, L. & Tissières, A. (1978) Two hybrid plasmids with *Drosophila melanogaster* DNA sequences complementary to mRNA coding for the major heat shock protein. *Cell* 14, 921–929.

So, M., Gill, R. & Falkow, S. (1975) The generation of a ColEl-Ap^r cloning vehicle which allows detection of inserted DNA. *Molec. Gen. Genet.* 142, 239–249.

Southern, E. M. (1975) Detection of specific sequences among DNA fragments separated by gel electrophoresis. *J. Mol. Biol.* 98, 503–517.

Spradling, A., Penman, S. & Pardue, M.-L. (1975) Analysis of *Drosophila* mRNA by *in situ* hybridization: Sequences transcribed in normal and heat-shocked cultured cells. *Cell* 4, 395–404.

Spradling, A., Pardue, M.-L. & Penman, S. (1977) Messenger RNA in heat-shocked *Drosophila* cells. *J. Mol. Biol.* 109, 559–587.

Tissières, A., Mitchell, H. K. & Tracy, U. M. (1974) Protein synthesis in salivary glands of *Drosophila melanogaster:* Relation to chromosome puffs. *J. Mol. Biol.* 84, 389–398.

DISCUSSION

CRICK: When you say "coding" you mean "messenger"?

ARTAVANAS-TSAKONAS: When I say "coding", I mean complementary to mature message.

CRICK: So it does not mean coding in the sense of being translated?

ARTAVANIS-TSAKONAS: Right.

DAWID: I wanted to ask whether you have perhaps done a Berk-Sharp experiment (Berk & Sharp 1977) to look for short R-loops, and whether you have looked for a possible nuclear precursor to the 70 k protein mRNA?

ARTAVANAS-TSAKONAS: We have not yet done a Berk-Sharp experiment, so that we cannot exclude very small intervening sequences; as far as the second part of the question is concerned Marc Edouard Mirault is trying to identify a possible precursor.

LEICK: How large a fraction of the newly synthesized RNA is heat-shock specific?

ARTANANIS-TSAKONAS: The majority of the newly synthesized polyA$^+$RNA under heatshock conditions appears to code for the seven heatshock proteins indicated in the first Figure. However, this is not the only RNA which is being synthesized under those conditions. For example, as Spradling *et al.* (1977) have shown, there are at least 12 polyA$^+$RNA species which are products of the mitochrondrial genome as well as polyA$^-$ species representing histone mRNAs. In addition he finds approximately 25 chromosomal sites, other than the heatshock puffs, which hybridize weakly with RNA labeled under heatschock.

PARDUE: The nuclear RNA hybridized *in situ* to the same polytene bands as the cytoplasmic RNA. When ^{3}H-uridine labeling is begun as little as 2 min. after the beginning of heatshock the pattern of hybridization of nuclear RNA to polytene

---

Berk, A. S. & Sharp, P. A. (1977) *Cell* 12, 721–732.

bands changes to resemble that of the heatshock cytoplasmic RNA. The sequences in nuclear RNA are changed, apparently reflecting differences in transcription. The processing of the ribosomal RNA stops, and the processing of 5S RNA also stops.

RICH: I wanted to just make a comment about another aspect of this system in work which is going on in collaboration with Dr. Pardue, and carried out by Bob Storti and others. They have been able to make a very efficient cell-free system from *Drosophila* which can translate mRNAs. If you take the total messenger RNA from heatshocked cells, translate it in a wheat germ or reticulocyte system, you will get both heatshock and normal cell proteins. If you translate them in a heatshock system, they will only translate the heatshock message, whereas translating them in the non-heatshock system will translate the normal mRNAs as well. So now we may be able to find out what it is that controls the system.

PLESNER: The slide you showed of heatshocked proteins resembles very closely the picture we get when we starve our cells, e.g. *Tetrahymena* cells. This is work by a collaborator, K. Kristiansen. This selective synthesis of relatively few proteins – whether these are pre-existing or new species – must necessarily mean that the synthesis of the majority of cellular proteins is inhibited. We observe concomitantly a transition of the ribosomal potein S6 from a non-phosphorylated to an almost fully phosphorylated form and interpret this as part of a translational control mechanism (Kristiansen *et al.* 1978). My question is now: Have you observed the same in your system or heard of anyone who has?

ARTAVANIS-TSAKONAS: No, we have not.

Kristiansen, K., Plesner, P. & Krüger, A. (1978) Phosphorylation *in vivo* of ribosomes in *Tetrahymena pyriformis. Eur. J. Biochem.* 83, 395–403.

The Genome of Hypotrichous Ciliates

David M. Prescott, John M. Heumann, Marshal Swanton & Robert E. Boswell

The group of ciliated protozoa called hypotrichs provide special advantages for the study of the organization of genes in chromosomes and for the study of gene structure. Like other ciliates, hypotrichs contain two kinds of nuclei: micronuclei and macronuclei. The micronucleus contains a diploid complement of chromosomes but is transcriptionally inert. It apparently functions only in sexual exchange of DNA. When two cells mate (conjugate), their micronuclei undergo meiosis and the two cells exchange haploid micronuclei (see below). The macronucleus contains many fold more DNA than the micronucleus but in hypotrichs this DNA is not organized into chromosomes. All of the DNA occurs in gene-sized molecules, and these gene-sized molecules serve as the templates for all RNA synthesis (except mitochondrial) in the cell. The macronucleus forms from a micronucleus after cell mating, and hence the gene-sized molecules of the macronucleus arise by excision from micronuclear chromosomes during macronuclear formation.

Cytology of Macronuclear Formation from a Micronucleus in Hypotrichs
When cells mate, each micronucleus undergoes meiosis to form four haploid micronuclei. The cells exchange haploid micronuclei through a cytoplasmic bridge, and each migratory micronucleus fuses with a stationary, haploid micronucleus to form a new diploid micronucleus. The unused haploid micronuclei degenerate as do the old macronuclei. The mating cells then separate. The new diploid micronucleus in each exconjugant cell divides by mitosis (without cell division), and one of the daughters develops into a new macronucleus. The entire process takes several days. After formation of the new

Department of Molecular, Cellular and Developmental Biology, University of Colorado, Boulder, Colorado 80309 USA.

SPECIFIC EUKARYOTIC GENES, Alfred Benzon Symposium 13, Munksgaard 1979

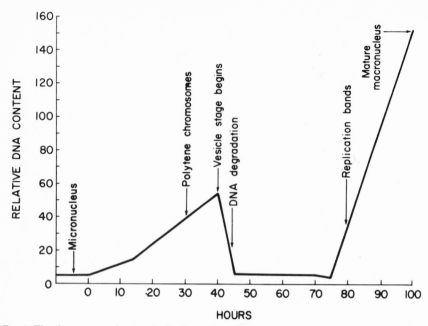

Fig. 1. The time course of events in the formation of a macronucleus from a micronucleus after conjugation in *Oxytricha sp.*

macronucleus, the cell resumes vegetative growth and reproduction with a cell cycle time of 6 to 8 hours under optimal growth conditions.

Formation of a macronucleus is diagrammed in Fig. 1. It begins with several successive rounds of DNA synthesis in the micronucleus destined to form a macronucleus. This synthesis results in the formation of polytene chromosomes (Ammermann 1964). When the polytene chromosomes have formed, they are transected through each interband by a septum (Kloetzel 1970). Transection is followed by enclosure of each chromosomal band into a vesicle within the nucleus. Thus, each band becomes a physically separate entity (Ammermann 1971), and the developing macronucleus is converted from a bag of polytene chromosomes to a bag containing thousands of vesicles, each vesicle containing a short segment of a chromosome.

Following the cutting up of polytene chromosomes, most of the DNA in each vesicle is degraded (Prescott & Murti 1973); overall, >90% of the total DNA in the developing macronucleus is destroyed. Next, the vesicle organization disappears, and the remaining DNA, which is now in gene-sized pieces, goes through approximately six rounds of replication to produce the mature, DNA-rich macronucleus.

Changes in DNA during Formation of the Macronucleus

The molecular weight of DNA in micronuclear chromosomes is high, i.e. $>$ several hundred million daltons, and has a genome size of about 6×10^8 base pairs (bp) (Lauth et al. 1976). During formation of a macronucleus the DNA undergoes two dramatic changes. First, the molecular weight of the DNA is drastically reduced, in accordance with the cytological changes described above, i.e. transection of the chromosomes at the polytene stage and subsequent destruction of $>90\%$ of the DNA. As a result macronuclear DNA occurs in gene-sized molecules. Electrophoresis of macronuclear DNA in a 1% agarose gel (Fig. 2) shows that these gene-sized molecules range in size from 450 bp to 30,000 bp. A continuum of sizes is present but certain sizes are represented in larger numbers, giving rise to a banding pattern in the gel that is superimposed on the continuum. The banding pattern in Fig. 2 is constant from one DNA preparation to the next and is characteristic of Oxytricha sp. Two other hypotrichs, Euplotes aediculatus and Stylonychia pustulata, have their own characteristic banding patterns of macronuclear DNA (J. Heumann, unpublished).

The sizes of DNA molecules have also been measured by electron microscopy, providing the size distribution shown in Fig. 3. From these data we obtained a number average molecular weight for macronuclear DNA of 1.50×10^6 daltons or 2270 bp ($\pm 3.4\%$).

Extensive DNA sequence diminution also takes place during formation of a macronucleus from a micronucleus. Evidence for a loss of sequences was first obtained by comparing the profiles of optical density of micronuclear and macronuclear DNAs after isopycnic centrifugation in cesium chloride (Bostock & Prescott 1972). The profile of micronuclear DNA is complex, reflecting the presence of at least four major density components. The profile for macronuclear DNA shows the presence of a single density component. The differences between micronuclear and macronuclear DNAs are also observed in melting curves (Bostock & Prescott 1972). The melting curve for micronuclear DNA is complex, reflecting the presence of multiple components, while the curve for macronuclear DNA shows the presence of a single component. The loss of the several density components of micronuclear DNA occurs in two stages. During development of the polytene chromosomes, one or more of the high density

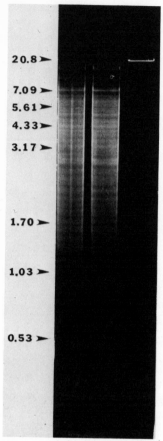

Fig. 2. Separation of native macronuclear DNA of *Oxytricha sp.* by size on a 1% agarose gel. The numbers to the left indicate sizes in kilobase pairs. The left well and the center well contain two separate preparations of native macronuclear DNA. The well on the right side contains λ CI DNA cut with Eco R1 and SV40 DNA cut with Hind 111 to provide size markers.

components is under-replicated. Loss of lower density DNA occurs in the vesicle stage of breakdown of the polytene chromosomes (Spear & Lauth 1976).

Quantitative analysis of the decrease in sequence complexity was achieved by measuring the rates of reassociation of micronuclear and macronuclear DNAs (Lauth *et al.* 1976). The reassociation kinetics for micronuclear DNA show at least two components, reflecting the presence of repetitious sequences and unique sequences; about 30% of the DNA consists of repetitious sequences and about 70% are unique. Macronuclear DNA reassociates as a single second order reaction, showing that most or all sequences are present at about the same frequency. From the reassociation curve the kinetic complexity of macronuclear DNA is estimated to be 3.6×10^{10} daltons. The kinetic complexity of the unique sequence DNA in the micronucleus is about 8.5×10^{11}. In comparing this with the kinetic complexity of macronuclear DNA (3.6×10^{10}), we can estimate that about 96% of the unique sequences present in micronuclear DNA are destroyed in formation of a macronucleus. (Arguments why repetitious DNA sequences of the micronucleus cannot represent more than a small fraction of the sequences in the macronucleus are presented elsewhere (Lauth *et al.* 1976). Indeed, for a number of reasons that cannot be detailed here it is likely that most of the repetitious sequences of the micronucleus are lost during formation of the macronucleus.)

From the analysis of reassociation kinetics we may conclude that the macronucleus contains only about 4% of the unique sequences present in the micronucleus. This conclusion is important because little or no RNA is synthesized in the micronucleus, and all of the RNA (except mitochondrial RNA) needed for cell functions is transcribed from DNA templates in the macronucleus. This leads us to the conclusion that ~96% of the unique

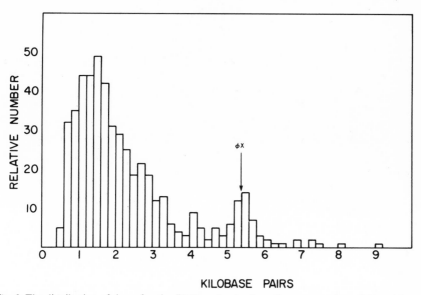

Fig. 3. The distribution of sizes of native DNA molecules from the macronucleus of *Oxytricha sp.* determined by electron microscopy. The number average molecular size ranges from 430 to 9,675 base pairs with a number average size of 2,270 base pairs. The peak at ~5,400 bases is due to single stranded ØX DNA (5,370 bases) included for calibration purposes.

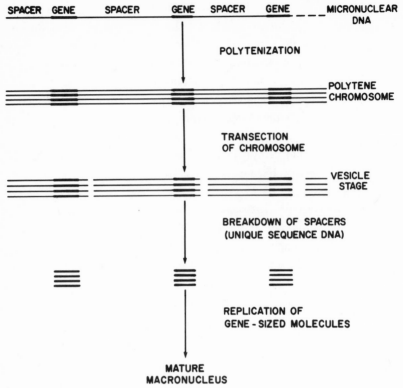

Fig. 4. A scheme for processing of micronuclear chromosomal DNA to form the gene-sized DNA molecules of the macronucleus. The scheme explains the observed change in molecular weight and sequence complexity of DNA and is consistent with the cytological findings on macronuclear development.

sequence DNA in the chromosomes of the micronucleus is nongenetic in the traditional sense and probably serves a purpose other than gene structure.

The Arrangement of Macronuclear Genes in Micronuclear Chromosomes

The cytological events of macronuclear development coupled with the changes in DNA during development lead rather forcefully to a model of how macronuclear genes are arranged in micronuclear chromosomes (Prescott & Murti 1973). First, we know from the band by band transection of the polytene chromosome and the subsequent destruction of most of the DNA in each band (during the vesicle stage) that the macronuclear sequences must be dispersed throughout the chromosome. It may be reasonably assumed that each band yields one or more specific macronuclear molecules. The DNA destroyed during the vesicle stage is believed to be nongenetic DNA that separates the macronuclear sequence in one band from the macronuclear sequence in the next band. This nongenetic DNA, moreover, is unique sequence DNA. Thus, as shown in Fig. 4, we conclude that most of the DNA of micronuclear chromosomes is nontranscribed spacer, separating the sequences that give rise to the gene-sized molecules of the macronucleus.

We have called the nongenetic DNA between gene sequences "spacer" in analogy with the nontranscribed spacer DNAs that are present between the successive copies of rRNA, tRNA, and histone genes in other organisms. The function of these nontranscribed spacer sequences is not known, and we can offer no compelling hypothesis for the function of the putative spacers in hypotrichs. Since the chromosomes of the micronucleus do serve in meiosis and the sexual exchange of DNA, it may be that spacers have a role connected with these activities, e.g. serving as regions for crossing over during meiosis.

Finally, we suggest that much of the unique sequence DNA (96% in *Oxytricha sp.*) in virtually all eukaryotes (yeast may be an exception) may serve as spacers between gene sequences and their associated control regions.

The Number of Kinds of DNA Molecules in the Macronucleus and their Multiplicity
The kinetic complexity of macronuclear DNA is 3.6×10^{10} daltons, and the number average molecular weight of the DNA molecules is 1.50×10^{6}. Therefore, the number of kinds of molecules is $\dfrac{3.6 \times 10^{10}}{1.50 \times 10^{6}}$ or ca. 24,000. If we accept the hypothesis that each molecule is a gene with attached control regions (Prescott *et al.* 1973), then we conclude that *Oxytricha sp.* contains ca. 24,000 different genes (Table I).

The multiplicity of each kind of molecule (gene) can also be calculated. From microspectrophotometry we know that the macronucleus contains about 3.5×10^{13} daltons of DNA (Lauth *et al.* 1976). We know from EM measurements that the number average molecular weight of macronuclear DNA is 1.50×10^{6} daltons. The total number of molecules per macronucleus is $\dfrac{3.5 \times 10^{13}}{1.50 \times 10^{6}}$ or ca. 23×10^{6}. Since there are ca. 24,000 kinds of molecules, each kind of molecule must be present in just under 1,000 copies per macronucleus. *Oxytricha sp.* has two macronuclei per cell and hence just under 2,000 copies of each DNA molecule per cell.

Table I

Characteristics of micronuclear and macronuclear DNAs of Oxytricha sp.

	Molecular size		Amount per nucleus	Sequence complexity	No. of molecules per nucleus
Macronuclear DNA	*Range* 3.0×10^5 to 2.0×10^7 daltons or 450 to 30,000 BP	*Number avg.* 1.50×10^6 daltons or 2,270 BP	58 pg or 3.5×10^{13} daltons or 5.30×10^{10} BP	3.6×10^{10} daltons or 5.5×10^7 BP	2.3×10^7
Micronuclear DNA	$>$several hundred$\times 10^6$		0.66 pg or 4×10^{11} daltons or 6.1×10^8 BP (haploid amounts)	ca. 8.5×10^{11} daltons or ca. 1.3×10^9 BP	Unknown, presumably ca. 120 (haploid number of chromosomes)

Fine Structure of Macronuclear DNA Molecules
The first major clue about the fine structure of macronuclear DNA molecules
came from the observation that heat denaturation of purified DNA followed by
rapid cooling led to the formation of single stranded circles by most of the DNA
(Wesley 1975). The single stranded circles were presumed to be held together by
a short duplex region, or neck, formed by complementary sequences present at
the ends of a single stranded molecule as shown below.

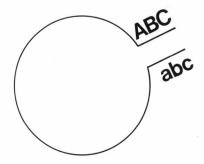

The duplex necks have been prepared in pure form by digestion with S1
nuclease and characterized (Herrick & Wesley 1978). The necks prepared by S1
digestion are 23 bp long, although this may be an underestimate of their true
length since S1 may nibble nucleotides from necks because of transient opening
of the ends of the duplex regions during preparation. The purified necks
reassociate extremely rapidly $(Cot\,{}^{1}\!/_{2} = 1.1 \times 10^{-5}\ mol \cdot liter^{-1} \cdot sec)$, and the
reassociated necks melt at the same temperature as the original, native necks.
Thus, all of the macronuclear molecules contain the same neck sequence at their
ends, and all molecules apparently share the structure,

ABC	cba
abc	CBA

The significance of the inverted terminal repeat at the ends of the molecules is
not known. One obvious possibility is that they are recognition sites for excision
of the gene-sized molecules from the polytene chromosomes during macronuclear development.

The nucleotide sequence at the ends of native macronuclear DNA molecules
has been determined by Lawn (1977), revealing that at least most of the 24,000

different kinds of molecules share the same 26 bp sequence at both ends. Sequencing of purified neck DNA (23 bp) obtained by S1 digestion of single stranded circles confirmed that the neck sequences are derived from the ends of native molecules and must be at least 26 bp.

Thus, the generalized model of the macronuclear DNA molecule generated by characterization of neck DNA is substantiated by the sequencing data. The sequence of the inverted terminal repeat sequence is,

5′C C A A G G G T C A A A G T T T C C C C G T T T T T − − − − − − −
3′G G T T C C C A G T T T C A A A G G G G C A A A A A − − − − − − −

This sequence in itself has not given any clues as to its function.

Measurements of contour length had suggested that single stranded molecules capable of forming single stranded circles were on the average shorter than native molecules. This led to the idea that native molecules contain site specific single strand interruptions, presumably nicks with copies of the inverted terminal repeat sequences on each side of the interruption (Wesley 1975). We have recently done several experiments to examine this possibility, including measurement of contour lengths of single stranded and native molecules, and have found no evidence of single strand interruptions (Heumann *et al.*, in preparation).

Finally, macronuclear DNA molecules are associated with histones to form nucleosomes (Lawn *et al.* 1978). The repeat length of DNA in a nucleosome is 220 ± 5 bp, and nucleosome cores prepared by prolonged digestion of isolated macronuclei contain 140 bp.

Coding (Gene) Functions of Particular Size Classes of Macronuclear DNA Molecules

The coding functions of several size classes of macronuclear DNA molecules have been identified by hybridizing radioactive RNAs or DNAs of known function to native macronuclear DNA blotted from agarose gels to nitrocellulose filters (Southern 1975). [125]I ribosomal RNA (26S + 17S) of *Oxytricha sp.* hybridizes to a single prominent band identifiable in a stained gel (Fig. 2) (Lawn *et al.* 1978). Evidently this band is prominent because ribosomal genes are repeated ca. 20 times relative to the average kind of DNA molecule in the macronucleus. Thus, there are ca. 20,000 rRNA genes per macronucleus. The DNA hybridizing to rRNA has a size of ca. 7,000 bp. The large and small rRNAs contain a total of ca. 6,000 bases. 5S rRNA hybridizes to a DNA of ca. 690 bp

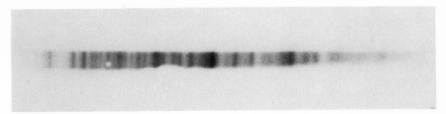

Fig. 5. Hybridization of [32]P cRNA copies from a plasmid (pSp2) containing the histone genes H4, H2B, and H1 of the sea urchin *Strongylocentrotus purpuratus*. Genes for these three histones are present in multiple size classes of DNA. The plasmid containing the histone genes was kindly provided by Lawrence Kedes.

(Rae & Spear 1978), and tRNAs hybridize to DNA ranging in size from 500 bp to ca. 7,000 bp (Fraser, unpublished). Nick translated DNA or radioactive cRNAs transcribed *in vitro* from cloned sea urchin histone genes hybridize to multiple size classes of DNA molecules (Fig. 5) (Boswell, unpublished). Thus we are able to associate particular genes with specific size classes of DNA molecules, which will simplify the task of isolating genes of known function for construction of recombinant plasmids. The actin gene sequence from *Dictyostelium* has also been shown to cross hybridize with at least one size class of macronuclear DNA by the Southern procedure (unpublished results).

Construction of Bacterial Plasmids Containing Macronuclear DNA Molecules
Macronuclear DNA molecules have been inserted into the bacterial plasmid pBR322 (Bolivar *et al.* 1977) and cloned into *E. coli* to produce a set of colonies that collectively will contain the entire macronuclear genome.

The procedure involves the restriction of the plasmid DNA at the single restriciton site for the endonuclease Pst 1. A small number of guanosine residues (<10) are added to the 3'-OH end of linearized plasmid with deoxynucleotidyl transferase. Similarly a small number of cytosine residues are added to the 3'-end of intact macronuclear DNA and annealed with the tailed vehicle. The reannealed molecules are then cloned into *E. coli* by a modification of the procedure of Wensink *et al.* (1974). The clones containing recombinant plasmids are selected by their resistance to tetracycline and sensitivity to ampicillin. The advantage of this method over other methods is that the Pst 1 restriction sequence is regenerated at each end of the inserted macronuclear DNA sequence, allowing the cloned 'gene' to be conveniently excised from the bacterial plasmid with the restriction enzyme Pst 1.

A clone bank of macronuclear DNA sequences can now easily be established. From the equation $P = 1 - (1-f)^n$, where n = the number of colonies and f = the fraction of the genome represented by the average macronuclear DNA piece, one can calculate the number of colonies, each containing a single macronuclear DNA molecule, that would be required to achieve a 95% probability of including any particular molecule. This number is ca. 65,000 for *Oxytricha sp.*

The frequency of transformation using the procedure described above is ca. $12 - 15 \times 10^3$ transformants per μg of DNA, which means that only 5 - 6 μg of macronuclear DNA are required for the construction of a clone bank.

This clone bank is being screened by the colony hybridization procedure of Grunstein & Hogness (1975) for histone gene sequences, using as a probe the histone gene repeat from the sea urchin. This repeat contains all five histone gene sequences and has been shown to cross hybridize with several size classes of macronuclear DNA (see above). Based on the number of bands observed on Southern blots, we estimate that there may be one or two histone-containing colonies per 5,000 total colonies. This probe is, however, nonhomologous and caution must be exercised in the interpretation of results with such cross hybridization. The preparation of histone mRNA from *Oxytricha sp.* will avoid potential problems with cross hybridization.

The colony bank will be screened for colonies containing *Oxytricha* transfer RNA using the specifically labeled homologous tRNA. The gene for actin can also be selected using the nonhomologous actin sequence from *Dictyostelium* as a probe.

Ribosomal genes from *Stylonychia pustulata* are located in a single prominent band in a 1% agarose gel of macronuclear DNA. This band has been excised and the DNA cloned into *E. coli* as described above. Most of the colonies show cross hybridization with homologous rRNA and contain inserts of about 7,000 bp.

Cloned macronuclear DNA sequences are of great interest because these molecules are intact functional genes and must contain all of the information for their expression, regulation, and replication. The specific gene sequences will therefore be used to characterize the "genes" of *Oxytricha* with respect to common features between genes, the presence of intervening sequences, control regions, and the location of specific genes within polytene chromosomes.

ACKNOWLEDGMENT
This work is supported by a grant from the National Institutes of General Medical Sciences (#GM 19199) to D. M. Prescott.

REFERENCES

Ammermann, D. (1964) Riesenchromosomen in der makronukleusanlage des ciliaten *Stylonychia spec. Naturwissenschaften 51, 249.*

Ammermann, D. (1971) Morphology and development of the macronuclei of the ciliates *Stylonychia mytilus* and *Euplotes aediculatus. Chromosoma* 33, 209–238.

Bolivar, F., Rodriguez, R. L., Greene, P. S., Betlach, M. D., Heyneker, H. L. & Boyer, H. W. (1977) Construction and characterization of new cloning vehicles. II. A multipurpose cloning system. *Gene* 2, 95–113.

Bostock, C. J, & Prescott, D. M. (1972) Evidence of gene diminution during the formation of the macronucleus in the protozoan, *Stylonychia. Proc. Natl. Acad. Sci. USA* 69, 139–142.

Grunstein, M. & Hogness, D. S. (1975) Colony hybridization: A method for the isolation of cloned DNAs that contain a specific gene. *Proc. Natl. Acad. Sci. USA* 72, 3961–3965.

Herrick, G. & Wesley, R. D. (1978) Isolation and characterization of a highly repetitious inverted terminal repeat sequence from *Oxytricha* macronuclear DNA. *Proc. Natl. Acad. Sci. USA* 75, 2626–2630.

Kloetzel, J. A. (1970) Compartmentalization of the developing macronucleus following conjugation in *Stylonychia* and *Euplotes. J. Cell Biol.* 47, 395–407.

Lauth, M. R., Spear, B. B., Heumann, J. & Prescott, D. M. (1976) DNA of ciliated protozoa: DNA sequence diminution during macronuclear development of *Oxytricha. Cell* 7, 67–74.

Lawn, R. M. (1977) Gene-sized DNA molecules of the *Oxytricha* macronucleus have the same terminal sequence. *Proc. Natl. Acad. Sci. USA* 74, 4325–4328.

Lawn, R. M., Heumann, J. M., Herrick, G. & Prescott, D. M. (1978) The gene-sized DNA molecules in *Oxytricha sp. Cold Spring Harbor Symp. Quant. Biol.* 42, 483–492.

Prescott, D. M. & Murti, K. G. (1973) Chromosome structure in ciliated protozoans. *Cold Spring Harbor Symp. Quant. Biol.* 38, 609–618.

Prescott, D. M., Murti, K. G. & Bostock, C. J. (1973) Genetic apparatus of *Stylonychia sp. Nature* 242, 576, 597–600.

Rae, P. M. M. & Spear, B. B. (1978) Macronuclear DNA of the hypotrichous ciliate *Oxytricha fallax. Proc. Natl. Acad. Sci. USA.* 75, 4992–4996.

Southern, E. M. (1975) Detection of specific sequences among DNA fragments separated by gel electrophoresis. *J. Mol. Biol.* 98, 503–517.

Spear, B. B. & Lauth, M. R. (1976) Polytene chromosomes of *Oxytricha*: Biochemical and morphological changes during macronuclear development in a ciliated protozoan. *Chromosoma* 54, 1–13.

Wensink, P. C., Finnegan, D. J., Donelson, J. E. & Hogness, D. S. (1974) A system for mapping DNA sequences in the chromosomes of *Drosophila melanogaster. Cell* 3, 315–325.

Wesley, R. D. (1975) Inverted repetitious sequences in the macronuclear DNA of hypotrichous ciliates. *Proc. Natl. Acad. Sci. USA* 72, 678–682.

DISCUSSION

LEICK: You mentioned that you had some amicronucleate strains. Since the DNA in the macronucleus is in small pieces, is there any evidence that the cells get senile during vegetative growth?

PRESCOTT: Yes, I believe Ammermann has evidence in *Stylonychia* that many generations after conjugation the cells begin to die out. If during the decline they are allowed to conjugate, senescence is removed and the cells are rejuvenated. The amicronucleated strains that we created in the lab do die out. Some have gone through many generations. Recently I isolated some amicronucleated strains from nature, but I don't know much about their growth yet, but since they occur in nature, I have some hope that they will proliferate for a long time.

PAUL: How does the macronucleus divide in this organism, is it by amitotic division?

PRESCOTT: The macronucleus divides amitotically. Presumably that is possible because there are so many copies of everything. Although in *Tetrahymena* the DNA in the macronucleus is in chromosomal-sized molecules, they are still present in multiple copies. The macronucleus divides rather sloppily with unequal distribution of DNA between the two daughter macronuclei, but the multiple copies of the chromosomes in *Tetrahymena* or gene-sized molecules in hypotrichs make up for the lack of precision of the macronuclear division mechanism, at least for some generations.

BIRNSTIEL: The histone genes of the related *Stylonychia* have been mapped by Dr. Susan Elsevier in my lab and Dr. Lipps in Tübingen. In these experiments, the labeled histone genes of the sea urchin were shown to hybridize to approximately 20 bands of *Stylonychia* DNA of distinct molecular weights, ranging from a few hundred nucleotide base pairs to a few kb. Each of these bands hybridized uniquely to just one of the five kinds of single gene fragments. Hence, in the *Stylonychia* macronucleus the histone genes cannot be tandemly arranged as they are in the sea urchin. It follows that in these species transcription of the histone genes must be predominantly monocistronic.

SCHAFFNER: This finding makes me wonder if most of the (macronuclear) genes are clustered together in the micronuclear chromosomes, leaving vast chromosomal regions completely devoid of genes. What pattern do you observe if you hybridize nick-translated macronuclear DNA in situ to polytene chromosomes?

PRESCOTT: Dick Lawn prepared some recombinant DNA plasmids with pSC101 in David Hogness' lab, and we hybridized to chromosomes cRNA copied from macronuclear sequences in plasmids. Hybridization occurred in single bands. That told us that those particular macronuclear sequences (of unidentified functions) each came from single bands in polytene chromosomes.

SCHAFFNER: Have you found a restriction endonuclease type enzyme in *Stylonichia*?

PRESCOTT: We have been looking for restriction type enzymes and so far have not found any. We have not developed the right test substrates. The correct substrate is micronuclear DNA, and until recently we could not obtain that in sufficient quantity to search for the restriction enzymes.

KLENOW: Are the base sequences in the spacers preserved during the evolution?

PRESCOTT: We cross hybridized macronuclear DNAs of two *Oxytricha* species, and observed approximately 70% homology. With micronuclear DNA there is essentially no measurable cross hybridization. That suggests that the gene sequences in the macronucleus have been maintained during evolution, whereas the spaces between them have drifted so that they no longer are homologous.

II. Structural Organization of the Transcriptional Unit in Chromosomal DNA

Ribosomal DNA and Related Sequences in *Drosophila melanogaster*

Igor B. Dawid & Eric O. Long

Ribosomal DNA (rDNA) in *Drosophila melanogaster* is a family of repeated sequences. These sequences are arranged in two chromosomal loci, one nucleolus organizer each on the X and the Y chromosome. As is the case with rDNA from other higher eukaryotes, *Drosophila* rDNA is arranged in tandem arrays of repeating units. Each repeating unit contains a region that codes for rRNA and a nontranscribed spacer. *Drosophila* rDNA is characterized by a feature that was at first considered unusual but has rapidly become commonplace: an interruption within the coding sequence. Interruptions occur in a fraction of the genes for 28S rRNA and have been called ribosomal insertions (Glover & Hogness 1977, White & Hogness 1977, Wellauer & Dawid 1977, Pellegrini *et al.* 1977). Shortly thereafter a number of viral and eukaryotic genes were found to be interrupted by sequences that do not code for the final product of these genes. Such sequences are most frequently called intervening sequences (Tilghman *et al.* 1978a) and are transcribed into mRNA precursors (Tilghman *et al.* 1978b). We shall continue to use the term insertions for such sequences in *Drosophila* rDNA.

Sequences homologous to the ribosomal insertions occur at different locations in the *Drosophila* genome (Dawid & Botchan 1977). These non-rDNA insertion DNA molecules, as they are named in an operational definiton, are a middle-repetitive group of sequences that are interspersed with other sequences of DNA.

In the present article we summarize our experiments on the structure of rDNA

Carnegie Institution of Washington, Department of Embryology, Baltimore MD 21210, and Laboratory of Biochemistry, National Cancer Institute, Bethesda, MD 20014, U.S.A.

SPECIFIC EUKARYOTIC GENES, Alfred Benzon Symposium 13, Munksgaard 1979

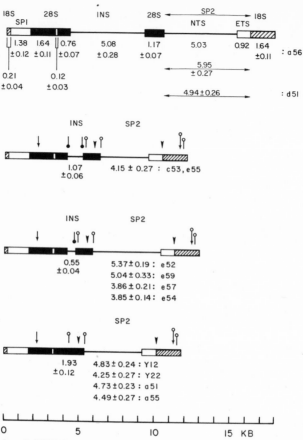

Fig. 1. Maps of cloned rDNA fragments representing full-length repeating units. Each map shows a repeat with one particular size class of insertion. The 28S RNA sequences are shown as heavy bars and the 18S regions as hatched bars. Transcribed spacer regions including the gap in the 28S gene are shown as open bars. Below each region the size with standard deviation is given in kb. At the right end the name of each clone is listed, e.g. a56 standing for Dmra56. In the case of cloned fragments with the same insertion size (or no insertion) different spacer lengths are listed under each other with the corresponding clone designations. The lengths of all regions in the molecules are shown at the top (a56); in the lower maps only those regions are labeled that differ in length from the corresponding region in a56. Restriction sites are indicated as follows: ↓*Sma*I, ꝗ*Hind*III, ↓*Bam*HI,▼*Hae*III. Not all *Hae*III sites are shown; there are no additional *Hae*III sites in the spacer but other sites in the rest of the molecule have not been mapped.

using information based on the study of several cloned fragments. We describe results which show that the ribosomal insertion is not transcribed into rRNA precursor in *Drosophila* embryo cells, raising the possibility that ribosomal insertions in *Drosophila* and intervening sequences in many other eukaryotic genes may have different physiological implications. Last, we present some preliminary observations on the structural arrangements in non-rDNA insertion sequences.

STRUCTURE OF CLONED FRAGMENTS OF D. MELANOGASTER rDNA

We have cloned fragments produced from rDNA with the restriction endonuclease *Eco*RI. In most rDNA repeats there is a single *Eco*RI site in the 18S rRNA gene, so that digestion with this enzyme leads to repeat-length fragments. We have studied 19 such fragments. These DNA molecules were distributed into four classes with respect to the presence of an insertion in the 28S gene region. Repeats without an insertion (continuous repeats) and repeats with insertions of 0.5, 1 and 5 kb were represented. The structure of these cloned fragments is given in Fig. 1. Within each class there is some length variation due to differences in the nontranscribed spacer.

We have studied the sequence relations between different insertions and between spacers of variable length by heteroduplex mapping in the electron microscope (Wellauer & Dawid, 1979), and by cross hybridization using labeled restriction fragments from internal regions of insertions (Dawid & Wellauer 1978). These experiments lead to the conclusion that the 0.5 and 1 kb insertions are homologous to rightmost 0.5 or 1 kb of the 5 kb insertion. Therefore, we group these three size classes of insertions together as type 1 insertions. Type 1 insertions also occur in lengths larger than 5 kb up to about 6.5 kb, but such molecules are relatively rare.

Type 1 insertions are not internally repeated, at least at the level of detectability of restriction enzyme analysis, heteroduplex mapping by electron microscopy and reassociation kinetics. This is surprising since the size of the 1 kb insertion had suggested that it might be a duplication of the 0.5 kb sequence. However, the data clearly exclude the presence of a diret or an inverted duplication in the 1 kb insertion. In contrast, nontranscribed spacers are internally repeated, as will be shown below.

About 16% of all rDNA repeats in *D. melanogaster* carry an insertion which contains at least one *Eco*RI site (Wellauer *et al.* 1978). As a result we obtained in our sample of cloned fragments some molecules that represent about half of a repeating unit of rDNA. The maps of such cloned fragments are shown in Fig. 2. Fragments Dmra54 and Y25 have analogous structures, but the sequences that interrupt the 28S gene in these molecules are not homologous to each other. In

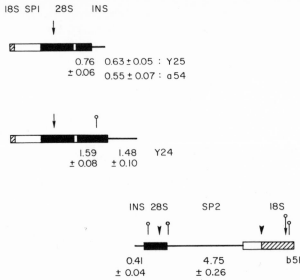

Fig.2. Maps of cloned *Eco*RI rDNA fragments of less than repeat size. The meaning of symbols is described in the legend to Fig. 1.

clone DmrY24 the 28S gene is interrupted at an unusual position, different from all other cases of cloned or uncloned molecules that we have studied. We have not investigated this cloned fragment in detail. Clone Dmrb51 is an example of a "right half" of a repeat. The sequence that interrupts the 28 S gene is homologous to the insertion sequence that is part of an unusual molecule that we describe below. Insertions in the cloned fragments shown in Fig.2 are not homologous to any part of the 5 kb insertion of type 1. Such insertions, which are characterized by the presene of EcoRI sites, are grouped together as type 2 insertions. Whether all type 2 insertions share some sequences or whether more sequence types occur is not known at present.

One unusual rDNA molecule was obtained as a recombinant clone (Fig. 3). The structure of this molecule appears to have arisen by a recombination event. It could be the result of a deletion of an entire 18S gene and parts of the surrounding spacers, or there might have been a translocation of a 28S gene with parts of its surrounding spacers into the spacer of another repeat. There is good evidence that this rearrangement occurred in the fly and is not a cloning artifact since a molecule with very similar structure has been found in the electron microscope among uncloned rDNA molecules from *Drosophila*.

The chromosomal distribution of different rDNA structures has been studied

(Wellauer *et al.* 1978). On the X chromosome about 65% of all repeats are interrupted; of these, about 50% carry type 1 insertions while the rest are mostly of type 2. On the Y chromosome only 16% of all repeats are interrupted and most if not all of these repeats carry type 2 insertions. Type 1 insertions are very rare in Y chromosomal rDNA if they occur at all. The chromosomal distribution of rare forms of rDNA like DmrY24 (Fig.2), Dmrc52 (Fig. 3), or Dm207 described by Glover (1977) is not known.

INTERNAL STRUCTURE OF NONTRANSCRIBED SPACERS

The nontranscribed spacer in *Xenopus laevis* rDNA has been found to vary in length between different repeating units and to have an internally repetitious sequence arrangement (Wellauer *et al.* 1976, Botchan *et al.* 1977). We have obtained similar information on the spacer in *Drosophila* in two different ways. A detailed heteroduplex analysis in the electron microscope that will be reported separately (Wellauer & Dawid, 1979) demonstrated that pairs of cloned rDNA repeats formed heteroduplexes containing deletion loops at variable position. Such loops are thought to arise from misalignment of internally repetitive regions during reannealing. Loops were found throughout most of the length of the nontranscribed spacer suggesting that repetitive elements are present in this region. Nontranscribed spacers in X and Y chromosomal rDNA are homologous to each other (Wellauer *et al.* 1978).

Additional information was obtained by restriction mapping, using four different rDNA clones. Two clones are derived from X chromosomal rDNA, one being a continuous gene (a55) and the other a gene with a 5 kb insertion (a56). The third clone is derived from the Y chromosome and carries a continuous gene (Y22). The fourth clone carries a 0.5 kb insertion but its

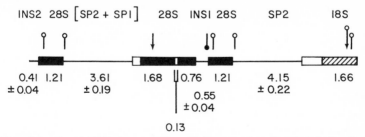

Fig. 3. Map of the cloned rDNA fragment Dmrc52. The meaning of symbols is described in the legend to Fig. 1.

chromosomal origin is not known (e54). Furthermore, clone a56 has the longest and e54 the shortest spacer in our collection of cloned rDNA fragments. The HindIII fragments containing the spacer (see Fig. 1) were end-labeled at their 5' ends, and digested with HaeIII. The large spacer fragment, now labeled at one end, was isolated by gel electrophoresis and used for partial digest mapping. These maps were confirmed and refined by analyzing various digests of unlabeled spacer fragments. The results of the mapping with several restriction enzymes are shown in Fig. 4.

These analyses led to the following conclusions. Spacers are internally repetitive, as shown by the regular 250 bp interval between AluI sites. The number of these repeated elements varies from one repeat to another. All clones have a conserved 1.0 kb long fragment at the right end of the spacer, generated by AluI-HaeIII digestion. Most of this fragment codes for the external transcribed spacer (see Fig. 1). There is no striking difference in the organization and structure of spacers derived from the X or the Y chromosome, or from repeats with or without insertions.

The occurrence of internal repeats is a common feature among spacers of rDNA (Wellauer et al. 1976) and other gene families such as 5S DNA (Fedoroff

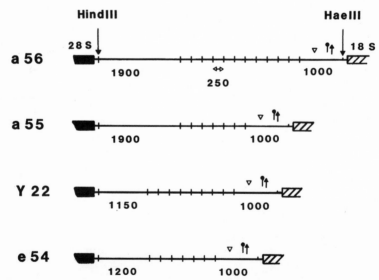

Fig. 4. Restriction map of spacers from cloned *D. melanogaster* rDNA. The sites of restriction by the following endonucleases are indicated: *Alu*I, (vertical bar across the horizontal line); the sizes of the *Alu*I fragments are given in bp. *Taq*I, (∇); *Hinf*, (↑); *Hha*I, (↑). Sixteen other restriction endonucleases tested did not cut the *Hind*III-*Hae*III spacer fragment.

& Brown 1978). The functional implications of these structures are not known but it has been suggested that internally repetitive spacers are sites of unequal recombination within gene clusters and are thus important in the evolution of gene families (Smith 1973, Wellauer *et al.*1976, Fedoroff & Brown 1978).

SEARCH FOR TRANSCRIPTS OF RIBOSOMAL INSERTION SEQUENCES

More than half of all rDNA repeating units located on the X chromosome and about 16% of the units on the Y chromosome are interrupted by insertion sequences. Furthermore, DNA elements homologous to type 1 insertions occur outside the nucleolus organizer loci, bringing the total amount of insertion-like sequences in a diploid cell to several hundred copies (Dawid & Botchan 1977). To test whether these sequences are transcribed we looked for RNA molecules in *Drosophila* embryos that are homologous to type 1 insertion sequences. A large excess of unlabeled RNA was hybridized with highly labeled fragments from cloned rDNA which contain the entire 5 kb insertion element. Hybrid formation was assayed by digestion with the single strand-specific nuclease S1. Cells derived form 3- to 18-h embryos were separated into crude nuclear and cytoplasmic fractions and total RNA was extracted from each for this test.

Several controls were carried out. Aliquots of the annealed samples were digested with RNase under conditions that destroy hybrids before treatment with S1. Any labeled DNA remaining S1 resistant under these conditions was subtracted from the experimental result. We tested separately that duplex DNA is recovered intact after the RNase/S1 treatment. The RNA and DNA were tested by gel electophoresis after incubation to guard against extensive degradation. The labeled DNA probe was shown to be able to self-reassociate to about 90% S1 resistance. Further, the same RNA preparations used in these tests were annealed with a labeled restriction fragment of rDNA that is derived from a gene region (coding for rRNA) . The RNA hybridized to this gene fragment with the expected kinetics when making reasonable assumptions about the abundance of rRNA in the total RNA samples.

The experimental reactions between total nuclear or cytoplasmic RNA from embryos and labeled insertion sequences failed to show any hybridization at all. The sensitivity of the experiment was such that we should have detected one RNA copy of insertion sequences per cell on the average. It is possible that a small fraction of the insertion sequence is transcribed or that a larger part, even all of it, could be transcribed at some frequency in certain cells that constitute a

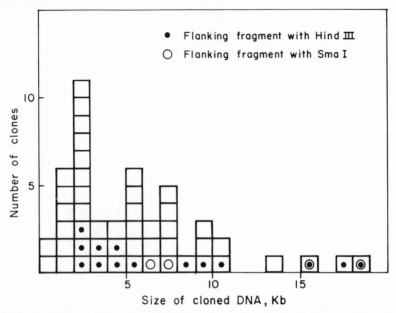

Fig.5. Size distribution of cloned non-rDNA insertion molecules. Each clone was digested with *Hind*III and *Sma*I and the digests were searched for fragments that contain flanking sequences, i.e. regions that do not hybridize with ribosomal insertions. The presence of such flanking fragments in a clone is indicated by a solid circle in the case of *Hind*III fragments, and by an open circle for *Sma*I fragments.

small portion of the embryo cell population. The major result, however, is the absence of transcripts of insertions at substantial frequencies. If one were to hypothesize that ribosomal genes carrying insertions are transcribed into mature rRNA by a mechanism that involved transcription across the insertion followed by splicing, one would expect a rather large number of nascent transcripts with insertion sequences to occur. It is known that an embryo cell contains about 5000 nascent transcripts of rRNA precursor (McKnight & Miller 1976). Considering these numbers it is irrelevant in the context of rRNA production whether insertion transcripts occur at a level of less than one copy per average cell. If they did this might be of interest in a different context, but with respect to ribosomal RNA production we conclude that interrupted genes are probably not used in the *Drosophila* embryo. The possible transcription of interrupted genes by the polymerases jumping across the interruption is not excluded by our data but should have been seen in electron micrographs of transcription units if it occurred frequently. The situation in other cells and tissues has not been tested so far.

Unless the situation in other tissues proves to be very different from that in the embryo, it would appear that the interrupted ribosomal genes in *Drosophila* are substantially different in character from other interrupted genes in various eukaryotes. In these other cases all copies of the gene (often a single copy) are interrupted and produce functional RNA by transcription of the intervening sequence followed by RNA splicing. Such a mechanism is not important in rRNA synthesis in *Drosophila* embryos. Functional rRNA must be made from those copies of the ribosomal genes that carry a continuous 28S sequence in the genome.

HETEROGENEITY IN NON-rDNA INSERTION SEQUENCES

Sequences homologous to type 1 ribosomal insertions occur outside the nucleolus organizer region (Dawid & Botchan 1977). This material is present in multiple copies and arranged in an irregular way interspersed with DNA of unrelated sequence. We attempted to study in more detail the organization of these non-rDNA insertion-like molecules. For that purpose we have isolated about 50 recombinant clones carrying such DNA. *Drosophila* embryo DNA was sheared randomly, and non-rDNA insertion DNA was purified partially by density gradient centrifugation as described previously (Dawid & Botchan 1977). The DNA fragments were then inserted into pMB9 (Bolivar *et al.* 1977) by the poly(dA:dT) tailing method (Wensink *et al.* 1974). Transformants were screened by hybridization with insertion sequences by a modification of the method of Grunstein & Hogness (1975).

The cloned DNA fragments selected for study have a heterogenous size distribution as shown in Fig. 5. As a first characterization we digested the recombinant plasmids with *Hind*III and *Sma*I and tested the fragments for hybridization with ribosomal insertion sequences by the method of Southern (1975). We wanted to find fragments that do not hybridize with insertion sequences and therefore would represent "flanking DNA", i.e. regions interspersed with non-rDNA insertions. Since the restriction map of the vector is known we could exclude the trivial case of fragments derived from the vector only. Sixteen of the cloned DNAs did contain regions that are not homologous to ribosomal insertions (se Fig. 5). These "flanking" fragments have various sizes suggesting that they represent various sequences. Several of these flanking

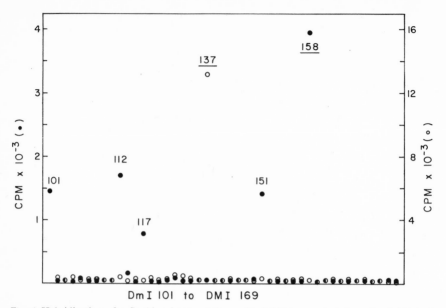

Fig. 6. Hybridization of a flanking fragment from pDmI 137 (open circles) or pDmI 158 (solid circles) to filter-bound DNA from the other cloned non-rDNA insertion molecules. The points along the ordinate represent individual clones arranged consecutively. Positive hybridizations are numbered, and self-reactions are underlined. pDmI 137 hybridizes only to itself, while pDmI 158 hybridizes to four other clones as well.

sequences were isolated, labeled by nick translation and hybridized with filter-bound samples of all the cloned non-rDNA insertion DNA molecules. Fig. 6 shows two cases with different results. A flanking sequence derived from pDmI 137 hybridized only to itself and not at all with any of the other cloned DNAs. Thus, this flanking sequence is unique in our cloned sample. Flanking sequence from pDmI 158 hybridized to four other cloned DNAs in addition to itself. Other examples not shown gave similar results with flanking sequences hybridizing to a variable number of representatives from our collection of cloned DNAs.

These results support and extend our earlier conclusions (Dawid & Botchan 1977) regarding the nature of non-rDNA insertion DNA. These DNA sequences occur in blocks of several kb interspersed with a variety of other DNA sequences. Some of the flanking sequences, as we call them, are again representatives of middle-repetitive DNA, but we do not know whether unique sequences occur in this position. A particular flanking sequence may be found next to insertion-like sequences at variable frequencies.

Many questions regarding non-rDNA insertions remain unanswered. Our experiments regarding the low abundance of transcripts of insertions in embryos are valid for non-rDNA insertions as well as for rDNA. However, it is possible that a small number of transcripts which would be quantitatively unimportant in rRNA production could be biologically important when derived from non-rDNA insertions.

REFERENCES

Bolivar, F., Rodriguez, R.L., Betlach, M.C. & Boyer, H.W. (1977) Construction and characterization of new cloning vehicles I. Ampicillin-resistant derivatives of the plasmid pMB9. *Gene 2*, 75–93.

Botchan, P., Reeder, R.H. & Dawid, I.B. (1977) Restriction analysis of the non-transcribed spacers of *Xenopus laevis* ribosomal DNA. *Cell 11*, 599–607.

Dawid, I.B. & Wellauer, P.K. (1978) Ribosomal DNA and related sequences in *Drosophila melanogaster. Cold Spring Harbor Symp. Quant. Biol. 42*, 1185–1194.

Dawid, I.B. & Botchan, P. (1977) Sequences homologous to ribosomal insertions occur in the *Drosophila* genome outside the nucleolus organizer. *Proc. Natl. Aca. Sci. U.S.A. 74*, 4233–4237.

Fedoroff, N.V. & Brown, D.D. (1978) The nucleotide sequence of oocyte 5S DNA in *Xenopus laevis.* I. The AT rich spacer. *Cell 13*, 701–716.

Glover, D.M. (1977) Cloned segment of *Drosophila melanogaster* rDNA containing new types of sequence insertion. *Proc. Natl. Acad. Sci. U.S.A. 74*, 4932–4936.

Glover, D.M. & Hogness, D.S. (1977) A novel arrangement of the 18S and 28S sequences in a repeating unit of *Drosophila melanogaster* rDNA. *Cell 10*, 167–176.

Grunstein, M. & Hogness, D.S. (1975) Colony hybridization: a method for the isolation of cloned DNAs that contain a specific gene. *Proc. Natl. Acad. Sci. U.S.A. 72*, 3961–3965.

McKnight, S.L. & Miller, O.L.Jr. (1976) Ultrastructural patterns of RNA synthesis during early embryogenesis of *Drosophila melanogaster. Cell 8*, 305–319.

Pellegrini, M., Manning, J. & Davidson, N. (1977) Sequence arrangement of the rDNA of *Drosophila melanogaster. Cell 10*, 213–224.

Smith, G.P. (1973) Unequal crossover and the evolution of multigene families. *Cold Spring Harbor Symp. Quant. Biol. 38*, 507–513.

Southern, E.M. (1975) Detection of specific sequence among DNA fragments separated by gel electrophoresis. *J. Mol. Biol. 98*, 503–517.

Tilghman, S.M., Tiemeier, D.C., Seidman, J.D., Peterlin, B.M., Sullivan, M., Maizel, J.V. & Leder, P. (1978a) Intervening sequence identified in the structural portion of a mouse β-globin gene. *Proc. Natl. Acad. Sci. U.S.A. 75*, 725–729.

Tilghman, S.M., Curtis, P.J., Tiemeier, D.C., Leder, P. & Weismann, C. (1978b) The intervening sequence of mouse β-globin gene is transcribed within the 15S β-globin mRNA precursor. *Proc. Natl. Acad. Sci. U.S.A. 75*, 1309–1313.

Wellauer, P.K. & Dawid, I.B. (1977) The structural organization of ribosomal DNA in *Drosophila melanogaster. Cell 10*, 193–212.

Wellauer, P. K. & Dawid, I. B. (1979) Ribosomal DNA in *Drosophila melanogaster* II. Heteroduplex mapping of cloned and uncloned rDNA. *J. Mol. Biol.,* in press.

Wellauer, P.K., Dawid, I.B. & Tartof, K.D. (1978) X and Y chromosomal ribosomal DNA of Drosophila: comparison of spacers and insertions. *Cell 14*, 269–278.

Wellauer, P.K., Dawid, I.B., Brown, D.D. & Reeder, R.H. (1976) The molecular basis for length heterogeneity in ribosomal DNA from *Xenopus laevis*. *J. Mol. Biol. 105*, 461–486.

Wensink, P.C., Finnegan, D.J., Donelson, J.E. & Hogness, D.S. (1974) A system for mapping DNA sequences in the chromosomes of *Drosophila melanogaster*. *Cell 3*, 315–325.

White, R.L. & Hogness, D.S. (1977) R-loop mapping of the 18S and 28S sequences in the long and short repeating unit of *Drosophila melanogaster* rDNA. *Cell 10*, 177–192.

DISCUSSION

PARDUE: Are you talking only about type I sequences that you have localized elsewhere? What do you know about type II?

DAWID: We have done some experiments with type II. We have not been able to find non-ribosomal insertion-type sequences of type II. If there were 10 copies of type II somewhere else I may not have seen them yet, if there were a hundred, we certainly would have seen them, and they are not there.

HOGNESS: In Laird's results using another type spread, it is clear that distribution of "Christmas trees" and spacers is different. I am not going as far as to saying it is different in embryonic than it is in nurse cells, and so by looking at embryos you may still be looking at rather restricted population.

CRICK: Could we just continue on this business of the type I ribosomal insertions. That period is the period before hatching?

DAWID: Yes, that is true. That is just before hatching.

CRICK: If you had to guess, for *Drosophila*, when it needed to make rapidly large amounts of ribosomes, what would you guess? It would be extremely interesting if it was found that in one tissue these genes were used, and in another tissue they were not. I have a feeling that that may not be the ideal tissue to look for this kind of phenomenon.

DAWID: That may be true. Rates of rRNA synthesis in different tissues are not known. However, McKnight & Miller (1977) have found that rRNA synthesis is activated rapidly at the blastoderm stage. There is no good reason known to me to expect another stage to be more active. Perhaps nurse cells might be expected to be most active in rRNA synthesis, but we have not studied them. No EM data known to me show a large proportion of long transcription units (about 13 kb) that would be expected if the insertion were transcribed into RNA.

McKnight, S. L. Jr. (1977) *Cell* 12, 795–804.

HOGNESS: But the other reason for thinking of nurse cells in this regard is that you may not only want to make a lot ribosomal RNA, but you may want to store it in some stable form and then be able to trigger it in its useful form with conversion with its useful form at one time, and one could imagine that insertion sequences were useful in that regard.

WEISSMANN: When you were looking for possible transcripts, were you pulse-labeling the embryos?

DAWID: No. That was cold RNA plus hot DNA, and then looking for S1-resistant hybrids.

WEISSMANN: And the steady-state level of this precursor molecule?

DAWID: It is no more than one per cell, but that is the point. You cannot really splice in any easy way before you have traversed the insertion. If you do make a precursor which goes all the way across, and splice it at the moment where the polymerase has gotten across, that would leave about 50 nascent chains hanging off the 5 kb insertion region, and since there are 50–100 genes/cell that would already account for 1,000 copies. So if you want to make the precursor and splice it to make a product the way the β-globin mRNA does, you would at least have to go across with your polymerase to the other end before you can splice. And that we would easily see.

FLAVELL: You would not have picked up a transcript of only a small segment of this region. I think David Glover did Southern blots which would detect such transcripts. This could explain such a discrepancy.

DAWID: That is true. We would have only seen transcripts if you transcribed a large fraction of the 5 kb segment. But again, if you want to really make rRNA from such a gene, you have to get the whole thing transcribed.

Functional Organization of the Histone Genes in the Sea Urchin *Psammechinus:* A Progress Report

M. Birnstiel, R. Portmann, M. Busslinger, W. Schaffner, E. Probst & A. Kressmann

The repeated histone genes of the sea urchin are an interesting example of developmentally controlled genes. As there are histone variants at the protein level, variant DNA clones can be isolated. Clone h22 and h19 are such variant clones coding for different H2A's and H1's proteins. While the DNA sequences of the structural genes are easily interpreted, we have no simple way of interpreting the DNA sequences upstream and downstream from the structural genes. The procedure of studying the evolution of such sequences reveals some conservative motifs which may have a function in the regulation of histone gene expression. To understand their real function we must study the expression of such potential regulatory sequences in an *in vivo* system. Injection of cloned genes into the *Xenopus* oocyte may well provide a means of detecting and analyzing such signal sequences.

HISTONE GENES ARE CLUSTERED

In the sea urchin *Psammechinus* the histone genes for the five histone proteins form a genetic unit in that they are clustered together on the chromosomal DNA (Portmann *et al.* 1976, Schaffner *et al.* 1976). Fig. 1 depicts such a DNA unit which was cloned from the sea urchin *Psammechinus* and then reclaimed from a λ vector (Clarkson *et al.* 1976). The stretch of DNA comprising the five histone genes is about 6000 bp long (Portmann *et al.* 1976, Schaffner *et al.* 1976). Much of the DNA is AT-rich spacer DNA. In Fig. 1 the DNA has been melted out and

Institut für Molekularbiologie II der Universität Zürich, 8057 Zürich, Switzerland.

SPECIFIC EUKARYOTIC GENES, Alfred Benzon Symposium 13, Munksgaard 1979

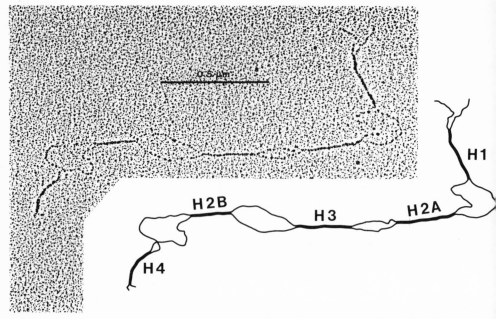

Fig. 1. Partially denatured histone DNA unit. (cf. Portmann *et al.* (1976).

rendered single-stranded and can be identified as four bubbles and two forks.
The structural genes are to be found within the unmelted regions, one each per
double-stranded section in a series H4, H2B, H3, H2A and H1. From
sequencing data (Schaffner *et al.* 1978) it is known that in each double-stranded
section the structural genes lie towards the "right" so that the unmelted, and
hence GC-rich sections lying to the "left" constitute prelude regions to the
structural genes. Since histone genes are a repeated gene family and are arranged
in a tandem array, one may imagine that in the chromosomal DNA the large
fork near the H1 end would link up with the small fork near the H4 gene of the
next tandem repeat. It is further known that transcription proceeds in the
direction H4→H1, i.e. all coding sequences lie on the same DNA strand (Gross
et al. 1976).

HISTONE GENES ARE REGULATED AT THREE LEVELS
Since our main interest is to understand how these histone genes function in the
sea urchins and how they are regulated, we should first of all ask what kind of
regulatory processes might be expected.

Since H1 proteins occur only in half molar concentrations relative to other histone proteins (reviewed by Kornberg & Thomas 1974) yet H1 genes are found once per repeat, it follows that there must be some regulation of the H1 protein levels, either during transcription, translation or at a post-translational level. The appearance of histone mRNAs in the cytoplasm and the production of histones as such are clearly regulated during the cell cycle, but it is still a matter of considerable controversy whether this regulation is transcriptional or post-transcriptional.

Another type of regulation which is of considerable interest is the developmental regulation of histone production. There is now conclusive evidence that different histone species of an individual are not all the same and that specialized tissues may have histone "variants" of distinct primary structure. Such tissue-specific sequence diversity was first recognized and then established by protein sequencing for the H1 proteins (reviewed by Elgin & Weintraub 1975) which are known to be rapidly evolving proteins also. More recently, extensive sequence variation has been found also for the H2A and H2B proteins within a single species, most elegantly documented in the sea urchin. Cohen et al. (1975) were the first to point out that during the early sea urchin development there is a synthesis of a consecutive series of H2B variants a, γ, δ distinguishable from one another by electrophoretic parameters. More recently, direct protein sequencing of the H2B's enabled von Holt and co-workers to distinguish as many as eight distinct kinds of H2B proteins which could be classified as embryonic, or belonging to the gut, or to spermatocytes (Brandt et al. 1978). Since the H2B species show quite disparate sequences, especially near the N-terminus of the molecule (Brandt & von Holt 1978) it may be assumed that genes coding for different H2B variants within an individual have been separated from each other for a very long time in evolution. A similar pattern of sequence divergence is also emerging for the H2A proteins but at present the data are still limited (cf. Schaffner et al. 1978).

DIVERGENT HISTONE DNA CLONES CODE FOR HISTONE VARIANTS
Divergent subsets of histone genes which now experience tissue specific expression must have accumulated – at the level of the DNA sequence – mutations of at least two kinds: those leading to amino acid substitutions with selective advantage for the animal or which are at least selectively neutral, and those mutations leading to synonymous codons with no direct effects on amino

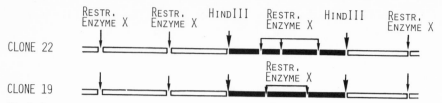

Fig. 2. General scheme for screening of histone DNA variants.

acid composition (Weinberg *et al.* 1972). One would therefore expect that when histone genes are cloned from the sea urchin, first, that not all cloned units would be the same. Second, since the demand for the synthesis of specific histone variants differs drastically for specific developmental stages, one would expect some subsets of genes to be found more frequently than others.

By screening numerous histone DNA clones, we are able to verify this prediction (Portmann *et al.,* unpublished results). The DNA was cloned into a λ vector, the histone DNA being inserted at the HindIII site (Clarkson *et al.* 1976). When each individual recombinant DNA is restricted first with HindIII and then a second restriction enzyme, two kinds of events take place: first, the inserted histone DNA is released. Second, the additional restriction enzyme may cleave of the λ DNA, with all the restriction fragments generated in this reaction held in common by all clones. The restriction fragments obtained from the inserted histone DNA will differ depending on the degree of sequence divergence found in the insert (Fig. 2).

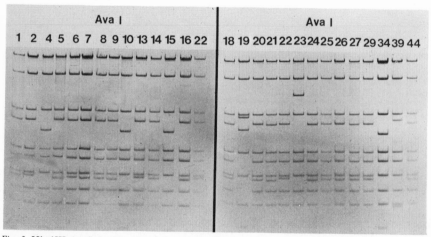

Fig. 3. HindIII-AvaI double-digest of a series of independently isolated λ-histone DNA recombinants.

Fig. 3 shows the result of such a screening with Hind III and Ava I. Most tracts of the electrophoretic analysis are identical to one another, or at least very similar, while others are distinctly different, e.g. clone 4, clone 19, etc. Screening

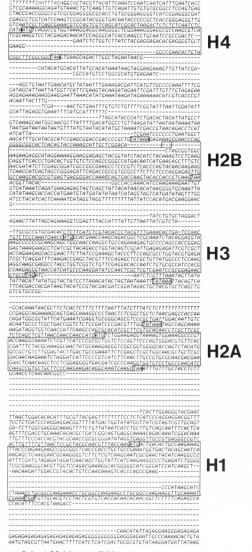

Fig. 4. Partial sequence of the h22 histone DNA clone. The positions of the "Hogness promotors" have been indicated in the 5′ regions of structural genes.

experiments of this type using a large number of clones have enabled us to subdivide the clones into four basic categories: First, a very large family of clones of the h22 type, obviously occurring with high frequency; another group of the h4 type which probably occurs in the genome perhaps 20–30 times; another of the clone 19 type occurring only a few times in the genome (S. Rusconi, unpublished results). A fourth class of divergent genes has also been found which occur at low frequency and which are as yet poorly characterized.

To prove that the different DNA classes code for specific histone variants, it is necessary to look at the DNA sequences in detail.

Fig. 4 depicts some sequences of clone h22, nearly 4000 bases having been sequenced. The structural genes for the H2A and H3 have been analyzed in their entirety and large sections of other genes as well. This venture has allowed us to confirm the basic features of the gene unit such as the nature of the gene arrangement, the direction of transcription, and the distribution and composition of spacers and genes (Schaffner *et al.* 1978).

Translation of the DNA sequence of the H2B and the H2A structural genes into the corresponding amino acid sequence by computer and comparison of these protein sequences with the protein data of von Holt's group (Brandt *et al.* 1978) reveal that clone h22 belongs to the embryonic gene programme (cf. Schaffner *et al.* 1978).

The divergent clone 19, representative of a very small family of histone genes within the sea urchin, has been analyzed in the same way. About 2500 bases have been sequenced and all the genes have been identified (M. Busslinger *et al.,* unpublished results, see also Fig. 5). From comparison with the von Holt protein sequences, it is clear that clone 19 also belongs to the general family of embryonic histone genes, but close inspection shows that the protein sequences coded for by this clone differ from those encoded by clone h22. Thus H2A encoded by these two clones differ from one another in at least one amino acid and by definition are therefore H2A variants (Busslinger *et al.,* unpublished results). However, it can most easily be seen that these are variant DNA clones from the H1 protein sequences.

Comparison of the two H1 proteins, translated from the DNA sequence by computer, reveals that they have quite different N-terminal sequences and only from amino acid 70 onwards is there an area of extensive sequence homology. This homology is also shared with trout and rabbit H1 proteins (Busslinger *et al.,* unpublished results).

Sequencing has also permitted other very interesting information about the structural genes for histones: 1. No introns – or split genes – have been discovered. 2. The 5′ prelude sequences to the structural genes are such that no histone protein precursor can be produced. 3. There are no piggyback

h19

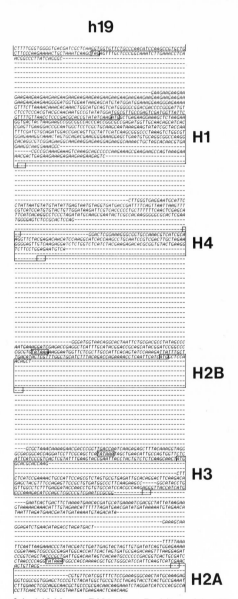

Fig. 5. Partial sequence of the h19 histone DNA clone. Positions of the "Hogness promotors" have been indicated.

arrangements of superimposed genes in histone DNA so that in contrast to viral DNA each histone DNA sequence codes for only a single protein species. Furthermore, the AT-rich DNA which has been sequenced so far cannot possibly code for additional large proteins (Schaffner *et al.* 1978).

SEQUENCES OF INTEREST CAN BE FOUND IN THE PRELUDES
TO STRUCTURAL GENES

The functional interpretation of the DNA sequences of structural genes is of course quite straightforward. However, outside the structural gene, in the prelude sequence in front of the initiator codon ATG and the sequence following the termination signal TAA, one would expect to find regulatory sequences such as those coding for the ribosome binding site of mRNA, maturation signals dictating the cleavage of precursor histone mRNAs, promotors, terminator signals for transcription and signals for DNA replication; but at present there are no guidelines as to how to identify such regulatory sequences. We can, however, argue as follows: It seems reasonable to suppose that mutations in regulatory sequences would be deleterious and that such sequences would therefore be conservative in evolution; on the other hand, unimportant sequences would show rapid evolutionary change.

Since we have considerable sequence data from two histone DNA clones known to have been separated from each other by a considerable evolutionary distance and having incurred a great many silent mutations to synonymous

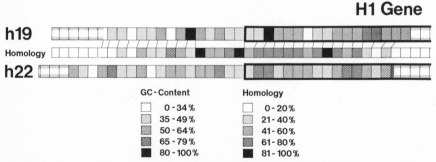

Fig. 6. Sequence comparison between the H1 region of clone h22 and clone 19. The upper and lower bands depict the GC content of this DNA region, while the middle band gives the percent homology between the two clones. For this operation all sequences were matched to give maximal homologies. The mispaired and the sequence gaps were then counted for each 20 nucleotide section of our "standard" clone h22. The number of "flaws" was related to the 20 nucleotide sections of clone h22.

```
C C G A A T T A C C T | A C T G T C T C T C A A - - G C A A C T (A T G) |  H3-GENE PSAMM.CLONE 19
C A C T G A N T C C A | A C T C T C T C C C A A - A T C A A C C (A T G) |  H3-GENE PSAMM.CLONE 22
A T C G C A C T A A G | A C T C T C T C T C A A T C T C C A T A (A T G) |  H4-GENE PSAMM.CLONE 22
A T C A C A C A A G A | A C T C T C T C T C A A -14B- - C A T C (A T G) |  H4-GENE STRONGYLOCENTROTUS *
```

```
G C A T C T T T A C A G A C C A G A A A A C T | C A A T T C A T C (A T G) |  H2B-GENE PSAMM.CLONE 19
G C T C T C T C A G C T C G T T A A C | C A A C C A A C - C A T C (A T G) |  H2A-GENE PSAMM.CLONE 22
C C G A T T T A T T C T A A C T C A T | C A A - C A A - - C A T C (A T G) |  H2A-GENE STRONGYLOCENTROTUS **
```

```
T T T G T T A A - C T C C G C T A C G C A A C G T T T A C | C A A G (A T G) |  H1-GENE PSAMM.CLONE 22
- - - - - - - - -   - - - -   - - - - -   - - -   - -   - - - -
T T T G T T A A C C T C C C - G A C G C A C C G T A T A T | C A A G (A T G) |  H1-GENE PSAMM.CLONE 19
```

*GRUNSTEINS LAB.   **KEDES' LAB.

Fig. 7. Comparison of the DNA sequences proximal to the initiator codon ATG. Such sequences might code for the ribosome attachment sites in mRNA.

codons in the structural genes, we have looked for conservative sequence blocks in the preludes of the structural genes. An example of this is shown in Fig. 6. The H1 prelude regions of the two DNA clones were matched in a computer for maximal sequence homology and the degree of homology charted in map units of 20 nucleotides. This operation reveals that there is conservation of a DNA region extending from the H1 structural gene over all of the prelude sequence. Hence, this prelude region is clearly distinct from the rapidly evolving AT-rich spacer DNA. Moving from the ATG initiator codon towards the spacer, it can be seen that the first nucleotide block of 20 is fairly conservative. It may be indicative of a conserved ribosomal attachment site sequence in the H1 mRNA. Further upstream the sequences are slightly more divergent. A conservative sequence block occurs at a position around −100 but after this there is hardly any sequence homology and we have now reached the AT-rich spacer DNA, which, as mentioned above, would be expected to evolve more rapidly.

Having seen indications of a possible imprint of a ribosome attachment coding sequence, we made a compilation of the DNA sequences immediately preceding the five histone genes and ordered the sequences according to their relatedness. These results are depicted in Fig. 7 and raise some interesting questions.

The putative ribosome attachment coding sequences of all the known H3 and H4 structural genes in both the clones and even those from a different sea urchin species (sequenced by Grunstein & Grunstein 1977) show extensive sequence homology over a stretch of about 20 nucleotides. The homologous section differs from the sequences preceding the H2A and the H2B and are in turn different again from the pre-H1 sequences. By any criteria, whether it be evolution, nucleosome structure or developmental diversity, the histones have always been classified into groups, one consisting of the H4 and the H3, and another consisting of H2A and H2B proteins, while the H1 proteins have always been considered as a separate group. It is thus very interesting that the putative ribosomal attachment sequences show a similar threefold division and we pose the question whether these sequences may not play a role in translational control of histone messenger expression.

Sequence comparison may also have revealed the promotor sequence (or part of it) for the polymerase II. Recently, Hogness & coworkers have sequenced the histone genes of *Drosophila*. Comparing the prelude sequence of the *Drosophila* genes with one another and with those of the sea urchin, he noted that the sequence TATAAA is held in common between *Drosophila* genes and some of the sea urchin histone genes (this volume). A computer search showed that the sequence TATAAA occurs in front of the H2A and the H2B in clone h22, about roughly 100 nucleotides removed from the structural genes (cf. Fig. 4). There are two sites in clone 19 (cf. Fig. 5). Hogness proposes that the TATAAA might represent a "Pribnov box" for the eukaryotic polymerase II. No putative promotor sequence has as yet been found proximal to the H4 or the H1 genes of any histone clone of any sea urchin. At face value this might mean that the H2B and the H3 genes are transcribed monocistronically, while the H2A, the H1 and H4 genes might be co-transcribed. If true, this would offer some explanation why sequence comparison between the preludes of H4, H2A, H2B and H1 did not reveal universally shared sequence homologies.

CLONED SEA URCHIN HISTONE GENES ARE EXPRESSED IN THE XENOPUS OOCYTES

With present day techniques it is possible to delete interesting conservative sequences (pinpointed by the above approach) or to mutagenize them, but to elucidate their function we must have some system for comparing their expression in their natural unmodified form. This is a general area of research which we have called Surrogate Genetics (Birnstiel & Chipchase 1977, Kressmann et al. 1978) and which more recently has also been called Reversed Genetics (Ch. Weissmann, Zürich; cf. this volume). The approach which we have been using is to inject the cloned sea urchin histone DNA into the nucleus of the living frog oocytes and to study its expression.

It is generally believed that the frog oocyte nucleus is used in these experiments because it is very large and can be injected easily. This is of course true, but the oocyte nucleus has other advantages. For one thing, it synthesizes RNA at a rate about 1000 times that of an average cell nucleus. Since it is already synthesizing large amounts of RNA it should be possible to insert some foreign genes for transcription without too much disturbance of the nuclear metabolism. But the oocyte is a very peculiar cell in that it has stored in it many components needed for the rapid development following fertilization which produces a highly structured embryo within hours; in view of this we may hope that the oocyte contains sufficient regulatory proteins to support the expression of injected foreign DNA.

The basic problem encountered in oocyte nucleus experiments is to find and inject the nucleus in an opaque egg. Our approach has been to first isolate the oocytes and centrifuge them gently (Kressmann et al. 1977) so that the nucleus rises to the top within the oocyte where its exact position can be seen through the displacement of pigment granules. These granules then form a dark ring surrounding the nucleus. Thus subcutaneous injection into the dead center of the ring automatically insures injection of the nucleus with a high success rate (Kressmann et al. 1977).

Using the oocyte system we have established the following major points: Cloned histone DNA in ligated, circularized form is transcribed rapidly, some 20% of all cellular RNA being derived from the injected DNA (Kressmann et al. 1977). This transcription is entirely dependent on polymerase II as determined by α-amanitin experiments (E. Probst, unpublished results). Sea urchin histone proteins H2A and H2B are produced in small amounts but there is as yet no conclusive evidence that sea urchin H3, H4 and H1 proteins are also synthesized. There is a clear discrepancy between the very intensive RNA synthesis supported by the injected histone DNA and the relatively small rate of histone protein production. This apparent discrepancy can be resolved by analysis of the RNA pattern produced by the oocyte. Sea urchin specific RNA was found to be of two kinds: a polydisperse RNA of ill-defined size accounting for most of the transcript and a class of discrete mRNA-like molecules which comigrated with the messengers for H2A and H2B proteins. Only traces of H3 mRNA-like molecules were observed; no messengers for H4 or H1 proteins were detectable (E. Probst & A. Kressmann, unpublished results).

We therefore conclude that while all of the RNA derived from injected histone DNA is transcribed by polymerase II, much of the RNA is of ill-defined size. Nevertheless, small amounts of H2A and H2B messenger-like molecules as well as H2A and H2B proteins are produced. Thus at least some regulatory sequences of the sea urchin genes appear to be recognized by the oocyte system.

ACKNOWLEDGMENT

This work was supported by the Swiss National Science Foundation, Grant No. 3.257.077 and the state of Zürich.

REFERENCES

Birnstiel, M. & Chipchase, M. (1977) Current work on the histone operon. Review article for *Trends in Biochemical Sciences* 2, 149–152.

Brandt, W. F. & von Holg, C. (1978) A histone H2B variant from the embryo of the sea urchin *Parechinus angulosus. Biochem. Biophys. Acta.* In press.

Brandt, W. F., Strickland, W. N., Strickland, M., Carlisle, L., Woods, D. & von Holt, C. (1978) A histone programme during the life cycle of the sea urchin. *Europ. J.* In press.

Clarkson, S. G., Smith, H. O., Schaffner, W., Gross, K. W. & Birnstiel, M. L. (1976) Integration of eukaryotic genes for 5S RNA and histone proteins into a phage lambda receptor. *Nucl. Acids Res.* 3, 2617–2632.

Cohen, L. H., Newrock, K. M. & Zweidler, A. (1975) Stage specific switches in histone synthesis during embryogenesis of the sea urchin. *Science* 190, 994–997.

Elgin, S. C. R. & Weintraub, H. W. (1975) Chromosomal proteins and chromatin structure. *Ann. Rev. Biochem.* 44, 725–774.

Gross, K., Schaffner, W., Telford, J. & Birnstiel, M. L. Molecular analysis of the histone gene cluster of *Psammechinus miliaris:* III. Polarity and asymmetry of the histone-coding sequences. *Cell* 8, 479–484.

Grunstein, M. & Grunstein, J. E. (1977) The histone H4 gene of *Strongylocentrotus purpuratus* DNA and mRNA sequences at the 5' end. *CSH Symp. Quant. Biol.* 42, 1083–1092.

Kornberg, R. D. & Thomas, J. O. (1974) Chromatin structure: oligomers of the histones. *Science* 184, 865–871.

Kressmann, A., Clarkson, S. G., Telford, J. L. & Birnstiel, M. L. (1977) Transcription of Xenopus tDNA[meet] and sea urchin histone DNA injected into the Xenopus oocyte nucleus. *CSH Symp. Quant. Biol.* 42, 1077–1082.

Kressmann, A., Clarkson, S. G., Pirrotta, V. & Birnstiel, M. L. (1978) Transcription of cloned tRNA gene fragments and subfragments injected into the oocyte nucleus of *Xenopus laevis*. *Proc. Natl. Acad. Sci. USA* 75, 1176–1180.

Portmann, R., Schaffner, W. & Birnstiel, M. (1976) Partial denaturation mapping of cloned histone DNA from the sea urchin *Psammechinus miliaris*. *Nature* 264, 31–34.

Schaffner, W., Gross, K., Telford, J. & Birnstiel, M. (1976) Molecular analysis of the histone gene cluster of *Psammechinus miliaris:* II. The arrangement of the five histone-coding and spacer sequences. *Cell* 8, 471–478.

Schaffner, W., Kunz, G., Daetwyler, H., Telford, J., Smith, H. O. & Birnstiel, M. L. (1978) Genes and spacers of cloned sea urchin histone DNA analyzed by sequencing. *Cell* 14, 655–671.

Weinberg, E. S., Birnstiel, M. L., Purdom, I. F. & Williamson, R. (1972) Genes coding for polysomal 9S RNA of sea urchins: Conservation and divergence. *Nature* 240, 225–228.

DISCUSSION

HOGNESS: What is the evidence in sea urchins that histone genes are transcribed by RNA polymerase II and not polymerase I or III?

BIRNSTIEL: There is as yet no evidence.

DAWID: I wonder, is there any new information on possible precursors *in vivo*, or no precursors, to histone messenger RNA?

BIRNSTIEL: Lulla Melli and Giovanni Spinelli working in my lab have found a 32 S RNA in very small amounts (unpublished results) which is large enough to span the entire histone DNA repeat unit. Also, Erik Weinberg (Baltimore) has evidence that at the mesenchyme-blastula stage there is high molecular weight histone RNA. However, it is clear that in a very short pulse experiment most of the histone mRNAs are already 9S. The difficulty at the moment consists in deciding whether the high molecular weight RNAs represent abortive read-through products or whether they may serve as a precursor to histone mRNA. The simplest way of unifying all the contradictory data from a variety of species would be to postulate that there are several sites of initiation of transcription in the histone gene repeat unit and that the stop signals for transcription are not always recognized. This would result in a situation where mono- and polycistronic transcription of the tandem genes would coexist, with one or the other aspect being accentuated in some species or in some specialized tissues.

CRICK: Do you know anything about supercoiling?

BIRNSTIEL: I have to refer you to the elegant work of Gurdon's group who have evidence that after injection of cloned circular DNA into the cell nucleus the DNA is preserved and maintained in a supercoil state.

GALL: You showed a sucrose gradient where one could see only a smear and a 4S peak, and then you showed a gel that had two very sharp bands. How do these compare?

BIRNSTIEL: The interpretation of our results is that most of the transcripts are polydisperse, but within this mixture of molecules there are two sharp messenger RNA-like bands detectable by gel electrophoresis. They amount to only a few percent of the total newly synthesized histone DNA-specific RNAs.

GALL: Are those two bands specific histones or are they mixtures?

BIRNSTIEL: Each of these bands appears to hybridize specifically to subclones of histone DNA containing a single H2A or H2B gene. On this basis one would argue that these bands are not mixtures of mRNA.

GALL: H3 and H4 are not being made?

BIRNSTIEL: Not detectably.

JELINEK: What happens if you take the region larger than 9S out of the gel, do you get bands?

BIRNSTIEL: The answer is yes. Burckhardt, using his contact hybridization technique, was able to obtain from the living sea urchin embryo RNA of high molecular weight and therefore confirm the results of Melli and Spinelli. These RNA bands may be enhanced by the use of DRB. It is possible that the oocyte histone DNA transcripts also contain minor components of distinct high molecular weights but the situation has not yet been fully analyzed.

BORST: You were raising the possibility that you put in so many genes that the processing system is overwhelmed – so that you now get all kinds of transcripts which are improperly processed. One way of testing that could be to look for other transcripts, normal transcripts in the system, and see whether you also get processing defects there, e.g. of the normal ribosomal RNA. Have you looked at that?

BIRNSTIEL: Ribosomal RNA is processed normally in the presence of the histone DNA.

CRICK: Is there a good technical reason why you have to inject so much DNA into the eggs?

BIRNSTIEL: Yes, it is a matter of sensitivity, especially if one wants to see the RNA transcripts.

FLAVELL: If you inject SV40, is the T-antigen synthesized?

BIRNSTIEL: Drs. Hans Türler and Duri Rungger (1978) have evidence that this is indeed the case.

Türler, H. & Rungger, D. (1978) *Proc. Nat. Acad. Sci. USA* (in press).

The Structure and Organization of Linked Mammalian Globin Genes

*Tom Maniatis, Edward F. Fritsch, Elizabeth Lacy, Richard M. Lawn &
Richard C. Parker*

One of the best studied examples of eukaryotic gene regulation is the differential
expression of mammalian globin genes during embryonic and adult red cell
development. Although the timing of embryonic, fetal and adult globin gene
expression has been established and the gene products (globin proteins and
mRNA) extensively characterized, the molecular events leading to globin gene
activation during development are not understood (see Bunn *et al.* 1977, and
Nienhuis & Benz 1977, for reviews). One approach to the question of the
mechanism of globin gene regulaton is to study the structure and organization
of isolated globin genes. Although an individual globin gene represents only one
five millionth of the DNA in a mammalian cell, recent advances in the
development of molecular cloning techniques have made it possible to obtain a
number of globin genes and their associated sequences in the amounts required
for detailed biochemical studies. The first globin sequences to be cloned and
amplified in bacteria were double-stranded DNA copies of globin mRNA
(Rougeon *et al.* 1975, Maniatis *et al.* 1976, Higuchi *et al.* 1976, Rabbits 1976).
These cDNA clones have been used to determine the nucleotide sequence of
globin mRNA (Efstratiadis *et al.* 1977, Liu *et al.* 1977), to map restriction sites
flanking globin genes in genomic DNA (Jeffreys & Flavell 1977a,b), and to
identify and isolate globin genes and their surrounding sequences (Tilghman *et
al.* 1977, Maniatis *et al.* 1978).

Globin genes were first isolated from genomic DNA using a combination of
gene enrichment and recombinant DNA techniques (Tilghman *et al.* 1977). We

Division of Biology, Calfornia Institute of Technology, Pasadena, California 91125 U.S.A.

SPECIFIC EUKARYOTIC GENES, Alfred Benzon Symposium 13, Munksgaard, 1979.

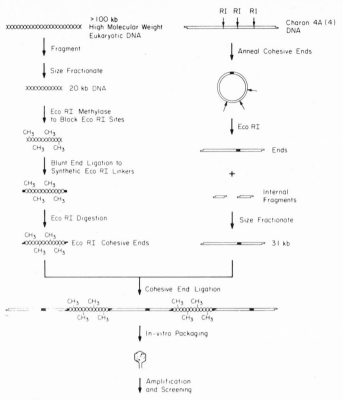

Fig. 1. Schematic diagram illustrating the strategy used to construct libraries of random eukaryotic DNA fragments. (Maniatis *et al.* 1978, reprinted with permission).

have recently established a procedure for gene isolation which does not require partial purification of the gene prior to cloning (Maniatis *et al.* 1978). The essential features of this procedure are illustrated in Fig. 1. High molecular weight DNA is randomly fragmented and then size fractionated on sucrose gradients to obtain molecules of approximately 20 kilobases (kb). These molecules are then adapted for cloning in bacteriophage λ in the following manner. First, the eukaryotic DNA is treated with the enzyme EcoRI methylase which renders EcoRI sites within the eukaryotic DNA resistant to cleavage by EcoRI. Next, the methylated DNA is ligated to a synthetic dodeca-nucleotide duplex DNA molecule bearing an EcoRI site (EcoRI linker) using the blunt end joining activity of T4 DNA ligase. Finally, the methylated eukaryotic DNA is dgested with EcoRI. Because the EcoRI sites in the eukaryotic DNA are blocked by methylation, only the EcoRI sites within the synthetic DNA are cleaved. This produces random, high molecular weight DNA fragments bearing EcoRI cohesive ends which are suitable for insertion into an appropriate cloning vector.

The Charon 4A strain of bacteriophage λ (Blattner 1977) was used as a cloning vector. As shown in Fig. 1, λ Charon 4A DNA is cleaved three times by Eco RI to produce two internal fragments and two end fragments. The internal fragments carry genes which are not essential to phage viability and therefore can be removed and replaced with eukaryotic DNA. The internal fragments are separated from the end fragments by annealing the cohesive ends of the intact Ch4A DNA, digesting the circular DNA with EcoRI and fractionating the products on a sucrose gradient. The 31 kb end fragments are readily separated from the 7 and 8 kb internal fragments. Recombinant phage molecules can then be obtained by joining the 31 kb end fragments of the vector to the eukaryotic DNA through ligation of the EcoRI cohesive ends.

Because of the enormous complexity of the mammalian genome, a very large number of independent phage recombinants is required if the collection of cloned sequences (cloned library) is to contain all of the sequences present in the genome. For example, the calculated number of independently derived recombinant phages necessary to achieve a 99% probability of having any given DNA sequence in the library (for 20 kb DNA inserts) is nearly 7×10^5 (Maniatis et al. 1978). To obtain the necessary number of phage recombinants, we employed a highly efficient procedure for introducing phage DNA into bacteria which involves in vitro packaging of the phage DNA into viable phage particles (Sternberg et al. 1977). This procedure is from 10 to 50 times more efficient than calcium chloride transfection procedures. Once a large number of viable phage recombinants is obtained, the in vitro packaged phage can be amplified 10^6-fold by low density growth in bacteria on agar plates, with no apparent loss in sequence complexity (Maniatis et al. 1978). The amplified phage then constitute a permanent library of genomic DNA which can be screened repeatedly.

Recently, a rapid in situ plaque hybridization procedure has been developed which makes it possible to screen many hundreds of thousands of phage recombinants at a time (Benton & Davis 1977). The procedure involves plating approximately 10,000 phage on an agar plate, transferring phage DNA from the resulting plaques onto a nitrocellulose filter, fixing the DNA to the filter and hybridizing with ^{32}P-labeled hybridization probes. Plaques which carry the sequence of interest are identified by autoradiography. By aligning the resulting autoradiogram with the agar plates, the plaques which hybridize can be identified, picked and purified. Using this procedure, it is possible to screen a mammalian DNA library (7×10^5 independent plaques) in 1–2 weeks.

The library approach to gene isolation offers several advantages: 1) several different genes can be isolated in a single step by screening a library with a mixture of gene probes, 2) isolation of a set of overlapping clones, all of which contain a given gene, permits study of sequences extending many kilobases from the gene in the 5' and 3' direction, and 3) distant regions along the chromosome can be obtained by rescreening the library using terminal fragments of the initially selected clones. Rescreening is facilitated by the fact that the entire genome can be rapidly screened.

Using this procedure of gene isolation, we have obtained a number of different globin genes from libraries of rabbit and human DNA. Restriction endonuclease cleavage analyses and hybridization experiments have revealed that a number of these globin genes are closely linked.

Characterization of Linked Globin Genes

Mammalian globin genes constitute a relatively simple gene family comprising a number of members (a and non-a types) which almost certainly evolved from a single ancestral gene by duplication and subsequent sequence divergence (Bunn *et al.* 1977). Genetic (Weatherall & Clegg 1972) and cell fusion (Diesseroth *et al.* 1977, 1978) studies have shown that the a and non-a types of globin genes are located on different chromosomes, but that both types are arranged in closely linked clusters. Models for the mechanism of hemoglobin switching have emphasized the possible relationship between the organization of genetically linked globin genes and the control of their temporal expression, but until now this possibility could not be examined at the molecular level. In fact there was no direct evidence for close physical linkage between globin genes. We present here the current status of our analysis of the organization of linked rabbit and human β-globin genes, utilizing cloned large fragments of rabbit or human genomic DNA-bearing globin sequences.

Linked Rabbit β-Globin Genes

As shown in Table I, there are at least four to six different globin genes in rabbit. Two types of globin chains (designated χ and ε) are found in nucleated red blood cells derived from yolk sac islets (Steinheider *et al.* 1974). At least two different ε chains (y and z) with similar but nonidentical amino acid sequences have been detected. After 20 days of the 32-day gestation period, the fetal liver becomes the

Table I

Globin gene families of rabbit and human

		Embryonic	Fetal	Adult
Rabbit	a	χ		a
	non-a	$\varepsilon(y)$		$\beta,(\beta$ minor$)$
		$\varepsilon(z)$		
Human	a	ζ		a_1,a_2
	non-a	ε	AγGγ	δ, β

center for erythropoiesis and only the a- and β-globin proteins are synthesized (Kitchen & Brett 1974). Until recently, there was no evidence for more than one adult β-globin gene. However, a β-like mRNA sequence has been identified in proerythroblasts and basophilic erythroblasts of bone marrow from anemic rabbits which is clearly different from the adult β-globin gene (Clissold *et al.* 1977). Although it is possible that the presence of β-like mRNA in immature erythroid cells results from anemia-induced activation of an embryonic gene, the temporal expression of this mRNA during red cell maturation is strikingly similar to that of the δ gene of human (Roberts *et al.* 1972) and a minor hemoglobin is in fact found in immature erythroid cells from nonanemic rabbits (Borsook 1968).

Although the possibility of genetic linkage between different β-related genes in rabbit has not been studied, such linkage has been demonstrated in other mammals (Bunn *et al.* 1977, Russell & McFarland 1974, Gilman & Smithies 1968, Popp 1974, Weatherall & Clegg 1972). For example, in mouse, the adult β-major and β-minor genes are linked to each other and to an embryonic ε gene (Gilman & Smithies 1968, Popp 1973). In the process of analyzing several clones selected from a library of rabbit DNA by hybridization to a β-globin probe, we have identified one or more β-related genes closely linked to the adult β-globin gene.

From a screen of 750,000 recombinant phage, four independent rabbit β-globin clones were isolated. Restriction mapping and hybridization experiments on the DNA from these clones revealed that two clones (designated RβG2 and RβG5), contain β-globin related sequences in addition to the adult β-globin gene.

Bam HI and Kpn I restriction enzyme maps indicate that the β-related gene is located approximately 9 kb to the 5' side of the adult β-globin gene (Fig. 2). Preliminary mapping experiments on RβG5 DNA revealed the presence of a possible third linked β-globin gene, which mapped in the 5' direction from the β-related sequence.

The identities of the β-related sequences in RβG2 and RβG5 have not yet been determined. To decide whether the related genes are embryonic β-globin and/or adult β-minor globin genes, we are preparing cDNA clones from mRNA isolated from the blood islands of 12-day rabbit fetuses and from the bone marrow of anemic adult rabbits. Once the β-related genes are identified, it will then be possible to establish the order of linkage of the genes in the rabbit β-globin family. Furthermore, it should also be possible to determine whether there are more linked β-like genes by using terminal fragments from the β clones to rescreen the library.

The Human Globin Gene Family

As shown in Table I, there are at least eight members of the human globin gene family (Bunn et al. 1977). In contrast to the developmental pattern of expression

λCh4A RβG2 – 48.5kb
Rabbit DNA insert – 18.9kb

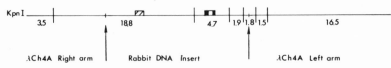

Fig. 2. Bam HI and KpnI restriction maps of the rabbit β-globin genomic clone RβG2. The vertical lines indicate the positions of Bam HI and KpnI cleavage sites. The approximate number of kilobase pairs between restriction sites are also indicated. The hatched box represents the approximate position of the β-related sequence in the cloned DNA. The interrupted solid box represents the position of the adult β-globin gene. The clear area indicates the presence of a 600 bp noncoding intervening sequence (Jeffreys & Flavell 1978b). A smaller (125 bp) intervening sequence located nearer to the 5' end of the coding region (between codons 30 and 31) is not shown (unpublished). Experiments have not yet been performed to determine whether the minor β gene contains an intervening sequence. The horizontal arrow (5'→3') indicates the orientation of the β-globin gene with respect to the direction of transcription. The orientation of the β-globin gene is not yet known. The vertical arrows show the junction between the rabbit DNA insert and λ Ch 4A DNA.

in rabbit, where only one switch in the expression of hemoglobin types occurs (embryo to adult), two switches occur in human. In the early embryo, the ζ and ε genes are expressed in erythroid cells thought to be derived from the yolk sac. The human ζ chain is analogous to the embryonic χ chain of rabbit in that primary structure of the two globins resembles that of their respective adult a-globin chains (Kamazura & Lehmann 1975).

When the site of red blood cell production changes from the yolk sac to the fetal liver, the adult a-globin and fetal γ-globin genes are expressed. In some human populations, the a chain locus is thought to be duplicated (Bunn et al. 1977). At least two structural genes for the γ chains exist in humans, coding for polypeptide chains which have either glycine (Gγ) or alanine (Aγ) in position 136 of their amino acid sequence (Schroeder et al. 1972). Just prior to birth, the adult β- and δ-globin chains appear and by 6 months HbA ($a_2\beta_2$) and HbA$_2$($a_2\delta_2$) represent greater than 98% of the hemoglobin in peripheral blood. There is thought to be only one copy each of the β- and δ-globin structural genes per haploid genome.

Linked Human Globin Genes
The linkage relationships and chromosomal locations of the ε and δ genes are not known. Cell fusion experiments have shown that a-globin gene(s) are located on chromosome 16 (Deisseroth 1977) and that non-a genes are located on chromosome 11 (Deisseroth 1978). Analysis of two structural mutants, hemoglobins Lepore and Kenya (Huisman et al. 1972) suggest that the γ, β and δ genes are closely linked. In hemoglobin Lepore the N-terminal amino acid sequences of δ-globin are joined to the C-terminal sequence of β-globin, while the Aγ and β-globin genes are fused in a similar fashion in hemoglobin Kenya (Baglioni 1962). This information and other genetic data are consistent with either of the following gene arrangements: 5'Gγ-Aγ-δ-β3' of 5' Aγ-δ-β-Gγ-3' (Weatherall & Clegg 1972). Until now physical linkage of globin genes has not been demonstrated.

The human globin gene system presents the possibility of using mutants to establish relationships between the structure and organization of globin genes and the mechanisms of their differential expression. In order to characterize globin genes and their associated DNA sequences, we constructed a human DNA library by the methods described above using human fetal liver DNA (a gift of B. G. Forget). The library was screened using ^{32}P-labeled nick-translated human a, β and γ globin cDNA plasmids (pJW101, pJW102, pJW151,

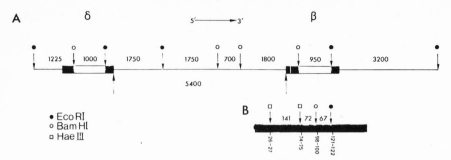

Fig. 3. Location of δ- and β-globin genes in HβG2 DNA. (A) The globin gene-containing region of HβG2 DNA is shown. Arrows pointing down indicate restriction endonuclease sites of EcoRI (●) and Bam HI (○). Sizes of the fragments are given in base pairs. The boxed regions denote the δ- and β-globin genes. The filled boxes represents the mRNA sequence and open boxes represent noncoding intervening sequences. The size of the intervening sequence in the 5′ segment of the β-globin gene is not known. The arrows pointing up delineate the distance between the linked genes. (B) The positions of EcoRI, BamHI, and HaeIII cleavage sites in the β-globin cDNA sequence (Marrota *et al.* 1977). Only those Hae III cleavage sites 5′ to the Bam HI site are shown. The positions of the codons containing each of the restriction endonuclease sites are also given. (Lawn *et al.* 1978; reprinted with permission).

respectively; the cDNA plasmids were a gift of B. G. Forget and co-workers [Wilson *et al.* 1978]). We have initially studied two clones which hybridize the β-globin probe (designated HβG1 and HβG2) (Lawn *et al.* 1978).

Detailed restriction endonuclease cleavage analysis and hybridization experiments revealed that both clones carry two β-related globin genes, separated by approximately 5.4 kb of DNA. Partial nucleotide sequence analysis identified the two genes and the δ- and β-globin genes. Hybridization experiments using probes specific for the 5′ and 3′ regions of the β-globin gene indicated that the orientation of the two genes with respect to the direction of transcription is 5′-δ-β-3′. Fig. 3 shows the organization of the δ- and β-globin genes in cloned genomic DNA. Similar conclusions were reached by Flavell *et al.* on the basis of genomic blotting experiments (Flavell *et al.*, this symposium).

Non-coding Intervening Sequences in the δ- and β-Globin Genes
Large non-coding intervening sequences in the β- and δ-globin genes were revealed by comparing the location of Bam HI and Eco RI sites within the regions which hybridize the β-globin probe in HβG2 to the corresponding sites in the β-globin mRNA sequence (Fig. 3). The EcoRI and Bam HI sites in the β-globin mRNA sequence are separated by 67 base pairs. In HβG2 approximately

950 base pairs of DNA separate these sites. Similarly, EcoRI and BamHI sites within the δ-globin gene are separated by 1000 base pairs. Thus, in both genes the coding sequences in genomic DNA are interrupted by at least 900 base pairs of non-coding sequences. This conclusion was verified directly by nucleotide sequence analysis (Lawn *et al.* 1978) which showed that the non-coding insert in both genes is located between codons for amino acids 104 and 105. A second intervening sequence in the human β-globin gene has been located somewhere between the codons for amino acids 24 and 74.

It is interesting to note that an intervening sequence of approximately 600 bp is located between the codons for amino acids 104 and 105 of the rabbit β-globin (Jeffreys & Flavell 1977b, Efstratiadis, Lacy & Maniatis, unpublished results, Weissman *et al.*, this symposium) and the mouse β-globin genes (Tilghman *et al.* 1978a). A second, smaller non-coding intervening sequence has been located in the mouse (Tilghman 1978a) and rabbit (Efstratiadis *et al.*, unpublished, Weissman *et al.*, this symposium) β-globin genes, located between codons 30 and 31. Although the functional significance of the intervening sequences is not understood, the non-coding sequences in the mouse β-globin genes are transcribed in the nucleus (Tilghman *et al.* 1978) and presumably removed before the message sequence is transported to the cytoplasm.

Nucleotide sequence analysis and cross hybridization experiments between the large intervening sequences in the δ- and β-globin genes have shown that only the sequences surrounding the junction between coding and non-coding sequence are conserved. The bulk of the intervening sequences show little if any

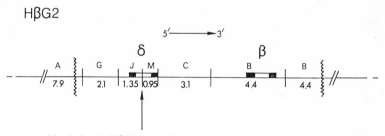

HβG2

Fig. 4. A map of Pst I sites in HβG2 DNA. The vertical lines indicate the position of Pst I cleavage site. The wavy lines represent the junction between the λ Ch 4A DNA and inserted human DNA. The region of HβG2 DNA containing the human DNA insert is shown. The Pst I site between fragments J and M of HβG2 (marked by an arrow) is absent in HβG1. A fragment 2.3 kb in length (Pst fragment G of HβG1) replaces the Pst J and M fragments of HβG2. Filled boxes represent the message coding region of each gene and open boxes represent the large intervening sequence in each gene. The small intervening sequence in the 5′ end of the β-globin gene is not shown. (Lawn *et al.* 1978; reprinted with permission).

homology (Lawn *et al.* 1978). A similar observation was made when comparing the intervening sequences within the mouse β_{major} and β_{minor} globin genes (Tiemeier *et al.* 1978).

In addition to differences in the large intervening sequences in the δ- and β-globin genes, we have detected sequence polymorphism in the intervening sequences of the δ-globin gene. Analysis of the two independently isolated clones, HβG1 and HβG2, revealed the presence of a Pst I recognition site in the intervening sequence of the δ-gene in HβG2 DNA which is not present in the δ-globin gene of HβG1 (see Fig. 4). We concluded that the human DNA fragments in HβG1 and HβG2 were derived from homologous chromosomes which are heterozygous with respect to the Pst I site in the intervening sequence of the δ-globin gene (Lawn *et al.* 1978). A similar polymorphism in an intervening sequence of the ovalbumin gene has been observed by Weinstock *et al.* (1978) and Garapin *et al.* (1978).

DISCUSSION

The intergene distances observed for the linked globin genes described above are remarkably similar. The number of base pairs separating Bam HI cleavage sites within the two members of linked rabbit β- and human β-globin genes is approximately 9 and 7 kb, respectively. In the case of the linked human and rabbit β-globin genes, the β-related sequence is located to the 5' side of the adult β-globin gene. Although the β-related globin genes in rabbit have not yet been identified with a particular globin mRNA, it is possible that one of these genes codes for the β-like mRNA expressed in immature adult erythroid cells of anemic rabbits (Clissold *et al.* 1978). Both the human δ gene and the minor β gene in rabbit have sequences which are similar but not identical to the respective β-globin genes and are expressed primarily during the early stages of adult erythropoiesis. The relationship, if any, between the close linkage and sequential expression of the genes can now be approached using cloned genomic DNAs as hybridization probes to nuclear RNA.

The existence of well-defined functional deficiencies in human hemoglobin expression (thalassemias) provides the opportunity for studying the relationships between globin gene organization and function (Weatherall & Clegg 1972). The availability of cloned genomic globin DNA with its associated non-coding sequences will extend the utility of this approach by making it possible to detect structural changes in sequences not accessible to cDNA probes. For example, the cloned δ- and β-globin intervening sequences can be used to identify the origin of the intervening sequence in Hb Lepore DNA. Once structural differences in DNA from any thalassemic individual have been detected by genomic blotting, the genetic defect can be studied at the level of nucleotide sequence by cloning the affected gene. The gene isolation procedure described should allow the rapid isolation of mutant globin genes. Relatively small amounts of DNA are required and the procedure is not affected by changes in restriction endonuclease cleavage sites which flank the affected genes since randomly fragmented DNA, rather than a specific restriction fragment, is cloned. Thus, thalassemias resulting from large deletions or sequence rearrangements as well as those resulting from single base changes will be accessible to structural analysis. Studies of this kind should identify the molecular basis of thalassemias and possibly provide insight into human genetic disorders in general.

ACKNOWLEDGMENTS

We are grateful to Diana Quon and Catherine O'Connell for excellent technical assistance. This work was supported by a grant from the National Institutes of Health and the National Science Foundation. R.M.L. and E.F.F. were supported by postdoctoral fellowships from the American Cancer Society and the Damon Runyon-Walter Winchell Cancer Fund, respectively. T.M. is a recipient of a Rita Allen Foundation Career Development Award.

REFERENCES

Baglioni, C. (1962) The fusion of two polypeptide chains in hemoglobin Lepore and its interpretation as a genetic deletion. *Proc. Nat. Acad. Sci. USA* 48, 1880–1885.

Benton, W. D. & Davis, R. W. (1977) Screening λgt recombinant clones by hybridization to single plaques *in situ. Science* 196, 180–182.

Blattner, F. R., Williams, B. G., Blechl, A. E., Thompson, K. D., Faber, H. E., Furlong, L. A., Grunwald, D. J., Kiefer, D. O., Moore, D. D., Schumm, J. W., Sheldon, E. L. & Smithies, O. (1977) Charon phages: Safer derivatives of bacteriophage lambda for DNA cloning. *Science* 196, 161–169.

Borsook, H. (1968) The change of hemoglobin synthesis from minor to major in the course of erythroblast maturation. *Ann. N. Y. Acad. Sci.* 149, 416–422.

Bunn, H. F., Forget, B. G. & Ranney, H. M. (1977) *Human Hemoglobins.* W. B. Saunders & Co., Philadelphia.

Clissold, P. M., Arnstein, H. R. V., Chesterton, C. J. (1977) Quantitation of globin mRNA levels during erythroid development in the rabbit and discovery of new β-related species in immature erythroblasts. *Cell* 11, 353–361.

Deisseroth, A., Nienhuis, A., Turner, P., Velez, R., Anderson, W. F., Ruddle, F., Lawrence, J., Creagen, R. & Kucherlapate, R. (1977) Localization of the human alpha globin structural gene to chromosome 16 in somatic cell hybrids by molecular hybridization assay. *Cell* 12, 205–218.

Deisseroth, A., Nienhuis, A., Lawrence, J., Giles, R., Turner, P. & Ruddle, F. (1978) Chromosomal location of human β globin gene on human chromosome II in somatic cell hybrids. *Proc. Nat. Acad. Sci. USA* 75, 1456–1460.

Efstratiadis, A., Kafatos, F. C. & Maniatis, T. (1977) The primary structure of rabbit β-globin mRNA as determined from cloned DNA. *Cell* 10, 571–585.

Garapin, A. C., Cami, B., Rosham, W., Koorilsky, P., LePennec, J. P., Perrin, F., Gerlinger, P., Cochet, M. & Chambon, P. (1978) Electron microscopy and restriction enzyme mapping reveal additional intervening sequences in the chicken ovalbumin split gene. *Cell* 14, 629–639.

Gilman, J. G. & Smithies, O. (1968) Fetal hemoglobin variants in mice. *Science* 160, 885–886.

Higuchi, R., Paddock, G. V., Wall, R. & Salser, W. (1976) A general method for cloning eukaryotic structural gene sequences. *Proc. Nat. Acad. Sci. USA* 73, 3146–3150.

Huisman, T. H. J., Wrightstone, R. N., Wilson, J. B., Shroeder, W. A. & Kendall, A. G. (1972) Hemoglobin Kenya, the product of fusion of δ and β polypeptide chains. *Arch. Biochem. Biophys.* 153, 850–853.

Jeffreys, A. J. & Flavell, R. A. (1977a) A physical map of the DNA regions flanking the rabbit β globin gene. *Cell* 12, 429–439.

Jeffreys, A. J. & Flavell, R. A. (1977b) The rabbit β globin gene contains a large insert in the coding sequence. *Cell* 12, 1097–1108.

Kamuzora, H. & Lehmann, H. (1975) Human embryonic haemoglobins including a comparison by hemology of the human ζ and a chains. *Nature* 256, 511–513.

Kitchen, H. & Brett, I. (1974) Embryonic and fetal hemoglobin in animals. *Ann. N. Y. Acad. Sci.* 241, 653–670.

Lawn, R. M., Fritsch, E. F., Parker, R. C., Blake, G. & Maniatis, T. (1978) The isolation and characterization of linked δ and β globin genes from a cloned library of human DNA. (*Cell*, in press.)

Liu, A. Y., Paddock, G. V., Heindell, H. C. & Salser, W. (1977) Nucleotide sequences from a rabbit alpha globin gene inserted in a chimeric plasmid. *Science* 196, 192–194.

Maniatis, T., Sim, G. K., Efstratiadis, A. & Kafatos, F. C. (1976) Amplification and characterization of a β globin gene synthesized *in vitro. Cell* 8, 163–182.

Maniatis, T., Hardison, R. C., Lacy, E., Lauer, J., O'Connell, C., Quon, D., Sim, G. K. & Efstratiadis, A. (1978) The isolation of structural genes from libraries of eukaryotic DNA. *Cell.* 15, 687–699.

Nienhuis, A. W. & Benz, E. J. (1977) Regulation of hemoglobin synthesis during development of the red cell. *New. Engl. J. Med.* 297, 1318–1328, 1371–1381, 1430–1436.

Popp, R. A. (1973) Sequence of amino acids in the major and minor β chains of the diffuse hemoglobin from BALB/c mice. *Biochim. Biophys. Acta* 303, 61–67.

Rabbits, T. H. (1976) Bacterial cloning of plasmids carrying copies of Rabbit globin mRNA. *Nature* 260, 221–225.

Roberts, A. V., Weatherall, D. J. & Clegg, J. B. (1972) The synthesis of human hemoglobin A2 during erythroid maturation. *Biochem. Biophys. Res. Comm.* 47, 81–87.

Rougeon, F., Kourilsky, P. & Mach, B. (1975) Insertion of a rabbit β globin sequence into an *E. coli* plasmid. *Nucl. Acid. Res.* 2, 2365–2377.

Russell, E. S. & McFarland, E. C. (1974) Genetics of mouse hemoglobins. *Ann. N. Y. Acad. Sci.* 41, 25–38.

Schroeder, W. A., Shelton, J. R., Shelton, J. B. (1972) World-wide occurrence of non-allelic genes for the δ chains of human fetal haemoglobin in newborns. *Nature (New Biology)* 240, 273–274.

Steinheider, G., Melderis, H. & Ostertag, W. (1974) Mammalian embryonic hemoglobins. *International Symp. on the Synthesis, Structure and Function of Hemoglobin,* eds. Martin, H. & Novicke, L., pp. 222–235. Lehmans, Munich.

Sternberg, N., Tiemeier, D. & Enquist, L. (1977) *In vitro* packaging of a λ *Dam* vector containing Eco RI DNA fragments of *E. coli* phage Pl. *Gene* 1, 255–280.

Tiemeier, D. C., Tilghman, S. M., Polsky, F. I., Seidman, J. G., Leder, A., Edgell, M. H. & Leder, P. (1978) A comparison of two cloned mouse β globin genes and their surrounding and intervening sequences. *Cell* 14, 237–245.

Tilghman, S. M., Tiemeier, D. C., Polsky, E., Edgell, M. H., Seidman, J. G., Leder, A., Enquist, L. W., Norman, B. & Leder, P. (1977) Cloning specific segments of the mammalian genome: Bacteriophage λ containing mouse globin and surrounding gene sequences. *Proc. Nat. Acad. Sci. USA* 74, 4406–4410.

Tilghman, S. M., Tiemeier, D. C., Seidman, J. G., Peterlin, B. M., Sullivan, M., Maizel, J. & Leder, P. (1978a) Intervening sequences of DNA identified in the structural portion of a mouse β globin gene. *Proc. Nat. Acad. Sci. USA* 75, 725–729.

Tilghman, S. M., Curtis, P. J., Tiemeier, D. C., Leder, P. & Weissman, C. (1978b) The intervening sequence of a mouse β globin gene is transcribed within the 15S β globin mRNA precursor. *Proc. Nat. Acad. Sci. USA* 75, 1309–1313.

Weatherall. D. J. & Clegg, J. B. (1972) *The Thalassemia Syndromes.* 2nd ed. Blackwell Scientific Publications, Oxford.

Weinstock, R., Sweet, R., Weiss, M., Cedar, H. & Axel, B. (1978) Intragenic DNA spacers interrupt the ovalbumin gene. *Proc. Nat. Acad. Sci. USA* 75, 1299–1303.

Wilson, J. T., Wilson, L. B., deRiel, J. K., Villa Komaroff, L., Efstratiadis, A., Forget, B. G. & Weissman, S. M. (1978) Insertion of synthetic copies of human globin genes into bacterial plasmids. *Nucleic Acids Res.* 5, 563–581.

DISCUSSION

FLAVEL: Alec Jeffreys is doing a systematic study of polymorphism in this system, and he has picked up the same polymorphism which Tom Maniatis described. He finds that it is relatively rare, in fact, he analyzed 50 individuals and found, I believe, one. He has also found a second type polymorphism, but he has not mapped this one to my knowledge.

MANIATIS: It is interesting in this regard that intervening sequences within β-globin genes of mouse, rabbit and man are located in exactly the same position within the coding sequence, but the nucleotide sequence of these non-coding regions is quite different within two related genes in the same species (Tremeier *et al.* 1978). Moreover, as Charles Weissmann will discuss, the intervening sequences in the β-globin genes of different species are quite different. In contrast, the amino acid and nucleotide sequences of mammalian β-globin genes are highly conserved. Thus, it seems that, except for the junctions between coding and non-coding sequences, there is little, if any selective pressure to maintain the nucleotide sequence of non-coding interruptions in globin genes. The polymorphism within the human δ-globin intervening sequence may be more extensive than indicated by the presence of new *Hpa*I site.

Comparison of Cloned Rabbit and Mouse β-globin Genes: Strong Evolutionary Divergence of Two Homologous Pairs of Introns

Johan van den Berg[1], *Albert van Ooyen*[1], *Ned Mantei*[1], *Anton Schamböck*[1], *Gerard Grosveld*[2], *Richard A. Flavell*[2] *& Charles Weissmann*[1]

Analysis of several eukaryotic genes has shown that the nucleotide sequences coding for one polypeptide chain are frequently arranged in noncontiguous blocks (for a review see Williamson 1977). The sequences lying between these blocks, the so-called intervening sequences (Tilghman *et al.* 1978a) or introns (Gilbert 1978), are not present in the mature mRNA; at least in one instance it has been shown that they are transcribed into an mRNA precursor and must therefore be eliminated during its processing (Curtis *et al.* 1977a, Curtis *et al.* 1977b, Tilghman *et al.* 1978b).

Tilghman *et al.* (1977) have cloned a 7000 base pair segment of mouse genomic DNA containing a β-globin gene, and have shown that the gene consists of two, perhaps three blocks of coding sequences separated by an intron of 550 nucleotides, and possibly by a second unidentified, shorter intron, respectively (Tilghman *et al.* 1978a). Jeffreys & Flavell (1977a) have shown, by restriction site analysis of chromosomal DNA, that the rabbit β-globin gene is arranged in at least two blocks, separated by 600 base pairs.

To determine whether the sequences coding for the β-globin gene of the mouse and the rabbit were interrupted at homologous positions, and to compare the nucleotide sequences of the homologous introns of the two organisms, we

[1] Institut für Molekularbiologie I, Universität Zürich, Switzerland.
[2] Section for Medical Enzymology and Molecular Biology, Laboratory of Biochemistry, University of Amsterdam, Amsterdam, The Netherlands.

SPECIFIC EUKARYOTIC GENES, Alfred Benzon Symposium 13, Munksgaard 1979

10*

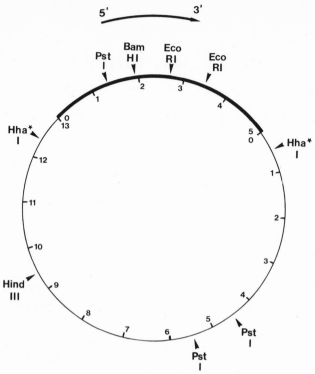

Fig. 1. Orientation of the rabbit β-globin-specific chromosomal DNA in the hybrid plasmid Z-pCRI/RchrβG-1.

The location of the HindIII and PstI sites on pCRI are from Armstrong *et al.* (1977). Only the two HhaI sites closest to the insert are indicated; pCRI, but not the insert, contains many additional HhaI sites. The thick line represents the inserted rabbit DNA KpnI-fragment, the thin line the pCRI DNA. "0" indicates the erstwhile EcoRI-site of pCRI. The numbers indicate the distances in 1000 base pairs (kb). The arrow indicates the direction of transcription. The beginning and the end of the arrow indicate approximately the start and the end of the mature β-globin mRNA as determined by sequence analysis (data not shown).

cloned a 5100 base pair rabbit DNA fragment containing a β-globin gene, prepared restriction maps of the cloned mouse (Tilghman *et al.* 1977) and rabbit chromosomal DNA, and determined the sequence of several segments of interest, in particular the ones containing the junctions between the introns and the coding regions.

Preparation and characterization of a hybrid plasmid containing the rabbit β-globin gene and neighboring regions

Cleavage of rabbit DNA with KpnI gives rise to a 5100 base pair fragment containing in its middle portion all β-globin-specific sequences detectable by hybridization under stringent conditions (Jeffreys & Flavell 1977b). This fragment was enriched by preparative agarose gel electrophoresis (Tonegawa *et al.* 1977), elongated with dAMP residues, hybridized to EcoRI-cleaved, dTMP-elongated pCRI, and transfected into *E.coli* X1776. One colony out of about 60,000 was identified as containing rabbit β-globin-specific DNA by the Grunstein–Hogness assay and designated as Z-pCRI/RchrβG-1 or R-chrG for short.

The overall size of the plasmid R-chrG, about 18,000 base pairs, was estimated by adding up the lengths of the three fragments, 8500, 8500 and 1500 base pairs, obtained after digestion with PstI. The largest fragment arising after cleavage of pCRI with HhaI has 1400 base pairs and contains the EcoRI site; the largest fragment found after cleavage of R-chrG with HhaI has 6200 base pairs. Thus, the insert consists of no less than about 4800 base pairs (including the AT-linker segments).

The orientation of the insert relative to pCRI was derived by mapping the BamHI and PstI sites relative to the HindIII site of pCRI (Fig. 1). As shown in Fig. 2, the order of the restriction sites on the KpnI fragment plus strand (i.e. the strand containing the same sequence as the mRNA) is (5′)-PstI-BamHI-(3′); the HindIII site is proximal to the 5′ end of the globin plus strand.

The partial restriction map of the chromosomal globin gene was compared with that of the cloned β-globin cDNA in PβG-1 (Maniatis *et al.* 1976, Efstratiadis *et al.* 1977) (Fig. 2) using the single BamHI site as reference point. There is a one-to-one correspondence between several sites mapping between the BamHI site (position 0) and the MboII recognition site at position − 175 base pairs. However, the EcoRI, BspI (an isoschizomer of HaeIII) and BglII sites, located between 0 to +175 base pairs in the cDNA sequence, are displaced by about 580 base pairs to the right. This displacement delineates the intron previously identified (Jeffreys & Flavell 1977a). A further discrepancy between map distances in the chromosomal and cDNA sequences was noted; The MboII site at − 175 base pairs is preceded by a BspI site at − 217 and an MboII site at − 230 base pairs in the cDNA sequence; these distances are increased by about 125 base pairs in the chromosomal sequence, defining a second, smaller intron.

Comparison of the cloned rabbit and mouse β-globin chromosomal DNA fragments by restriction mapping

A partial restriction map of the chromosomal mouse β-globin gene cloned by

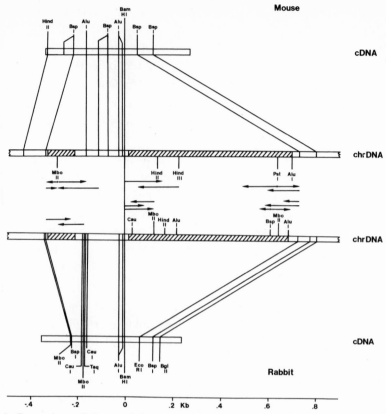

Fig. 2. Comparison of the restriction maps of the cloned β-globin cDNA and the cloned chromosomal DNA segments containing the β-globin genes from rabbit and mouse.

The restriction maps of the rabbit and mouse β-globin cDNAs were derived from their nucleotide sequences (Efstratiadis *et al.* 1977, N. Mantei, unpublished results), that of the chromosomal β-globin genes was derived from partial restriction analysis (Smith & Birnstiel 1976). The map represents only the segment of the cloned DNA corresponding to the β-globin-specific sequences. Horizontal arrows indicate the sequenced region discussed in this paper. Hatched areas represent introns. The distances are given in 1000-base per units (kb) as measured from the BamHI site.

Tilghman *et al.* (1977) is compared with that of a mouse β-globin cDNA clone, Z-pCRI/McβG-1 (M-cG for short) in Fig. 2. Five restriction sites, from the single BamHI site (taken as reference point) to the AluI site at −165 base pairs, are present at identical distances on both sequences. The BspI sites located at +48 and +116 base pairs on the cDNA clone are however displaced by about 600 base pairs to the right on the chromosomal clone, indicating the intron discovered by Tilghman *et al.* (1978a). A second intron of about 120 base pairs is revealed by the displacement of both a HindII and a BspI site, which on the cDNA sequence are located at -325 and -217 base pairs and on the chromosomal sequence at -440 and -335 base pairs, respectively. An MboII site is present at -277 base pairs on the chromosomal DNA fragment and is missing on the cDNA; as shown by nucleotide sequence analysis, this site lies within the small intron. A BspI site at -258 base pairs on the cDNA is lacking on the chromosomal DNA; this is attributed to the different origin of the cDNA and chromosomal DNA (van den Berg *et al.,* submitted for publication).

The mouse and rabbit chromosomal DNA segments may be compared using as a point of reference the BamHI site, which is present at homologous positions in both globin DNA sequences, namely within the val-asp-pro codons (amino acids 98–100) (Dayhoff 1972). It is clear that both globin genes contain two introns each, of similar length and in similar positions.

The analysis carried out so far would not reveal additional, very small introns at other locations within the gene, or even large ones at the extremities of the gene. However, nucleotide sequence analysis has demonstrated the absence of further introns in at least the rabbit chromosomal β-globin gene (unpublished data).

Comparison of nucleotide sequences of rabbit and mouse β-globin DNA
Nucleotide sequence analysis of cloned rabbit and mouse chromosomal DNA was carried out by the procedure of Maxam & Gilbert (1977), in the regions indicated by horizontal arrows in Fig. 2. The complete nucleotide sequence of the β-globin cDNA in plasmid Z-pCRI/McβG-1 has been determined (N. Mantei, unpublished data). The amino acid sequence encoded by the cloned mouse cDNA (which was prepared from mRNA isolated from Porton Swiss mice by R. Williamson) agrees at the critical positions 13, 20, 139 with the structure given for β^s-globin (an allele of β-major globin) of C57BL mice, as reported by Popp (1973) and amended by Gilman (1976).

The chromosomal DNA MβG2 cloned by Tilghman *et al.* (1978a) is from the plasmacytoma MOPC-49 of a Balb/c mouse and should therefore code for a globin of the β^d series (Gilman 1976, Popp & Bailiff 1973). The coding sequences, as far as they have been determined by us (unpublished results), are those of β^d-major and not of β^d-minor globin at the critical amino acid positions 58, 73, 76, 77 and 80, as given by Gilman (1976). In the case of the rabbit, the encoded amino acid sequence is that of the β-globin described by Best *et al.*

(1969), both in the cDNA (Efstratiadis *et al.* 1977) and chromosomal DNA (Fig. 3, data shown only in part).

The location of both the small and the large introns relative to the coding sequence is the same in rabbit and mouse. The small introns have been depicted

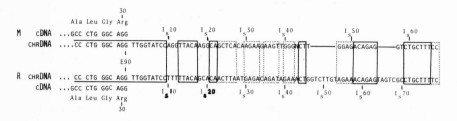

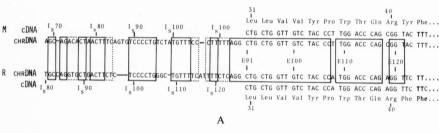

A

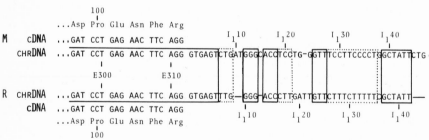

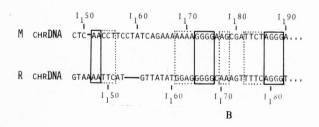

B

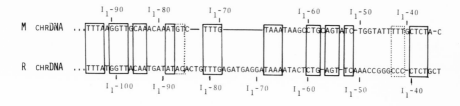

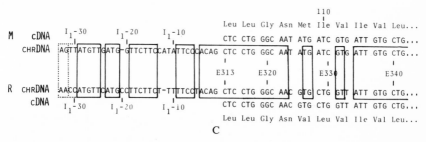

C

Fig. 3. Comparison of nucleotide sequences of the introns of the rabbit and mouse chromosomal β-globin genes at the junctions with the coding regions.

The regions indicated by horizontal arrows in Fig. 2 were sequenced by the method of Maxam & Gilbert (1977). Comparison of the nucleotide sequences of the region comprising (A) the small intron, (B) the beginning of the large introns and (C) the end of the large introns. M cDNA: mouse β-globin cDNA (Z-pCRI/McβG-1; N. Mantei, unpublished data). M chrDNA: Mouse chromosomal β-globin gene (MβG-2). R cDNA: Rabbit β-globin cDNA (PβG-1; from Efstratiadis *et al.* (1977)). R chrDNA: Rabbit chromosomal β-globin gene (Z-pCRI/RchrβG-1). Closed boxes indicate identical sequences, dotted boxes sequences differing at most by transitions.

in Fig. 3A as starting after the Arg^{30} triplet A-G-G and terminating with the sequence T-Py-A-G-G; both could equally well start with or within the sequence A-G-G; following the Gly^{29} triplet, and terminate with T-Py, T-Py-A or T-Py-A-G. The large introns (Fig. 3B and C) have been drawn as following the A-G-G triplet of Arg^{104} and terminating with the sequence C-A-G. In this case the introns might also start within the Arg codon, following the A-G, and terminate with the sequence C-A.

The small introns differ somewhat in length, that of the rabbit (126 nucleotides) exceeding its counterpart in the mouse by 11 nucleotides. The large intron of the mouse is not yet completely sequenced but it seems to comprise about 550–600 base pairs (Tilghman *et al.* 1978a); the large intron of the rabbit is 580–600 base pairs in length.

The large and the small introns show few similarities. One feature they share is the occurrence of strikingly long pyrimidine tracts within the last 30 nucleotides, another is the high T-content (31–39% as compared to 23–25% in the coding sequences). As far as the flanking sequences are concerned, the interpretation given in Fig. 3 suggests that both large and small introns are preceded by the sequence C-A-G-G- and followed by -C-T-N-C-T-G. However, because of the indeterminacy mentioned above as to the precise position at which the introns start, this feature remains uncertain.

In Fig. 3A the nucleotide sequences of the small introns of the rabbit and the mouse were lined up, introducing gaps so as to maximize the homologies. Identical sequences of two or more nucleotides are indicated by a black, continuous frame, while sequences related by nucleotide transitions are framed by dotted lines. The first nine nucleotides from the 5′ ends of the introns are identical; elsewhere several blocks of six to eight nucleotides can be matched. Figs. 3B and C show a comparison of the 5′ and 3′ terminal regions of the large introns, matched in the same fashion. As shown in Table I, the most similar segments of corresponding rabbit and mouse introns are located within 10 nucleotides of the junctions.

DISCUSSION

Most likely the large and small introns of the rabbit and mouse β-globin genes have a common origin because they (1) are located at the same position relative to the coding sequences, (2) have about the same lengths and (3) show more sequence similarities than would be expected on a chance basis. To facilitate comparison of sequences, we introduce the "similarity index", a number which results from the subtraction of the percent gaps, transitions and transversions required to render the sequences identical, from 100 (Table I). Thus, the index of identical sequences is 100 and that of two random sequences of equal length and identical base composition is 25. Random sequences of unequal base composition or unequal length may have indices below 25. This index is not entirely satisfactory, for example, because it does not take into account that two nucleic acids having a number of identical nucleotide positions should be considered more related if these positions were all contiguous rather than scattered. Moreover the index does not reflect the possibility that different types of mutations occur with different probabilities, and that the occurrence of one deletion of 10 nucleotides is more likely that of 10 deletions of one nucleotide.

However, there are at present insufficient data to justify the introduction of appropriate weighting factors.

Using the similarity index (S.I.) for what it is worth, the β-globin coding sequences as well as the mRNA leader sequence of rabbit and mouse appear closely related (S.I. 81 and 75, respectively). If one considers the so-called silent substitution sites, i.e. the codon positions in which nucleotide substitutions do not cause amino acid changes, the similarity index is only 63. The small and large introns have values of 55 and 50, respectively, and are thus as related, as the sequences following the termination triplet of the globin gene, which have a value of 53.

Assuming that the introns of rabbit and mouse are derived from common ancestral sequences and that the mutation rate is about the same for all nucleotides, it would seem that the strongest constraint (lowest mutation acceptance rate) is on the replacement sites (as defined in Kafatos *et al.* 1977) within the coding regions, followed by the 5' terminal leader sequence and the silent substitution sites; the least constraint is on the introns except for about 10 nucleotides at each junction, and the region following the 3' end of the coding region. The high mutation acceptance rate of the introns may also have led to the sequence diversity of the large introns of cloned mouse β-major and β-minor globin DNA detected by heteroduplex analyses (Tiemeier *et al.* 1978).

The strong evolutionary divergence suggests that if any function is associated with the introns it is not dependent on a unique primary structure of a substantial part of the sequence. Why have homologous introns diverged so widely and yet retained about the same length in mouse and rabbit rather than being largely deleted? Two possibilties must be envisaged: (1) There is little or no selective advantage in losing part or all of the intron and/or insufficient time has elapsed for such deletions to establish themselves in the population. (2) The presence of an intron with a certain length has a functional significance. What functions could these be? A somewhat remote possibility is that nucleosome or higher order structure of the chromatin is dependent on some structural feature provided by the introns. It has also been proposed that the presence of introns facilitates recombination and thereby provides selective advantage (Gilbert 1978). As regards translation, we may note that one or more stop codons prevent translation through the small and large introns; however, at least short polypeptides could be synthesized from internal intron sequences, from an initiation site within the intron, or from a start codon in an intron to a stop codon in the coding sequence. At the level of RNA synthesis and processing, one

Table I

Comparison of nucleotide sequences of cloned chromosomal rabbit and mouse β-globin DNA[+]

Segment	Base composition (%)				A+T / G+C	Nucleotides compared (R/M)	Gaps§	Sequence comparison			Similarity index#
	A	T	G	C				Transitions	Transversions	Total°	
1. Coding sequence (including AUG)											
Total	21	25	31	23	0.84(R)	441/441	0	49	35	84(19%)	81
	20	23	30	27	0.75(M)						
Replacement substitution sites (raw data)											
Total						441/441	0	16	19	35(8%)	92
Silent substitution sites (raw data)*						132/132	0	33	16	49(37%)	63
2. 5' proximal noncoding mRNA sequence●	32	27	13	28	1.4(R)	53/52	1	8	4	13(25%)	75
	31	27	15	27	1.4(M)						
3. 3' proximal noncoding mRNA sequence	26	34	18	22	1.5(R)	95/134	41	16	7	64(47%)	53
	31	32	16	21	1.7(M)						
4. Small intron											
Total	21	34	21	23	1.2(R)	126/115	19	26	13	58(45%)	55
	22	31	24	23	1.1(M)						
5' and 3' proximal segments (10 base pairs each)						20/20	0	4	1	5(25%)	75
Middle segment						106/95	19	23	12	53(48%)	52
5. Large intron											
Total	24	39	17	20	1.7(R)	189/185	30	42	29	101(50%)	50
	23	34	22	21	1.3(M)						
5' and 3' proximal segments (10 base pairs each)						20/20	0	3	1	4(20%)	80
Middle segment						169/165	30	40	28	98(54%)	46

should note that the mouse β-globin 15 S messenger RNA precursor contains the large (Tilghman *et al.* 1978b) (and most likely also the small) intron and that it is processed to the mature mRNA with a halflife of a few minutes (Curtis *et al.* 1977a, Curtis *et al.* 1977b). This processing involves the elimination of the introns by a reaction designated "splicing" (Chow *et al.* 1977, Klessig 1977, Dunn & Hassell 1977, Lewis *et al.* 1977) and is thought to involve excision of the intron transcript and rejoining of the RNA ends, in one or several steps (Knapp *et al.* 1978). Undoubtedly the enzyme(s) responsible for such a precise operation has specific substrate requirements. These may be satisfied by specific nucleotide sequences at or about the cleavage sites, and it is in fact striking that the homologies between rabbit and mouse introns are most pronounced around the junctions of the introns with the coding regions. In addition juxtaposition of the cleavage sites could require certain secondary and tertiary structures which may come about by a variety of nucleotide sequences but require a certain length of the intron. Finally, the possibility should be considered that the excised introns themselves fulfill some function, for example at the regulatory level.

In seeking features common to the large and small introns, we have noted the sequence C-A-G-G- at the 5′ junction region of both introns. In the case of the small intron, the 3′ junction region is Py-A-G-G, and the excision of the intron formally appears like an internal crossingover event at any one of four positions:

....CAGG   PyAGG....

Legend to table 1.

[+] Abbreviations: R, rabbit; M, mouse.

§ Gaps are introduced into the compared sequences to align for maximal homology, as shown in Fig. 3. Gaps are counted by the number of nucleotides they comprise.

• AUG triplet excluded. The 15 nucleotides at the 5′ terminal region of the mouse β-globin mRNA are from Baralle & Brownlee (1978). The rabbit sequence is as given by Efstratiadis *et al.* (1977).

* See Kafatos *et al.* (1977).

° Values in parentheses are percent based on "adjusted sequence length" which is obtained by adding the number of base pairs and the number of unpaired bases (opposite gaps) of the aligned sequences. For example in Fig. 3A, the adjusted sequence length of the small introns is 130.

Similarity index is computed as 100 − (% gaps (nucleotides) x c + % transitions x b + % transversions x c). The factors a, b and c are presently taken as 1. Percentages are calculated relative to "adjusted sequence length"°.

The situation is rather dissimilar in the case of the large introns where cutting and rejoining does not occur within a region of homology:

....CAGG̅G̅   CA̅G̅CTCCTG....

Other junctions between introns and their neighboring regions have been sequenced: six pairs for the ovalbumin gene (Breathnach *et al.* 1978), four pairs for immunoglobulin genes (Tonegawa *et al.* 1978, S. Tonegawa, personal communication) and six pairs in SV40 late and early genes (Reddy *et al.* 1978, S. M. Weissman, personal communication). The fact that the regions at the globin intron junctions are more conserved than in the midpart could mean that they play a role in splicing. There is a feature common to all intron junctions, namely a potential cleavage site following either the Pu or the G of a Pu-G sequence at the junction; the Pu-G sequence is frequently but by no means always part of the C-A-G-G sequence which has been noted previously (Tonegawa *et al.* 1978). There may be several different recognition sequences and perhaps more than one enzyme system for cutting and rejoining; alternatively, or in addition, some as yet unrecognized secondary or tertiary structure may constitute or contribute to the recognition target.

SUMMARY

Cloned β-globin genes of both mouse and rabbit each contains a large and a small intervening sequence (intron) of about equal length at precisely the same positions relative to the coding sequence. The homologous introns show some sequence similarity, paticularly at the junctions with the coding sequence. They most likely arose from a common ancestral sequence and diverged substantially during evolution.

ACKNOWLEDGMENTS

We thank Dr. P. Leder for providing us with the mouse β-globin gene hybrid λgtWES·MβG2. The work was supported by grants of the Schweizerische Nationalfonds and the Kanton of Zürich, the Netherlands Foundation for Chemical Research (SON) with financial aid from the Netherlands Organization for the Advancement of Pure Research (ZWO), and the Koningin Wilhelmina Fonds.

REFERENCES

Armstrong, K. A., Hershfield, V. & Helinski, D. R. (1977) Gene cloning and containment properties of plasmid Col El and its derivatives. *Science* 196, 172–174.

Baralle, F. E. & Brownlee, G. G. (1978) AUG is the only recognizable signal sequence in the 5′ non-coding regions of eukaryotic mRNA. *Nature* 274, 84–87.

Best, J. S., Flamm, U. & Braunitzer, G. (1969) The primary structure of the β-gene of rabbit hemoglobin. *Z. Physiol. Chemie* 350, 563–580.

Breathnach, R., Benoist, C., O'Hare, K., Gaunon, F. & Chambon, P. (1978) The ovalbumin gene: Evidence for a leader sequence in mRNA and DNA sequences at the exon-intron boundaries. *Proc. Natl. Acad. Sci. USA.* In press.

Chow, L. T., Gelinas, R. E., Broker, T. R. & Robert, R. J. (1977) An amazing sequence arrangement at the 5′ ends of adenovirus 2 messenger RNA. *Cell* 12, 1–8.

Curtis, P. J., Mantei, N., van den Berg, J. & Weissmann, C. (1977a) Presence of a putative 15 S precursor to β-globin mRNA but not to α-globin mRNA in Friend cells. *Proc. Natl. Acad. Sci. USA* 74, 3184–3188.

Curtis, P. J., Mantei, N. & Weissmann, C. (1977b) Characterization and kinetics of synthesis of 15 S β globin RNA, a putative precursor of β globin mRNA. *Cold Spring Harbor Symp. Quant. Biol.* 42, 971–984.

Dayhoff, M. O. (1972) *Atlas of Protein Sequence and Structure.* Vol. V. National Biomedical Res. Found., Washington, D.C.

Dunn, A. R. & Hassell, J. A. (1977) A novel method to map transcripts: Evidence for homology between an adenovirus mRNA and discrete multiple regions of the viral genome. *Cell* 12, 23–36.

Efstratiadis, A., Kafatos, F. C. & Maniatis, T. (1977) The primary structure of rabbit β-globin mRNA as determined from cloned DNA. *Cell* 10, 571–585.

Gilbert, W. (1978) Why genes in pieces? *Nature* 271, 501.

Gilman, J. G. (1976) Mouse hemoglobin beta chains. *Biochem. J.* 159, 43–53.

Grunstein, M. & Hogness, D. S. (1975) Colony hybridization: A method for the isolation of cloned DNAs that contain a specific gene. *Proc. Natl. Acad. Sci. USA* 72, 3961–3965.

Jeffreys, A. J. & Flavell, R. A. (1977a) The rabbit β-globin gene contains a large insert in the coding sequence. *Cell* 12, 1097–1108.

Jeffreys, A. J. & Flavell, R. A. (1977b) A physical map of the DNA regions flanking the rabbit β-globin gene. *Cell* 12, 429–439.

Kafatos, F. C., Efstratiadis, A., Forget, B. G. & Weissmann, S. M. (1977) Molecular evolution of human and rabbit β-globin mRNAs. *Proc. Natl. Acad. Sci. USA* 74, 5618–5622.

Klessig, D. F. (1977) Two adenovirus mRNAs have a common 5′ terminal leader sequence encoded at least 10 kb upstream from their main coding regions. *Cell* 12, 9–21.

Knapp, G., Beckmann, J. S., Johnson, P. F., Fuhrman, S. A. & Abelson, J. (1978) Transcription and processing of intervening sequences in yeast tRNA genes. *Cell* 14, 221–236.

Lewis, J. B., Anderson, C. W. & Atkins, J. F. (1977) Further mapping of late adenovirus genes by cell-free translation of RNA selected by hybridization to specific DNA fragments. *Cell* 12, 37–44.

Maniatis, T., Kee, S. G., Efstratiadis, A. & Kafatos, F. C. (1976) Amplification and characterization of a β-globin gene synthesized *in vitro. Cell* 8, 163–182.

Maxam, A. M. & Gilbert, W. (1977) A new method for sequencing DNA. *Proc. Natl. Acad. Sci. USA* 74, 560–564.

Popp, R. A. (1973) Sequence of amino acids in the β chain of single hemoglobins from C57BL, SWR and NB mice. *Biochim. Biophys. Acta* 303, 52–60.

Popp, R. A. & Bailiff, E. G. (1973) Sequence of amino acids in the major and minor β chains of the diffuse hemoglobin from balb/c mice. *Biochim. Biophys. Acta.* 303, 61–67.

Reddy, V. B., Thimmappaya, B., Dhar, R., Subramanian, K. N., Zain, B. S., Pan, J., Ghosh, P. K., Celma, M. L. & Weissmann, S. M. (1978) The genome of Simian virus 40. *Science* 200, 494–502.

Smith, H. O. & Birnstiel, M. L. (1976) A simple method for DNA restriction site mapping. *Nucleic Acids Res.* 3, 2387–2398.

Tiemeier, D. C., Tilghman, S. M., Polsky, F. I., Seidman, J. G., Leder, A., Edgell, M. H. & Leder, P. (1978) A comparison of two cloned mouse β-globin genes and their surrounding and intervening sequences. *Cell* 14, 237–245.

Tilghman, S. M., Tiemeier, D. C., Polsky, F., Edgell, M. H., Seidman, J. G., Leder, A., Enquist, L. W., Norman, B. & Leder, P. (1977) Cloning specific segments of the mammalian genome: Bacteriophage λ containing mouse globin and surrounding gene sequences. *Proc. Natl. Acad. Sci. USA* 74, 4406–4410.

Tilghman, S. M., Tiemeier, D. C., Seidman, J. G., Peterlin, B. M., Sullivan, M., Maizel, J. V. & Leder, P. (1978a) Intervening sequence of DNA identified in the structural portion of a mouse β-globin gene. *Proc. Natl. Acad. Sci. USA* 75, 725–729.

Tilghman, S. M., Curtis, P. J., Tiemeier, D. C., Leder, P. & Weissmann, C. (1978b) The intervening sequence of a mouse β-globin gene is transcribed within the 15 S β-globin mRNA precursor. *Proc. Natl. Acad. Sci. USA* 75, 1309–1313.

Tonegawa, S., Brack, C., Hozumi, N. & Schuller, R. (1977) Cloning of an immunoglobulin variable region gene from mouse embryo. *Proc. Natl. Acad. Sci. USA* 74, 3518–3522.

Tonegawa, S., Maxam, A. M., Tizard, R., Bernard, O. & Gilbert, W. (1978) Sequence of a mouse germ-line gene for a variable region of an immunoglobulin light chain. *Proc. Natl. Acad. Sci. USA* 75, 1485–1489.

Williamson, B. (1977) DNA insertions and gene structure. *Nature* 270, 295–297.

DISCUSSION

FLAVELL: What is the efficiency of mutagenesis with the hydroxycytosine DNA?

WEISSMANN: In this particular experiment which I described here, which is I suppose the best one we have done, the efficiency in obtaining mutants is 2%, that means that 2% of the DNA molecules were resistant to EcoRI. The theoretical value in this particular experiment would have been as judged from the amount of hydroxycytosine substitution which was obtained. The reason for this difference in the theoretical and the found efficiencies presumably has to do with repair processes. When you put the hydroxycytosine substituted DNA into the cell you get repair or perhaps preferential excision of the hydroxycytosine.

ENGBERG: Did you give an explanation for the sequence similarity towards the ends of the introns?

WEISSMANN: I would think that the conservation of sequences towards the ends of the introns has to do with processing. In other words, the enzymes which are responsible for excision and ligation are bound to have rather high specificity for these sites, and so the sequences which confer the specificity onto the RNA are likely to be conserved.

ENGBERG: By selective pressure?

WEISSMANN: Yes. There is another question which you might really also ask: The sequences within the introns have diverged very extensively. You can see that the sequences of rabbit and mouse coding regions, and even the silent regions within the coding region, are conserved relatively well. So you would conclude that if the sequences within the introns diverge so strongly, there is no selective pressure to maintain these particular sequences. If this is so, then of course you can ask why these intervening sequences have not simply been deleted. I suppose there are two possible answers to that: One is, there has not been enough time to eliminate them, or that there is so little selective advantage in diminishing the intervening sequence that the mutants in which this deletion has occurred do not spread, or have not had time to spread through the population. The other, I think, more likely explanation is that by and large you need not a particular sequence, but a particular length for some purpose. For the most part it may not matter what it is, as long as it is there. This might have something to do with the overall conformation of the messenger RNA precursor. Or you may have proteins interacting with the messenger precursor, perhaps in connection with processing, which require a certain length (and perhaps a few more or less specific sequences).

ENGBERG: So you would expect that there will be no similarities between the sequences of the different intervening sequences?

WEISSMANN: I think that the large β-globin intron does not cross hybridize with other parts of the genome.

CRICK: It seems to me that there are quite a number of distinct ideas here which have been touched on. It is of course true that there has to be some recognition site for the processing enzyme. We don't know whether there is more than one set of processing enzymes, and I would be astonished if it were the same set for the tRNA as for your particular case. We simply have no idea how many there are. There is also the problem of bringing together the roots of the intervening sequences. When you have a series of them – especially in the ovalbumin genes, where you have seven – it is a problem to bring the right ones together. If you have too simple a way of bringing them together, you have the danger of assorting them wrongly, unless there is a time sequence so that you process one after the other. When we come to look at the homology of the intervening sequences, we have to realize there may be in certain cases special control mechanisms. If we may loosely compare the enzymes that do the processing, e.g. to an RNA polymerase there may be molecules analogous to repressor molecules which are used for control. We might have control at a coarse level with perhaps 10 or 20 different enzymes for processing intervening sequences. If you deleted one of them, then you wouldn't process that particular message. That would be a way of switching off very large numbers of genes, always assuming that if you don't do the processing, you don't get message and the RNA is then destroyed. You might also have a fine level of control, something to sit on one or two transcripts, not necessarily on all of them, to be used for fine tuning. We can all agree there will be some control at the transcriptional level. It is highly unlikely that all the control is done just by RNA processing.

When you come to the matter of the size of the RNA-loop, we have to remember that, as far as we know, RNA is not naked in the nucleus. There are packaging proteins. For all we know the length of intervening sequences is quantitized, perhaps because of the way they are around on the packaging proteins. If you look at the actual sequences, it is difficult to see how they are recognized in a simple way. There are some features which are statistically significant, but they are not very compelling. So one is pushed towards something which Alex Rich and others emphasized to me, that we are seeing the effects of the secondary and tertiary structure of the RNA. I would remind you that in the case of tRNA where we saw the secondary structure of the clover leaf very well, it was very difficult for people to reconstruct the tertiary structure. In fact it was a failure. The reason is that there are a great many possible ways.I think that we may have to face the fact that this is not a problem that you can easily do with a computer. We have to ask, if we can isolate this material before it is processed, does it have a tertiary structure? Can it be explored by enzymes such as S1, by chemical methods and so on. The distressing thing we heard yesterday is that in *Drosophila* there is as yet no genuine case of an intervening sequence. So I think all we can do at this stage is to explore ideas, and in particular think of the different experimental methods we shall need in order to approach these rather complex problems.

Physical Mapping of Globin Genes: Application of the Study of Human Genetic Diseases

R.A. Flavell, J.M. Kooter, P.F.R. Little* & E. De Boer

INTRODUCTION

The mammalian genome contains about 3×10^9 base pairs of DNA while the average structural gene is only about 2000 base pairs long. Since most mammalian genes occur only once per haploid genome, each gene comprises only about one part in 10^6 of the total DNA. Until recently, this fact has greatly impeded the analysis of single-copy genes, although considerable information has accumulated on the eukaryotic genes which are present in multiple copies per genome.

There are two approaches which have made it possible to study single-copy genes:

1. To purify the gene in question – this has become possible with the advent of recombinant DNA technology.

2. To develop sensitive methods which are capable of detecting a single-copy gene amid the background of the total DNA extracted from the mammalian nucleus.

METHODOLOGY

The results described in this article have been obtained by the analysis of single-copy genes, in this case the β-related globin genes of rabbit and man, in total

Section for Medical Enzymology and Molecular Biology, Laboratory of Biochemistry, University of Amsterdam, P.O.Box 60.000, 1005 GA Amsterdam, The Netherlands and * Department of Biochemistry, St. Mary's Hospital Medical School, University of London, England.

SPECIFIC EUKARYOTIC GENES, Alfred Benzon Symposium 13, Munksgaard 1979

chromosomal DNA. We have used the "blotting" method (Southern 1975) in conjunction with filter hybridization to detect the β-globin gene family.

Mammalian DNA is cleaved with a given restriction endonuclease which generates about 10^6 different fragments. The digested DNA is electrophoresed on an agarose gel and transferred to a nitrocellulose filter (Southern 1975). The globin DNA-containing fragments are then detected by hybridization with a ^{32}P-labeled β-globin cDNA plasmid. Since the methodology is described elsewhere (Jeffreys & Flavell 1977a, b) we will not reiterate it here. It is, however, worthwhile to point out the differences between the information obtained by the analysis of single-copy genes by the "blotting" approach and the isolation of a recombinant DNA containing the single-copy gene.

The two major advantages of the blotting approach are:

1. The method examines the gene sequence as it is in the mammalian DNA itself, not after many poorly controlled steps, including replication in bacteria where point mutations and even deletions in DNA sequences can occur. Also secondary modifications present on the mammalian DNA, such as DNA methylation, will be lost during cloning; conversely, secondary modifications may be introduced into the DNA by bacterial enzyme systems.

2. The method is amenable to the simultaneous analysis of genes from many individuals. This enables us to score for alterations in the primary structure of sequences, within or neighboring a structural gene, such as polymorphisms; perhaps more useful is the possibility of probing for mutations which result in defects in gene expression.

At present the method requires about 5–30 μg of total mammalian DNA for a single analysis. Since in practice up to 30 μg of total DNA can be obtained from 1 ml of blood, the method can be applied to the screening of large numbers of different individuals.

The blotting method also suffers limitations, e.g. the information that can be obtained is greater with cloned DNA segments (e.g. DNA sequencing). The two methods should, therefore, be considered to be complementary rather than alternatives.

A DISCONTINUOUS β-GLOBIN GENE IN RABBITS

By using Southern's blotting methodology we constructed a physical map of restriction endonuclease cleavage sites in and around the rabbit β-globin gene (Jeffreys & Flavell 1977b). A detailed analysis of this physical map showed that the β-globin gene was not a continuous DNA sequence on the chromosome, but instead consisted of at least two noncontiguous blocks of DNA interrupted by a 600 base pair non-β-globin DNA sequence (Jeffreys & Flavell 1977b), which we shall call here an "intron" (Gilbert 1978). Since this map could be compared with the known DNA sequence of the β-globin structural gene (Efstratiadis et al. 1977), it could be stated that the interruption occurred somewhere within the sequence coding for amino acids 101–120 of the 146 amino acid β-globin chain. Otherwise the sequence of the chromosomal globin gene appeared to be colinear with the cDNA sequence (Jeffreys & Flavell 1977b). The same structural organization was found for a mouse β-globin gene in a simultaneous study (Tilghman et al. 1978). More recent studies on a cloned rabbit β-globin gene have shown that in fact two interruptions occur in the β-globin structural gene sequence – the one described (Jeffreys & Flavell 1977b) and a second small intron close to the 5'-end of the gene (Van den Berg et al. 1978). The same split-gene structure has been described for a large number of eukaryotic genes (see e.g. Gilbert 1978), including several animal viral genes where the original observation was made (Berget et al. 1977, Chow et al. 1977, Klessig 1977). There are, however, also continuous genes in eukaryotes, e.g. the ribosomal 5S RNA genes (Fedoroff & Brown 1978), certain tRNA genes of *Xenopus* (Clarkson & Müller, personal communication) and yeast and (probably) the sea urchin histone genes (Birnstiel & Kedes, personal kommunications). The eukaryotic genome functions, therefore, with both continuous and split genes; there is no strong indication as of yet for a functional distinction of these two groups of gene types and conjecture at this stage does not seem productive.

THE β- AND δ-GLOBIN GENES IN NORMAL HUMANS

More recently we have turned our attention to the human globin genes. Considerable information has accumulated on the biochemistry, genetics, ontogeny and pathology of the human globin genes. Considering the non-α-globin genes, the hemoglobin molecule utilizes sequentially during development ε chains in the embryonic stages, γ chains (coded for by at least two non-allelic γ-globin genes) during fetal life and β- and (at a low level) δ-globin chains during normal adult life.

To detect the β-related globin genes in human DNA we used a human β-globin cDNA plasmid pHβG1 (Little et al. 1978) as a hybridization probe. Human placental DNA was restricted with EcoRI, BglII, BamHI or PstI.

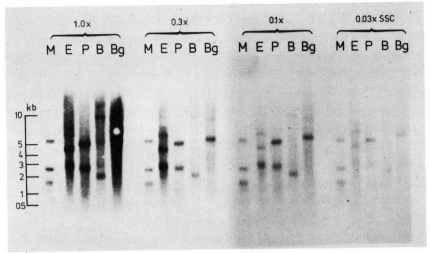

Fig. 1. Detection of DNA fragments containing the β-related globin genes in digests of human DNA with EcoRI, PstI, BamHI or BglII. 30 μg of human DNA cleaved with EcoRI (E), PstI (P), BamHI (B) or BglII (Bg) was denatured with alkali and electrophoresed in a 1.2% agarose gel. Hybridization markers (M) were 10 pg rabbit plasmid pβG1 DNA × HindIII plus 25 pg DNA × EcoRI × AvaI × HindIII and were treated as the human DNA. The denatured DNA was transferred by blotting to a nitrocellulose filter. The filter was cut into strips and the strips carrying the human DNA hybridized to ^{32}P-labeled pHβG1 DNA and the marker strips hybridized with ^{32}P-labeled pβG1 DNA. After hybridization the unbound labeled probe was washed from the strips in 3 × SSC at 65°C (SSC is 0.15 M NaCl, 0.015 M Na citrate, pH 7.0). Duplicate strips were further washed at 65°C in lower concentrations of SSC as indicated. Labeled components on each strip were subsequently detected by autoradiography. All details of hybridizations and washing procedures are described in Jeffreys & Flavell (1977a,b). (From Flavell *et al.* 1978, with permission of the publishers.)

Following hybridization, duplicate strips were subjected to increasingly stringent washes as done previously for the rabbit β-related globin genes (Jeffreys & Flavell 1977a).Fragments from a single given digest show different stabilities (Fig. 1). For example, a 5.0 kb PstI fragment appears to form hybrids more stable to a 0.03 x SSC wash than the 2.3 kb PstI component. Since the probe used in these experiments is specific for the β-globin genes, the experiment suggests that the hybrids which are most stable are formed with the β-globin gene. The β- and δ-globin genes differ by 10 amino acids and exhibit an 8% difference at the nucleotide level as calculated from T_m measurements of DNA-RNA hybrids (Comi *et al.* 1977). This suggests that the δ-gene should form well, but not perfectly matched hybrids with the pHβG1 probe; the 2.3 kb PstI component behaves in this way.

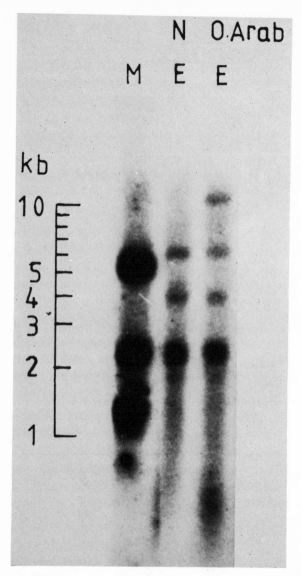

Fig. 2. β- and *δ*-globin gene fragments in EcoRI digests of DNA from a person heterozygous for Hb 0-Arab. DNA prepared from normal placenta or from peripheral blood from a person heterozygous for Hb 0-Arab was digested to completion with EcoRI. 15 μg of each DNA digest were denatured with alkali, applied to a 1.2% agarose gel in a 3 × 2 × 10 mm deep slot, electrophoresed and transferred and the *β-* and *δ*-globin fragments detected by filter hybridization as described in Fig. 1. Strips were given a final wash with 0.1 × SSC at 65°C. Hybridization markers were those used in Fig. 1 and were hybridized with ³²P-labeled p*β*G1 DNA. Human DNA samples were hybridized with ³²P-labeled pH*β*G1 DNA. (From Flavell *et al.* 1978, with permission of the publishers.)

A more rigorous identification of these genes is, however, necessary. The human β-globin structural gene contains an EcoRI site at the sequence coding for amino acids 121–122 (Glu-Phe) (Marotta *et al.* 1977). It follows that mutation of either of these two amino acids will remove the intragenic EcoRI site at this position. EcoRI cleavage should give rise to a fragment that is equal in size to the sum of the two EcoRI fragments contiguous at the intragenic EcoRI site.

We have utilized the variant Hb O-Arab where glutamic acid 121 has been replaced by lysine (GAA→AAA). DNA from humans with normal hemoglobins shows fragments of 6.5, 4.0, 2.3 and 1.9 kb (Fig. 2), yet the DNA from a patient heterozygous for Hb O-Arab contains these bands together with a new 10.9 kb band (Fig. 2). The 10.9 kb band can only be formed from the 6.5 and 4.0 kb fragments. Thus, the O-Arab experiment identifies these fragments unequivocally as being derived from the β-globin gene active in adult humans.

A PHYSICAL LINKAGE MAP OF THE HUMAN δ- AND β-GLOBIN GENES

The use of restriction enzymes in single and double digests makes it possible to construct a map of restriction endonuclease cleavage sites within and surrounding the genes in question. The construction of the two maps of sites around the δ- and β-globin genes, respectively, is fully described in Flavell *et al.* (1978). Mears *et al.* (1978) have also constructed separate δ- and β-globin gene maps containing some of the sites shown in Fig. 3. The maps from both groups show no significant inconsistencies.

The mapping of the cleavage sites of certain restriction endonucleases which generate large β+δ-globin DNA fragments has established the δ-β intergene distance and the gene order. Evidence for δ-β-gene linkage was provided by the following (Flavell *et al.* 1978):

a) XbaI yields a single, strongly hybridizing fragment of 12.3 kb. BglII splits this fragment at a single site into single δ- (7.5 kb) and β-gene-containing (5.2 kb) fragments.

b) Similarly, BclI and TaqYI cut the XbaI fragment at single sites between the β- and δ-genes to generate the predicted double digest fragments.

These data are summarized in the map in Fig. 3. The major points to arise from this study are:

1. The coding sequence of the β- and probably the δ-globin gene contains an intron of 800–1000 base pairs. This is found within the same region (coding for

amino acids 101–120) as the major introns in the rabbit and mouse globin genes (Jeffreys & Flavell 1977b, Tilghman *et al.* 1978).

2. The genes are approximately 7000 base pairs apart, with the δ-gene to the 5'-side of the β-gene (relative to the messenger RNA coded within the gene). To our knowledge this is the first measurement of its kind for two single-copy mammalian genes.

3. Both genes are transcribed from the same DNA strand.

4. There is little homology between the pattern of restriction endonuclease cleavage sites surrounding the δ- and β-globin genes, respectively. The calculated divergence (Upholt 1977) for the extragenic regions of the δ- and β-genes is about 25% compared with 8% for the coding regions (Comi *et al.* 1977). Two explanations are possible:

a) The extragenic regions were homologous, but have since diverged considerably.

b) The region duplicated at the time of creation of the second locus was small and restricted to the gene plus only the immediate flanking regions. This newly duplicated segment was translocated into a nonhomologous region of the chromosome.

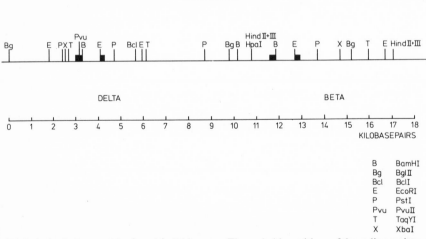

Fig. 3. A physical map of the β- and δ-globin genes. The probable positions of the coding regions of the two globin genes are shown as filled boxes. It should be stressed that the only extragenic cleavage sites which can be detected for a given enzyme by this analysis are those closest to the gene examined. Although the β- and δ-genes are presented as being composed of two coding segments in each case, the possibility that these segments are further split cannot be excluded from these data. (From Flavell *et al.* 1978, with permission of the publishers.)

Recently the δ-β region has been isolated as a recombinant DNA and direct restriction site analysis shows essentially the same sequence organization as that shown in Fig. 3 (Lawn, R., Fritsch, E., Parker, R. & Maniatis, T., this symposium.)

The availability of plasmids containing the fetal γ-globin cDNAs permits the same type of analysis to be performed for the γ-genes. Using one such γ plasmid (described in Little *et al.* 1978), we have recently constructed a map of the cleavage sites around two linked γ-globin genes (unpublished).

ANALYSIS OF ABNORMAL GLOBIN GENES

The availability of the β- and δ-globin gene map enables us to score for deletions, insertions or other rearrangements of DNA sequences within or near to these genes in the DNA of patients who have defective globin genes. In this respect the sensitivity of the method and the capacity for the analysis of many samples simultaneously are useful.

GENETIC DEFECTS IN THE HUMAN β-GLOBIN GENE FAMILY

The functioning of the β-related globins may be disrupted in a number of ways:

a) Abnormal globin proteins may be produced: this usually results from amino acid substitutions in the globin polypeptide caused by point mutations; more rarely deletions or even fusions cause alterations in the β-globin polypeptide sequence.

b) The level of normal β- or δ-globin chains can be reduced or even zero in the diseases known as the β-thalassemias. The levels of globin messenger RNA found in β-thalassemia and in normal humans have been determined using cDNA hybridization. Furthermore, information has been obtained on the presence or absence of the β- and δ-globin gene sequences in these diseases (Ottolenghi *et al.* 1976, Tolstoshev *et al.* 1976). However, these methods measure only gross alterations in the level of the globin coding sequences and cannot measure changes in the sequences that are not transcribed into globin messenger RNA.

The development of the gene mapping techniques described above enables the globin gene analysis to be extended to the flanking sequences: specifically, we can ask whether deletions of these sequences are the cause of the malfunctioning of globin genes in the thalassemias.

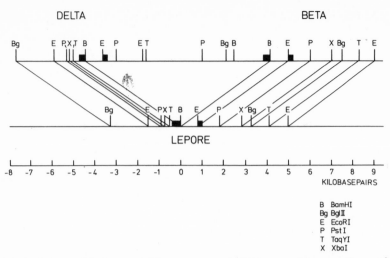

Fig. 4. A physical map of the Lepore globin gene compared with the map of the normal human β- and δ-globin genes. (From Flavell *et al.* 1978, with permission of the publishers.)

HB LEPORE

Hb Lepore is a β-like chain with an N terminal δ-protein sequence fused to a C terminal β sequence. Homozygous hemoglobin Lepore is rare, but since Hb Lepore is only produced in low amounts, Hb Lepore-β-thalassemia double heterozygotes behave as "clinically homozygous β-thalassemia". It was suggested (Baglioni 1962) that Hb Lepore was the product of an unequal crossing over, caused by pairing of β- and δ-genes at meiosis instead of β-β and δ-δ pairing. However, the discovery of RNA splicing (Berget *et al.* 1977, Chow *et al.* 1977, Klessig 1977) raises the possibility that Hb Lepore results from a fusion at the RNA rather than DNA level (Jeffreys & Flavell 1977b). To determine the molecular structure of the Hb Lepore gene we have mapped the restriction endonuclease cleavage sites around the Hb Lepore gene. From the map in Fig. 4

Fig. 5. β- and δ-globin gene fragments in digests of DNA from patients homozygous for β-thalassemia. DNA was isolated from either blood or spleen from patients with homozygous β-thalassemia as described in Jeffreys & Flavell (1977a) and digested to completion with PstI. The samples were analyzed for the β-δ-globin genes as described by Flavell *et al.* (1978). Patient 5 is described in Comi *et al.* (1977): Patient 11 in Tolstoshev *et al.* (1976). Patients 2,3 and 10 have been diagnosed as β⁰-thalassemia (Southern Italian; Ottolenghi, personal communication) and the remainder as homozygous β⁺-thalassemics. 1, 4, 8 and 12 show control normal DNA.

we conclude that Hb Lepore results from a gene fusion rather than an RNA splicing error, at least in this patient. The data fit with the unequal crossing over model (Baglioni 1962) and the deletion of DNA in the Hb Lepore gene is about 9000 base pairs. This suggests that this DNA cannot contain essential genes since Hb Lepore patients manifest no apparent illness apart from the anemia caused by the hemoglobinopathy and its secondary consequences. (We assume here

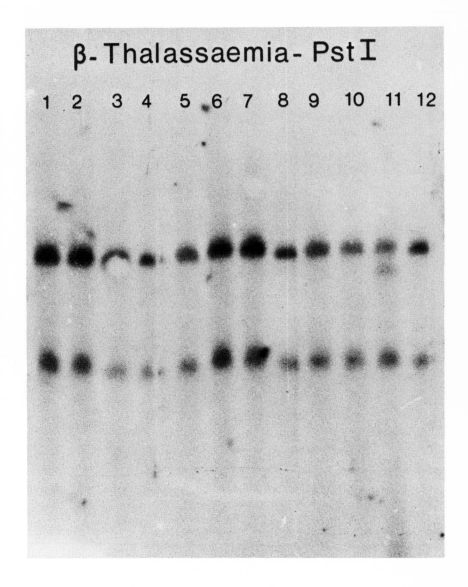

that the nonglobin coding intergenic DNA has not been translocated to another position in the genome, although we have no formal evidence for this.)

THE β-THALASSEMIAS

$\delta\beta^0$-Thalassemia is a rare condition that is characterized by the complete absence of β- and δ-globin chains. Previous studies using cDNA hybridizations have shown that at least partial deletion of the β- or δ-globin genes has occurred although the extent of the deletion could not be defined (Ottolenghi *et al.* 1976). We have analyzed DNA from two (sibling) patients homozygous for $\delta\beta^0$-thalassemia and also from peripheral blood of two patients heterozygous for the condition. Analysis of this DNA cleaved with endonuclease XbaI shows a new globin-specific band at about 2.7 kb and a second faint band at 4.4 kb. In the $\delta\beta^0$ homozygotes these are the only ($\beta+\delta$) bands detectable in the XbaI digest, whereas in heterozygotes the bands are found together with the 12.3 kb XbaI $\beta+\delta$ band found in DNA from non-thalassemics. This suggests that a large deletion of DNA sequences between the δ- and β-globin genes has also occurred in $\delta\beta^0$-thalassemia, although alternative rearrangements – such as inversions – could also explain such results.

The structure of the globin genes in β^0- and β^+-thalassemia is different to the $\delta\beta^0$-thalassemia genes. It had already been shown that most – if not all – of the β-globin structural gene sequence is present in β^0-thalassemia (Tolstoshev *et al.* 1976). We have recently shown that in β^0-thalassemia and β^+-thalassemia cases (Italians, Greek and Turkish-Cypriots and Indians) the pattern of globin DNA fragments seen in Southern blots is unchanged when compared with DNA from normal individuals. Fig.5 shows PstI digests from a series of β-thalassemias in which most patients show a normal pattern of 5.0 and 2.3 kb bands; only normal bands are seen in XbaI and EcoRI digests. This shows that large deletions of the regions flanking the β-globin gene do not occur in β-thalassemia. However, in one case (number 11 in Fig. 5), a second β-globin band is present. This thalassemia gene is the result of a 600 base pair deletion to the 3'-side of the β-globin gene (unpublished data) and this patient carries this gene, together with a β-thalassemic gene which shows no apparent deletion. Our analysis is not capable of detecting small deletions or point mutations, both of which may be the change underlying β-thalassemia in the majority of these cases. Clearly, if we want to find out more about the structure of the β-thalassemic globin genes, we shall have to clone these DNAs and perform sequence comparisons with normal globin genes.

USE OF GENE MAPPING FOR THE ANTENATAL DIAGNOSIS OF THE THALASSEMIAS

The technique of amniocentesis has made the isolation of fetal cells a simple matter. Fetal DNA may be prepared from cells of 12–16 week fetuses and the globin genes analyzed directly. This has been done successfully (Kan *et al.* 1976) by conventional cDNA analysis for a case of α-thalassemia. The mapping techniques described here are more sensitive than the cDNA analysis and can be used for the diagnosis of $\delta\beta^0$-thalassemia and Hb Lepore. At present the more common β^0- or β^+-thalassemias would not be amenable to this approach. However, it is possible that the cloning of the human δ- and β-globin genes will provide probes that are specific even for a small lesion, should this turn out to be the cause of these conditions. Ultimately, this approach may become a general method for the analysis and diagnosis of genetic defects in man.

ACKNOWLEDGMENTS

This work was supported in part by grants to R.A.F. and P. Borst from The Netherlands Foundation for Chemical Research (SON) with financial aid from The Netherlands Organization for the Advancement of Pure Research (ZWO) and a grant from the British Medical Research Council to R. Williamson.

REFERENCES

Baglioni, C. (1962) The fusion of two peptide chains in haemoglobin Lepore and its interpretation as a genetic deletion. *Proc. Natl. Acad. Sci. U.S.A. 48,* 1880–1886.

Berget, S.M., Moore, C. & Sharp, P.A. (1977) Spliced segments at the 5' terminus of adenovirus 2 late mRNA. *Proc. Natl. Acad. Sci. U.S.A. 74,*3171–3175.

Chow, L.T., Gelinas, R.E., Broker, T.R. & Roberts, R.J. (1977) An amazing sequence arrangement at the 5' ends of adenovirus 2 messenger RNA *Cell, 12* 1–8.

Comi, P., Giglioni, B., Barbarano, L., Ottolenghi, S., Williamson, R., Novakova, M. & Masera, G. (1977) The transcriptional and post-transcriptional defects in β^0-thalassemia. *Europ. J. Biochem. 79,* 617–622.

Efstratiadis, A., Kafatos, F.C. & Maniatis, T. (1977) The primary structure of rabbit β-globin mRNA as determined from cloned DNA. *Cell 10,* 571–585.

Fedoroff, N.V. & Brown, D.D. (1978) The nucleotide sequence of the repeating unit in the oocyte 5S ribosomal DNA of *Xenopus laevis. Cold Spring Harbor Symp. Quant. Biol. 42,* 1195–1200.

Flavell, R.A., Kooter, J. M., De Boer, E., Little, P.F.R. & Williamson, R. (1978) Analysis of the human β-δ-globin gene loci in normal and Hb Lepore DNA: Direct determination of gene linkage and intergene distance. *Cell. 15,* 25–41.

Gilbert, W. (1978) Why genes in pieces? *Nature 271,* 501–502.

Jeffreys, A.J. & Flavell, R.A. (1977a) A physical map of the DNA regions flanking the rabbit β-globin gene. *Cell 12,* 429–439.

Jeffreys, A.J. & Flavell, R.A. (1977b) The rabbit β-globin gene contains a large insert in the coding sequence. *Cell 12,* 1097–1108.

Kan, Y.W.,Golbus, M.S. & Dozy, A.M. (1976) Prenatal diagnosis of alphathalassemia: Clinical application of molecular hybridization. *New Engl. J. Med. 295,* 1165–1167.

Klessig, F.D.(1977) Two adenovirus mRNAs have a common 5' terminal leader sequence encoded at least 10 kb upstream from their main coding regions. *Cell 12,* 9–21.

Little, P.,Curtis, P.,Coutelle, Ch., Van den Berg, J., Dalgleish, R., Malcolm, S., Courtney, M., Westaway, D. & Williamson, R. (1978) Isolation and partial sequence of recombinant plasmids containing human a-, β- and γ-globin cDNA fragments. *Nature 273,* 640–643.

Marotta, C.A., Wilson, J.T., Forget, B.G. & Weissman, S.M. (1977) Human β-globin messenger RNA.III. Nucleotide sequences derived from complementary DNA. *J. Biol. Chem. 252,* 5040–5053.

Mears, J.G., Ramirez, F., Leibowitz, D. & Bank, A. (1978) Organization of human β- and δ-globin genes in cellular DNA and the presence of intragenic inserts. *Cell.* In press.

Ottolenghi, S.,Comi, P., Giglioni, B.,Tolstoshev, P.,Lanyon, W.G., Mitchell, G.J., Williamson, R., Russo, G., Musumeci, S., Schiliro, G., Tsistrakis, G.A., Charache, S., Wood, W.G., Clegg, J.B. &Weatherall, D.J. (1976) $\delta\beta$-Thalassemia is due to a gene deletion. *Cell 9,* 71–80.

Southern, E.M. (1975) Detection of specific sequences among DNA fragments separated by gel electrophoresis. *J. Mol. Biol. 98,* 503–517.

Tilghman, S.M., Tiemeier, D.C., Seidman, J.G., Peterlin, B.M., Sullivan, M., Maizel, J.V. & Leder P. (1978) An intervening sequence of DNA identified in the structural portion of a mouse β-globin gene. *Proc. Natl. Acad. Sci. U.S.A. 75,* 725–729.

Tolstoshev, P., Mitchell, J., Lanyon, G., Williamson, R., Ottolenghi, S., Comi, P., Giglioni, B., Masera, G., Modell, B., Weatherall, D.J. & Clegg, J.B. (1976) Presence of gene for β-globin in homozygous β^0-thalassemia. *Nature 259,* 95–98.

Upholt, W.B. (1977) Estimation of DNA sequence divergence from comparison of restriction endonuclease digests. *Nucl. Acids Res. 4,* 1257–1266.

Van den Berg, J., Van Ooijen, A., Mantei, N., Schamböck, A., Grosveld, G.C., Flavell, R.A. & Weissmann, C. (1978) Comparison of cloned rabbit and mouse β-globin genes: Strong evolutionary divergence of two homologous pairs of introns. *Nature,* submitted.

DISCUSSION

WEISSMANN: You said before that the deletion you observed proved that there is no essential gene betwen the β-and δ-gene. This conclusion is inoperative if what you think is a deletion is really a translocation.

FLAVELL: Obviously, another way of creating this is to translocate some or all of that DNA elsewhere in the gene. And we could not detect that unless we could do blots for this region which we have not done.

MANIATIS: I understand that the one β° thalassemia DNA that showed a deletion is homozygous for β°, but there is deletion in only one of the two β° alleles?

FLAVELL: Yes, there are two forms of the disease, one is the type where you cannot detect any difference in the blotting pattern, and the second has a deletion.

Organization and Structure of Immunoglobulin Genes

S. Tonegawa

No manuscript was received for this communication, but permission from the author to print the following summary of his lecture has been obtained.

We have been studying organization and structure of immunoglobulin genes by various biochemical methods including gene cloning. These studies established that a complete, active immunoglobulin gene in plasma cells arises as a result of somatic sequence rearrangement that takes place during differentiation of lymphocyte precursor cells. This DNA rearrangement brings previously distant V (amino terminal half) and C (carboxyl terminal half) coding segments to proximity, presumably into a single transcription unit. Occurrence of rearrangement is restricted only to the pair of immunoglobulin DNA segments that are expressed in a close coupling of the rearrangement event and gene activation.

Detailed structure of a λ chain gene in the pre- and post-rearrangement states were revealed by DNA sequencing. Based on these results we shall present specific models of the DNA rearrangement.

Basel Institute for Immunology, 487 Grenzacherstrasse, CH-4005 Basel 5, Switzerland.

SPECIFIC EUKARYOTIC GENES, Alfred Benzon Symposium 13, Munksgaard 1979

Structure and Expression in Bacteria of Growth Hormone Genes

Howard M. Goodman, Peter H. Seeburg, Joseph A. Martial, John Shine, Axel Ullrich & John D. Baxter

INTRODUCTION

We have recently described the isolation and amplification in bacteria of the DNA sequences complementary to mRNA for the polypeptide hormones rat insulin (Ullrich *et al.* 1977), rat growth hormone (RGH; Seeburg *et al.* 1977a) and human chorionic somatomammotrophin (HCS; Shine *et al.* 1977). Two of these hormones, growth hormone (GH) and chorionic somatomammotrophin (CS), along with prolactin, are a set of closely related polypeptides whose genes probably arose by duplication from a common ancestral precursor (Niall *et al.* 1971, Bewley *et al.* 1972). This hypothesis is consistent with the high degree of nucleotide sequence homology found when the cloned gene structures are compared (Shine *et al.* 1977). The expression of these genes is also affected by other hormones. Thus this system is interesting for the study of the regulation, structure, and expression of related genes. In addition to information about structure and regulation, application of recombinant DNA methods may also provide an alternate source of the hormones via their synthesis in bacteria. Since nonprimate growth hormones have little activity in humans and it has not been possible to extract enough human hormone from pituitaries to meet all the therapy needs, it is of particular importance to obtain human growth hormone gene sequences. We report here our findings on the isolation of a portion of the gene sequences coding for human growth hormone and on the synthesis of rat growth hormone by bacteria. More details of the methodology are described elsewhere (Seeburg *et al.* 1978a,b).

The Howard Hughes Medical Institute, Department of Biochemistry & Biophysics and the Metabolic Research Unit, University of California, San Francisco, California 94143.

SPECIFIC EUKARYOTIC GENES, Alfred Benzon Symposium 13, Munksgaard 1979

```
                25                                          40
      Ala Phe Asp Thr Tyr Gln Glu Phe Glu Glu Ala Tyr Ile Pro Lys Glu Gln Lys Tyr Ser Phe Leu Gln AsN Pro Gln Thr
5'...GCC UUU GAC ACC UAC CAG GAG UUU GAA GAA GCC UAU AUC CCA AAG GAA CAG AAG UAU UCA UUC CUG CAG AAC CCC CAG ACC

                60
      Ser Leu Cys Phe Ser Glu Ser Ile Pro Thr Pro Ser AsN Arg Glu Glu Thr Gln Gln Lys Ser AsN Leu Glu Leu Leu Arg
      UCC CUC UGU UUC UCA GAG UCU AUU CCG ACA CCC UCC AAC AGG GAG GAG ACA CAA CAG AAA UCC AAC CUA GAG CUG CUC CGC

                80                                         100
      Ile Ser Leu Leu Ile Gln Ser Trp Leu Glu Pro Val Gln Phe Leu Arg Ser Val Phe Ala AsN Ser Leu Val Tyr Gly
      AUC UCC CUG CUG AUC CAG UCG UGG CUG GAG CCC GUG CAG UUC CUC AGG AGU GUC UUC GCC AAC AGC CUG GUG UAC GGC

                                                          120
      Ala Ser Asp Ser AsN Val Tyr Asp Leu Leu Lys Asp Leu Glu Glu Gly Ile Gln Thr Leu Met Gly Arg Leu Glu Asp Gly
      GCC UCU GAC AGC AAC GUC UAU GAC CUC CUA AAG GAC CUA GAG GAA GGC AUC CAA ACG CUG AUG GGG AGG CUG GAA GAU GGC

                140
      Ser Pro Arg Thr Gly Gln Ile Phe Lys Gln Thr Tyr Ser Lys Phe Asp Thr AsN Ser His AsN Asp Ala Leu Leu Lys
      AGC CCC CGG ACG GGG CAG AUC UUC AAG CAG ACC UAC AGC AAG UUC GAC ACA AAC UCA CAC AAC GAU GCA CUA CUC AAG

                160                                        180
      AsN Tyr Gly Leu Leu Tyr Cys Phe Arg Lys Asp Met Asp Lys Val Glu Thr Phe Leu Arg Ile Val Gln Cys Arg Ser Val
      AAC UAC GGG CUG CUC UAC UGC UUC CGC AAG GAC AUG GAC AAG GUC GAG ACA UUC CUG CGC AUC GUG CAG UGC CGC UCU GUG

                191
      Glu Gly Ser Cys Gly Phe
      GAG GGC AGC UGU GGC UUC UAG CUGCCCGGGGUGGCAUCCUGUGACCCCUGCCCCCAGUGCCUCUCCUGGCC...3'
```

Fig. 1. Primary structure of HGH (amino acids 24–191) and the sequence of the DNA corresponding to HGH mRNA determined from the cloned 550 base pair fragment (Seeburg *et al.* 1978). Numbers above the sequence indicate the amino acid number of HGH. The palindrome in the region corresponding to the 3'-noncoding portion of the mRNA is underlined.

ANALYSIS OF RECOMBINANT DNA CONTAINING HUMAN GROWTH HORMONE
GENE SEQUENCES

RNA containing human growth hormone (HGH) mRNA was isolated from
HGH producing tumors of pituitary origin by the guanidinium thiocynate-
CsCl density gradient method which we described previously (Ullrich *et al.* 1977,
Seeburg *et al.* 1977b). Double-stranded cDNA was synthesized from the mRNA
by reverse transcription. A 550 base pair fragment from this cDNA was obtained
by digestion with HaeIII endonuclease. This fragment was purified to >99% in
a manner exactly analogous to that developed previously for HCS gene
sequences (Shine *et al.* 1977). This involved polyacrylamide gel electrophoresis,
internal cleavage with endonuclease *Pvu*II, isolation and subsequent religation
of the cleaved pieces, and re-electrophoresis. The self-complementary decanuc-
leotide linkers, pC-C-A-A-G-C-T-T-G-G, containing the cleavage site for endonuclease *Hind*III, were ligated to the *Hae*III fragment. After digestion with
*Hind*III to produce cohesive termini, the fragment freed of linkers was ligated to
the *Hind*III cut plasmid vector pBR322 (Bolivar *et al.* 1977b). The EK2 host
strain X1776 was transformed with this recombinant DNA in accordance with
NIH guidelines in a P3 physical containment facility, and ampicillin-resistant-
tetracycline-sensitive recombinants were selected. All recombinants contained
the correct *Hae*III fragment from HGH cDNA.

The inserted DNA from one recombinant was removed by *Hind*III endonuclease digestion and its nucleotide sequence analyzed using the chemical
degradation method of Maxam & Gilbert (1977). The nucleotide sequence of
growth hormone mRNA, deduced from the sequence of the cloned DNA is
shown in Fig. 1. This sequence agrees (except for two bases) with the sequence
which is partially predictable from the known amino acid sequence of HGH (Li
& Bewley 1976). The *Hae*III fragment corresponds to amino acids 24 to 191 of
the coding region and part of the 3'-untranslated region of the mRNA. The
codons used in this region of the HGH sequence are shown in Table I. In some
cases, there is a marked selectivity in the use of one triplet over another for the
same amino acid. In particular, there is a strong preference for the third position
of the codon to be C or G rather than U or A.

Comparison of the HGH sequence with the sequence of HCS (Shine *et al.*
1977) shows that these two hormones differ by only 22 amino acids in the region
studied (amino acids 24–191). The amino acid homology is therefore 86.9%
while comparison of the nucleotide sequences shows an even greater homology
of 93.4%. Furthermore, the two mRNAs are almost identical in the 3'-

Table I
Codon utilization in human growth hormone mRNA

AA	Codon	#	AA	Codon	#	AA	Codon	#	AA	Codon	#
Phe	UUU	2	Ser	UUU	3	Tyr	UAU	3	Cys	UGU	2
"	UUC	9	"	UCC	4	"	UAC	5	"	UGC	2
Leu	UUA	–	"	UCA	3	Term	UAA	–	Term	UGA	–
"	UUG	–	"	UCG	1	"	UAG	1	Trp	UGG	1
Leu	CUU	–	Pro	CCU	–	His	CAU	–	Arg	CGU	–
"	CUC	7	"	CCC	4	"	CAC	1	"	CGC	3
"	CUA	4	"	CCA	1	Gln	CAA	2	"	CGA	–
"	CUG	10	"	CCG	1	Gln	CAG	10	"	CGG	1
Ile	AUU	1	Thr	ACU	1	Asn	AAU	–	Ser	AGU	1
"	AUC	6	"	ACC	3	"	AAC	8	"	AGC	5
"	AUA	–	"	ACA	4	Lys	AAA	1	Arg	AGA	–
Met	AUG	2	"	ACG	1	"	AAG	8	"	AGG	4
Val	GUU	–	Ala	GCU	–	Asp	GAU	2	Gly	GGU	–
"	GUC	3	"	GCC	4	"	GAC	8	"	GGC	5
"	GUA	–	"	GCA	1	Glu	GAA	6	"	GGA	–
"	GUG	4	"	GCG	–	"	GAG	8	"	GGG	3

Codons given only for amino acids 24–191.   AA=amino acids; #=the number of times the codon was used; Term=termination codon.

untranslated region where they differ by only two out of 54 bases; there is also one additional base in the HGH mRNA. Finally, the palindromic sequence found in this region in HCS mRNA (Seeburg *et al.* 1977b, Shine *et al.* 1977) is almost completely conserved in HGH mRNA.

EXPRESSION OF GROWTH HORMONE IN BACTERIA

To construct a plasmid suitable for expressing the rat growth hormone gene in bacteria we used the recombinant plasmid, pRGH-1 (Seeburg *et al.* 1977). This contains sequences corresponding to the entire coding sequence for pre-RGH, the 3'-untranslated region of the mRNA and most of the 5'-untranslated sequence (shown schematically in Fig. 2). The cDNA had been inserted into the *Hind*III site of the plasmid pBR322. The 800 base pair *Hind*III insert in pRGH-1 was transferred to the *Hind*III site of the plasmid pMB9 (Bolivar *et al.* 1977a). The new plasmid contains a single *Pst*I site in the pre-sequence of the RGH insert (Fig. 2, see also Fig. 3). The region between the *Pst*I and *Bam*HI site of this plasmid was replaced with a similarly digested piece from the plasmid pBR322.

This resulted in a plasmid where the RGH gene could be read in phase under the control of the ampicillin resistance gene of pBR322. The steps involved in the construction of this "expression plasmid" are outlined in Fig. 3.

The complete DNA nucleotide sequences of the insert in pRGH-1 (Seeburg *et al.* 1977a) and the β-lactamase gene of pBR322 (Sutcliffe 1978) are known. Inspection of these two sequences indicates that by joining them at their respective *Pst*I sites the correct phasing of pre-RGH gene sequences is maintained (Fig. 4). The product expected from this region of the plasmid is a polypeptide of 395 amino acids (molecular weight 44,300). This consists of the 23 amino acids of the pre-sequence of β-lactamase, the 159 N-terminal amino acids of β-lactamase (Sutcliffe 1978), the 23 amino acids of the pre-sequence of pre-RGH and then all of the 190 amino acids of RGH. It is noted that three amino acids of the pre-sequence of RGH are lost by cleavage at the *Pst*I site and one is restored (alanine at position 24) by reformation of the site; this residue is also the 182nd amino acid of β-lactamase.

The proteins synthesized by the "expression plasmid" and pBR322 in the minicell producing *E. coli* strain P678-54 (Adler *et al.* 1966) were examined on SDS-polyacrylamide gels. There are several differences in the proteins made by

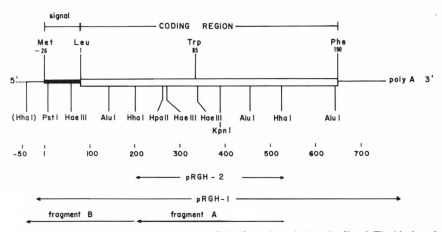

Fig. 2. Physical map of rat growth hormone mRNA from the polyA to the 5' end. The black and white boxes span the coding region and the signal region coding for the mature hormone, respectively. Characteristic amino acids and their respective positions are shown above the boxed areas for orientation. The locations of the cleavage sites in the corresponding DNA for restriction endonucleases *Alu*I, *Hae*III, *Hha*I, *Hpa*II, *Kpn*I and *Pst*I were determined from growth hormone cDNA and from cloned growth hormone DNA. It is uncertain whether the left most *Hha*I site exists or whether this site represents the 5' end of growth hormone mRNA. Nucleotide numbers are given below the symbols for the endonucleases (Reprinted from Seeburg *et al.* 1977a).

CONSTRUCTION OF PLASMID
TO EXPRESS GROWTH HORMONE

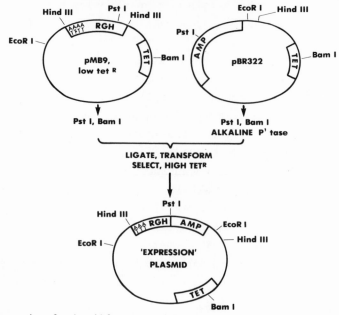

Fig. 3. Construction of a plasmid for rat growth hormone expression. The 800 base pair *Hind*III fragment in pRGH-1 (see Fig. 2) was transferred to the *Hind*III site of pMB9. This plasmid is resistant to tetracycline at low levels (5 μg/ml) since insertion of DNA molecules containing poly dA.dT regions into the *Hind*III site allows expression of the tet® gene at reduced levels. The orientation of the insert was determined by double digestion with *Eco*RI and *Pst*I. The *Pst*I-*Bam*HI fragment of this plasmid was replaced by the *Pst*I-*Bam*HI fragment of pBR322 by cleavage, ligation, and selection for high tet® (20 μg/ml) after transformation. As the single *Pst*I site in pMB9 plasmid resides in the presequence of the RGH gene (see Fig. 2), the structure of the final "expression plasmid" is as shown. The figure is not drawn to scale.

the two types of plasmids as would be expected (data not shown). The most striking difference is the prominent appearance in minicells containing the expression plasmid of a new polypeptide of about 47,000 d. This is within 6% of the molecular weight expected for the fusion product between the β-lactamase fragment and pre-RGH described above. Missing from the strain carrying the "expression plasmid" are the two polypeptides, pre-β-lactamase and β-lactamase, which are present in the strain with pBR322. During cleavage of its 23 amino acid pre-sequence, β-lactamase is transported into the periplasmic space. In one experiment, a large portion (17%) of the β-lactamase present in strain

P678-54 containing pBR322 was released into the medium when spheroplasts were formed in the presence of high osmotic pressure medium. Under the same conditions only about 1% of the 47,000 d. polypeptide from P678-54 containing the "expression plasmid" is released. All these results strongly suggest that pre-RGH, linked to a portion of pre-β-lactamase, is being synthesized but not secreted in cells with the "expression plasmid".

IMMUNOLOGICAL DETECTION OF GROWTH HORMONE SYNTHESIS
IN BACTERIA

Immunological studies were performed to obtain a more direct indication of whether the "expression plasmid" was making RGH. *E. coli* colonies containing this plasmid were screened for their content of RGH using the sensitive solid phase immunological method developed by Broome & Gilbert (1978). Briefly, colonies on an agar plate are lysed *in situ* using CHCl₃ vapor. The antigen present in the cells (i.e. RGH) is bound to a polyvinyl plastic disk coated with antibody against RGH. The bound antigen is specifically labeled using

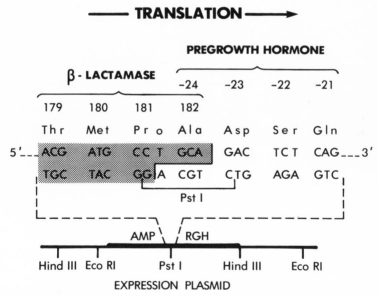

Fig. 4. Nucleotide sequence in the region of the *Pst*I site of the "expression plasmid". The nucleotide sequence and restriction sites in the vicinity of the *Pst*I joining site of the "expression plasmid" are shown. The sequence of pre-RGH is from Seeburg *et al.* (1977a) and of β-lactamase from Sutcliffe (1978).

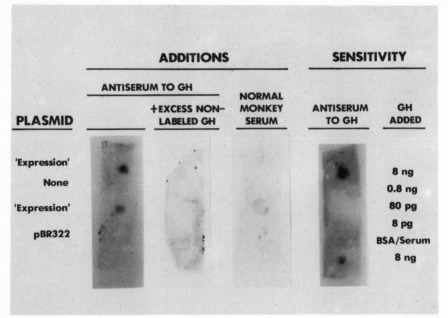

Fig. 5. Immunological detection of growth hormone synthesis in bacteria. Bacterial colonies containing the "expression plasmid" were assayed for growth hormone synthesis using the solid phase immunological screening method of Broome & Gilbert (1978) with the exception that their "wash buffer, W.B." was replaced with 10 mg/ml gelatin, 0.1% NP40 in PBS. Bacterial colonies of *E. coli* P678-54 containing no plasmid ("None"), pBR322, or the "expression plasmid" were grown on agar in petri dishes. After exposure to CHCl₃ vapor for 20 min, the colonies were put in contact with polyvinyl plastic strips which were precoated with anti-RGH-IgG. These strips were washed, incubated overnight at 4° with 10^6cpm of affinity column purified [^{125}I]anti-RGH-IgG, washed and exposed to X-ray film. Each strip was exposed to four colonies in the order shown under the heading "Plasmid". One strip was incubated with [^{125}I]antiRGH-IgG that had been preincubated with 5 µg of RGH. This showed no reaction. Another strip was coated with normal monkey serum IgG (preimmune) in place of anti-RGH-IgG. This showed a slight reaction with cells containing the "expression plasmid", since antigen (i.e. RGH) sticks to plastic even in the absence of anti-RGH-IgG. The sensitivity of the assay was measured by applying varying amounts of pure RGH (8 ng, 0.8 ng, 80 pg, 8 pg, and 8 ng) to an agar plate and screening as above. The sample with 8 ng is readily visible while a control protein spot consisting of BSA and calf serum showed no reaction.

[^{125}I]anti-RGH-IgG and the colonies producing RGH are detected by radio-autography.

Using affinity column purified anti-RGH-IgG with a specific activity of 5.3 µCi/µg, colonies containing the "expression plasmid" were readily labeled while the host cell or colonies containing pBR322 were not labeled at all (Fig. 5). Parallel sensitivity assays indicate that 8 ng of purified RGH gives a strong positive reaction (Fig. 5). Assuming 10^6 bacteria per colony, these results suggest that there are about 20,000 molecules of fused growth hormone per cell. In other preliminary studies with the use of direct radioimmunoassay of extracts of the bacteria, a value of only 200 molecules per cell was obtained. This latter calculation may be an underestimate, since it is based on the unlikely assumption that the fused protein has about the same affinity for the antibody as authentic RGH. In any event, the results suggest that substantial quantities of growth hormone are being produced by the "expression plasmid".

Several additional controls suggest that the immunological reactions are specific for growth hormone. Treatment of the polyvinyl with the IgG component of preimmune monkey serum in place of anti-RGH-IgG (Fig. 5) or the use of $[^{125}I]$-normal monkey serum-IgG as a probe (data not shown) also failed to label any colony. Finally, incubation of the $[^{125}I]$-anti RGH-IgG probe with a 250-fold (w/w) excess of RGH for 1 h at room temperature prior to its use, also gave no sign of labeling the colonies (Fig. 5). In other experiments, every colony containing the "expression plasmid" gave a strong positive response, while no reaction has ever been detected from the host cells or cells containing pBR322.

DISCUSSION

The experiments presented here indicate that gene sequences for polypeptide hormones can be accurately replicated in bacteria. The studies with rat growth hormone gene sequences also show that the nucleotide sequence coding for a polypeptide hormone can be transcribed and translated by the bacteria. Furthermore, although precise quantification is not yet available, the data suggest that RGH can be produced by the bacteria at a rate comparable to some of the major bacterial proteins such as β-galactasidase. It may therefore be possible to adapt recombinant DNA technology to the large scale production of polypeptide hormones and other important proteins. These conclusions are further supported by the recent demonstration of synthesis of rat insulin in bacteria (Villa-Komaroff *et al.* 1978).

As emphasized earlier, it is of major importance, particularly with growth hormone, to produce the human protein. The current studies with cDNA to HGH mRNA represent a step in that direction. In addition, analysis of the structure of this cloned DNA provides comparative information about related genes. Of particular interest was the finding of sequence homology not only in the coding portion of the gene, but also in the sequences corresponding to the 3'-noncoding portion of the mRNA. Save for a AAUAAA sequence near the poly A segment (Seeburg *et al.* 1975a), strong sequence homology has not been reported with other mRNAs. Thus, the possibility must be considered that these sequences and the palindrome are in some way important for the expression of these two related genes.

ACKNOWLEDGMENTS

This work was supported by NIH grants CA 14026 and AM 19997 and by a grant from Eli Lilly and Company. H.M.G. and J.D.B. are investigators of the Howard Hughes Medical Institute. We are especially indebted to Dr. Charles B Wilson for provision of HGH-producing tumors and to Robert D. Ivarie and Julie Morris for help with the immunological studies.

REFERENCES

Adler, H. I., Fischer, W. D., Cohen, A. & Hardigree, A. A. (1966) Miniature *Escherichia coli* cells deficient in DNA. *Proc. Natl. Acad. Sci. USA* 57, 321–326.

Bewley, T. A., Dixon, J. S. & Li, C. H. (1972) Sequence comparison of human pituitary growth hormone, human chorionic somatomammotrophin, and ovine pituitary growth and lactogenic hormones. *Int. J. Peptide Prot. Res.* 4, 281–287.

Bolivar, F., Rodriguez, R. L., Betlach, M. C. & Boyer, H. M. (1977a) Construction and characterization of new cloning vehicles I. Ampicillin-resistant derivatives of the plasmid pMB9. *Gene* 2, 75–93.

Bolivar, F., Rodriguez, R. L., Greene, P. L., Betlach, M. C., Heyneker, H. L., Boyer, H. W., Crosa, J. H. & Falkow, S. (1977b) Construction and characterization of new cloning vehicles II. A multipurpose cloning system. *Gene* 2, 95–113.

Broome, S. & Gilbert, W. (1978) Immunological screening method to detect specific translation products. *Proc. Natl. Acad. Sci. USA* 75, 2746–2749.

Li, C. H. & Bewley, T. A. (1976) Studies on plasmin-modified human growth hormone and its fragments. In: *Growth Hormone and Related Peptides,* ed. Pecile, A. & Muller, E.E., pp. 14–32. Excerpta Medica, American Elsevier Publishing Co., Inc., New York.

Maxam, A. M. & Gilbert, W. (1977) A new method for sequencing DNA. *Proc. Natl. Acad. Sci. USA* 74, 560–564.

Niall, H. D., Hogan, M. L., Sauer, R., Rosenblum, I. Y. & Greenwood, F. C. (1971) Sequences of pituitary and placental lactogenic and growth hormones: Evolution from a primordial peptide by gene replication. *Proc. Natl. Acad. Sci. USA* 68, 866–869.

Seeburg, P. H., Shine, J., Martial, J. A., Baxter, J. D. & Goodman, H. M. (1977a) Nucleotide sequence and amplification in bacteria of the structural gene for rat growth hormone. *Nature 270,* 486–494.

Seeburg, P. H., Shine, J., Martial, J. A., Ullrich, A., Baxter, J. R. & Goodman, H. M. (1977b)

Nucleotide sequence of part of the gene for human chorionic somatomammotrophin: Purification of DNA complementary to predominant mRNA species. *Cell* 12, 157–165.

Seeburg, P. H., Shine, J., Martial, J. A., Baxter, J. D. & Goodman, H. M. (1978a) Construction and analysis of recombinant DNA containing human growth hormone gene sequences. In preparation.

Seeburg, P. H., Shine, J., Martial, J. A., Ivarie, R. D., Ullrich, A., Baxter, J. D. & Goodman, H. M. (1978b) Synthesis of growth hormone in bacteria. *Nature*. In press.

Shine, J., Seeburg, P. H., Martial, J. A., Baxter, J. D. & Goodman, H. M. (1977) Construction and analysis of recombinant DNA for human chorionic somatomammotrophin. *Nature* 270, 494–499.

Sutcliffe, J. G. (1978) Nucleotide sequence of the ampicillin resistance gene of pBR322. *Proc. Natl. Acad. Sci. USA.* 75, 3737–3741.

Ullrich, A., Shine, J., Chrigwin, J., Pictet, R., Tischer, E., Rutter, W. J. & Goodman, H. M. (1977) Rat insulin genes: Construction of plasmids containing the coding sequences. *Science* 196, 1313–1319.

Villa-Komaroff, L., Efstratiadis, A., Broome, S., Lomedico, P., Tizard, R., Naber, S. P., Chick, W. L. & Gilbert, W. (1978) A bacterial clone synthesizing/proinsulin. *Proc. Natl. Acad. Sci. USA.* 75, 3727–3731.

DISCUSSION

WEISSMANN: What is the possibility for cleaving the growth hormone out of the fused protein?

GOODMAN: Unfortunately, one cannot use CNBr cleavage which has been used successfully with somatostatin and insulin where there is no methionine in the coding region. So far we have very few good ideas. The question is whether it is ever going to be really necessary to take the hormone out of the fused protein. One of the next steps has to be to show not only just immuno-reactivity, but also biological activity of the products made. In some cases, the peptide fused to the hormone may not be toxic, and therefore, it may be possible to use the fusion product as obtained. Another hope which could be feasible is simply to construct a plasmid with the fusion site right at the function point between the presequence of beta-lactamase and the beginning of the hormone gene itself. Then one might hope that the hormone would be secreted as well as being cleaved at exactly the right point. However, it remains to be seen whether one can do that or not.

WEISSMANN: I suppose that there would be ways, e.g. of putting into the junction point a proline preceded by several lysines, thereby creating a region very susceptible to trypsin, and then using some exopeptidase to take off the proline.

GOODMAN: Yes, we have thought of that. Of course, one would like some analogue or some enzyme that is much more specific for a particular amino acid sequence. Then one could construct a linker that would have exactly the right DNA sequence to code for the proper cleavage site.

Movement of Foreign DNA into and out of Somatic Cell Chromosomes by Linkage to SV40

W. Schaffner, W. Topp & M. Botchan

SUMMARY

Rat cells were transformed with a recombinant virus in which the Simian virus (SV40) "early" region was linked to a segment of sea urchin histone DNA. The recombinant DNA became covalently integrated into the rat genome in the transformed cells. In the majority of these cell lines, the integrated recombinant DNA was present as a greater than unit length array containing head-to-tail duplications with at least one intact histone DNA moiety present. In several cell lines rescue of recombinant DNA indistinguishable from the input DNA was obtained after fusion of the transformed cells with permissive monkey cells.

INTRODUCTION

Simian virus 40 (SV40) has been envisioned as a eukaryotic vector (Jackson *et al.* 1972) and has recently been used to propagate segments of bacteriophage lambda DNA (Ganem *et al.* 1976, Nussbaum *et al.* 1976, Goff & Berg, 1976) or cloned bacterial and eukaryotic genes in a lytic infection cycle (Hamer *er al.* 1977, P. Berg, personal communication, D. Hamer, personal communication). The basic approach has been to construct chimeric DNA in which the viral "late" genes are replaced by foreign DNA, and to grow such recombinants in monkey cells in the presence of an SV40 helper virus that is defective in its "early" functions. The aim of these studies is of course to get expression of the linked

Cold Spring Harbor Laboratory, New York, U.S.A.

SPECIFIC EUKARYOTIC GENES, Alfred Benzon Symposium 13, Munksgaard 1979

genes under the direction of either SV40 or their own controlling elements. In fact, transcription of sequences inserted into SV40 has been detected during a lytic infection cycle (Goff & Berg, 1976, Hamer *et al.* 1977). A yeast tyrosine tRNA gene transcript was processed to tRNA size (Goff & Berg, personal communication). A hemoglobin β chain cDNA gene (Maniatis *et al.* 1976) inserted in the SV40 "late" region is transcribed under SV40 control and gives rise to β globin protein in the infected monkey cells (Berg, personal communication, Hamer, personal communication).

Upcroft *et al.* (1978) found free copies of a SV40-tRNA gene recombinant persisting in populations of permissive and nonpermissive cells.

The mode by which SV40 integrates and excises from host chromosomes indicates that transformation of nonpermissive cells could be a useful alternative to lytic growth for this type of experiment, since constraints due to packaging of the chimeric DNA molecule into viral particles can be bypassed. SV40 stably transforms nonpermissive cells such as mouse and rat cells. The essential functions for initiation and maintenance of the transformed state reside entirely in the "early" region of the SV40 genome, as indicated by transformation of rat cells with subgenomic fragments of SV40 (Graham *et al.* 1974). Upon transformation, SV40 DNA is covalently attached in a linear form to host DNA (Sambrook *et al.* 1968, Botchan *et al.* 1976). No specific integration site on the SV40 genome could be detected (Botchan *et al.* 1976, Ketner & Kelly, 1976), nor does there seem to be a unique attachment site in the host genome, as indicated by restriction analysis of integrated SV40 DNA in transformed cells (Botchan *et al.* 1976) and cytogenetic studies (Croce & Koprowski, 1975, Croce, 1977, Kucherlapati *et al.* 1978). The only viral prerequisite selected for in this system, seems to be the conservation of the "early" region, whose continuous expression is usually a necessary component for maintenance of SV40-induced cell transformation (Brugge & Butel, 1975, Martin & Chou, 1975, Osborn & Weber, 1975, Tegtmeyer, 1975, Steinberg *et al.* 1978).

After growth of transformed cells for many generations, the integrated SV40 DNA can be activated by fusing them with (permissive) african green monkey kidney cells. About 20% of the fused transformed cells start producing SV40 virus (Watkins, 1974, Botchan *et al.* 1978) which is usually indistinguishable from the input virus. How can the integrated SV40 DNA that is covalently attached to cellular DNA be exactly excised during the fusion process? In several laboratories, including our own, the structures found for integrated Papova virus DNA often contain large tandem head-to-tail duplications (Kelly *et al.*

1974, Botchan *et al.* 1976, Botchan *et al.* 1978, Birg *et al.* submitted, Gluzman, personal communication, Rogers & Southern, personal communication. Rigby & Berg, personal communication). Such duplications are thought to enable the viral DNA to be excised via recombination mechanisms (see Discussion).

Our aim was to find out if a foreign piece of DNA linked to SV40 could be integrated along with the viral DNA in order to answer the following questions: (1) Is the foreign DNA involved in the junction to host sequences, (2) does it also undergo partial duplication, (3) can this DNA be rescued together with SV40 DNA after fusion of the transfromed cell with monkey cells, and (4) is the original chimeric DNA molecule restored upon fusion?

In order to explore these problems, we prepared a recombinant between cloned sea urchin histone DNA (Clarkson *et al.* 1976, Schaffner *et al.* 1978) and SV40. Our data show that SV40 can be used to integrate a foreign DNA segment into rat cells, and that the foreign DNA can be rescued together with the vector from the vast excess of host DNA.

MATERIALS AND METHODS
Preparation of SV40-histone DNA recombinant
SV40 wild type DNA was cleaved with restriction endonucleases HpaII, BamHI and EcoRI. The HpaII-BamHI fragment containing the "early" region was recovered after agarose gel electrophoresis as described in Clarkson *et al.* (1978); 2 μg of the fragment were elongated with about 150 dT residues per end using terminal deoxynucleotidyl-transferase in the presence of Co^{++} (Roychoudhury *et al.* 1976).

A total of 2 μg of a cloned 6000 bp histone gene cluster of the sea urchin *Psammechinus miliaris* (Clarkson *et al.* 1976, Schaffner *et al.* 1978) were randomly cleaved with DNase I in presence of Mn^{++} in order to induce double-strand breaks (Melgar & Goldthwait, 1968) to a weight-average of about 2500 bp as judged by agarose gel electrophoresis. This DNA was then elongated with about 150 dA residues as described above. After phenol extraction and ethanol precipitation, 0.5 μg of SV40-polyT was mixed with 0.5 μg of histone DNA-polyA in 0.2 ml of Tris-buffered saline medium, heated to 65°C and slowly cooled to room temperature within 1 h; 0.2 ml of 1 mg/ml DEAE-Dextran in Tris-buffered saline medium were added. A 24-h-old monolayer of African green monkey kidney cells (CV-1 cells) were infected with the DNA according to Pagano *et al.* (1967). These cells had been infected 1.5 h previously with SV40 tsA 209 virus (Chou & Martin, 1974). Nine days later, plaques containing sea urchin

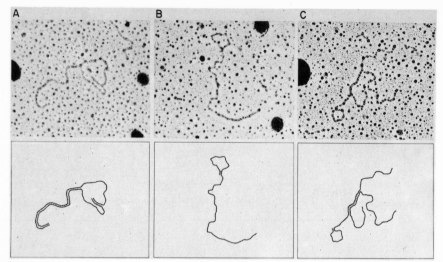

Fig. 1. Electron micrographic heteroduplex analysis of the DNA from SV40-histone DNA recombinant No. 35.

A) Heteroduplex molecule between SV40 wild type and clone 35 DNA. Both molecules were cleaved with BglI prior to denaturation and reassociation. The "bubble" indicates nonhomology between the SV40 wild type "late" region and the sea urchin histone insert of recombinant No. 35. The spreading conditions according to Caskye & Davidson (1977) may not have allowed for efficient basepairing between PolyA and PolyT.

B) Denatured single stranded molecule of the cloned sea urchin histone 6 kb DNA recovered from λh22 by HindIII digestion (Clarkson *et al.* 1976). A characteristic loop structure near the H1 gene (Portmann & Birnstiel, personal communication) permits the orientation of the molecule.

C) Heteroduplex between 6 kb histone DNA and SV40-histone DNA recombinant No. 35. The stem region indicates homologous segments between the histone gene cluster and the insert segment in recombinant No. 35.

histone DNA were identified according to the procedure of villareal & Berg (1977).

Transformation of rat cells

5×10^5 primary rat embryo cells were seeded in a 60-mm dish and infected with a mixture of tsA 209 virus and SV40-histone DNA recombinant grown up from plaque No. 35 at an m.o.i. of about 20. The ratio of tsA 209 to recombinant was about 3:1. One day later the cells were diluted 1000-fold and seeded at about 1000 cells per 60-mm dish. Only transformed cells form colonies under these conditions. A total of nine colonies were isolated and recloned in microwells. The incubation temperature for all steps was 39.5°.

Cell fusion

5×10^5 transformed cells were seeded with 1.5×10^6 CV-1 cells and fused with polyethylene glycol (Pontecorvo, 1975, Botchan *et al.* 1978). One day later the cells were lysed and low molecular weight DNA was extracted according to Hirt (1967).

Analysis of the integrated recombinant

Transformed cells were grown up in roller bottles. $2-3\times10^8$ cells were collected

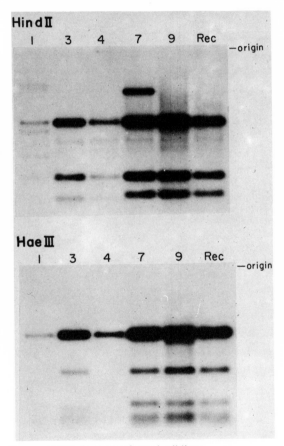

Fig. 2. Analysis of rescued DNA from transformed cell lines.

One day after fusion of transformed cells to monkey cells, low molecular weight DNA was extracted and subjected to restriction digestion, gel electrophoresis, blotting and hybridization to [32]-P-labeled SV40 wild type DNA probe. 1, 3, 4, 7, and 9: DNA from individual transformed cell lines. Rec: recombinant from plaque No. 35 used for transformation.

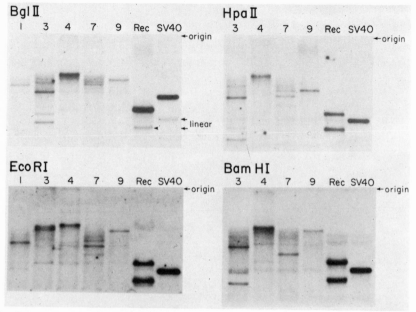

Fig. 3. Analysis of integrated DNA in transformed cell lines.

DNA from transformed cell lines was restricted by enzymes known not to cut the input recombinant, and hybridized to ^{32}P-labeled SV40 wild type DNA after electrophoresis and blotting. 1, 3, 4, 7 and 9: transformed cell lines. SV40: wild type DNA. Rec: recombinant DNA used for transformation.

from each cell line, and the DNA was extracted according to Botchan *et al.* (1974). Analysis of the integrated DNA was performed as described by Botchan *et al.* (1976).

RESULTS

A cloned sea urchin histone gene cluster was fragmented and individual DNA segments were recloned in an SV40 vector by lytic plaque formation using an SV40 tsA mutant as a helper virus as described in Materials and Methods. A total of 55 recombinant plaques were identified. One of these (No. 35) was used for subsequent studies. 10^7 CV-1 cells were infected with virus extracted from plaque No. 35. This infected cell lysate was used as a virus stock for transformation. In parallel, plaque 35 virus was plaque-purified once more and a stock prepared from it.

The DNA of recombinant No. 35 was analyzed by two different techniques. ^{32}P-labeled recombinant was hybridized to restriction fragments of the λh22 6 kb histone gene cluster. The hybridization showed that the histone DNA insert in SV40 consisted essentially of the whole spacer DNA between the genes H3 and H2A (Portmann *et al.* 1976). Sea urchin histone DNA spacers are relatively AT-rich and are not repetitious (Schaffner *et al.* 1978).

Further analysis of recombinant No. 35 DNA with restriction enzymes as well as electron microscopic heteroduplex analysis (Fig. 1) yielded no evidence for rearrangements of the histone DNA due to the cloning within SV40. However a

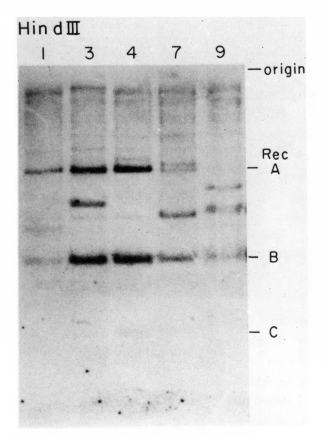

Fig. 4. Probing for duplications in the integrated recombinant DNA.

DNA from transformed cells was restricted by HindIII and analyzed as in Figure 2. A, B, C: Fragments found after HindIII digestion of circular recombinant No. 35 DNA used for transformation; fragment A contains the complete histone DNA insert. See text for further explanations.

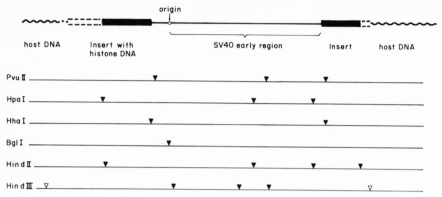

Fig. 5. Structure of integrated recombinant in transformed cell line No. 9.

The amount of head-to-tail duplication and the most likely junction points to cell DNA were deduced from restriction and probing with ^{32}P-labeled SV40 wild type DNA. Further possible restriction sites within the histone DNA insert or in the host cell DNA may have gone undetected by this approach.

rearrangement of the SV40 DNA near the original BamHl site was found (data now shown). Rat cells were transformed with the recombinant No. 35/tsA pool as described in Materials and Methods. Nine transformed cell lines were cloned and propagated at 39.5° for 15 passages. These cells were then fused with permissive monkey cells in order to detect free replicating recombinant DNA. Analysis of the low molecular weight DNA in the "Hirt supernatant" revealed that in all nine cell lines histone DNA was excised together with SV40 and replicated extrachromosomally. In five cell lines, Nos. 1, 3, 4, 7 and 9, the rescued DNA was the same size as the input recombinant. This replicating DNA was directly analyzed by restriction enzyme digestion followed by agarose gel electrophoresis and blotting of the DNA fragments onto nitrocellulose membrane filters (Southern 1975). The fragments were detected by hybridization to ^{32}P-labeled SV40 or histone DNA. The DNA replicating extrachromosomally in four of these cell lines turned out to be similar if not identical to the purified input recombinant No. 35 (Fig. 2). Fragments characteristic for tsA DNA could be detected neither in the chromosomal DNA prior to cell fusion (see below), nor in the extrachromosomally replicating DNA after fusion.

The integrated state of the recombinant in the five cell lines mentioned was also analyzed. It turned out that cell line No. 9 and probably lines Nos. 1 and 4 contain only one major insert, whereas lines Nos. 3 and 7 apparently have multiple inserts (Fig. 3). The transformation by SV40 of cells "semi-permissive" for viral replication often produces lines which maintain persistent copies of free SV40 DNA. However in our cell lines transformed by the SV40-histone DNA recombinant, as in other stably transformed rat lines, no free circular recombinant DNA was detectable.

Further restriction of chromosomal DNA with the enzymes HindII, HindIII, HhaI and BglI gave clues to the structure of the integrated recombinants. For cell lines Nos. 1, 3, 4 and 7, HindIII digestion yielded all three fragments generated from the circular recombinant, in addition to new fragments (Fig. 4). This indicates that in cell lines with one insert, the integated recombinant occurs as a head-to-tail partial duplication of more than unit length. In cell lines with multiple insets, the possibility existed that different unit length inserts would each contribute one or two of the three fragments. The presence of head-to-tail duplications in the cell lines Nos. 1, 3, 4 and 7 became however obvious after a digestion with Bgl I, an enzyme which cuts once in the SV40 origin of replication (data not shown). Clones 1, 3, 4 and 7 yielded a DNA fragment of unit genome length, which means that the duplications created an integrated molecule containing two SV40 origins of replication in the structure: junction fragment-origin-early region-histone DNA-origin-junction fragment.

With the experiments completed to date, the structure of the integrated DNA in cell line No. 9 could be clarified to a higher degree of resolution (Fig. 5). In this cell line the recombinant DNA is also partially duplicated. The junction with chromosomal DNA is probably mediated by sea urchin histone DNA on one right-hand side, whereas on the left-hand side it seems to occur via SV40 DNA.

DISCUSSION

We have shown that a recombinant between SV40 and sea urchin histone DNA can be used to transform rat cells. As an intact early region is required for SV40 cell transformation, one might suspect that integration would frequently interrupt genes inserted into the late region of the viral DNA which indeed has been previously demonstrated (Botchan et al. 1976). However, previous work also suggested that large duplications of the viral DNA might occur on occasion. Large partial head-to-tail duplications have been found for integrated Papova viruses in host chromosomes (Botchan et al. 1976, Botchan et al. 1978, Birg et al. submitted for publication, Rogers & Southern, personal communication, Rigby & Berg, personal communication) as well as in Adenovirus-SV40 hybrids (Kelly *et al.* 1974, Y. Gluzman, personal communication). It is unclear how such duplications arise, but it is conceivable that replicative intermediates rather than covalently closed circles are the substrate for the integration process.

Indeed as a result of partial head-to-tail duplications, a majority of the transformed lines described do contain one continuous sea urchin histone DNA moiety. This augurs well for studies aimed at selecting for expression of an integrated SV40-linked gene, since the linear sequence of DNA must often be conserved rather than interrupted during the integration process.

Because excision of viral DNA in transformed nonpermissive cells is very infrequent (discussed in Botchan *et al.* 1978), the question arises why it is so efficient after fusion to monkey cells. Replication of SV40 sequences still associated with chromosomal DNA is observed prior to the detection of free viral DNA after fusion. It involves perhaps multiple rounds of replication starting from a single origin as proposed for various systems (Mandal *et al.* 1974, Sambrook *et al.* 1974). This *in situ* SV40 replication which is dependent on the presence of a functional viral A gene (Botchan *et al.* 1978) is believed to create the proper substrate for this efficient excision.

Partial duplications are believed to be the structual prerequisite for *precise* excision of integrated viral DNA, presumably by recombination between homologous duplicated DNA segments, an idea first proposed for SV40 excision from Adenovirus-SV40 hybrid viruses (Kelly *et al.* 1974). The structure of the integrated SV40-histone DNA recombinant in cell line No. 9 suggests that precise excision may not depend on SV40 sequences but could be mediated by duplicated sea urchin histone DNA sequences (Fig. 5).

The fact that duplications also involve the sea urchin histone DNA insert and that the joining to host DNA can occur via this insert are consistent with the notion that there is no sequence requirement for SV40-mediated integration into the host genome (Botchan *et al.* 1976, Ketner & Kelly 1976). The same seems to be true for precise excision.

One interesting puzzle concerns the absence of tsA 209 helper DNA in the cells transformed by a mixture of tsA virus and SV40-histone DNA recombinant virus. The finding is peculiar in the light of the fact that tsA was present in excess over the recombinant, and that some of the resulting transformed cells even contain multiple copies of the recombinant molecule. Whatever the reason for the absence of tsA DNA from our transformants, it is very convenient, because analysis of the integrated DNA is facilitated, and the transformed cells are genetically incapable of producing infectious virus.

Taken together, we hope that this transforming system will enable us to introduce any gene into an appropriate host cell, and to recover it from the vast excess of host DNA after analysis of – or selection for – its activity.

ACKNOWLEDGMENTS

We thank Drs. J. Sambrook and Y. Gluzman for gifts of SV40 wild type DNA and tsA 209 virus, respectively, and J. Telford and Professor M. Birnstiel (University of Zürich) for sending us purified 6000 bp histone DNA. We are also grateful to Susanne Weirich for providing excellent technical assistance, and to Dr. T. Grodzicker for critical reading of the manuscript.

REFERENCES

Birg, F., Dulbecco, R., Fried, M. & Kamen, R. (1978) State and organization of polyoma virus DNA sequences in transformed rat cell lines. *J. Virol.* Submitted.

Botchan, M., McKenna, G. & Sharp, P.A. (1973) Cleavage of mouse DNA by a restriction enzyme as a clue to the arrangement of genes. *Cold Spring Harbor Symp. Quant. Biol.* 38, 38–395.

Botchan, M., Topp, W. & Sambrook, J. (1976) The arrangement of simian virus 40 sequences in the DNA of transformed cells. *Cell* 9, 269–287.

Botchan, M., Topp, W., Weirich, S. & Sambrook, J. (1978) Studies on SV40 excision from chromosomes. *Cold Spring Harbor Symp. Quant. Biol.* 43, In press.

Brugge, J. & Butel, J. (1975) Role of simian virus 40 gene A function in maintenance of transformation. *J. Virol.* 15, 619–635.

Casey, J. & Davidson, N. (1977) Rates of formation and thermal stabilities of RNA:DNA and DNA; DNA duplexes at high concentrations of formamide. *Nucleic Acids Res.* 4, 1539–1552.

Chou, J.Y. & Martin, R.G. (1974) Complementation analysis of simian virus 40 mutants. *J. Virol.* 13, 1101–1109.

Clarkson, S.G., Smith, H.O., Schaffner, W., Gross, K.W. & Birnstiel, M.L. (1976) Integration of eukaryotic genes for 5S RNA and histone proteins into a phage lambda receptor. *Nucleic Acids Res.* 3, 2617–2632.

Clarkson, S.G., Kurer, V. & Smith, H.O. (1978) Sequence organization of a cloned tDNA[met] fragment from *Xenopus laevis. Cell* 14, 713–724.

Croce, C.M. (1977) Assignment of the integration site for simian virus 40 to chromosome 17 in GM54VA, a human cell line transformed by simian virus 40. *Proc. Nat. Acad. Sci. U.S.A.* 74, 315–318.

Croce, C.M. & Koprowski, H. (1975) Assignment of gene(s) for cell transformation to human chromosome 7 carrying the simian virus 40 genome. *Proc. Nat. Acad. Sci. U.S.A.* 72, 1658–1660.

Ganem, D., Nussbaum, A.L., Davoli, D. & Fareed, G.C. (1976) Propagation of a segment of bacteriophage λ-DNA in monkey cells after covalent linkage to a defective simian virus 40 genome. *Cell* 7, 349–359.

Goff, S.P. & Berg, P. (1976) Construction of hybrid viruses containing SV40 and λ phage DNA segments and their propagation in cultured monkey cells. *Cell* 9, 695–705.

Graham, F.L., Abrahams, P.J., Mulder, C., Heijneker, H.L. Warnaar, S.O., de Vries, F.A.J., Fiers, W. & van der Eb, A.J. (1974) Studies on *in vitro* transformation by DNA and DNA fragments of human adenoviruses and simian virus 40. *Cold Spring Harbor Symp. Quant. Biol.* 39, 637–650.

Hamer, D. H., Davoli, D., Thomas, C. A. & Fareed, G. C. (1977) Simian virus 40 carrying an *Escherichia coli* suppressor gene. *J. Mol. Biol.* 112, 155–182.

Hirt, B. (1967) Selective extraction of polyoma DNA from infected mouse cell cultures. *J. Mol. Biol.* 26, 365–369.

Jackson, D.A., Symons, R.H. & Berg, P. (1972) Biochemical method for inserting new genetic information into DNA of simian virus 40: Circular SV40 molecules containing lambda phage genes and the galactose operon of *Escherichia coli*. *Proc. Nat. Acad. Sci. U.S.A.* 69, 2904–2909.

Kelly, T.J., Jr., Lewis, A.M., Jr., Levine, A.S. & Siegel, S. (1974) Structure of two adenovirus-simian virus 40 hybrids which contain the entire SV40 genome. *J. Mol. Biol.* 89, 113–126.

Ketner, G. & Kelly T.J., Jr. (1976) Integrated simian virus 40 sequences in transformed cell DNA: Analysis using restriction endonucleases. *Proc. Nat. Acad. Sci. U.S.A.* 73, 1102–1106.

Kucherlapati, R., Hwang, S.P., Shimizu, N., McDougall, J.K. & Botchan, M.R. (1978) A new chromosomal assignment for an SV40 integration site in human cells. *Proc. Nat. Acad. Sci. U.S.A.* In press.

Mandal, N.C., Crochet, M. & Lieb, M. (1974) Properties of polysogens containing 2 depressed λ N⁻ prophages. IV. A large number of integrated λ prophages. *Virology* 57, 85.

Maniatis, T., Kee, S.G., Efstratiadis, A. & Kafatos, F.C. (1976) Amplification and characerization of a β-Globin gene synthesized *in vitro*. *Cell* 8, 163–182.

Martin, R.G. & Chou, J.Y. (1975) Simian virus 40 functions required for the establishment and maintenance of malignant transformation. *J. Virol.* 15, 599–612.

Melgar, E. & Goldthwait (1968) Deoxyribonucleic acid nucleases. II. The effects of metals on the mechanism of action of deoxyribonuclease I. *J. Biol. Chem.* 243, 4409–4416.

Nussbaum, A.L., Davoli, D., Ganem, D. & Fareed, G.C. (1976) Construction and propagation of a defective simian virus 40 genome bearing an operator from bacteriophage lambda. *Proc. Nat. Acad. Sci. U.S.A.* 73, 1068–1072.

Osborn, M. & Weber, K. (1975) Simian virus 40. A gene function and maintenance of transformation. *J. Virol.* 15, 636–644.

Pagano. J.S., McCutchan, H.G. & Vaheri, A. (1967) Factors influencing the enhancement of the ineffectivity of poliovirus ribonucleic acid by diethylaminoethyl-dextran. *J. Virol.* 1, 891–897.

Pontecorvo, G. (1975) Production of mammalian somatic cell hybrids by means of polyethylene glycol treatment. *Somatic Cell Genetics* 1, 397–400.

Portmann, R., Schaffner, W. & Birnstiel, M.L. (1976) Partial denaturation mapping of cloned histone DNA from the sea urchin *Psammechinus miliaris*. *Nature* 264, 31–34.

Roychoudhury, R., Jay, E. & Wu, R. (1976) Terminal labelling and addition of homopolymer tracts to duplex DNA fragments by terminal deoxynucleotidyl transferase. *Nucleic Acids Res.* 3, 863–877.

Sambrook, J., Westhhal, H., Srinivasan, P.R. & Dulbecco, R. (1968) The integrated state of viral DNA in transformed cells. *Proc. Nat. Acad. Sci. U.S.A.* 60, 1288–1295.

Sambrook, J., Botchan, M., P. Gallimore, Ozanne, B., Pettersson, U., Willians, J. & Sharp, P. (1974) Viral DNA sequences in cells transformed by simian virus 40, Adenovirus type 2 and Adenovirus type 5. *Cold Spring Harbor Symp. Quant. Biol.* 39, 615–632.

Schaffner, W., Kunz, G., Daetwyler, H., Telford, J., Smith, H.O. & Birnstiel, M.L. (1978) Genes and spacers of cloned sea urchin histone DNA analyzed by sequencing. *Cell* 14, 655–672.

Southern, E.M. (1975) Detection of specific sequences among DNA fragments separated by gel electrophoresis. *J. Mol. Biol.* 98, 503–517.

Steinberg, B., Pollack, R., Topp, W. & Botchan, M. (1978) Isolation and characterization of T antigen negative revertants from a line of transformed rat cells containing one copy of the SV40 genome. *Cell* 13, 19–32.

Tegtmeyer, P. (1972) Simian virus 40 deoxyribonucleic acid synthesis: the viral replicon. *J. Virol.* 10, 591–598.

Tegtmeyer, P. (1975) Function of simian virus 40 genes A in transforming infection. *J. Virol.* 15, 613–618.

Upcroft, P., Skolnik, H., Upcroft, J. A., Solomon, D., Khoury, G., Hamer, D. & Fareed, G. C. (1978) Transduction of a bacterial gene into mammalian cells. *Proc. Nat. Acad. Sci. USA* 75, 2117–2121.

Villareal, L.P. & Berg, P. (1977) Hybridization *in situ* of SV40 plaques: Detection of recombinant SV40 virus carrying specific sequences of nonviral DNA. *Science* 196, 183–185.

Watkins, J.F. (1974) The SV40 rescue problem. *Cold Spring Harbor Symp. Quant. Biol.* 39, 355–362.

DISCUSSION

MANIATIS: Is the T-antigen required for a proper excision?

SCHAFFNER: Yes. Mike Botchan (Botchan *et al.* 1978) finds that nothing happens if rat cells transformed with a tsA mutant of SV40 are fused at high temperature with monkey cells.

WEISSMANN: It would be interesting to learn whether the integration occurs preferentially within the histone genes of the host cell.

SCHAFFNER: I don't know, but I would expect integration into a homologous site. In marked contrast to yeast cells (Hinnen *et al.* 1978) no DNA uptake into a homologous locus has been demonstrated for mammalian cells, just the opposite: Mike Botchan (personal communication) has re-transformed rat cells which contained already one integrated copy of SV40 DNA. In none out of more than forty cell lines analyzed was the second SV40 DNA integrated into the preexisting molecule.

Studies on the transfer of a herpes thymidine kinase gene including the cellular flanking sequences done by Axel and colleagues (M. Wigner, personal communication) also show uptake into nonhomologous loci. Apart from these findings, the sea urchin histone DNA segment present in recombinant No. 35 may have diverged considerably from the mammalian sequence.

Botchan, M., Topp, W., Weirich, S. & Sambrook, J. (1978) Studies on SV40 excision from chromosomes. *Cold Spring Harbor Symp. Quant. Biol.* 43, in press.
Hinnen, A., Hicks, J. B. & Fink, G. R. (1978) Transformation of yeast. *Proc. Nat. Acad. Sci. USA* 75, 1929–1933.

Mapping of the Transforming Gene of a Murine Sarcoma Virus by Transfection with Specific Fragments of Viral DNA

Poul Andersson*, Mitchell Goldfarb & Robert A. Weinberg

INTRODUCTION

Moloney sarcoma virus is a replication-defective retrovirus which is able to transform fibroblasts *in vitro* and generate fibrosarcomas *in vivo*. The replication of the Moloney sarcoma virus (Mo-MSV) genomic RNA appears to be identical to that of other retroviruses. However, its truncated genome of approximately 6 kb RNA prevents it from specifying many of the viral proteins required for independent replication. Rather, Mo-MSV must depend upon co-infection with a replication competent helper virus, whose RNA genome of approximately 9 kb contains all information required for genome replication and synthesis of virion components.

The helper viruses which complement Mo-MSV replication are thymic leukemia viruses. Besides a dependence upon a leukemia virus for its continued replication, Mo-MSV shares a second important relationship with these leukemia virus, since Mo-MSV was originally derived by passing Moloney leukemia virus (Mo-MLV) through a Balb/c mouse. A solid tumor of the infected animal was found to release the originally injected Mo-MLV along with a novel agent (Mo-MSV). Upon further *in vivo* passaging the later agent continued to induce sarcomas instead of thymic lymphomas usually induced by Mo-MLV *in vivo* (Moloney 1966).

Hybridization studies and RNA-DNA heteroduplex analysis by electron

Center for Cancer Research and Department of Biology, Massachusetts Institute of Technology, Cambridge, Mass. 02139, USA.
* Present address: Fibiger Laboratory, DK-2100 Copenhagen Ø, Denmark.

microscopy indicate that Mo-MSV derives about 70% of its genomic sequences from the Mo-MLV genome. However, these analyses indicate clearly that novel nucleotide sequences have been acquired by the Mo-MSV which are not present in the Mo-MLV parent (Hu *et al.* 1977). Rather, these new sequences are detectable in the DNA of uninfected mouse cells where they are present in one or two copies per haploid genome (Frankel & Fischinger 1976, 1977).

These newly acquired sequences are of considerable interest since their introduction into the Mo-MSV genome appears to have occurred concomitantly with the acquisition of a potent transforming gene by the virus. Nevertheless, in the case of Mo-MSV and other mammalian sarcoma viruses, no evidence exists to assign a genomic location of their transforming genes. Virtually no mutants exist in the transforming genes of the mammalian sarcoma viruses and the development of a genetic system has therefore been impossible.

To circumvent this problem, we have undertaken transfection experiments with *in vitro* synthesized Mo-MSV DNA to study aspects of viral transformation of NIH-3T3 mouse fibroblasts. This approach has allowed for a localization of the transforming gene within the Mo-MSV genome, and further, has provided an experimental system suitable in pursuing the mechanism of the transformation process.

RESULTS

Physical Mapping of in vitro *Synthesized Mo-MSV DNA.*

Mo-MSV DNA was synthesized by endogenous reverse transcription in detergent permeabilized clone G8-124 virus. This strain of Mo-MSV is minimally contaminated with the obligatory replication competent helper virus (Ball *et al.* 1973). The *in vitro* DNA synthesis was carried out under conditions favoring synthesis of very long DNA transcripts (Rothenberg & Baltimore 1977). Analysis of the synthesized DNA by alkaline agarose gel electrophoresis shows that the longest DNA molecules synthesized were 5.2 kb and 5.8 kb DNA species (Fig. 2, Lane b) which represent (−) strand transcripts complementary to viral genomic RNA. It has previously been reported (Rothenberg *et al.* 1977) that the limit length (−) strand DNA molecules synthesized *in vitro* in Moloney leukemia virus particles are 8.2 kb and 8.8 kb and that the synthesis of the 8.8 kb species is inhibited by the presence of Actinomycin D during the *in vitro* reaction. The 0.6-kb difference between the 8.2 kb and 8.8 kb (−) strand transcripts was subsequently located to the 3' end of the (−) strand transcripts

(Andersson, unpublished results). The finding of a similar difference of 0.6 kb between the longest (−) strand transcripts synthesized in Mo-MSV virions and of an inhibitory effect of Actinomycin D on the final extension of the 5.2 kb (−) strand transcript was used to orient the physical map of Mo-MSV DNA with respect to the ends of the Mo-MSV genomic RNA.

A mixture of a^{32}P-dATP-labeled 5.2 kb and 5.8 kb (−) strand transcripts was isolated by fractionation of total *in vitro* synthesized Mo-MSV DNA by alkaline sucrose gradient centrifugation. The single-stranded DNA was converted to double-stranded form using avian myeloblastosis virus reverse transcriptase for DNA-directed synthesis primed randomly by addition of a limit DNase I digest of calf thymus DNA (Summers 1975, Summers *et al.* 1975). This second DNA strand was synthesized with nonradioactive dNTPs. The resulting double-stranded DNA could be used as substrate for restriction endonucleases followed

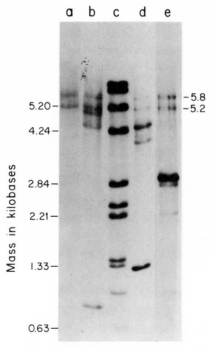

Fig. 1. Orientation of the physical map for *in vitro* synthesized Mo-MSV DNA. A mixture of ³²P-dATP-labeled 5.2 kb and 5.8 kb (−) strand DNA synthesized *in vitro* was converted to double-stranded form and subjected to cleavage with Hind III (Lane b), Hpa I (Lane d) or Sal I (Lane e). The resulting fragments were resolved by alkaline agarose gel electrophoresis (Berk & Sharp 1977). Each lane was added noncleaved DNA (seen in Lane a) to provide internal marker.

ANDERSSON ET AL.

by analysis of the cleavage products by alkaline agarose gel electrophoresis. When the mixture of 5.2 kbp and 5.8 kbp DNA was cleaved with endonucleases having a single recognition site within the 5.2 kb (−) strand transcript, three

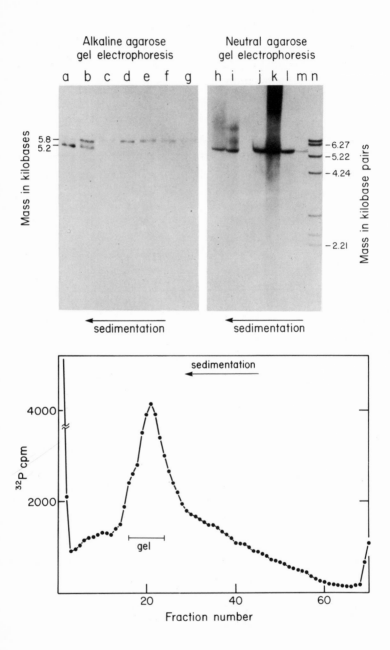

fragments were generated. We reasoned that one common fragment would originate from both molecular species, while two fragments would derive from that end where the 0.6 kb difference is found. In Fig. 1 Lane b, cleavage with Hind III can be seen to generate a common fragment of 0.9 kb and a doublet of fragments differing by 0.6 kb thus establishing a cleavage site for Hind III at 0.9 kb from the 5' end of the (−) strand transcripts. The known locations for the Hind III, Hpa I and Sal I cleavage sites within the Mo-MSV DNA were in turn used for a more detailed restriction endonuclease mapping using as substrate a 5.8 kbp double-stranded DNA species which could be readily isolated from the total *in vitro* synthesized Mo-MSV DNA.

Fig. 2 shows the sedimentation profile in a neutral sucrose gradient of ^{32}P-dATP-labeled Mo-MSV DNA synthesized in detergent permeabilized virions. A peak of radioactivity sedimenting at approximately 16S was further characterized by gel electrophoresis. Alkaline agarose gel electrophoresis of aliquots of individual gradient fractions showed that a 5.8 kb DNA species constituted a dominant species in the 16S DNA (Lanes c-g). Upon neutral agarose gel electrophoresis of aliquots of the peak fractions from the neutral sucrose gradient, it can be seen that a 5.8 kbp DNA species is present in these fractions (Lanes j and l). The pelleted material from the sucrose gradient centrifugation was enriched for the 5.2 kb DNA species (Lane a) when compared to unfractionated Mo-MSV DNA (Lane b). This isolation of the 5.8 kbp Mo-MSV DNA is based on the fact that the 5.2 kb (−) strand transcript as well as smaller (−) strand DNA products synthesized during the endogenous reverse transcription are single-stranded and /or associated with the RNA template and thus sediment more rapidly than the complete 5.8 kbp Mo-MSV DNA.

The sucrose gradient purified 5.8 kbp Mo-MSV DNA was used as substrate for a series of restriction endonucleases and a physical map of the Mo-MSV DNA was derived according to known principles. The orientation of the map relative to the ends of the Mo-MSV 30S genomic RNA was assured by the

---

Fig. 2. Characterization of *in vitro* synthesized Mo-MSV DNA. ^{32}P-dATP-labeled Mo-MSV DNA synthesized *in vitro* was subjected to velocity centrifugation in a 15–30% (w/v) neutral sucrose gradient. The sedimentation profile is shown in the lower part of the figure. Aliquots of individual sucrose gradient fractions indicated in the figure were analyzed by alkaline agarose gel electrophoresis as well as by neutral agarose gel electrophoresis. Lanes b, k: unfractionated Mo-MSV DNA. Lanes c–g and h–m; fractions from sucrose gradient peak. Lane a: pelleted material from sucrose gradient. Lane n: adenovirus 2 marker DNA cleaved with Sma I.

location of the cleavage sites for Hind III, Hpa I and Sal I derived above. The map is presented in Figs. 4 and 5 together with transfection data to be discussed below. This map is almost identical to a restriction endonuclease cleavage site map derived for Mo-MSV DNA extracted from recently infected cells (Dina *et al.* 1976, Dina 1978).

Transfection with in vitro *Synthesized Mo-MSV DNA.*
The strategy for determining the location of the transforming gene within the Mo-MSV genome depends on the ability of subgenomic fragments of *in vitro* synthesized Mo-MSV DNA to induce morphological transformation of NIH-3T3 mouse fibroblasts upon transfection.

Employing the transfection methodology described by others (Graham & van der Eb 1973) it has previously been reported that *in vivo* synthesized as well as *in vitro* synthesized Mo-MLV DNA was capable of inducing Mo-MLV production upon transfection into susceptible cells (Rothenberg *et al.* 1977). Also, Harvey sarcoma virus DNA extracted from cells shortly after infection as well as cellular DNA from cells transformed with Harvey sarcoma virus has been found to be biologically active, yielding foci of transformed cells upon transfection (Goldfarb & Weinberg, manuscript in preparation).

Using this transfection technique, we found that unfractionated *in vitro* synthesized Mo-MSV DNA was capable of inducing morphological transformation of NIH-3T3 mouse fibroblasts. The foci consist of overgrowing, rounded or spindle-shaped, highly refractile cells. This morphology is identical to that of Mo-MSV-induced foci and is easily distinguishable from spontaneous overgrowth of the NIH cells. The induced transformed phenotype was genetically stable since it was perpetuated during clonal isolation of transformed cells.

The transfected foci differed in one significant property from those induced by Mo-MSV infection. Since Mo-MSV is replication defective, cells singly infected by Mo-MSV will be transformed but will not produce virus particles. The Mo-MSV genome of such nonproducer cells can be rescued by subsequent superinfection with a complementing leukemia helper virus. The foci which we generated by transfection with *in vitro* synthesized Mo-MSV DNA were, however, not rescuable upon superinfection with helper virus in that no transforming virus particles emerged from the helper virus infected cells. This indicated that the transfection introduced enough of the Mo-MSV genome to elicit transformation. However, the Mo-MSV DNA in the transfected cells

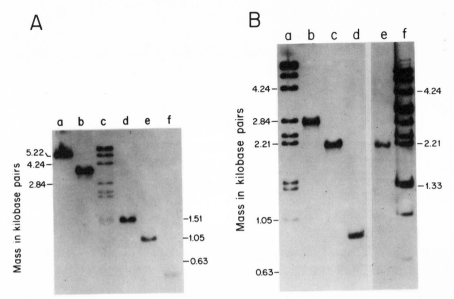

Fig. 3. Gel-purified fragments of Mo-MSV DNA. ^{32}P-dATP-labeled Mo-MSV DNA was synthesized *in vitro* and fractionated according to Fig. 2. The 5.8 kbp Mo-MSV DNA was cleaved with different endonucleases and the fragments were separated by neutral agarose gel electrophoresis. DNA in the excised gel pieces was recovered by equilibrium centrifugation in potassium iodide gradients (Birnie 1977). The figure shows the gel electrophoretic control of the purity of some of the isolated fragments used in subsequent transfection experiments.

Fig. 3A: Lane a: 5.8 kbp Mo-MSV DNA. Lane b: 3.8 kbp Hae II fragment. Lane d–f: 1.5 kbp, 1.0 kbp and 0.5 kbp Hae II fragments of 5.8 kbp ds DNA, respectively.

Fig. 3B: Lanes c and e: 2.1 kbp Sal I + Hind III fragment. Lane b: 2.8 kbp Sal I fragment. Lane d: 0.9 kbp Hind III fragment.

apparently was unable to specify RNA molecules which were complete and which could be packaged by the virions supplied by the rescuing helper virus. These arguments suggested that only subgenomic portions of the Mo-MSV DNA were established upon transfection.

This conclusion was strengthened by transfection with *in vitro* synthesized Mo-MSV DNA of different size classes isolated by velocity centrifugation of Mo-MSV DNA through neutral sucrose gradients. DNA sedimenting significantly slower than 5.8 kbp Mo-MSV DNA was found capable of inducing foci of transformed cells upon transfection. As expected, no transforming virus could be rescued from such transformed cells. This implies that subgenomic fragments of Mo-MSV DNA are biologically active and this observation formed the basis for subsequent transfection experiments with restriction-endo-nuclease-generated fragments of 5.8 kbp Mo-MSV DNA.

We point out one exception to the above-mentioned inability to rescue transforming particles from transfected foci. In transfection experiments employing gel purified 5.8 kbp Mo-MSV DNA synthesized *in vitro*, we have been able to rescue a transforming virus by superinfection with leukemia helper virus. However, even using this putatively complete viral DNA, only a small fraction of the foci generated by transfection was rescuable.

Transfection with Specific Mo-MSV DNA Fragments.

To determine the location of the transforming gene within the Mo-MSV genome, we have performed transfection experiments with gel-purified restric-tion endonuclease-generated fragments of the 5.8 kbp Mo-MSV DNA synthe-sized *in vitro*. The fragments were produced by cleavage of sucrose gradient purified 5.8 kbp DNA (as in Fig. 2) with one or two endonucleases with subsequent isolation of the individual fragments by agarose gel electrophoresis. An example of such preparations is seen in Fig. 3A, which shows resolution of the different fragments generated by Hae II cleavage of the Mo-MSV DNA (Lanes b, d, e, f) as well as gel-purified 5.8 kbp Mo-MSV DNA (Lane a). In Fig. 3B are shown preparations of an internal 2.1 kbp fragment produced by Sal I + Hind III (Lanes c, e). Lane b in Fig. 3B is a preparation of 2.8 kbp fragment derived from the left end of the Mo-MSV DNA (see Fig. 4) by Sal I cleavage. Lane d is a control for purified 0.9 kbp Hind III fragment from the right end of the DNA.

Transfection with DNA fragments lacking either of the ends of the 5.8 kbp DNA yielded foci of transformed cells (Fig. 4, Table I). Hind III and Hpa I were used to cleave off the right end of the 5.8 kbp Mo-MSV DNA, and Hae II cleavage resulted in removal of the left end of this DNA. Further, fragments lacking both ends of the 5.8 kbp DNA molecule were isolated from digests with Hind III + Hae II, Hae II + Hpa I, Hind III + Sal I or Kpn I. All these internal fragments proved biologically active (Fig. 4). This implies that any role that the ends of the Mo-MSV DNA may play during viral infection in directing integration of the viral DNA or in transcriptional control is not crucial to the expression of the transforming function.

We noticed on several occasions that DNA fragments produced by endo-nuclease cleavage in the genomic region 4.3 kbp to 4.9 kbp, while being able to induce foci of morphological transformed cells, did so at a substantially lower efficiency than uncleaved 5.8 kbp DNA or Hae II or Sal I digested DNA. We wished to pursue this discrepancy in transfection efficiencies but we found it difficult to obtain quantitatively reliable results in transfection experiments with isolated DNA fragments. A different approach was therefore taken to evaluate the significance of the apparent quantitative effect of endonuclease cleavage in the right part of the Mo-MSV DNA. This will be discussed below.

Referring to Fig. 4 it can be seen that a 1.5-kbp region extending from 2.8 kbp to 4.3 kbp on the physical map of the Mo-MSV DNA, which is defined by the locations of the cleavage sites for Sal I and Kpn I, is common to all DNA fragments exhibiting biological activity in the transfection assay. In Fig. 4 the heteroduplex data of Hu *et al.* (1977) have been superimposed on the derived

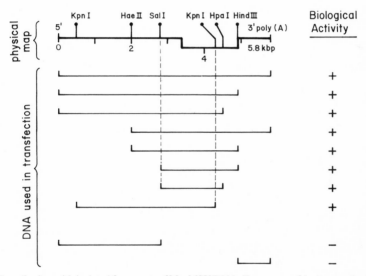

Fig. 4. Transfection with isolated fragments of Mo-MSV DNA. Fragments of *in vitro* synthesized 5.8 kbp Mo-MSV DNA were isolated as in Fig. 3. DNA samples for transfection were precipitated with NIH-3T3 cellular DNA as carrier and each sample was used to transfect two 60-mm plates with a total of 10^6 NIH-3T3 cells. The transfection was performed essentially as described by others (Graham & van der Eb 1973). The plates were split to six 100-mm plates following adsorption of DNA to the cells and the plates were scored for foci of transformed cells after 2 to 3 weeks. Each DNA species has been tested for biological activity in several independent experiments with separate preparations of the given DNA fragment. The notation + indicates that 1 to more than 50 foci were observed per plate. The notation − indicates that no focus forming activity was detected. A detailed account for two such transfection experiments is provided in Table I.

The indented portion of the thick line in the physical map of the 5.8 kbp DNA, shown in the upper part of the figure, delineates the location of the non-Mo-MLV nucleotide sequences present in the Mo-MSV genome according to the heteroduplex data of Hu *et al.* (1977).

Table I

Transfection with gel-purified fragments of 5.8 kbp Mo-MSV DNA

DNA spanning (kbp)	Isolated from digest with	Transfection expt. II			Transfection expt. IV		
		Mass of DNA (pmol$\times 10^3$)	Foci/plate	Foci/ Six plates	Mass of DNA (pmol$\times 10^3$)	Foci/plate	Foci/ Six plates
0−5.8	0	6.53	8,11,13,14,14,15	75	9.14	4,4,5,6,6,7	32
0−4.9	Hind III	3.92	2,3,5,5,6,7	28	17.5	1,1,2,2,3*	11
2.0−5.8	Hae II	10.2	M,M,M,M,M,M**	>100			
2.8−4.9	Hind III+Sal I				18.3	3,3,3,4,4,5	22
0−2.8	Hind III+Sal I				16.7	0,0,0,0,1,1	2***
4.9−5.8	Hind III				37.1	0,0,0,0,0,0	0

* plate lost

** M indicates "too many to count"

*** Preparation contaminated with c. 10% 2.8−5.8 kb Sal I fragment. New preparation without transforming activity.

physical map for the 5.8 kbp DNA. It can be seen that the minimal transforming region, as defined by these experiments, consists of nucleotide sequences of Moloney leukemia virus origin (2.8 kbp to 3.4 kbp map units) as well as of non-Mo-MLV sequences (3.4 kbp to 4.3 kbp map units). We are presently trying to further limit the size of the minimal transforming region.

DNA fragments which did not include the minimal transforming region were found to be biologically inactive when tested for transforming capability by transfection (Fig. 4, Table I). One such region spanning 0 to 2.8 kbp on the physical map of the Mo-MSV DNA is of Mo-MLV origin and encodes internal structure proteins (the gag gene products). It may thus be concluded that these products are of no major significance in establishment and maintenance of transformation. However, it is possible that genomic regions outside the minimal transforming region may exert a modifying effect on the final transformed phenotype. We mention that cells transformed with the 3.8 kbp Hae II endonuclease-generated fragment spanning 2.0 kbp to 5.8 kbp on the physical map (Fig. 4), exhibit a distinctive phenotypic trait with very low substrate adherence. This is evidenced by the presence of a high number of floating, viable cells found in cultures late in the transfection assay. This distinctive phenotype has only been observed consistently with the 3.8 kbp Hae II fragments.

Transfection with Total Endonuclease Digests of 5.8 kbp Mo-MSV DNA.
As mentioned previously, a different protocol was used in order to obtain a more quantitative assay of the effects of endonuclease digestions on the transformation efficiency of Mo-MSV DNA. Rather than isolating restriction endonuclease-generated fragments of the 5.8 kbp Mo-MSV DNA prior to transfection, the total unfractionated endonuclease digests were assayed directly for biological activity. The 5.8 kbp DNA used for these experiments was either isolated by sucrose gradient centrifugation according to Fig. 2 or further purified by neutral agarose gel electrophoresis as in Fig. 3. The 5.8 kbp Mo-MSV DNA was cleaved with a series of restriction endonucleases in the presence of salmon sperm carrier DNA to prevent any rejoining of Mo-MSV fragments which might occur by annealing of staggered, complementary ends of cleaved DNA molecules. The outcome of transfection experiments with such digests is given in Fig. 5. As expected from the previous transfection experiments with isolated DNA fragments (Fig. 4), cleavage with Sal I or Kpn I did not abolish the biological effect of the 5.8 kbp Mo-MSV DNA. The location of the minimal

ANDERSSON ET AL.

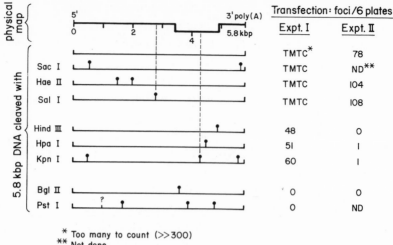

```
*  Too many to count (>>300)
** Not done
```

Fig. 5. Transfection with total digests of 5.8 kbp Mo-MSV DNA. 5.8 kbp Mo-MSV DNA synthesized *in vitro* was isolated by sucrose gradient centrifugation (expt. I) or by neutral agarose gel electrophoresis according to Fig. 3 (expt. II). In expt. I, 40 ng 5.8 kbp DNA cleaved with one of the indicated restriction endonucleases was used to transfect two 60-mm plates of NIH-3T3 cells. These plates were split to six plates, and the number of foci per six plates is given in the figure. In expt. II, 20 ng total endonuclease digest of 5.8 kbp Mo-MSV DNA was used in each transfection.

transforming region on the Mo-MSV genome (2.8 kbp map units to 4.3 kbp map units, Fig. 4) would predict that cleavage of the 5.8 kbp Mo-MSV DNA with Bgl II or Pst I might render the DNA biologically inactive since these enzymes have a cleavage site within the minimal transforming region. As can be seen in Fig. 5, Expt. I, cleavage with these enzymes did in fact destroy the biological activity of the Mo-MSV DNA.

The Hae II and Sal I digests of the 5.8 kbp DNA were found not only to give rise to foci of transformed cells but additionally to do so with approximately the same efficiency as the noncleaved 5.8 kbp DNA. This implies that the left end of the 5.8 kbp Mo-MSV DNA can be separated from the minimal transforming region without affecting quantitatively the biological activity. In contrast, a dramatic reduction in focus forming activity was observed when the right end of the 5.8 kbp DNA was separated from the minimal transforming region by cleavage with Kpn I, Hpa I or Hind III (Fig. 5). This finding was unexpected since these three enzymes all cut the 5.8 kbp Mo-MSV DNA outside of the previously defined minimal transforming region. They nevertheless have a profound effect on the biological activity of the Mo-MSV DNA which was reduced by as much as a factor of 100 (Fig. 5, Expt. II). These surviving foci cannot be attributed to incomplete cleavage of the 5.8 kbp DNA since isolated DNA fragments ending at the Kpn I, Hpa I and Hind III sites as seen before (Fig. 4), were in fact able to induce formation of foci of transformed cells.

Finally, we found Sac I endonuclease digests of the Mo-MSV DNA to be as active in focus formation as non-cleaved 5.8 kbp DNA (Fig. 5, Expt. I) indicating that cleavage at the extreme right end of the 5.8 kbp DNA is not able to effect a reduction in biological activity. We conclude that a region between the Hind III cleavage site and the right Sac I cleavage site, spanning 4.9 kbp to 5.6 kbp on the physical map of the Mo-MSV DNA, is of importance in determining the transformation efficiency as assayed by transfection. Any enzyme which severs this 4.9 kbp to 5.6 kbp sequence from the minimal transforming region creates a severe reduction in yield of foci of transformed cells. Possible explanations for this finding will be considered in the discussion.

DISCUSSION

The ability to synthesize *in vitro* relatively large amounts of 5.8 kbp Mo-MSV DNA allows studies of the molecular basis for Mo-MSV-induced cellular transformation. In the present work we describe the successful assignment of the transforming region of the Mo-MSV genome to a defined subgenomic fragment of *in vitro* synthesized 5.8 kbp Mo-MSV DNA.

Transfection with the 5.8 kbp Mo-MSV DNA synthesized *in vitro* yielded foci of transformed NIH-3T3 cells upon transfection. The foci were morphologically indistinguishable from virus-induced foci. A conservative estimate of the specific biological activity of the 5.8 kbp DNA synthesized *in vitro* is $0.5–1 \times 10^4$ foci per μg DNA. However, sarcoma virus DNA synthesized in virus-infected cells seems to be at least 100-fold more efficient in eliciting foci of transformed cells upon transfection (Goldfarb & Weinberg, manuscript in preparation). Another difference between *in vivo* and *in vitro* synthesized sarcoma virus DNA is the ability of transforming virus to be rescued from cells transfected with *in vivo* synthesized DNA. In contrast, as seen here, cells transformed by *in vitro* synthesized 5.8 kbp Mo-MSV DNA only occasionally yield transforming virus particles upon attempted rescue. These data together suggest that the *in vitro* synthesized Mo-MSV DNA may have minor structural defects which affect the efficiency of integration of the viral DNA into host cell DNA. Further, the lack of rescue of transforming virus from such transformed cells suggests that only a fragment of the *in vitro* synthesized 5.8 kbp DNA became established in most of the transfected cells.

Transfection experiments with restriction endonuclease-generated fragments of the 5.8 kbp Mo-MSV DNA have defined a region within the Mo-MSV genome which includes the gene specifying the transforming property of Mo-MSV. This region spans 2.8 kbp to 4.3 kbp on the physical map of the Mo-MSV DNA and currently represents our maximum estimate for the size of the transforming region. Referring to Fig. 4 it can be seen that this minimal transforming region consists of nucleotide sequences of cellular as well as Mo-MLV origin. The transformation protein may thus be a fused protein coded partly by cellular nucleotide sequences and partly by Mo-MLV sequences. Our experiments would indicate that the maximum possible Mo-MLV contribution to any such fused protein would derive from 0.6 kbp Mo-MLV nucleotide sequences located in the left part of the minimal transforming fragment (Fig. 4). Alternatively, the transforming function of Mo-MSV may be encoded by nucleotide sequences of solely cellular origin. Since these non-MLV sequences in the Mo-MSV genome are present in normal mouse cell DNA, the question may be raised why these sequences are not being expressed to the same extent in normal cells as the identical sequences introduced into the cell by transfection with Mo-MSV DNA.

Transfection experiments with unfractionated restriction endonuclease digests of the 5.8 kbp Mo-MSV DNA (Fig. 5) suggested that a region in the right end of the 5.8 kbp Mo-MSV DNA, while not itself specifying the transforming property, may influence quantitatively the efficiency of transformation by Mo-MSV DNA upon transfection. This region maps at 4.9 kbp to 5.6 kbp on the physical map of the 5.8 kbp Mo-MSV DNA and its separation from the minimal transforming region (from 2.8 kbp map units to 4.3 kbp map units) results in a significant decrease in transformation efficiency (Fig. 5). Three possibilities may be considered. 1) This region may contain a site which recombines with cellular DNA sequences at a higher frequency than surrounding Mo-MSV DNA nucleotide sequences, thus potentiating a higher integration frequency. 2) The indicated region may encode a protein which promotes expression of the genetic information contained within the minimal transforming region of the Mo-MSV DNA. 3) The right end region of the Mo-MSV DNA may encode an RNA sequence influencing the expression of RNA sequences to its left. Such influence might be exerted if the right end RNA sequence represented a noncoding part of a (−) strand transcript from the minimal transforming region.

The latter two hypotheses imply that the expression of the transforming gene in cells transfected by Mo-MSV DNA fragments lacking the right end region is impaired relative to expression of the gene in cells transformed by DNA fragments including the right end region. Although we have not yet performed an adequate quantitative evaluation of the level of expression of the transforming gene in the various DNA fragment transformed cells, we have observed that foci induced by fragments or total endonuclease digests involving cleavage with Kpn I, Hpa I or Hind III, all which separates the right end region from the minimal transforming region, take longer to develop than foci induced by transfection with 5.8 kbp ds DNA or Hae II or Sal I endonuclease digests of the viral DNA. We have no further evidence which would give one of the explanations preference over the others, but the three hypotheses can be tested experimentally.

REFERENCES

Ball, J. K., McCarter, J. A. & Sunderland, S. M. (1973) Evidence for helper independent murine sarcoma virus. 1. Segregation of replication-defective and transformation-defective viruses. *Virol.* 56, 268–284.

Berk, A. J. & Sharp, P. A. (1977) Sizing and mapping of early adenovirus mRNAs by gel electrophoresis of Sl endonuclease-digested hybrids. *Cell* 12, 721–732.

Dina, D., Beemon, K. & Duesberg, P. (1976) The 30S Moloney sarcoma virus RNA contains leukemia virus nucleotide sequences. *Cell* 9, 299–309.

Dina, D. (1978) The "sarcoma-specific" region of Moloney murine sarcoma virus 124. *Proc. Natl. Acad. Sci. USA* 75, 2694–2698.

Frankel, A. E. & Fischinger, P. J. (1976) Nucleotide sequences in mouse DNA and RNA specific for Moloney sarcoma virus. *Proc. Natl. Acad. Sci. USA* 73, 3705–3709.

Frankel, A. E. & Fischinger, P. J. (1977) Rate of divergence of cellular sequences homologous to segments of Moloney sarcoma virus. *J. Virol.* 21, 153–160.

Graham, F. L. & Van der Eb, A. J. (1973) A new technique for the assay of infectivity of human adenovirus 5 DNA. *Virol.* 52, 456–467.

Hu, S., Davidson, N. & Verma, I. M. (1977) A heteroduplex study of the sequence relationships between the RNAs of M-MSV and M-MLV. *Cell* 10, 469–477.

Moloney, J. B. (1966) A virus-induced rhabdomyosarcoma of mice. *Nature* 22, 139–142.

Rothenberg, E. & Baltimore, D. (1977) Increased length of DNA made by virions of murine leukemia virus at limiting magnesium ion concentration. *J. Virol.* 21, 168–178.

Rothenberg, E., Smotkin, D., Baltimore, D. & Weinberg, R. A. (1977) *In vitro* synthesis of infectious DNA of murine leukemia virus. *Nature* 269, 122–126.

Summers, J. (1975) Physical map of polyoma viral DNA fragments produced by cleavage with a restriction enzyme from *Haemophilus Aegyptius,* endonuclease R · Hae III. *J. Virol.* 15, 946–953.

Summers, J., O'Connel, A. & Millman, I. (1975) Genome of hepatitis B virus: restriction enzyme cleavage and structure of DNA extracted from Dane particles. *Proc. Natl. Acad. Sci. USA* 72, 4597–4601.

DISCUSSION

FLAVELL: Is it the idea that the gene in the 3' region has a leader?

ANDERSSON: Yes, that is a possible interpretation. It implies, however, that the (+) strand of the MSV DNA is transcribed, and we have at present little evidence for the existence of such mRNA species.

FLAVELL: Has the corresponding gene in chicken viruses been located?

ANDERSSON: The avian *src* gene has been mapped towards the 3' end of the viral genomic RNA, and this genomic region included nucleotide sequences which are also present in the DNA of normal chicken cells. The situation is thus similar to the murine system. A possible product of the avian *src* gene has recently been identified by several groups which would indicate that the transforming function is specified by the (−) strand viral DNA.

Initiation Sites for Replication of Mammalian Cell DNA

Igor Tamm, Barbara R. Jasny* & Joel E. Cohen

Replication of DNA in mammalian cells in S phase is initiated at about 50,000–100,000 sites (Hand & Tamm 1974, Jasny *et al.* 1978, Cohen *et al.* 1978). In general, replication proceeds bidirectionally from the origins (Huberman & Riggs 1968, Edenberg & Huberman 1975). There appear to be many more potential initiation sites than those activated during S phase. Evidence for this comes from work in developing organisms (Callan 1972, 1974) and with 5-fluoro-2′-deoxyuridine (Taylor & Hozier 1976, Taylor 1977). We have recently carried out a detailed examination of DNA chain initiation by light microscopic DNA fiber autoradiography in muntjac, mouse (L–929), and bovine (MDBK) cells in culture (Jasny *et al.* 1978, Cohen *et al.* 1978). Exponentially growing cells were labeled with high specific activity ^{3}H-thymidine for 10 minutes and then with low specific activity ^{3}H-thymidine for 3 hours. The modal inter-initiation site distance is 5–15 μm (15,000–45,000 base pairs) in all three cell types, but the individual measurable distances between the activated sites vary from 3.4 to 432 μm. Statistical tests of randomness, applied to the distribution of inter-initiation distances, show a nonrandom frequency distribution of the distances between activated initiation sites for all three cell types.

MEAN DISTANCE BETWEEN ACTIVATED INITIATION SITES

We have used three methods to obtain estimates of, or lower bounds on, the mean inter-initiation distances on the unbroken DNA fiber. The ranges of estimates are 8–23 μm for muntjac cells, 22–45 μm for MDBK cells, and 14–63

The Rockefeller University, New York, New York 10021 U.S.A.

* Dept. of Microbiology, State University of New York, Stony Brook, N.Y. 11794 U.S.A.

SPECIFIC EUKARYOTIC GENES, Alfred Benzon Symposium 13, Munksgaard 1979

Table I

Inter-initiation site distance and number of activated sites in mammalian DNA

Species	Cells	Mean inter-initiation distance, μm	Length of DNA, m*	Estimated number of activated sites per diploid genome	Reference
Muntjac	Muntjac	16	1.2	75,000	Cohen *et al.* 1978
Cattle	MDBK	34	1.8	53,000	Cohen *et al.* 1978
Mouse	L-929	39	1.8	46,000	Cohen *et al.* 1978
Mouse	L-929	45	1.8	40,000	Hand and Tamm 1974
Cattle	MDBK	17	1.8	106,000	Hand and Tamm 1974
Syrian hamster	BHK	30†	2.0	67,000	Hand and Tamm 1974
African green monkey	CV-1	42			Hand and Tamm 1974
Human	HEK	23	2.0	87,000	Hand and Tamm 1974

* Per diploid set of chromosomes; mouse, cattle, man from Altman & Katz (1976); muntjac from Green & Bahr (1975); Syrian hamster from S.Ohno, personal communication; a value for African green monkey was not available.

† In Chinese hamster (B14FAF28) the range of values is 5–180 μm and the range of distribution at one half peak height is 15–55 μm (Huberman & Riggs 1968); DNA length=2.0 m (S. Ohno, personal communication).

μm for L cells (Cohen *et al.* 1978). The center values of these estimates are recorded in the summary of available data in Table I. It can be seen that the estimates of the mean inter-initiation distance and of the number of activated sites in mammalian DNA (diploid) do not differ by more than a factor of 2–3 when derived by a variety of techniques. Most values for the number of activated sites fall within the 50,000–100,000 range, which corresponds to a range of 20–40 μm (60,000–120,000 base pairs) for most of the mean inter-initiation distances.

INVERTED REPEAT SEQUENCES

The physical nature of replication origins in mammalian cell DNA has not been established. It is reasonable to suppose that there are specific recognition sites in DNA for proteins that function in the initiation of new DNA chains and that such recognition sites share common nucleotide sequences. Furthermore, since DNA replication proceeds bidirectionally from most origins, the initiation sites may be expected to be structures with twofold rotational symmetry.

Regions of inverted complementary sequences, which are widely distributed in DNA (Davidson *et al.* 1973, Wilson & Thomas 1974, Schmid & Deininger 1975, Cech & Hearst 1975) may represent potential initiation sites for DNA replication (Bollum 1975, Edenberg & Huberman 1975). Inverted complementary sequences with twofold rotational symmetry are of the type

...A B C C' B' A'...
...A' B' C' C B A...

where A and A', B and B' and C and C' represent complementary sequences. The structure ... A B C C' B' A' ... in a single strand of DNA is commonly referred to as a pair of inverted repeat sequences and we shall follow this practice. In double-stranded DNA, a pair of inverted repeat sequences in one strand has a complement in the other strand. Numerical estimates of pairs of inverted repeats in nuclear DNA are commonly given in terms of one strand. Such estimates thus refer to regions in the double-stranded DNA containing inverted repeats. Two kinds of inverted repeat DNA structures have been recognized: 1) those which contain no or only a few intervening nucleotides between members of a pair of inverted repeats (Wilson & Thomas (1974) likened the inverted repeats without spacers to palindromes); 2) those in which the members of a pair of inverted repeats are separated by a spacer sequence of variable length.

The mean length of a member of a pair of repeat sequences is 300 bases in the human genome (Deininger & Schmid 1976). Such sequences show considerable homology, but not complete sequence identity (Robertson *et al.* 1977, Jelinek 1977, Jelinek *et al.* 1978, Jelinek 1978). These important findings are summarized elsewhere in this volume (Jelinek 1979).

MEAN DISTANCE BETWEEN PAIRS OF INVERTED REPEAT SEQUENCES
A key question is whether there are enough of the homologous inverted repeats in DNA to account for initiation sites for replication. The average center-to-center distance between pairs of inverted repeat sequences may be estimated for several mammalian species (Table II). Wherever comparison is possible, there are enough inverted repeats to account for initiation sites. Indeed, if initiation takes place in inverted repeat regions, there appears to be redundancy of such sites which would protect against failure in the critical process of genome reduplication (see data in human and hamster cells). The most extensive evidence is available for human cells (Wilson & Thomas 1974, Deininger & Schmid 1975, Jelinek *et al.* 1978) and it appears that there are 400,000–900,000

Table II

Center-to-center distance between pairs of inverted repeats and number of inverted repeat regions in mammalian DNA

Species	Cells	Mean center-to-center distance, μm	Estimated number per diploid genome		Reference
			Total	Inverted repeats without spacers	
Human	Placental	2.1–4.5	440,000–950,000	160,000–340,000	Deininger & Schmid 1976
Human	HeLa	5*	unknown	400,000	Wilson & Thomas 1974
Human	HeLa (hnRNA)		400,000–800,000		Jelinek *et al.* 1978
Chinese hamster	CHO		600,000		Jelinek 1978
Mouse†			~200,000	~80,000	Cech & Hearst 1975, Wilson & Thomas 1974, Ryskov *et al.* 1973

*Adjacent pairs of inverted repeats lacking spacers.

† In mouse cell (SVT2) DNA, Cech & Hearst (1975) reported pairs of inverted repeats to be separated by a mean distance of 25 μm, which is equivalent to 72,000 structures in the diploid genome. About 40% (29,000) lack spacers. Wilson & Thomas (1974) reported that the mean center-tocenter distance between clusters of inverted repeats without spacers in mouse cell (L) DNA is 62.1 μm, which gives an estimate of 30,000 for the total number of clusters. This estimate of the number of clusters is essentially the same as that of Cech & Hearst (1975) for individual regions (29,000). The reasons for this discrepancy are not clear. An analysis of the hnRNA of mouse Ehrlich's ascites cells suggested (Ryskov *et al.* 1973) that the total number of pairs of inverted repeats in the diploid mouse cell genome may be 600,000. This estimate is probably too high, because the length of the repeated sequences may be greater (Cech & Hearst 1975) than the value (100 nucleotides) used in making this calculation (Ryskov *et al.* 1973). As an intermediate figure we suggest that there may be about 200,000 pairs of inverted repeats in mouse DNA.

inverted repeat regions per genome, of which 36% lack spacers (Deininger & Schmid 1975).

The data from *Triturus* and *Xenopus laevis* are also compatible with the possibility that inverted repeat sequences are potential origins for DNA replication. The distances between activated initiation sites in DNA of somatic cells of mature *Triturus* are in the range of 100–350 μm or greater (Callan 1972, 1974), while in the embryos in the neurula stage most of the initiation sites are about 40 μm apart. Inverted repeats without spacers are distributed in *Triturus* DNA at an average center-to-center distance of 8.7 μm (Wilson & Thomas 1974). In *Xenopus* the inter-initiation distances are in the range of 18–128 μm (Callan 1972) while the mean distance between pairs of inverted repeats is about 10 μm (Perlman *et al.* 1976).

COMMENTS

Clearly, the inverted repeat sequences possess the fundamental properties expected of replication initiation sites in eukaryotic DNA. Homologous inverted repeats appear to be interspersed between stretches of unique nonrepetitious sequences in eukaryotic DNA. Inverted repeats without spacers would appear to be the preferred structures for the initiation of bidirectional replication. Unidirectional replication from origins has been reported to occur with low frequency (Edenberg & Huberman 1975). Whether this is entirely physiological is an open question. It should be noted that inverted repeat sequences have been demonstrated in segments of viral DNA containing initiation sites for DNA replication, as for example in simian virus 40 (SV40) (Subramanian *et al.* 1977, Hsu & Jelinek 1977).

The hypothesis that multifocal initiation of mammalian DNA replication occurs in homologous inverted repeat regions in DNA can be tested experimentally. This hypothesis does not exclude a possible role for inverted repeat sequences in the regulation of transcription (Bollum 1975) or in posttranscriptional processing of RNA (Jelinek *et al.* 1978).

ACKNOWLEDGMENTS

We thank Dr. Warren Jelinek for permission to quote unpublished results. This work was supported by Research Grant CA-18608 and by Program Project Grant CA-18213 awarded by the National Cancer Institute, and by National Science Foundation Grant BMS (DEB) 74–13276. B. R. J. was a Predoctoral Trainee under the Institutional National Research Service Award CA-09256 from the National Cancer Institute.

REFERENCES

Altman, P.L. & Katz, D.D. (1976) *Biological Handbooks I, Cell Biology,* Fed. Amer. Soc. Exp. Biol., 454 pages. Bethesda, Maryland.
Bollum, F.J. (1975) Mammalian DNA polymerases. In: *Progress in Nucleic Acid Research and Molecular Biology,* ed. Cohn, W.E., pp. 109–144. Academic Press, New York.
Callan, H.G. (1972) Replication of DNA in the chromosomes of eukaryotes. *Proc. R. Soc. Lond. B. 181,* 19–41.
Callan, H.B. (1974) DNA replication in the chromosomes of eukaryotes. *Cold Spring Harbor Symp. Quant. Biol. 38,* 195–203.
Cech, T.R. & Hearst, J.E. (1975) An electron microscopic study of mouse foldback DNA. *Cell 5,* 429–446.

Cohen, J.E., Jasny, B.R. & Tamm, I. (1978) The spatial distribution of initiation sites for mammalian DNA replication: A statistical analysis. *J. Molec. Biol.,* in press.

Davidson, E.H., Hough, B.R., Amenson, C.S. & Britten, R.J. (1973) General interspersion of repetitive with nonrepetitive sequence elements in the DNA of *Xenopus. J. Molec. Biol. 77,* 1–23.

Deininger, P.L. & Schmid, C.W. (1976) An electron microscope study of the DNA sequence organization of the human genome. *J. Molec. Biol. 106,* 773–790.

Edenberg, H.J. & Huberman, J.A. (1975) Eukaryotic chromosome replication. *Ann. Rev. Genet. 9,* 245–284.

Green, R. & Bahr, G.F. (1975) Comparison of G-, Q-, and EM-banding patterns exhibited by the chromosome complement of the Indian Muntjac, *Muntiacus muntjak,* with reference to the nuclear DNA content and chromatin ultrastructure. *Chromosoma (Berl.) 50,* 53–67.

Hand, R. & Tamm, I. (1974) Initiation of DNA replication in mammalian cells and its inhibition by reovirus infection. *J. Molec. Biol. 82,* 175–183.

Hsu, M.-T. & Jelinek, W.R. (1977) Mapping of inverted repeated DNA sequences within the genome of simian virus 40. *Proc. Natl. Acad. Sci. U.S.A. 74,* 1631–1634.

Huberman, J.A. & Riggs, A.D. (1968) On the mechanism of DNA replication in mammalian chromosomes. *J. Molec. Biol. 32,* 327–341.

Jasny, B.R., Cohen, J.E. & Tamm, I. (1978) The organization of DNA replication in a mammalian cell line. In: *DNA Synthesis: Present and Future,* ed. Kohiyama, M. & Molineaux, I., pp. 175–188. Plenum Press, New York.

Jelinek, W.R. (1977) Specific nucleotide sequences in HeLa cell inverted repeated DNA: Enrichment of sequences found in double-stranded regions of heterogeneous nuclear RNA. *J. Molec. Biol. 115,* 591–601.

Jelinek, W.R. (1978) Inverted, repeated DNA from CHO cells studied with cloned DNA fragments. *Proc. Natl. Acad. Sci. U.S.A. 75,* 2679–2683.

Jelinek, W.R. (1979) Inverted repeats in the genomes of mammalian cells. In: *Alfred Benzon Symposium XIII, Specific Eukaryotic Genes,* ed. Engberg, J., Klenow, H. & Leick, V. Munksgaard, Cohagen.

Jelinek, W., Evans, R., Wilson, M., Salditt-Georgieff, M. & Darnell, J.E. (1978) Oligonucleotides in hnRNA: similarity of inverted repeats and RNA from repetitious DNA sites. *Biochemistry 17,* 2776–2783.

Perlman, S., Phillips, C. & Bishop, J.O. (1976) A study of foldback DNA. *Cell 8,* 33–42.

Robertson, H.D., Dickson, E. & Jelinek, W. (1977) Determination of nucleotide sequences from double-stranded regions of HeLa cell nuclear RNA. *J. Molec. Biol. 115,* 571–589.

Ryskov, A.P., Saunders, G.F., Farashyan, V.R. & Georgiev, G.P. (1973) Double-helical regions in nuclear precursor of mRNA (pre-mRNA). *Biochim. Biophys. Acta 312,* 152–164.

Schmid, C.W. & Deininger. P.L. (1975) Sequence organization of the human genome. *Cell 6,* 345–358.

Subramanian, K.N., Dhar, R. & Weissman, S.M. (1977) Nucleotide sequence of a fragment of SV40 DNA that contains the origin of DNA replication and specifies the 5′ ends of "early" and "late" viral RNA. *J. Biol. Chem. 252,* 355–367.

Taylor, J.H. (1977) Increase in DNA replication sites in cells held at the beginning of S phase. *Chromosoma (Berl.) 62,* 291–300.

Taylor, J.H. & Hozier, J.C. (1976) Evidence for a four micron replication unit in CHO cells. *Chromosoma (Berl.) 57,* 341–350.

Wilson, D.A. & Thomas, C.A.Jr. (1974) Palindromes in chromosomes. *J. Molec. Biol. 84,* 115–144.

III. Organization and Function of Extrachromosomal Elements

The Structure and Function of the Mitochondrial DNA of *Drosophila melanogaster*

M. Berninger[1], T. Cech[2], J. Fostel[1], D. Potter[1], M. Scott[1] & M. L. Pardue[1]

Mitochondrial DNA (mtDNA) is a circular molecule in all animals which have been studied, with the exception of *Tetrahymena* and *Paramecia* (Borst 1977). Although the size of the molecule varies with species, mtDNAs from different species of higher animals fall within the relatively narrow size range of 15,000 to 19,000 base pairs (Borst 1972, Klukas & Dawid 1976). Studies on a variety of organisms suggest that there has also been little divergence in the functions of the mtDNA. This apparent evolutionary constancy is not surprising in view of the indispensability of mitochondria in most cells; however this constancy would not have been expected from DNA sequence comparisons since these show significant sequence divergence of the mtDNA even between closely related species (Dawid 1972a, Jakovcic *et al.* 1975).

The mtDNA has been shown to code for the RNAs of the two subunits of the mitochondrial ribosome and for a number of transfer RNAs (Borst 1972, Dawid 1972b, Nass & Buck 1970, Aloni & Attardi 1971, Angerer *et al.* 1976). In addition to coding for many, if not all, of the structural RNAs of the protein synthesizing machinery in the mitochondrion, mtDNA codes for a small number of poly(A)$^+$ RNAs (Hirsch *et al.* 1974, Ojala & Attardi 1974). These RNAs appear to be messenger RNAs since they are found on polysomes and are released by puromycin (Hirsch & Penman 1974). The number and size of these mRNAs show strong evolutionary conservation. Animals as distantly related as

[1] Biology Department, Massachusetts Institute of Technology, Cambridge, Mass. 02139 U.S.A.
[2] Chemistry Department, University of Colorado, Boulder, Colo. 80390 U.S.A.

human, hamster, mosquito and *Drosophila* all show similar patterns of mitochondrial poly(A)$^+$ RNA on polyacrylamide gels (Hirsch *et al.* 1974).

The most extensive genetic and biochemical studies of the proteins coded for by mtDNA have been carried out on yeast. Evidence from this system shows that the mitochondrial genome codes some eight to ten hydrophobic polypeptides, several of which are components of the enzyme systems of the mitochondrial inner membranes (Schatz & Mason 1974, Tzagoloff *et al.* 1975a,b). In these mitochondrial enzyme systems the mitochondrially coded polypeptides are associated with other polypeptides which are encoded by the nuclear genome, indicating cooperative interactions between the two separated genetic systems. Although there is much less evidence on the products of animal mitochondrial genomes, there are reasons to believe that the products will be found to be similar to those in yeast (O'Brien 1977).

Studies on animal mitochondrial genomes have lagged behind the studies on yeast largely because of difficulties in using classical genetic techniques on animal mitochondria. In the last few years, however, biochemical techniques have been developed which make it possible to map sites complementary to RNA transcripts, as well as some other aspects of chromatin structure, directly on the mtDNA. Using these techniques, we have begun to analyze the mitochondrial genome of *Drosophila melanogaster.*

MITOCHONDRIAL RNA TRANSCRIPTS

When cultured cells from *Drosophila melanogaster* (the Schneider line 2 which has been adapted to spinner culture) are grown in the presence of high doses of actinomycin D, these cells incorporate ^{3}H-uridine into a limited number of RNA species (Spradling *et al.* 1977). ^{3}H-RNA from cells labeled in 5 μg/ml actinomycin D is resolved by polyacrylamide gel electrophoresis into 12 sharp bands ranging in size from approximately 500 nucleotides to 1800 nucleotides (Fig. 1). Some smaller ^{3}H-RNAs are also produced but they have not yet been studied.

The 12 large RNA species produced in the presence of actinomycin D are all mitochondrial transcripts (Spradling *et al.* 1977). These RNAs hybridize to mitochondrial DNA but not to nuclear DNA. They include the two mitochondrial ribosomal RNAs as well as 10 additional poly(A)$^+$ RNAs and appear to give an accurate picture of the mitochondrial transcripts when cells are grown at their normal growth temperature of 25°C. The electrophoretic gel pattern of ^{3}H-RNA

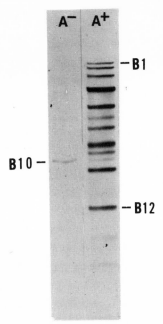

Fig. 1. Fluorograph showing the large mitochondrial RNAs (B-1 through B-12) of *D. melanogaster*. B-10 is the only RNA seen in the poly(A)⁻ fraction. (For technical reasons the RNA loaded on the (A)⁻ lane was prepared from one-fifth the number of cells used for the (A)⁺ lane.) RNA B-10 shows limited binding to oligo(dT)-cellulose and a faint band of B-10 can be seen in the (A)⁺ lane. Cells were labeled with ³H-uridine (25 Ci/mmole, 100 μCi/ml) in the presence of 5 μg/ml actinomycin D for 4 h at 3×10⁷ cells/ml (10X normal growth concentration). RNA was extracted from cells, fractionated on oligo(dT)-cellulose into poly(A)⁺ and poly(A)⁻ fractions and electrophoresed on a 2.5 to 5% polyacrylamide gel. The fluorograph was exposed for 24 h.

from cells labeled in the presence of actinomycin D is similar to that of ³H-RNA isolated from purified mitochondria of cells labeled in the absence of actinomycin. When the cells are moved to 37°C actinomycin D prevents the appearance of any new mtRNA although mtRNA synthesis continues at 37°C when actinomycin D is not present. These experiments suggest that actinomycin D is excluded from *Drosophila* mitochondria at 25°C although the drug can enter the mitochondria during the 37°C "heat shock".

The preferential blocking of nuclear RNA synthesis by actinomycin D allows preparation of radiochemically pure mtRNA in amounts several fold greater than can be obtained from isolated mitochondria and makes it practical to obtain individual gel fractions of the mtRNA for genetic mapping (Bonner *et al.* 1978). ³H-RNA from cells labeled in the presence of actinomycin D was

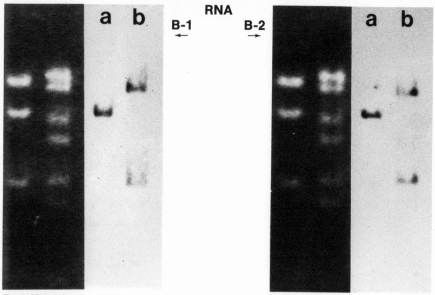

Fig. 2. Hybridization of RNA to *D. melanogaster* mtDNA fragments generated by restriction enzyme cleavage. RNA eluted from bands B-1 and B-2 (see Fig. 1) was hybridized to filters prepared by the method of Southern from 1.4% agarose gels containing restriction enzyme cleavage fragments of mtDNA. For each RNA fraction a photograph of the agarose gel showing DNA fragments stained by ethidium bromide is shown on the left. On the right is the fluorograph of RNA hybridized to the DNA transferred from that gel. In each case lane *a* contains mtDNA cleaved by Hae III, lane *b* contains mtDNA cleaved by Hind III mixed with mtDNA cleaved by Hpa II. The pattern of hybridization maps the hybridization of both RNAs to the same region of the mtDNA (Fig. 3).

separated on polyacrylamide gels. Individual bands of radioactive RNA were cut out and eluted from the gel. These RNA fractions were each hybridized to preparations of mtDNA which had been cleaved with several restriction enzymes.

Each of the purified RNAs was found to hybridize to a particular set of the DNA fragments generated by restriction enzyme cleavage (Fig. 2). When compared to the map of restriction enzyme cleavage sites on mtDNA, the set of DNA fragments to which a given RNA hybridized was always found to be consistent with a single location for the DNA sequences homologous to that RNA (Fig. 3). Our results with RNAs B-4 and B-10, the large and small mitochondrial ribosomal RNAs respectively, confirm the mapping of these RNAs established by Klukas & Dawid (1976). Sites of hybridization by the mitochondrial RNAs were distributed rather evenly over approximately 75% of the mitochondrial genome. None of the RNAs hybridized within the very A + T-rich region that makes up the remaining 25% of the mtDNA (Bultmann & Laird 1973, Polan *et al.* 1973, Wolstenholme 1973, Peacock *et al.* 1974, Klukas & Dawid 1976).

In each of our experiments the heavy hybridization to one (or two) fragments of DNA which characterized a given RNA fraction was accompanied by a low level of hybridization to the other fragments of mtDNA in the restriction enzyme digest. We believe that the low level hybridization is specific because there was no hybridization to fragments of bacteriophage lambda DNA run in the same experiments. However we have not yet determined whether this hybridization could be due to a small amount of sequence homology among the RNAs or to low levels of cross-contamination between the RNA fractions.

In several cases two or more RNA species map within the same region of the

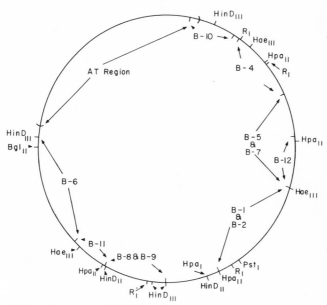

Fig. 3. Map of *D. melanogaster* mtDNA showing sites of RNA hybridization. The location of restriction enzyme cleavage sites was derived by analysis of the sizes of fragments generated by digestion of mtDNA by several different enzymes, both in digestions with only one enzyme and in double digestions in which the DNA was cut by two different enzymes simultaneously. The results of double digests are compatible with a single arrangement of cleavage sites. RNAs were mapped according to the restriction enzyme fragments with which they hybridized in experiments such as that shown in Fig. 2. For each of the RNAs the hybridization of the RNA to restriction enzyme fragments was consistent with a single location on the genome.

Fig. 4. Autoradiograph of proteins synthesize by *D. melanogaster* cell cultures in the presence of emetine (E) or cycloheximide (C). Synthesis of these proteins is inhibited by chloramphenicol. The pattern of drug sensitivity tentatively identifies these proteins as products of translation by mitochondrial ribosomes. (See text for discussion of polypeptide sizes.) 24×10^6 cells (12 ml of cultured cells in suspension) of the Schneider Line 2 were concentrated 10-fold and incubated in methionine-free medium in the presence of 100 μg/ml emetine or cycloheximide. After 5 min, ^{35}S-methionine was added to a final concentration of 50 μCi/ml. Labeling was for 1 h, after which a crude mitochondrial fraction was prepared by centrifuging cytoplasm at 6000 xg for 10 min. The resulting pellet was resuspended in sample buffer and loaded onto a 10 to 15% SDS-polyacrylamide gradient gel.

genome but have not yet been ordered within that region. This is the case for RNAs B-1 and B-2, RNAs B-5, B-7 and B-12, as well as RNAs B-8 and B-9. Each of these groups of RNAs bind to DNA fragments which, as estimated by gel mobilities, are shorter than the sum of the lengths of the RNAs in the group. These results suggest that RNAs within a group might share identical or complementary sequences, possibilities which are now being investigated.

Products of mitochondrial protein synthesis

We have examined the products of mitochondrial protein synthesis by using drugs which have been shown in other organisms to distinguish synthesis on mitochondrial ribosomes from that on cytoplasmic ribosomes. Doses of 100 μg/ml of either cycloheximide or emetine produced an inhibition of 97% of the total protein synthesis in the *Drosophila* cells. These drugs both prevent protein synthesis by cytoplasmic ribosomes in other eukaryotic cells (Schatz & Mason 1974). The 3% of the total protein synthesis continuing in the *Drosophila* cells in the presence of cycloheximide or emetine was almost totally eliminated by the addition of 1 mg/ml of chloramphenicol, a drug which acts on mitochondrial ribosomes in eukaryotic cells (Schatz & Mason 1974).

Drosophila cultured cells grown in the presence of emetine or cycloheximide produce a specific small class of proteins (Fig. 4). On the basis of mobility in the polyacrylamide gel, it would appear that these proteins have molecular weights of 33,000, 30,000, 26,000, 23,000, 21,000 and 10,000 daltons. *D. melanogaster* embryo cells grown for 1 h in 100 μg/ml emetine produce the same set of proteins as well as two faint protein bands of 37,000 and 36,000 daltons. The molecular weights determined from gel mobilities may be quite inaccurate since the mitochondrial translation products are expected to be hydrophobic polypeptides which may run quite anomalously in gel electrophoresis. However the molecular weights correspond well with those of some of the mitochondrial translation products in yeast (Schatz & Mason 1974) and mouse cells (Lansman & Clayton 1975).

We have as yet no direct evidence that the mitochondrial translation products are encoded by transcripts of the mtDNA, although there are some reasons to believe that this is the case. The mitochondrial translation products identified by our drug studies are all within the size range which could be encoded by the RNA transcripts of the *Drosophila* mtDNA.

Mitochondrial chromatin structure

The *Drosophila* mtDNA molecule, like the mtDNA of almost all animals, can be isolated as a covalently closed supercoiled molecule. However little is known about either the conformation of the DNA or its association with other molecules within the intact mitochondrion. Previous electron microscopic studies of osmotically ruptured *Drosophila* mitochondria (Chooi & Laird 1976) showed polysomelike structures associated with mitochondrial DNA but did not resolve other aspects of mitochondrial chromatin structure.

One technique for studying the state of DNA *in vivo* involves crosslinking the DNA with the me₃psoralen (4,5',8-trimethylpsoralen) photoreaction. Me₃psoralen is a small heterocyclic molecule that intercalates into DNA. Long

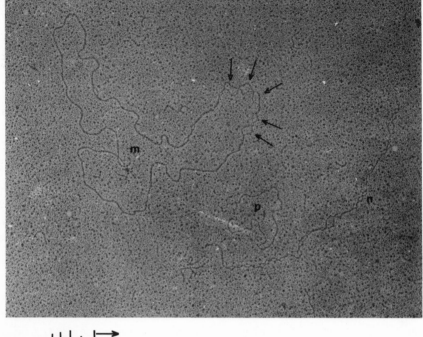

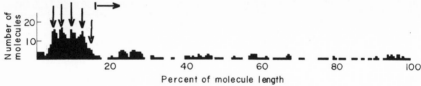

Fig. 5. DNA-protein interactions in the *D. melanogaster* mitochondrial genome as deduced from me₃psoralen crosslinking patterns. Freshly collected 6–12 h embryos were dechorionated and then gently homogenized in Minimal Robb's Medium without amino acids. The homogenization produced a mixture of clumps of cells, whole cells, and broken cells. Me₃psoralen (1.75 mg/ml in dimethylsulfoxide) was added to a final concentration of 6 μg/ml, and the mixture was irradiated for 2 min with 100 mW/cm² long wavelength ultraviolet light (365 nm). The me₃psoralen addition and irradiation were repeated a total of five times. The temperature was controlled at 22°C. Mitochondria were then isolated and their DNA purified. (a) Electron micrograph of the crosslinked mtDNA. The DNA was totally denatured in the presence of glyoxal and spread for electron microscopy as described by Cech & Pardue (1976). The arrows indicate the closely spaced set of uncrosslinked "bubbles" that was observed on 80% of the mtDNA molecules (m). The remainder of the molecule is heavily crosslinked and therefore appears predominantly double-stranded. A fragment of nuclear DNA (n), which contaminated the mtDNA preparation, shows the 200 base pair periodicity of crosslinks that is indicative of a nucleosome structure (Hanson *et al.* 1976). The single-stranded ØX174 DNA (p) was added to the sample before glyoxal denaturation to serve as a molecular weight standard (5375 bases). (b) Histogram showing the positions of uncrosslinked, single-stranded regions in the mtDNA after cleavage with Bgl II restriction endonuclease. The set

wavelength ultraviolet light (365 nm) will then produce a photochemical reaction between me₃psoralen and pyrimidines on opposite strands of the double helix and covalently crosslink the two polynucleotide strands. The photochemical crosslinking can be done *in vivo*. Since the covalent crosslinks are stable, the DNA can be purified and the distribution of the me₃psoralen crosslinks determined by analyzing the DNA spread under totally denaturing conditions in the electron microscope. It has been shown that when DNA is photoreacted in nuclei or intact cells of mouse or *Drosophila,* the me₃psoralen reacts primarily with the DNA between nucleosomes (Cech & Pardue 1977, Wiesehahn *et al.* 1977), producing crosslinks at intervals of 200 base pairs along the DNA (Cech *et al.* 1977, Hanson *et al.* 1976, Wiesehahn *et al.* 1977). Thus the purified crosslinked DNA still reflects some aspects of its *in vivo* chromatin structure.

When cells from *Drosophila melanogaster* embryos were photoreacted to high levels with me₃-psoralen, the pattern of crosslinking produced in the mtDNA was distinctly different from that in the nuclear DNA (Fig. 5a). The nuclear DNA showed the same pattern of 200 base pair repeats reported by Hearst and his co-workers (Hanson *et al.* 1976, Wiesehahn *et al.* 1977) for the nuclear DNA of *Drosophila.* The mtDNA, however showed four or five closely spaced bubbles of uncrosslinked DNA. These covered about 10% of the length of the molecule. The remaining 90% of the contour length was heavily crosslinked. The few bubbles of denatured DNA in the larger region were small and randomly distributed. Based on our previous studies of the crosslinking of protein-free DNA (Cech *et al.* 1977) we interpret such a pattern as reflecting ≥1 crosslink/100 base pairs. 80% of the mtDNA molecules examined showed this pattern of crosslinking; the remaining 20% appeared predominantly double-stranded over their entire length. All of the electron microscope preparations were spread under totally denaturing conditions as measured by the denaturation of partially crosslinked double-stranded bacteriophage molecules which had been added to the preparations.

Control experiments allow us to conclude that the pattern of me₃psoralen crosslinking found on the mtDNA is a reflection of the state of the DNA *in vivo*. Me₃psoralen forms bonds between pyrimidines on opposite strands of the DNA

---

of five uncrosslinked bubbles (vertical arrows) have been oriented with respect to the Bgl II site by analysis of molecules cleaved with Xho or Hae III. The horizontal arrow indicates the origin and direction of replication as mapped by Goddard & Wolstenholme (1978).

double helix and therefore such crosslinks would be precluded from stretches of DNA where pyrimidines are confined to one of the two polynucleotide strands. However we have not found evidence of long stretches in the mtDNA where me₃psoralen binding is prohibited solely on the basis of DNA sequence. When purified mtDNA was crosslinked *in vitro,* to approximately the same level as was reached in the *in vivo* experiment, the "bubbles" of uncrosslinked DNA were all quite small and distributed in an apparently random pattern over the molecules. To test the possibility that a supercoiled DNA molecule might have regions where me₃psoralen intercalation was prohibited for structural reasons, we performed a similar experiment using isolated supercoiled mtDNA molecules. Again only small regions of denaturation were detected and these regions were distributed randomly over the molecules.

The regions of the mtDNA which are protected against psoralen crosslinking *in vivo* have been mapped on the DNA relative to three restriction enzyme cleavage sites. Fig. 5b shows the data obtained from molecules cleaved with the Bgl II enzyme. Combined with data obtained from other experiments in which the mtDNA was cleaved with the enzymes Xho I or Hae III, this histogram shows that the five prominent uncrosslinked regions map at a discrete site within the A+T-rich region, extending from one end almost to the center of this region. The four largest uncrosslinked regions are similar in bubble size (394±13 base pairs) and repeat unit size (500±5 base pairs). The four bubbles occur together almost invariably. There is a fifth smaller bubble (208±71 base pairs) which is seen on only 43% of the molecules bearing the four larger bubbles. However this may reflect the lower probability of detection of a small bubble rather than a lower frequency of occurrence.

The specificity of the pattern and location of the uncrosslinked portions of the A+T-rich region is most easily interpreted as a reflection of the binding of site-specific proteins or protein complexes to the DNA. However a convincing demonstration of this assumption will require the isolation and characterization of the protein-mtDNA complex. Some intriguing functional possibilities for such proteins provide the incentive to undertake such studies. The close proximity of the presumed binding regions to the origin of replication (Goddard & Wolstenholme 1978) suggests that such proteins could be involved in mtDNA replication and/or could serve to bind the mtDNA molecule to the inner mitochondrial membrane. The me₃psoralen crosslinking data and the unidirectional origin of replication both indicate an asymmetry in the A+T-rich region that makes its nucleotide sequence another interesting topic for investigation.

The psoralen crosslinking data show clearly that the portion of the mtDNA which is transcribed is not in the nucleosome structure typical of nuclear DNA. The electron microscopic analysis would not detect protected regions in the DNA smaller than 150 base pairs. Protein associations which are labile enough to be disrupted by the intercalation or photoreaction of psoralen would not protect the DNA from crosslinking. Therefore these data do not permit us to draw further conclusions about possible associations between the major portion of the mtDNA and proteins.

SUMMARY

The mtDNA of *Drosophila melanogaster* appears to have transcription units distributed over approximately 75% of its length. No RNA transcription has been detected from the A+T-rich region that makes up the remaining 25% of the genome. The transcription units produce RNA species of sizes appropriate to code for the known products of mitochondrial translation.

The mtDNA does not share the nucleosome pattern of chromatin structure found in nuclear DNA. *In vivo* psoralen treatment yields uniformly heavy crosslinking over most of the genome, suggesting that if any proteins are associated with this DNA they are either less tightly bound or smaller than the nucleosomes of nuclear DNA. In contrast to the transcribed portions of the mtDNA, one half of the A+T-rich section contains specific regions that are protected from psoralen crosslinking *in vivo*. The origin of replication of the mtDNA is located in the center of the A+T-rich region, suggesting that the protection from psoralen binding could be due to membrane attachment or to replication proteins.

ACKNOWLEDGMENTS

We thank Dr. Sarah Elgin for the *Drosophila* embryos used in these experiments, Drs. I. T. Young and M. Eden for the use of the computer facilities at the M.I.T. Research Laboratory of Electronics, and Bradley Slosberg for technical assistance. This work was supported by grants from the National Cancer Institute and the National Institute of General Medical Sciences.

REFERENCES

Aloni, Y. & Attardi, G. (1971) Expression of the mitochondrial genome in HeLa cells. IV. Titration of mitochondrial genes for 16s, 12s and 4sRNA. *J. Mol. Biol.* 55, 271–276.

Angerer, L., Davidson, N., Murphy, W., Lynch, D., & Attardi, G. (1976) An electron microscope study of relative positions of the 4s and ribosomal RNA genes in HeLa cell mitochondrial DNA. *Cell* 9, 81–90.

Bonner, J.J., Berninger, M., & Pardue, M.L. (1978) Transcription of polytene chromosomes and of the mitochondrial genome in *Drosophila melanogaster. Cold. Spr. Harb. Symp. Quant. Biol.* 42, 803–813.

Borst, P. (1972) Mitochondrial nucleic acids. *Ann. Rev. Biochem.* 41, 333–376.

Borst, P. (1977) Structure and function of mitochondrial DNA. In: International Cell Biology, 1976–1977, eds. Brinkley, B.R. & Porter, K.R. pp. 237–244. Rockefeller Press, New York.

Bultmann, H. & Laird, C.D. (1973) Mitochondrial DNA from *Drosophila melanogaster. Biochim. Biophys. Acta* 299, 196–209.

Cech, T. & Padue, M.L. (1977) Crosslinking of DNA with trimethylpsoralen is a probe for chromatin structure. *Cell* 11, 631–640.

Cech, T., Potter, D., & Pardue, M.L. (1977) Electron microscopy of DNA crosslinked with trimethylpsoralen: a probe of chromatin structure. *Biochem.* 16, 5313–5321.

Chooi, W.Y. & Laird, C.D. (1976) DNA and polysome-like structures in lysates of mitochondria of *Drosophila melanogaster. J. Mol. Biol.* 100, 493–518.

Dawid, I.B. (1972a) Evolution of mitochondrial DNA sequences in *Xenopus. Dev. Biol.* 29, 139–151.

Dawid, I.B. (1972b) Mitochondrial RNA in *Xenopus laevis.* I. The expression of the mitochondrial genome. *J. Mol. Biol.* 63, 201–216.

Goddard, J.M. & Wolstenholme, D.R. (1978) Origin and direction of replication in mitochondrial DNA molecules from *Drosophila melanogaster. Proc. Natl. Acad. Sci. U.S.A.* 75, 3886–3890.

Hanson, C.V., Shen, C.-K. J., & Hearst, J.E. (1976) Crosslinking of DNA in situ as a probe for chromatin structure. *Science* 193, 62–64.

Hirsch, M., & Penman, S. (1974) The messenger-like properties of the poly(A)$^+$ RNA in mammalian mitochondria. *Cell* 3, 335–339.

Hirsch, M., Spradling, A., & Penman, S. (1974) The messenger-like poly(A)-containing RNA species from the mitochondria of mammals and insects. *Cell* 1, 31–35.

Jakovcic, S., Casey, J., & Rabinowitz, M. (1975) Sequence homology between mitochondrial DNAs of different eukaryotes. *Biochem.* 14, 2043–2050.

Klukas, C.K., & Dawid, I.B. (1976) Characterization and mapping of mitochondrial ribosomal RNA and mitochondrial DNA in *Drosophila melanogaster. Cell* 9, 615–625.

Lansman, R.A., & Clayton, D.A. (1975) Mitochondrial protein synthesis in mouse L-cells; effect of selective nicking of mitochondrial DNA. *J. Mol. Biol.* 99, 777–793.

Nass, M.M.K., & Buck, C.A. (1970) Studies on mitochondrial tRNA from animal cells. II. Hybridization of aminoacyl-tRNA from rat liver mitochondria with heavy and light complementary strands of mitochondrial DNA. *J. Mol. Biol.* 58, 187–198.

O'Brien, T.W. (1977) Transcription and translation in mitochondria. In: *International Cell Biology,* 1976–1977, eds. Brinkley B.R. & Porter, K.R. pp. 244–255. Rockefeller Press, New York.

Ojala, D., & Attardi, G. (1974) Expression of the mitochondrial genome in HeLa cells. II. Evidence for complete transcription of mitochondrial DNA. *J. Mol. Biol.* 55, 251–270.

Peacock, W.J., Brutlag, D., Goldring, E., Appels, R., Hinton, C.W., & Lindsley, D.L. (1974) The organization of highly repeated DNA sequences in *Drosophila melanogaster* chromosomes. *Cold Spr. Harb. Symp. Quant. Biol.* 38, 405–416.

Polan, M.L., Friedman, S., Gall, J.G., & Gehring, W. (1973) Isolation and characterization of mitochondrial DNA from *Drosophila melanogaster. J. Cell Biol.* 56, 580–589.

Schatz, G., & Mason, T.L. (1974) The biogenesis of mitochondrial proteins. *Ann. Rev. Biochem.* 43, 51–87.

Spradling, A., Pardue, M.L., & Penman, S. (1977) Messenger RNA in heat-shocked *Drosophila* cells. *J. Mol. Biol.* 109, 559–587.

Tzagoloff, A., Akai, A. & Needleman, R.B. (1975a) Assembly of the mitochondrial membrane system: characterization of nuclear mutants of *Saccharomyces cerevisiae* with defects in mitochondrial ATPase and respiratory enzymes. *J. Biol. Chem.* 250, 8228–8235.

Tzagoloff, A., Akai, A., Needleman, R.B., & Zulch, G. (1975b) Assembly of the mitochondrial membrane system: cytoplasmic mutants of *Saccharomyces cerevisiae* with lesions in enzymes of the respiratory chain and in the mitochondrial ATPase. *J. Biol. Chem.* 250, 8236–8242.

Wiesehahn, G.P., Hyde, J.E. & Hearst, J.E. (1977) The photoaddition of trimethylpsoralen to *Drosophila melanogaster* nuclei: a probe for chromatin substructure. *Biochem.* 16, 925–932.

Wolstenholme, D. (1973) Replicating DNA molecules from eggs of *Drosophila melanogaster. Chromosoma* 43, 1–18.

DISCUSSION

GALL: Is there any evidence that the mitochondrial DNA in *Drosophila* or any other species is attached to membranes, perhaps at the point where the bubbles are?

PARDUE: That is one thing we were looking for. There is some evidence of membrane binding in the mouse system, but as far as *Drosophila* goes, there is no evidence.

DAWID: The direction of replication was drawn to be towards the ribosomal RNA which is the other way around from the way it is in vertebrate mitochondrial DNAs. Is that definitely so?

PARDUE: That is what David Wolstenholme told us.

DAWID: What is the molecular weight of the 12 RNAs, if you add them up?

PARDUE: We are using 2.5 to 5% gels containing seven molar urea. If you are willing to believe those numbers, they add up so that they would just squeeze nicely into this region. But you have already convinced us that gels might not be the best way to measure sizes of RNAs. We have not seen any easy evidence that any of these RNAs may be precursors of other RNAs. Of course we have been doing our experiments using 1- and 2-h pulses.

DAWID: Do you have any suggstions for overlaps in sequence?

PARDUE: We do have those RNAs that look like they are too big to fit side by side on the DNA fragments to which they bind but it is a very weak evidence. If you look at the blots after longer exposures, you will see heavy bands of hybrids; in addition you will see lighter bands of hybridization that are specific for the mitochondrial DNA, because we run the lambda DNA in the same gel, and there is no hybridization to the lambda DNA. The low level hybrids could be due to cross-contamination of RNA fractions or they could be caused by some sequence homology. We will be better able to study this after we have cloned mitochondrial DNA.

BORST: Did you see any D-loops in the psoralene-treated or non-psoralene-treated DNA?

PARDUE: A lot of people have looked for D-loops, nobody has seen them before. But we would like to look at some more material before we say anything about what we see in the psoralene DNA.

LEICK: How many of these 12 poly-A-containing RNAs were identified?

PARDUE: The fourth largest RNA is the large mitochondrial ribosomal RNA. The poly-A⁻ Rna is the small mitochondrial ribosomal RNA. We don't have any idea of what any of the other RNAs do.

ARTAVANAS-TSAKONAS: Has anybody cloned everything on the mitochondrial DNA?

PARDUE: So far, I don't think anybody has. We have got 20 independent isolates of that same *Hind* III fragment that you all have, and nothing else so far. We have just started trying the cloning in a lambda vector.

16*

The Genes for Ribosomal RNA in Yeast Mitochondrial DNA

P. Borst

INTRODUCTION

The biosynthesis of mitochondria requires the close cooperation of genes in two cellular locations, in the nucleus and in the mitochondrial matrix space. The genes at the mitochondrial location are situated in mtDNA and in the yeast *Saccharomyces* this DNA is circular and contains from 68,000 to 76,000 base pairs, depending on the strain. The genes identified in this mtDNA include genes for the ribosomal RNAs (rRNAs) and transfer RNAs (tRNAs) used in mitochondrial protein synthesis and for eight mitochondrial proteins. Most of these proteins are part of enzyme complexes of the mitochondrial inner membrane; three of the seven subunits of cytochrome *c* oxidase, one (of the seven) subunits of the bc_1 complex, three (of the 10) subunits of the ATPase complex. Together these proteins account for less than 10% of the total mitochondrial protein, both on a weight and a number basis. The other mitochondrial proteins are specified by nuclear genes, they are made on cell-sap ribosomes and imported into the mitochondrion.

Why precisely these eight proteins are made inside mitochondria is unclear and this is underlined by recent results of Sebald and co-workers with the smallest subunit of the ATPase complex. In yeast this subunit is specified by a mitochondrial gene and made on mitochondrial ribosomes; in *Neurospora* the homologous protein is specified by a nuclear gene, made on cell-sap ribosomes and imported. This suggests that there is no profound evolutionary wisdom in the distribution of genes between mitochondrial and nuclear DNA.

The construction of a restriction map of yeast mtDNA by Sanders *et al.* (1977)

Section for Medical Enzymology and Molecular Biology, Laboratory of Biochemistry, University of Amsterdam, P.O.Box 60,000, 1005 GA Amsterdam, The Netherlands.

SPECIFIC EUKARYOTIC GENES, Alfred Benzon Symposium 13, Munksgaard 1979

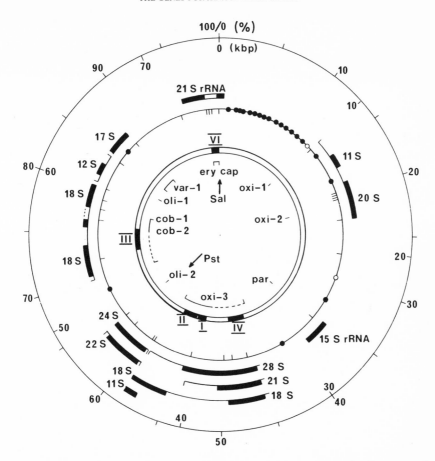

Fig. 1. The genetic and physical map of yeast mtDNA. The genetic map was obtained by co-retention of markers in petite mutants (Schweyen *et al.* 1978). The markers are indicated within the inner ring; ery, erythromycin resistance; cap, chloramphenicol resistance; oli, oligomycin resistance; par, paromomycin resistance. Oxi-1, 2, 3, structural genes for subunits of cytochrome *c* oxidase; cob, structural gene for apo-cytochrome *b*. The physical map is of mtDNA from *S. cerevisiae* strain KL14-4A (Sanders *et al.* 1977). The black bars in the inner ring represent the major insertions present in this mtDNA and absent in the mtDNA from *S. carlsbergensis.* The outer ring gives the position of recognition sites for endonucleases HindII+III and EcoRI and the approximate position of 4S RNA genes. The open circles are tRNA$_{met}$ genes. The approximate position of some of the other transcripts is given outside the outer ring, the bars indicating the uncertainty in the exact position. The transcription map is more complex than shown here and especially in the oxi-3 region many more overlapping transcripts have been found (Van Ommen, G. J. B., pers. commun.). The open part of the 21S rRNA represents the intervening sequence (see Fig. 2). Sa1 and Pst indicate the single recognition site for restriction endonuclease SalI and PstI, respectively. From Borst & Grivell (1978).

has made it possible to accurately map RNAs and genes for proteins on this DNA (see Fig. 1). The work of our group with yeast has been reviewed recently (Borst *et al.* 1977, Borst & Grivell 1978) and I refer to these papers for further reference to our work and that of others. In this paper I shall limit myself to the rRNAs and the nature of genes involved in resistance of mitochondrial protein synthesis to antibiotics.

MITOCHONDRIAL RIBOSOMES

The early studies by Grivell *et al.* (1971) showed that yeast mitochondria contain 73S ribosomes that can catalyze the poly(U)-directed synthesis of polyphe at the same rate as *Escherichia coli* ribosomes, if supplied with a high-speed supernatant from *E. coli*. The ability to utilize soluble enzymes from *E. coli* does not mean that the yeast mitochondrial ribosome is a close imitation of a bacterial ribosome. It cannot exchange its 50S and 37S subunits, for instance with *E. coli* ribosomes, whereas chloroplast ribosomes do (Grivell & Walg 1972). Our attempts to make a fully homologous protein-synthesizing system from yeast mitochondria have failed thus far, probably as a result of high ribonuclease activity.

MITOCHONDRIAL rRNAs

Only two rRNAs have been found in yeast mitochondrial ribosomes, a 21S RNA from the large subunit and a 15S RNA from the small subunit. There is no trace of 5S or 5.8S rRNAs in clean mitochondria (Grivell & Reijnders 1974). Since the 5S RNA sequence is apparently essential for ribosomal function in all ribosomes studied, it is likely that a 5S analogue must be hidden somewhere in the yeast ribosome, either co-migrating with 4S RNA or covalently attached to the 21S rRNA. A specific 5S rRNA has been found in the mitochondrial ribosome of higher plants (Cunningham *et al.* 1976), which looks more like a bacterial ribosome in other respects as well.

With 21 mole percent G+C, the rRNAs are very low in G+C and they tend to unfold rather easily in low salt, resulting in low migration rates through gels or in sucrose gradients. Under fully denaturing conditions they appear to be larger than the *E. coli* rRNAs and our best estimates of the molecular weights, using denaturing gels, electron microscopy or sedimentation equilibrium, are 1.30 and 0.70×10^6 (Reijnders *et al.* 1973).

THE 21S rRNA GENE IS SPLIT

Our early hybridization experiments showed that yeast mtDNA contains at most one gene for each of the rRNAs. This was confirmed by mapping these genes on the restriction map. In addition, these experiments showed unexpectedly that the genes for the two RNAs are about 30,000 base pairs (bp) apart on the mtDNA. There are many tRNAs and genes for at least two proteins between the 21S and 15S rRNA genes (Fig. 1) and both rRNAs can be made independently in petite mutants that contain only a small segment of wild-type mtDNA. This and other evidence (see Borst & Grivell 1978) suggests that these genes contain separate promotors and that they are not transcribed into one giant precursor RNA. The coordinate synthesis of both rRNAs in a 1:1 ratio must, therefore, be effected in a different fashion than in other biological systems. We have since found a great distance between the rRNA genes in *Tetrahymena* mtDNA as well, but in this case there is also a duplication of the large, but not of the small rRNA gene (Goldbach *et al.* 1978).

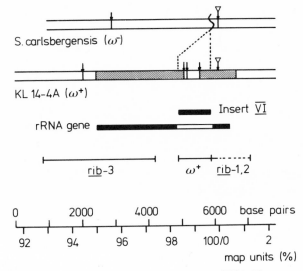

Fig. 2. A physical map of the large (21S) rRNA gene in yeast mtDNA. The two top bars show the position of Hind II+III (↓) and SalI (∇) recognition sites on an ω⁻ and ω⁺ mtDNA. The position of insert VI, the rRNA and the approximate positions of genetic markers on the ω⁺ DNA are also indicated. Fragments that hybridize with rRNA in a HindII+III × HapII double digest are hatched in the ω⁺ DNA; the intervening sequence in the rRNA gene is left open. Rib-1 is identical to cap in Fig. 1; rib-3 to ery; rib-2 is a second erythromycin (spiramycin) resistance locus. Rib-1 and rib-2 are most probably located in the region indicated by the continuous line, but a position more to the right (indicated by the broken line) is not excluded. The map unit scale is for KL14-4A mtDNA and it is identical to the scale in Fig. 1. From Borst & Grivell (1978).

The fine-structure restriction map of the gene for the 21S rRNA led to a second surprise: the rRNA was found to hybridize with non-adjacent fragments of the DNA, as indicated with the hatched fragments in Fig. 2. Although this finding immediately suggested that the rRNA gene is split, the hybridization experiments in themselves were inconclusive, because of the presence of duplications of part of the rRNA gene in this region (Borst *et al.* 1977). Moreover, Rabinowitz and co-workers (Hendler *et al.* 1976) who analyzed duplexes of rRNA and mtDNA by R-looping had detected no intervening sequence. Unambiguous evidence for the presence of an intervening sequence, however, was obtained by us in two ways:

1. The rRNA sequences hybridizing with fragments to the left of the SalI site (Fig. 2) were isolated by pre-hybridization and shown not to hybridize with sequences to the right of the SalI site.

2. The rRNA was hybridized to a HaeIII fragment which spans the SalI site and the putative intervening sequence. Electron micrographs of the hybrids showed a 1150 bp DNA loop between two hybrid sections (Bos *et al.* 1978).

On the basis of these results the rRNA gene contains at least one intervening sequence, as indicated in Fig. 2. Although intervening sequences have previously been found in the nuclear rRNA genes of *Drosophila,* it has not yet been possible to decide if these split genes yield mature rRNA. With yeast mtDNA this is certain, because no other gene is present. A further interesting aspect of the yeast rRNA gene is that the intervening sequence varies in size in different yeast strains. I shall return to this below.

THE NATURE OF CHLORAMPHENICOL AND ERYTHROMYCIN RESISTANCE IN YEAST

Yeast mutants in which mitochondrial protein synthesis is highly resistant to chloramphenicol or erythromycin arise spontaneously at high frequency and can be readily isolated and maintained. Most of these mutations show cytoplasmic inheritance and other properties characteristic of mutations in mtDNA. In 1969 I first raised the possibility that resistance in these mutants might be the consequence of alterations in the nucleotide sequence of 21S rRNA

a) Even if antibiotic resistance in bacteria is due to alterations in ribosomal proteins rather than rRNA, the interaction of rRNA and protein in the ribosome (Borst 1971). The rationale for this suggestion was two fold:
is such that alterations in the RNA might result in secondary alterations in the tertiary structure or position of ribosomal proteins.

b) Bacteria have multiple genes for rRNA and, unless an alteration in the rRNA sequence would confer a highly dominant advantage, one would never pick it up because the cell would be killed by an excess of sensitive ribosomes blocking translation in the presence of the antibiotic. Yeast mitochondria contain only a single gene for the rRNA of the large subunit and any alteration in this gene will readily be purified in the progeny by mitotic segregation. Hence, if antibiotic resistance can arise at all by alterations in the nucleotide sequence of rRNA, mitochondria are the place to look for it.

The idea that alterations in the primary sequence of rRNA are responsible for antibiotic resistance was taken up in Gif and in Amsterdam. In Gif, Slonimski and co-workers showed by a genetic and physical analysis of the mtDNA segments retained in petite mutants, that genetic markers for antibiotic resistance were indeed closely linked to the 21S rRNA gene (Faye *et al.* 1974). The work in Amsterdam consisted of two phases. First, Grivell and co-workers tried to eliminate all other alternative explanations for antibiotic resistance. These are:

a) A permeability barrier to the uptake of the antibiotic by the cell or its mitochondria or inactivation of the antibiotic

b) An alteration of the amino acid sequence or the secondary modification of the proteins of the mitochondrial ribosome

c) An alteration of the secondary modification of the rRNA.

Alternative (a) was eliminated by Grivell *et al.* (1973) by demonstrating that resistance was retained in isolated mitochondrial ribosomes. Alternative (b) was made less attractive by Groot's finding (1974) that all proteins of the large ribosomal subunit in yeast mitochondria are made on cell-sap ribosomes. Since there is no evidence that messenger RNAs (mRNAs) are exported from mitochondria and translated outside, this would imply that the genes for all the proteins of the large ribosomal subunit are in the nucleus. Alterations in mtDNA could, therefore, only affect these proteins if these mutations were in genes for enzymes that modify mitochondrial proteins. No such enzymes are known to be made in mitochondria, but this does not mean much. More significant is that no alterations in isoelectric point were found in the mitochondrial ribosomal proteins from any of these mutants (Grivell *et al.* 1973, Faye 1977).

Alternative (c) was rendered unlikely by a thorough study of the secondary modification of rRNA, which showed that the 21S rRNA contains only two ribose methyl groups, one pseudo-uridine residue and no methylated bases

(Klootwijk *et al.* 1975). It is not known whether the enzymes that introduce secondary modifications in mtRNAs are specified by mitochondrial or nuclear genes, although the latter seems more likely because no mitochondrial mutants are known that affect the biosynthesis of the large ribosomal subunit and that map outside the region of the large rRNA gene. However, the very meager secondary modification of the rRNA in itself makes it highly unlikely that alterations in this modification could account for all forms of antibiotic resistance. Several loci are known that affect antibiotic resistance and at each locus different mutations lead to distinguishable phenotypes (see Grivell *et al.* 1973). It is inconceivable that this could result from changes in two ribose methyl groups and one pseudo-uridine. It should also be noted that resistance to kasugamycin, erythromycin or thiostrepton in bacteria has been linked (see Cundliffe 1978) to an alteration in the secondary modification of rRNA, but in all these cases the alteration affects base methylation which is absent in yeast rRNA.

In our second approach direct evidence was sought for the location of mutations conferring chloramphenicol or erythromycin resistance within the rRNA gene by mapping these mutations precisely on the mtDNA using petite mutants. Cytoplasmic petite mutants are deletion mutants in which 10–99.9% of the mtDNA is lost, depending on the mutant. Although such mutants cannot make functional mitochondria, they can still transmit the genetic markers present on the DNA segment retained. By determining the wild-type mtDNA sequence retained in a series of petites that carry a chloramphenicol resistance marker, one can determine the position of this marker on wild-type mtDNA, because this marker should be located in the mtDNA segment that all these petites have in common. The results of such an analysis by Heyting of our group is included in Fig. 2. The positions of all three major antibiotic resistance loci- *rib*-1 (chloramphenicol), *rib*-2 (erythromycin, spiramycin) and *rib*-3 (erythromycin) – overlap the 21S rRNA gene, in agreement with the idea that these loci are part of this gene.

Very recently, Knight (1978) has identified four additional loci at which antibiotic-resistant mutants cluster. These loci all lie between *rib*-1, 2 and *rib*-3. Although there is still no proof that also these mutations are in the 21S rRNA gene, there is no reasonable alternative explanation for the sum total of all results now available.

It is clear that a detailed analysis of the nature of the sequence alterations in rRNA in these mutants, the position of the alterations and their effect on the structure of the RNA should be of great interest in obtaining further insight into the role of rRNA in ribosomal function.

THE ω LOCUS IS WITHIN THE RIBOSOMAL GENE

The polarity locus ω affects the transmission of markers around it in crosses. In $\omega^+ \times \omega^-$ crosses the markers associated with the ω^+ allele are preferentially transmitted; no polarity is observed in $\omega^+ \times \omega^+$, $\omega^- \times \omega^-$, $\omega^+ \times \omega^n$ or $\omega^- \times \omega^n$ crosses (Dujon et al. 1976). In mapping studies analogous to those described in the previous section, we (Borst et al. 1977) and the Gif group (Jacq et al. 1978) independently found that the ω^+ allele is closely correlated with a 1050 bp insertion (insert VI). All ω^+ strains studied contained this insertion, all ω^- and ω^n strains did not. The insertion was always completely transmitted to the ω^+ progeny in $\omega^+ \times \omega^-$ crosses.

The nature of ω has been discussed elsewhere (Dujon et al. 1976, Jacq et al. 1977, Heyting & Menke 1978). Here the point of interest is that insert VI overlaps the intervening sequence in the rRNA gene. Hence, this intervening sequence is 1050 bp shorter in ω^- and ω^n strains than in ω^+ strains (Fig. 2). Whether ω^- strains contain a short intervening sequence or none has not yet been determined.

The intervening sequence in the 21S rRNA gene is the first intervening sequence known to vary in size in variants of the same organism. It will probably be possible to construct strains containing only part of the ω^+ allele and in this way it should be possible to get a grip on the sequence requirements for splicing.

There are several observations that show an interaction between the ω locus and rib-1 (chloramphenicol resistance): first, about half of the C^S revertants from $\omega^- C^R$ (but not $\omega^+ C^R$) were found to be $\omega^n C^S$ (Dujon et al. 1976). Second, some $\rho^- C^R$ petites are able to integrate the C^R allele into ω^+ and ω^-, but not into ω^n strains (Dujon et al. 1976). Third, C^R mutations could not be introduced into ω^n strains (Dujon et al. 1976) and into one ω^+ strain (Heyting, C., personal communication). These observations can be explained by assuming that interaction between rib-1 and ω is required for proper splicing and that this interaction can be affected both by alterations at ω and at rib-1. It is likely, therefore, that ω^- contains a small intron rather than none.

WHY SPLIT GENES IN mtDNA?

It is likely that the rRNA gene is not the only split gene on mtDNA. There is strong circumstantial evidence that the structural gene for apo-cytochrome *b* contains at least two intervening sequences and suggestive evidence for a split arrangement of the structural gene for subunit I of cytochrome *c* oxidase (*oxi*-3 locus) (see Borst & Grivell 1978). If this is confirmed, this would link the three places on the map, where major sequence variations have been found, to split genes. When the mtDNAs of *Saccharomyces carlsbergensis* and *Saccharomyces cerevisiae* strain KL14–4A are compared (Sanders *et al.* 1977), the latter is found to contain five major insertions not present in the former (see Fig. 1). One of these (insert VI, 1050 bp) is in the rRNA gene, as already mentioned; one (insertion III, 3000 bp) is in the cytochrome *b* (*cob*) region; three (insertions I, II and IV, totalling 5000 bp) in the *oxi*-3 region.

Why are (some) mitochondrial genes split and why should the intervening sequence be a site of major sequence variation? Explanations for nuclear genes in pieces are of three types:

1. Gilbert (1978) has suggested that genes in pieces increase the evolutionary flexibility in several ways: by increasing the size of the gene, intragenic recombination can increase; splicing errors allow the formation of novel gene products without sacrificing the original gene; and – most importantly – if the intervening sequences ("introns") are between functional domains in the protein, faulty recombination between the introns of different genes may generate new functional proteins by combining functional domains of old ones.

2. Scherrer & Marcaud (1968) have suggested years ago on theoretical grounds that gene expression in a complex genome can be more precisely controlled in a step-wise (cascade) fashion, than exclusively at the level of transcription. The presence of intronic sequences in pre-mRNAs could increase the possibilities for selection at the processing step.

3. Intronic sequences are present to prevent the primary transcript to function before secondary modification is complete (O'Farrell *et al.* 1978).

None of these suggestions account too well for the introns in yeast mtDNA. The complexity of mtDNA is low and it would not seem to require a cascade to control its expression. There is also no evidence in mitochondria for the imaginative creation of new proteins from old ones in the course of evolution, because the same six to seven proteins appear to be made on mammalian mitochondrial ribosomes that are also made on yeast mitochondrial ribosomes. Recombination of mtDNA occurs at high rate, however, and introns could contribute to the effectiveness of this process. If crossovers can only be initiated from a sequence that cannot easily be tolerated within a coding sequence, the presence of introns could confer a clear advantage. Explanation 3 can not be dismissed either. Once a splicing mechanism is available, introns may also get into non-tRNA genes, if they happen to be compatible with the splicing system.

The possible association of major inserts with introns is difficult to explain. The sequence of at least two of these inserts (IV and VI) is absent elsewhere in the genome and they are absent in *S. carlsbergensis* mtDNA without discernable deleterious effect on function. This shows that these sequences do not carry essential information. It is, therefore, possible that introns are locations where extra sequences are best tolerated, rather than functionally required.

Finally, the finding of introns in mtDNA may suggest to some that the endosymbiontic origin of mitochondria has become less likely. This conclusion seems unwarranted to me. We do not know yet whether intervening sequences are completely absent from prokaryotes and even if this is the case, this may be a late evolutionary development as pointed out by Doolittle (1978). The introns in mitochondrial genes could, therefore, reflect the sloppy organization of genes in the primitive prokaryote from which mitochondria originate.

ACKNOWLEDGMENTS

This work was supported in part by a grant to P.B. and G.S.P. Groot from The Netherlands Foundation for Chemical Research (SON) with financial aid from The Netherlands Organization for the Advancement of Pure Research (ZWO).

REFERENCES

Borst, P. (1971) Size, structure and information content of mitochondrial DNA. In: *Autonomy and Biogenesis of Mitochondria and Chloroplasts,* eds. Boardman, N.K., Linnane, A.W. & Smillie, R.M. pp.260–266. North-Holland, Amsterdam.

Borst, P. & Grivell, L.A. (1978) The mitochondrial genome of yeast. *Cell 15,* 705–723.

Borst, P., Bos, J.L. Grivell, L.A. Groot, G.S.P., Heyting, C., Moorman, A.F.M., Sanders, J.P.M., Talen, J.L., Van Kreyl, C.F. & Van Ommen, G.J.B. (1977) The physical map of yeast mitochondrial DNA anno 1977. In: *Mitochondria 1977: Genetics and Biogenesis of Mitochondria.* eds. Bandlow, W., Schweyen, R.J., Wolf, K. & Kaudewitz, F., pp. 213–254. De Gruyter, Berlin.

Bos, J.L., Heyting, C.,Borst, P.,Arnberg, A.C. & Van Bruggen, E.F.J. (1978) An insert in the single gene for the large ribosomal RNA in yeast mitochondrial DNA. *Nature. 275,* 336–338.

Cundliffe, E. (1978) Mechanism of resistance to thiostrepton in the producing organism *Streptomyces azureus. Nature 272,* 792–795.

Cunningham, R.S., Bonen, L.,Doolittle, W.F. & Gray, M.W. (1976) Unique species of 5S, 18S and 26S ribosomal RNA in wheat mitochondria. *FEBS Letters 69,* 116–122.

Doolittle, W.F. (1978) Genes in pieces: Were they ever together? *Nature 272,* 581–582.

Dujon, B., Bolotin-Fukuhara, M.,Coen, D., Deutsch, J., Netter, P., Slonimski, P.P. & Weill, L. (1976) Mitochondrial genetics. XI. Mutations at the mitochondrial locus ω affecting recombination of mitochondrial genes in *Saccharomyces cerevisiae. Mol. Gen. Gen. 143*, 131–165.

Faye, G. (1977) Analysis of mitochondrial ribosomal poteins of paromomycin and chloramphenicol resistant mutants of *Saccharomyces cerevisiae*. In: *Mitochondria 1977: Genetics and Biogenesis of Mitochondria* eds. Bandlow, W., Schweyen, R.J., Wolf, K. & Kaudewitz, F., pp. 575–578. De Gruyter, Berlin.

Faye, G., Kujawa, C. & Fukuhara, H. (1974) Physical and genetic organization of petite and grande yeast mitochondrial DNA. IV. *In vivo* transcription products of mitochondrial DNA and localization of 23S ribosomal RNA in petite mutants of *Saccharomyces cerevisiae. J. Mol. Biol. 88*, 185–203.

Gilbert, W. (1978) Why genes in pieces? *Nature 271*, 501–502.

Goldbach, R.W., Borst, P., Bollen-de Boer, J.E. & Van Bruggen, E.F.J. (1978) The organization of ribosomal RNA genes in the mitochondrial DNA of *Tetrahymena pyriformis* strain ST. *Biochim. Biophys. Acta 521*, 169–186.

Grivell, L.A. & Walg, H.L. (1972) Subunit homology between *Escherichia coli,* mitochondrial and chloroplast ribosomes. *Biochem. Biophys. Res. Commun. 49*, 1452–1458.

Grivell, L.A. & Reijnders, L. (1974) Yeast mitochondrial ribosomes. *Postçpy Mikrobiologii 13*, 67–80.

Grivell, L.A., Reijnders, L. & Borst, P. (1971) Isolation of yeast mitochondrial ribosomes highly active in protein synthesis. *Biochim. Biophys. Acta 247*, 91–103.

Grivell, L.A., Netter, P., Borst, P. & Slonimski, P.P. (1973) Mitochondrial antibiotic resistance in yeast: Ribosomal mutants resistant to chloramphenicol, erythromycin and spiramycin. *Biochim. Biophys. Acta 312*, 358–367.

Groot, G.S.P. (1974) The biosynthesis of mitochondrial ribosomes in *Saccharomyces cerevisiae*. In: *The Biogenesis of Mitochondria*. eds. Kroon, A. M. & Saccone, C., pp. 443–452. Academic Press, New York.

Hendler, F., Halbreich, A., Jakovcic, S., Patzer, J., Merten, S. & Rabinowitz, M.(1976) Characterization and translation of yeast mitochondrial RNA. In: *Genetics and Biogenesis of Chloroplasts and Mitochondria*. eds. Bücher, Th., Neupert, W., Sebald, W. & Werner, s., pp. 679–684. North-Holland, Amsterdam.

Heyting, C. & Menke, H.H. (1978) Fine-structure of the 21S ribosomal RNA region on yeast mitochondrial DNA. III. Physical location of mitochondrial genetic markers and the molecular nature of omega. *Mol. Gen. Gen.* In press.

Jacq, C., Kujawa, C., Grandchamp, C. & Netter, P. (1977) Physical characterization of the differences between yeast mitochondrial DNA alleles ω^+ and ω^-. In: *Mitochondria 1977: Genetics and Biogenesis of Mitochondria*. eds. Bandlow, W., Schweyen, R. J., Wolf. K. & Kaudewitz, F., pp. 255–270. De Gruyter, Berlin.

Klootwijk, J., Klein, I. & Grivell, L.A. (1975) Minimal post-transcriptional modification of yeast mitochondrial ribosomal RNA. *J. Mol. Biol. 97*, 337–350.

Knight, J.A. (1978) Isolation and characterization of new mutants in the ribosomal region of the mitochondrial genome of *Saccharomyces cerevisiae*. Abstr. 9th Intern. Conf. on Yeast Genetics and Molecular Biology, Rochester, N.Y., U.S.A., p. 26; Nr. 110.

O'Farrell, P.Z., Cordell, B., Valenzuela, P., Rutter, W.J. & Goodman, H.M. (1978) Structure and processing of yeast precursor tRNAs containing intervening sequences. *Nature 274*, 438–445.

Reijnders, L., Sloof, P. & Borst, P. (1973) The molecular weights of the mitochondrial ribosomal RNAs of *Saccharomyces carlsbergensis. Europ. J. Biochem. 35*, 266–269.

Sanders, J.P.M., Heyting, C., Verbeet, M.Ph., Meijlink, F.C.P.W. & Borst, P. (1977) The organization of genes in yeast mitochondrial DNA. III. Comparison of the physical maps of the mitochondrial DNAs from three wild-type *Saccharomyces* strains. *Mol. Gen. Gen. 157,* 239–261.

Scherrer, K. & Marcaud, L. (1968) Messenger RNA in avian erytoblasts at the transcriptional and translational levels and the problem of regulation in animal cells. *J. Cell Physiol. 72,* Suppl. 1, 181–212.

Schweyen, R.J., Weiss-Brummer, B., Backhaus, B. & Kaudewitz, F. (1978) The genetic map of the mitochondrial genome in yeast. Map positions of drug ^{r} and mit$^-$ markers as revealed from population analysis of ρ^- clones in *Saccharomyces cerevisiae. Mol. Gen. Gen. 159,* 151–160.

DISCUSSION

PARDUE: When you said you looked upon your intervening sequence in Southern blots of DNA, was that mitochondrial DNA or nuclear DNA?

BORST: Mitochrondrial DNA.

PARDUE: Have you looked at nuclear DNA?

BORST: No. We still operate on the – maybe naïve – idea that the contact between mitochondrion and nucleus in present day yeast is blocked by the presence of the inner and outer mitochondrial membrane.

PARDUE: But maybe your insertion sequences are passing the membrane?

BORST: That is a possibility. It has to come from somewhere. My guess would be that it has come from one of the existing regions of the mitochondrial DNA, but this will be difficult to prove, if intervening sequences in yeast mtDNA evolve as rapidly as those in the β-globin gene in mammals. I cannot rule out, however, that the intervening sequence comes from the nucleus because the experiment has not been done.

PARDUE: How firmly does one know that there is no homology between the mitochondrial and nuclear DNA? By this I mean a homology of one or a few RNA coding units.

BORST: These experiments were done, maybe 10 years ago, and were not done at a high resolution. I think the experiments we did at that time showed that there must be much less than one complete copy of mitochondrial DNA in the nucleus, if there is any sequence homology at all. But now one could indeed do this much more precisely.

RICH: Can one make an analogy between the mitochondrial DNA and the DNA of a virus? The viruses frequently use the same piece of DNA for making different messages, either using different starts or stops or phase changes. Do you have any evidence for that in the mitochondrial DNA?

BORST: No, we do not have direct evidence, but in the *oxi*-3 region, Van Ommen and Groot in our lab have found several overlapping transcripts present in about the same amount. It is not obvious that one is the precursor of the other, so this could be analogous to the situation in SV40.

CRICK: The analogy should really not be pressed because the point about viruses is that they have a very restricted amount of DNA, and has to compact information on the DNA. As I understand it, in your case you have got rather a lot of DNA.

BORST: I agree, less than 20% of the total sequences are required to code for the known gene products. Also, of the remaining 80% more than half consists of very A-T rich sequences, which contain less than 5% G-C of unknown function. Since most of the transcripts are much longer than the size of the GC-rich segments in the DNA, part of the AT-rich segments must be transcribed. This has actually been verified in one case, the 21S transcript of the *oli*-1 region (see Fig. 1 of the preceding talk). Hensgens in our lab, has partially sequenced a 1,000 bp *Hap*II fragment containing this locus, which is known to code for the DCCD binding subunit of the mitochondrial ATPase complex. The amino acid sequence of this protein has been determined by Sebald and co-workers and this has allowed Hensgens to identify the C-and N-termini of the structural gene and to show that the gene is surrounded by long, very AT-rich segments. Since the 12S RNA hybridizes over most of this *Hap*II fragment, these AT-rich segments are included in this transcript.

One other comment on the biosynthesis of the DCCD binding protein in *Neurospora*. Whereas the structural gene for this protein is clearly on mtDNA in yeast, Sebald and co-workers have conclusively shown that the homologous protein in *Neurospora* is specified by a nuclear gene and made on cell-sap ribosomes. There is no doubt that the two proteins are functionally homologous and they share about 50% of their amino acid sequence. The conclusion seems unavoidable that there is no divine wisdom in the division of labor between nuclear and mitochondrial DNA and that in the course of evolution genes have been allocated to either location in a rather haphazard way.

DAWID: The insert VI, is that an AT-rich region?

BORST: We don't know.

PARDUE: Is the region that is actually coding for the protein very A-T rich also?

BORST: No, fortunately not. A-T rich sequences make sequencing difficult, because they contain no restriction sites.

Restriction Mapping and Interspecies Homology of Mitochondrial DNA from *Paramecium*

Donald J. Cummings, Richard A. Maki & Charles M. Paroda

INTRODUCTION

The mitochondrial DNA (mt DNA) of *Paramecium primaurelia* has been shown to be a linear genome of 27×10^6 daltons (Goddard & Cummings 1975). Replication of this DNA proceeds via a lariate intermediate terminating in a dimer length molecule which is then processed to two monomer length linear molecules (Goddard & Cummings 1977). The size of this genome and its unique mode of replication suggest many questions which can be answered only by a more detailed examination of the DNA. To obtain the necessary details, our laboratory is using restriction enzymes to study the DNA. Earlier, we reported (Maki & Cummings 1977) that *P. primaurelia* mt DNA is cleaved into six fragments by the restriction enzyme Eco R1 and a brief report of the Eco R1 map has recently appeared (Maki & Cummings 1978). This physical orientation of the genome is being correlated at the present with the genetics and biological function of the mt DNA.

The role of the mitochondrial genome in the biological function of the mitochondria is also being examined from another viewpoint. Knowles (1973) and Beale & Knowles (1976) have shown that antibiotic resistant mitochondria could be transferred only between certain species of *Paramecium*. Whether the control of this phenomenon is of nuclear or mitochondrial origin is not clear. Although the length and density of the mt DNA isolated from several species of *Paramecium* is the same, the Eco R1 restriction pattern for each species is unique (Maki & Cummings 1977). If the mitochondrial genome plays a significant role

---

University of Colorado Medical Center, Denver, Co 80262 USA.

SPECIFIC EUKARYOTIC GENES, Alfred Benzon Symposium 13, Munksgaard 1979

17*

in this restriction of transfer it may be reflected in the degree of homology between the mt DNAs of various species of *Paramecium*. It has been difficult to demonstrate genetic recombination in mitochondria from *Paramecium* (Adoutte 1977) and these homology studies may clarify this as well as help to determine the amount of evolutionary divergence between different species.

MATERIAL AND METHODS

The mitochondria were isolated and the DNA purified as described by Goddard & Cummings (1975). The mitochondrial ribosomes were isolated as described by Tait & Knowles (1977). The rRNA was purified by phenol extraction followed by ethanol precipitation. Reaction conditions for Eco R1 cleavage of mt DNA were as described by Green *et al.* (1974). The reaction conditions for Bam HI digestion were 20 mM Tris-HCl, ph 7.5, 7 mM MgCl$_2$, 2 mM 2-mercaptoethanol and 100 μg/l gelatin. The DNA fragments were analyzed by agarose gel electrophoresis. Gels were photographed under a longwave length ultraviolet lamp using a Polaroid camera with type 105 film and a Wratten 23A gelatin filter. Extraction of DNA from agarose gels was as described (Maki & Cummings 1977).

Mitochondrial rRNA was labeled with ^{125}I as described by Getz *et al.* (1972). The DNA fragments in agarose gels were transferred to nitrocellulose filters by the method of Southern (1975). Hybridization of the ^{125}I-labeled RNA to DNA on nitrocellulose filters was performed as described by Bell *et al.* (1977).

Mitochondrial DNA was labeled with ^{125}I according to the method of Davies

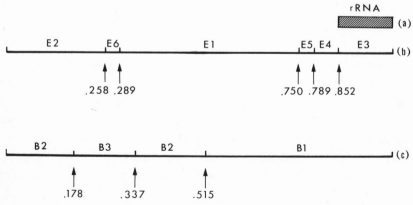

Fig. 1. Eco R1 and Bam HI restriction endonuclease maps of *Paramecium primaurelia*.

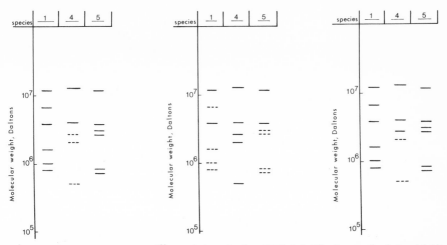

Fig. 2. Interspecies homology. a) ^{125}I-labeled species 1 mt DNA hybridized to species 1, 4 and 5. b) ^{125}I-labeled species 4 mt DNA hybridizazed to species 1, 4 and 5. c) ^{125}I-labeled species 5 mt DNA hybridized to species 1, 4 and 5.

(1972). Transfer of DNA fragments to nitrocellulose filters and hybridization of ^{125}I-labeled DNA on these filters was by the method of Bukhari *et al.* (1976).

RESULTS

Restriction endonuclease mapping. The digestion of *Paramecium primaurelia* mt DNA with Eco R1 generates six fragments (Maki & Cummings 1977). A restriction map of these fragments was constructed (Fig. 1b) using several enzymatic techniques. The basic methodology consisted of first comparing the Eco R1 cleavage pattern of the monomer length molecule with the dimer length molecule (Goddard & Cummings 1977). In the dimer length molecule there is a head to head covalent linkage of two monomers and therefore the Eco R1 pattern of this genome should differ from that of the monomer. Using this criterion, it was possible to establish Eco fragment E2 at one end of the linear genome. Second, incubating the mt DNA with Exo III followed by Eco R1 digestion enabled us to establish that Eco fragment E3 was located at the other end of the linear genome. Third, partial digestion of the mt DNA with Eco R1 was used to demonstrate that Eco fragment E2 was linked to E6, E6 to E1, E5 to E4, and E4 to E3.

Bam HI map. Bam HI cleaves the mt DNA into four fragments, although, because two fragments are of equal size, only three bands appeared by gel electrophoresis. Using the method of double digestion, i.e. Eco R1 fragments digested with Bam HI, it was possible to establish a Bam HI restriction (Fig. 1c).

Position of the rRNA genes. The rRNA extracted from purified ribosomes was shown to have two subunits, one of 21S and the other of about 14S by sucrose gradient centrifugation. Labeling of the rRNA *in vitro* with ^{125}I followed by hybridization to EcoRI fragments of mt DNA suggest that both the 21S and 14S subunits are located on Eco fragment 3 (Fig. 1a).

Interspecies homology between species 1, 4 and 5. Species 1 ^{125}I mt DNA was hybridized to the Eco R1 fragments of species 1, 4 and 5 immobilized on nitrocellulose strips (Fig. 2a). Species 1 mt DNA showed good hybridization to all *EcoRI* generated fragments of species 1 and species 5. In contrast, species 1 mt DNA showed homology only to the two larger molecular weight fragments of species 4 mt DNA.

Species 4 ^{125}I mt DNA hybridized to Eco R1 digests to species 1, 4 and 5 are shown in Fig. 2b. Species 4 mt DNA did not hybridize well to species 1 or 5 mt DNA. Species 4 mt DNA had homology only with Eco R1 fragments 1 and 3 of species 1 and fragments 1 and 2 of species 5.

Species 5 ^{125}I mt DNA hybridized to Eco R1 digests of species 1, 4 and 5 are shown in Fig. 2c. Species 5 exhibited good homology with species 1 but only showed homology with fragments 1, 2 and 3 of species 4.

A summary of these preliminary results are presented in Table 1. This table contains information on sequences that are homologous in the 3 mt DNAs examined.

DISCUSSION

The Eco R1 and Bam HI restriction endonuclease cleavage maps have been constructed for *Paramecium primaurelia* mt DNA. The genes for the 14S and 21S rRNA subunits have been located on Eco fragment E3. From the present data it can be concluded that since Eco fragment E3 is 5700 bp and the rRNA genes require about 1600 and 2900 bp, respectively, the two rRNA genes must be relatively close to each other and present in only one copy each. This is similar to several other systems studied (Ojala & Attardi 1977, David *et al.* 1976, Klukos & David 1976, Terpstra *et al.* 1976, Kroon *et al.* 1977) but differs from the relative position of the two rRNA genes found in yeast mt DNA (sanders *et al.* 1975).

The position of the rRNA genes relative to the origin of replication is quite interesting. In the circular mt DNAs which have been examined, the rRNA genes

Table I

Interspecies hybridization of Eco R1 restriction fragments of Paramecium mt DNA

^{125}I probe	Species 1						Species 4					Species 5					
Eco R1 fragments	1	2	3	4	5	6	1	2	3	4	5	1	2	3	4	5	6
Molecular weight ×10⁶	11.8	6.6	3.8	1.6	1.0	0.8	12.6	3.9	2.6	2.0	0.5	11.7	3.7	3.0	2.6	0.8	0.7
Species 1	+	+	+	+	+	+	+	+	−	−	−	+	+	+	+	+	+
Species 4	+	−	+	−	−	−	+	+	+	+	+	+	+	−	−	−	−
Species 5	+	+	+	+	+	+	+	+	+	−	−	+	+	+	+	+	+

are located near the termini for DNA replication (Ojala & Attardi 1977, Dawid *et al.* 1976, Kroon *et al.* 1977). In the linear mt DNA from *Paramecium,* the rRNA genes are also located near the termini for DNA replication which suggests that this may be a general feature of all mt DNAs.

Mitochondrial DNA from species 1 and 5 are homologous and have not diverged from one another to any great extent. The difference seen in the restriction pattern may be due therefore to single nucleotide mutations which would either add or delete Eco R1 restriction sites. These results do not, however, rule out the possibility of small deletions and insertions or possible small scale rearrangement of the genome (Bernardi *et al.* 1976).

Species 4 mt DNA has diverged from species 1 and 5 mt DNA. Since the average size of the mt genome in *Paramecium* is 27×10^6 daltons, there is a 25% divergence of species 4 mt DNA from species 1 mt DNA. This is similar to the 25% divergence between *Xenopus laevis* and *Xenopus mulleri* mt DNA (Dawid 1972) and between sheep and goat mt DNA (Upholt & Dawid 1977).

The results presented here indicate that there are areas of the mitochondrial genome that are conserved. The rRNA genes in particular, are conserved among the three species examined. The mt DNA probes and the rRNA probes hybridize to specific size fragments of the three species. Recent results in our laboratory show that the rRNA probe hybridizes to Eco R1 fragment 2 of species 4 and Eco R1 fragment 2 of species 5. This indicates that the rRNA genes are located on a Eco R1 fragment of $3.7 - 3.9 \times 10^6$ daltons in all these species. Species 4 mt DNA has diverged from species 1 and 5 but the rRNA genes and possibly other essential genes are conserved. On the other hand, areas of the mt genome may undergo extensive changes without affecting the survival of mitochondria. Whether these areas represent nonessential genes is not certain at present.

These results are interesting, also in regard to interspecies transfer of mitochondria (Knowles 1973, Beale & Knowles 1976). Species 4 cannot survive when transferred to any of the other species and vice versa. Mitochondria transferred from species 5 to species 1 occurs at a higher rate than species 1 mitochondria to species 5 cells. Beale & Knowles (1976) data were not extensive enough to prove the existence of a mitochondrially coded factor controlling compatibility and they concluded that compatibility was under nuclear control. Our results show that for species 4 which is incompatible with species 1 and 5, there is a divergence of nucleotide sequences. Therefore, it appears that the mitochondrial genome may play a role in mitochondrial compatibility. The mitochondrial genome may code for proteins that are essential to mitochondrial function, such as membrane assembly. Small or large changes in the poly-nucleotide sequences coding for these proteins or proteins may affect the nuclear-mitochondrial interaction resulting in incompatibility or different degrees of compatibility.

ACKNOWLEDGMENTS

The work reported here was supported by Grant BMS 75-11319 from the National Science Foundation and by Public Health Service Grant GM 21948 from the National Institute of General Medical Science.

REFERENCES

Adoutte, A. (1977) Ph.D. Thesis, University of Paris, France.

Beale, G. H. & Knowles, J. K. C. (1976) Interspecies transfer of mitochondria in *Paramecium aurelia*. *Molec. Gen. Genet.* 143, 197–201.

Bell, G. I., De Gennaro, L. J., Gelford, D. H., Bishop, R. J., Valenzuela, P. & Rutter, W. J. (1977) Ribosomal RNA genes of *Saccharomyces cerevisiae*. I. Physical map of the repeating unit and location of the regions coding for 5s, 5.8s, 18s and 25s ribosomal RNAs *J. Biol. Chem.* 252, 8118–8125.

Bernardi, G., Prunell, A., Fentz, G., Kopecka, H. & Strauss, F. (1976). In: *The Genetic Function of Mitochondrial DNA*, eds. Saccone, D. & Kroon, A. M., pp. 185–198. North-Holland, Amsterdam.

Bukhari, A. I., Froshauer, S. & Botchan, M. (1976) The ends of bacteriophage Mu DNA. *Nature* 264, 580–583.

Davies, M. B. (1972a) Labeling of DNA with [125]I. *Carneg. Instit. Yearbook,* 1972, 217–221.

Dawid, I. B. (1972b) Evolution of mitochondrial DNA sequences in *Xenopus. Develop. Biol.* 29, 139–151.

Dawid, I. B., Klukos, C. K., Obi, S., Ramires, J. L. & Upholt, W. B. (1976) in: *The Genetic Function of Mitochondrial DNA*, eds. Saccone, C. & Kroon, A. M., pp. 3–13. North Holland, Amsterdam.

Getz, M. J., Attenburg, L. C. & Saunders, G. F. (1972) The uses of RNA labeled *in vitro* with Iodine 125 in molecular hybridization experiments. *Biochim. Biophys. Acta* 287, 485–494.

Goddard, J. M. & Cummings, D. J. (1975) Structure and replication of Mitochondrial DNA from *Paramecium aurelia. J. Mol. Biol.* 97, 593–609.

Goddard, J. M. & Cummings, D. J. (1977) Mitochondrial DNA replication in *Paramecium aurelia*. Cross linking at the initiation end. *J. Mol. Biol.* 109, 327–344.

Green, P. J., Betoch, M. C., Goodman, H. M. & Boyer, H. W. (1974) In: *Methods in Molecular Biology,* ed. Wickner, R. B., Vol. 7, pp. 87–105, Dekker, New York.

Klukos, C. K. & Dawid, I. B. (1976) Characterization and mapping of mitochondrial ribosomal RNA and mitochondrial DNA in *Drosophila melanogaster. Cell* 9, 615–625.

Knowles, J. (1973) Ph.D. Thesis. University of Edinburgh, Scotland.

Kroon, A. M., Pepe, G., Bokker, H., Holtrop, M., Bollen, J. E., Van Bruggen, E. F. J., Contatore, P., Terpstra, P. & Saccone, C. (1977) The restriction fragment map of rat-liver mitochondrial DNA. A reconsideration. *Biochim. Biophys. Acta* 478, 128–145.

Maki, R. A. & Cummings, D. J. (1977) Characterization of mitochondrial DNA from *Paramecium aurelia* with Eco R1 and Hae II restriction endonucleases. *Plasmid* 1, 106–114.

Maki, R. A. & Cummings, D. J. (1978) Cleavage of species 1 mitochondrial DNA from *Paramecium aurelia* with the restriction endonuclease Eco R1. *Microbiology,* ed. Schlesinger, D., pp.119–120. Washington.

Ojala, D. & Attardi, G. (1977) A detailed physical map of Hela cell mitochondrial DNA and its alignment with the positions of known genetic markers. *Plasmid* 1, 78–105.

Sanders, J. P. M., Heyting, C. & Borst, P. (1975) The organization of genes in yeast mitochondrial DNA. I. The genes for large and small ribosomal RNA are far apart. *Biochim. Biophys. Res. Comm.* 65, 699–707.

Southern, E. M. (1975) Detection of specific sequences among DNA fragments separated by gel electrophoresis. *J. Mol. Biol.* 98, 503–517.

Tait, A. & Knowles, J. K. C. (1977) Characterization of mitochondrial and cytoplasmic ribosomes from *Paramecium aurelia. J. Cell Biol.* 73, 139–148.

Terpstra, P., Holtrop, M. & Kroon, A. M. (1976) In: *The Genetic Function of Mitochondrial DNA,* eds. Saccone, C. & Kroon, A. M., pp. 111–118. North Holland, Amsterdam.

Upholt, W. B. & Dawid, I. B. (1977) Mapping of mitochondrial DNA of individual sheep and goats: Rapid evolution in the D loop region. *Cell* 11, 571–583.

DISCUSSION

BORST: You suggest that in an interspecific transfer the mitochondria do not multiply in some cases because mitochondrial DNA cannot be recognized by the imported enzymes from the heterologous nucleus which are required for mitochondrial DNA replication. That is only one possibility, of course. The mitochondria and the nuclear system interact in the biosynthesis of several mitochondrial membrane protein complexes, so one could also envisage incompatibilities in this assembly process, in some nucleus-mitochondrion combinations.

CUMMINGS: That is correct.

BORST: A second point I might mention is that in *Tetrehymena* mtDNA – like in yeast mtDNA – the genes for the two ribosomal subunits are not adjacent. The gene for the large ribosomal subunit is subterminal in a duplication inversion, so there are two copies of that, one at both ends; the gene for the small subunit is more to the middle and is not duplicated (Goldbach *et al.* 1978).

CUMMINGS: What happens in the *Tetrahymena* that have a shorter duplication inversion?

BORST: I do not know, but I should add that we also do not know whether both genes are used in strains which appear to have two complete copies of the rRNA genes.

Goldbach, R. W., Borst, P., Bollen-de Boer, J. E. & Van Bruggen, E. F. J. (1978) *Biochem. Biophys. Acta* 521, 169–186.

Mitochondrial DNA from *Podospora Anserina* and the Occurrence of Multimeric Circular DNA in Senescent Cultures

Donald J. Cummings, Leon Belcour & Claude Grandchamp.

INTRODUCTION

Podospora anserina and other fungi exhibit vegetative death or senescence (Rizet 1953, Marcou 1961). Each vegetative culture of *Podospora* has a limited life span characterized by a period of active growth, (incubation distance, ID), transformation to a senescent state, followed by cessation of growth or death (Fig. 1). The life span, transformation rate, incubation distance and median length of growth (MLG) are specific for races of different geographic origin. Several investigators have shown that senescence is maternally inherited in both inter- and intraracial crosses and that a transmissible factor appears to be involved (Marcou 1961, Marcou & Schecroun 1959, Smith & Rubenstein 1973). The involvement of mitochondria is the most plausible mechanism for these observations and this has been corroborated by work with inhibitors of mitochondrial function (Tudzynski & Esser 1977) and with mitochondrial mutants (Belcour & Begel 1978). Certain properties of senescence such as cytochrome spectra and lifespan led Belcour & Begel (1978) to suggest that in some respects, senescence in *Podospora* resembles the rho^--mutation in yeast, *S. cerevisiae*. Genetic studies, electron microscopic, renaturation and density analysis have shown that large deletions can occur in rho^- mitochondrial DNA, resulting in a DNA population consisting of a multimeric set of circular molecules (Locker *et al.* 1974, Faye *et al.* 1973, Lazowska *et al.* 1974, Lazowska

Centre de Genetique Moleculaire du C.N.R.S., Gif-sur-Yvette, France.

SPECIFIC EUKARYOTIC GENES, Alfred Benzon Symposium 13, Munksgaard 1979

& Slonimski 1976). These properties allow us to further test the similarities between senescence in *Podospora* and *rho*⁻-mutations in yeast.

MATERIALS

Podospora anserina, races A and s, were grown in corn meal extract liquid medium, supplemented with yeast extract (Belcour & Begel 1977). All cultures, crosses, etc., were performed at 27° C. Senescent cultures were maintained and transferred on corn meal extract-agar plates grown at 30° C without illumination. When senescence was evidenced by pigmentation changes in the mycelium and cessation of growth, aliquots were taken for inoculation of liquid medium.

Mitochondrial DNA was prepared either by sand grinding of mycelia, at 0° C or by extraction of purified mitochondria.

Mitochondrial DNA was separated from nuclear DNA by DAPI CsCl density gradients. Williamson & Fennell (1975) showed that diamidino-2-phenylindole (DAPI) enhanced the separation of yeast nuclear and mitochondrial DNA. For *Podospora*, the two DNAs were separated by 13–15 mm which readily allowed their separation as well as permitted us to examine for other density species. Aurintricarboxylic acid (ATA) was present throughout to protect against nucleases (Hallick *et al.* 1977).

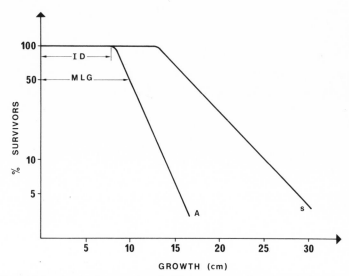

Fig. 1. Lifespan determination for races A and s. The percentage of survivors is plotted as a function of the distance grown in centimeters. ID-incubation distance; MLG-median length of growth.

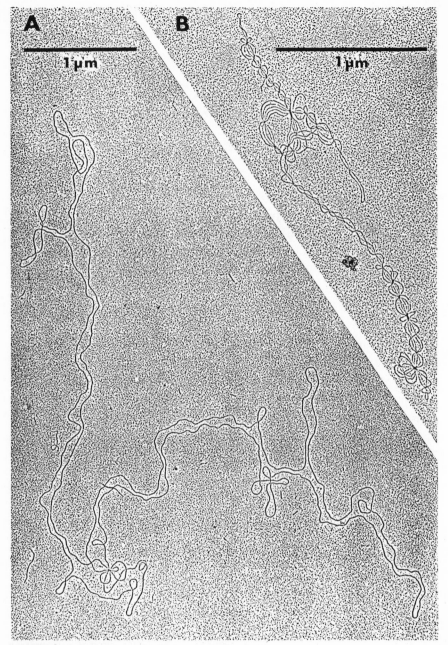

Fig. 2. Electronmicrograph of Mt DNA prepared from race s. A) circular molecule of 32 μm contour length; B) a highly organized molecule of about 30 μm.

Table I

Contour length of circular mitochondrial DNA

Race A	Race s
31.0	29.4
33.6	32.8
33.8	31.8
31.6	29.9
32.1	31.1
33.2	29.0
32.1	32.8
32.4	32.1
33.1	30.4

RESULTS

Mitochondrial DNA from young cultures was examined in the electron microscope using a modified Kleinschmidt technique (Inman & Schnos 1970). For both races A and s, about 1% of the DNA isolated with sand grinding and 2–4% of the DNA isolated from purified mitochondria consisted of circular molecules, 31 μm in contour length (Fig. 2). Table I lists the measurements taken for several molecules. These molecules are the longest mitochondrial molecules ever observed, with the possible exception of mitochondrial DNA from *Pisum sativum* (Kolodner & Tewari 1977). The density of these molecules in CsCl was 1.694 g/cm^3, compared with 1.713 g/cm^3 for nuclear DNA. No other density species or circular molecules of DNA were detected.

The contour length of mitochondrial DNA from senescent cultures of either races s or A was strikingly different. About 10 – 11% of the DNA molecules consisted of a multimeric set of circular molecules, with a monomer repeat unit of 0.89 μm. Fig. 3 is an electronmicrograph illustrating the size and appearance of these molecules. Most of the molecules were in the 1.8 and 2.7 μm classes. Out of about 200 molecules in five different experiments only 1 measured greater than 20 μm.

Analysis in the ultracentrifuge indicated that there were two density species of mitochondrial DNA from senescent cultures. The majority (75–90%) had the expected density of 1.694 g/cm^3 but the remaining DNA had a density of 1.699 g/cm^3. We were able to separate these two density species in a second DAPI-CsCl density gradient and examined them in the electron microscope. The normal density DNA contained less than 2% circular molecules whereas the

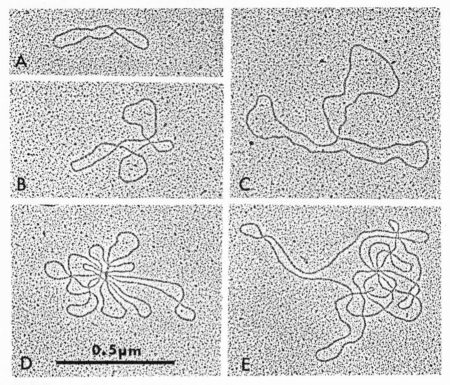

Fig. 3. Electronmicrographs of Mt DNA obtained from senescent race s. A) 0.89 μm; B) 1.77 μm; C) 2.92 μm; D) 4.45 μm; E) 5.85 μm.

heavy density DNA contained about 25% circular molecules with the expected multimeric size distribution.

Examination of these two DNAs by restriction endonucleases revealed that whereas mitochondrial DNA from young cultures had 16 Eco R1 sites, normal density DNA from senescent cultures had only 10. More significantly, the heavy DNA had no Eco R1 sites. Analysis with the restriction enzyme Hae III showed that normal DNA from young mycelia had about 40 sites but heavy DNA from senescent cultures had just one site, yielding a fragment of about 2500 bp (Fig. 4). This corresponded with the 2700 bp measured by electron microscopy for the monomeric unit. We concluded that the multimeric set of circular molecules observed in senescent cultures consisted of a tandemly repeated fragment of DNA.

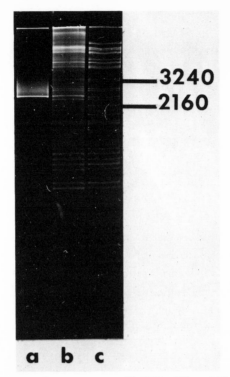

Fig. 4. Hae III digestion patterns for race s senescent Mt DNA. a) Heavy DNA; b) Light DNA; and c) race s young DNA included for comparison. Note that the heavy Mt DNA isolated from senescent cultures gave only one band, at about 2500 bp (see bp markers for comparison).

DISCUSSION

These results with Mt DNA isolated from senescent cultures of *Podospora anserina* were quite striking. Earlier, we discussed the similarities of senescence with the *rho⁻* mutation in yeast. This mutation leads to large-scale deletions in Mt DNA causing density shifts in the DNA and the generation of a multimeric set of tandemly repeating monomer units. Each independently derived *rho⁻* clone exhibited characteristic lengths of the monomeric repeat unit as well as density shifts in the DNA. We observed a density shift to a new population of Mt DNA and the occurrence of a multimeric set of circular molecules ranging in size from 0.89 μm to about 30 μm, with most in the lower size classes. It should be emphasized that the amount of these circular molecules was enhanced in DNA isolated from purified mitochondria. The results with endonuclease digestion indicate that this multimeric set of molecules is a tandemly repeated unit of about 2600 bp. The amplification of this fragment as a tandemly repeating structure raises interesting questions about its mechanism for replication. Although a rolling circle (Gilbert & Dressler 1968) is a possibility, for rho^- mutants Lazowska & Slonimski (1977) suggested that there are specific sites similar to transposable elements (Nevers & Saedler 1977) located at the covalent junctions of repetitions in the repeated units, and that recombination between these sites gives rise to the size distribution of the tandem repeats observed. A tandem repeat of a hexanucleotide has recently been found (Blackburn & Gall 1978) at the termini for nuclear ribosomal RNA genes in *Tetrahymena*. Whether this model is correct for rho^- mutants and whether it applies to the results obtained here is not known. Which genes this 2600 bp fragment contains in the *Podospora* mitochondrial genome is also not known. Since these tandemly repeated circles appear to be self-replicating, they must contain sequences essential for DNA replication. Another possibility may involve genes for ribosomal or transfer RNA since defects here would have a deleterious effect on continued protein synthesis which could lead to arrest of growth. Molecular hybridization studies will provide information on this point.

ACKNOWLEDGMENT

Donald J. Cummings is a Josiah Macy, Jr. Foundation Faculty Scholar whose permanent address is Department of Microbiology and Immunology, University of Colorado Medical Center, Denver Colorado 80262, U.S.A.

REFERENCES

Belcour, L. & Begel, O. (1977) Mitochondrial genes in *Podospora anserina*. Recombination and linkage. *Molec. Gen. Genet.* 153, 11–21.

Belcour, L. & Begel, O. (1978) Lethal mitochondrial genotypes in *Podospora anserina*. A model for senescence. *Molec. Gen. Genet.* In press.

Blackburn, E. H. & Gall, J. G. (1978) A tandemly repeated sequence at the termini of the extrachromosomal ribosomal RNA genes in *Titrahymena*. *J. Mol. Biol.* 120, 33–53.

Faye, G., Fukuhara, H., Grandchamp, C., Lazowska, J., Michel, F., Casey, J., Getz, G. S., Locker, J., Rabinowitz, M., Bolotin-Fukuhara, M., Coen, D., Deutsch, J., Dujon, B., Netter, P. & Slonimski, P. P. (1973) Mitochondrial nucleic acids in the petite colonie mutants: deletions and repetitions of genes. *Biochim.* 55, 779–792.

Gilbert, W. & Dressler, D. (1968) DNA replication: The rolling circle. *Cold Spring Harb. Symp. Quant. Biol.* 33, 473–484.

Hallick, R. B., Chelm, B. K., Gray, P. W. & Orozco, E. M. Jr. (1977). Use of aurintricarboxylic acid as an inhibitor of nucleases during nucleic acid isolation. *Nuc. Acids Res.* 4, 3055–3064.

Inman, R. B. & Schnös, M. (1970) Partial denaturation of thymine and 5-bromouracil-containing DNA in alkali. *J. Mol. Biol.* 49, 93–98.

Kolodner, R. & Tewari, K. K. (1972) Circular mitochondrial DNA (70×10^6 daltons) from pear leaves. *Fed. Proc.* 31, 876.

Lazowska, J., Michel, F., Faye, G., Fukuhara, H. & Slonimski, P. P. (1974) Physical and genetic organization of petite and grand yeast mitochondrial DNA. II. DNA-DNA hybridization studies and buoyant density determinations. *J. Mol. Biol.* 85, 393–410.

Lazowska, J. & Slonimski, P. P. (1976) Electron microscopy analysis of circular repetitive mitochondrial DNA molecules from genetically characterized Rho⁻ mutants of *Saccharomyces cerevisiae. Molec. Gen. Genet.* 146, 61–78.

Lazowska, J. & Slonimski, P. P. (1977) In: *Genetics and Biogenesis of Mitochondria,* ed. Bandlow, W., Schwegen, R. J., Wolf, K. & Kaudewitz, F. pp. 39–52. Walter de Gruyter, Berlin.

Locker, J., Rabinowitz, M. & Getz, G. S. Electron microscopic and renaturation kinetic analysis of mitochondrial DNA of cytoplasmic petite mutants of *Saccharomyces cerevisiae. J. Mol. Biol.* 88, 489–507.

Marcou, D. (1961) Notion de longévité et nature cytoplasmique du determinant de la senescence chez quelques champignons. *Ann. Sci. Natur. Botan.* II, 653–764.

Marcou, D. & Schecroun, J. (1959) La senescence chez *Podospora anserina* pourrait être dues à des particules cytoplasmiques infectantes. *C. R. Acad. Sci.* (Paris) 248, 280–283.

Nevers, N. & Saedler, H. (1977) Transposable genetic elements as agents of gene instability and chromosomal rearrangements. *Nature* 268, 109–115.

Rizet, G. (1953) Sur la longévité des souches de *Podospora anserina. C. R. Acad. Sci.* (Paris) 237, 838–840.

Smith, J. R. & Rubenstein, I. (1973) Cytoplasmic inheritance of the timing of senescence in *Podospora anserina. J. Gen. Microbiol.* 767, 297–304.

Tudzynski, P. & Esser, K. (1977) Inhibitors of mitochondrial function present senescence in the ascomycete *Podospora anserina. Molec. Gen. Genet.* 153, 111–113.

Williamson, D. H. & Fennel, D. J. (1975) In: *Methods in Cell Biology,* ed. Prescott, D. M. pp. 335–351. Academic Press, New York.

DISCUSSION

DAWID: How do you rejuvenate senescent cultures?

CUMMINGS: I have not investigated that, but Marcou showed years ago that you can rejuvenate the senescent culture simply by storing it in the refrigerator for a few months.

HOGNESS: Was that in the sense of nuclear regeneration?

CUMMINGS: Well as you know, it is very difficult to rule out the role of the nucleus.

HOGNESS: No, but the obvious test would be to do something to knock out the whole mitochondrial system, and then have an event which triggered regeneration and ask if the nuclear genes participated.

CUMMINGS: That has not been done. So far most of what was done by Marcou and Rizet, was done 20 years ago. I might say that their interpretation of the data has recently been taken up by Holliday in a so-called commitment theory of senescense of tissue culture cells; and if you looked at his curves side by side with what Rizet and Marcou did 20 years ago, the similarity is remarkable. Holiday thinks that the same sort of kinetic events occurs in tissue culture cells as occurs here, so perhaps you could ask your question in tissue culture cells as well.

SCHAFFNER: Did you also study this rejuvenation by storing the cells in the refrigerator and then analyzing if the original mitochondrial DNA is restored?

CUMMINGS: We did exactly that experiment, and the DNA was normal. It did not have these small circles.

SCHAFFNER: If I understood it correctly, you showed that *Eco*RI treatment of senescent mitochondrial DNA caused a few fragments to disappear.

CUMMINGS: In the so-called normal density DNA, I would interpret that as meaning that normal DNA density was perhaps on its way to being just that repeated fragment.

SCHAFFNER: I do not see an obvious way how one could from such repeated sequences reproduce the original mitochondrial DNA.

CUMMINGS: In all the experiments we never get more than 25% of the DNA being the heavy DNA; there always appears to be a majority amount of the so-called normal density DNA. In the regeneration experiment you can imagine that there is a mixture, even at the death stage, of normal density and heavy density. And it is the normal density, even a small fraction, that has all the *Eco*RI sites in it, i.e. regenerating. I am not at all saying it is just like in the petite mutants of yeasts; there, you lose the DNA and once it is gone, you cannot get back the whole genome.

Organization and Function of Kinetoplast DNA

B. A. Newton

INTRODUCTION

Trypanosomes have the distinction of being the organisms in which extra nuclear DNA was first detected. Bresslau & Scremin (1924) showed that the kinetoplast, an organelle situated close to the base of the flagellum of these protozoa, contains Feulgen-positive material; earlier Shipley (1916) had pointed out that this organelle, like mitochondria, is stained by Janus green. In some species of trypanosomes it was shown that the kinetoplast can be permanently eliminated by growth in the presence of dyes such as acriflavine (Werbitzki 1910, Gonder 1912), a phenomenon not observed in other organisms until the classical studies of Ephrussi *et al.* (1949) on respiratory-deficient mutants of *Saccharomyces cerevisiae*. Thus protozoologists were aware of the existence of extranuclear DNA, and had considered the possibility that it may be associated with mitochondrial function, well over 30 years before these concepts became acceptable to biochemists. However, it was not until the late 1950s that our present ideas about kinetoplast structure began to form. Further evidence for the presence of DNA in kinetoplasts was obtained by ^{3}H-thymidine incorporation and DNAase digestion (Cosgrove & Anderson 1954, Horne & Newton 1958) and electron microscopy showed it to be in the form of a fibrillar mass, frequently shaped as a concave disc (Horne & Newton 1958, Ris 1962), occupying a relatively small area of the single, branched mitochondrion which characterizes these unicellular flagellates (Pitelka 1961, Steinert 1964, Vickerman 1965). Kinetoplast DNA (kDNA) can be separated from nuclear DNA as a

Medical Research Council Biochemical Parasitology Unit, The Molteno Institute of Cambridge, Cambridge CB2 3EE, England.

SPECIFIC EUKARYOTIC GENES, Alfred Benzon Symposium 13, Munksgaard 1979

rapidly banding fraction by density gradient centrifugation of detergent lysed cells in cesium chloride (Du Buy *et al.* 1965) and Riou & Paoletti (1967) were the first to show that kDNA isolated in this way is in the form of small circular molecules (minicircles) which are often catenated to form dimers, trimers or oligomers. Work in a number of laboratories subsequently established that while minicircles (free or catenated) are a general feature of purified kDNA, the buoyant density, the contour length of individual minicircles and the amount of kDNA per cell vary considerably from species to species. Buoyant density measurements (Newton & Burnett 1972) indicate that the base composition of kDNA may range from 29–43% G+C; minicircles with contour lengths of 0.22 to 0.80 μm have been observed and cells may contain 0.7×10^{-14} to 4.0×10^{-14} g kDNA (corresponding to a 5–25% of total cell DNA) depending upon the species (reviewed: Simpson 1972, Borst 1976). On the basis of these measurements a single kinetoplast would contain $1-3 \times 10^4$ minicircles if all the DNA is in this form, however, evidence for the presence of some larger molecules in purified kDNA has been obtained by electron microscopy (Riou & Delain 1969, Renger & Wolstenholme 1970, Laurent & Steinert 1970). Clearly these findings raise many questions: How are the minicircles organized in the kinetoplast? How do they replicate and how does the kinetoplast divide? Do the minicircles contain genetic information which is transcribed and translated? What is the nature of the larger molecules? Are they an integral part of kDNA or contaminants? We can not answer all these questions, but since 1970 considerable progress has been made and in this paper some ideas about kinetoplast structure and function will be discussed in the light of recent research from a number of laboratories.

MOLECULAR ORGANISATION OF KINETOPLAST *DNA*

The finding of Du Buy *et al.* (1965) that kDNA behaves in an abnormal way in cesium chloride gradients was eventually explained by the work of Steinert and his collaborators (Laurent *et al.* 1971) who showed that detergent lysis of cells followed by phenol extraction yields large networks of DNA, each of which probably represents the total kDNA of a single cell (Fig. 1). Recent information about the molecular organisation of kDNA has come mainly from electron microscopy of such isolated networks but early ideas about the arrangement of minicircles within the kinetoplast were based on the study of thin sections of whole organisms.

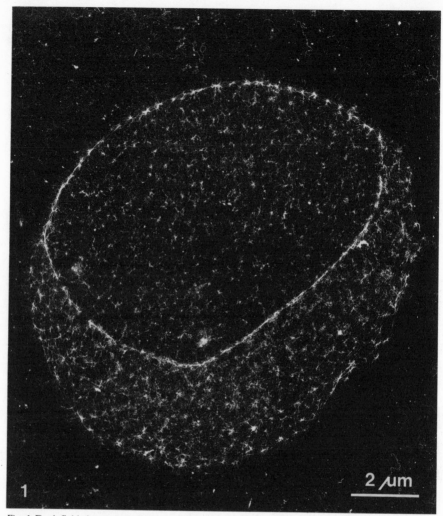

Fig. 1. Dark field electron micrograph of *Trypanosoma brucei* kDNA network isolated according to Laurent *et al.* (1971) and further purified by phenol extraction and buoyant density centrifugation in Cs Cl-ethidium bromide gradients. Marker DNA=PM2. [Preparation by Dr. D. C. Barker and electronmicrographs by Angela Wisby, Medical Research Council Biochemical Parasitology Unit, The Molteno Institute, University of Cambridge.]

Delain & Riou (1969) pointed out that the thickness of the kDNA disc seen in longitudinal sections of *Trypanosoma cruzi* corresponds to half the contour length of a minicircle. They suggested that the double-banded appearance of kDNA in the sections may result from minicircles, twisted to form a figure eight, being packed in ordered layers *in vivo*. However, the arrangement of kDNA fibrils in the kinetoplast of *T. cruzi* is not typical of other species and its significance remains unclear. Examination of purified networks by conventional and dark field electron microscopy has led to the conclusion that they are formed by catenation of minicircles: there is no evidence that RNA or protein forms part of the network structure. Networks are frequently seen in the form of 'baskets' or 'fishnets' due, perhaps, to the fact that the edge of networks may not be able to expand as much as the interior when spread on EM grids (Borst & Hoeijmakers 1978). Rosettes of minicircles are a common feature of such preparations, being most readily seen at the edge of networks where their centers appear regularly spaced at a distance corresponding to approximately half the circumference of a minicircle. Wolstenholme *et al.* (1974) have proposed that these rosettes are a basic structural unit of kDNA, formed, in the case of *Crithidia acanthocephali* kDNA, of 33 minicircles held together in a group by topological interlocking of each circle with a large number of other circles. Rosettes of minicircles have been isolated from sonicated networks of *Crithidia* but they are not always clearly visible in network preparations: Borst & Hoeijmakers (1978) failed to observe any rosettes in *Crithidia* networks released from cells by gentle lysis and fixed for electron microscopy without further purification and concluded that they are an artifact produced by stretching.

In support of electron microscope studies (Riou & Delain 1969, Renger & Wolstenholme 1970, Laurent & Steinert 1970) which suggested the kDNA may contain molecules larger than minicircles, Wesley & Simpson (1973) obtained evidence of a minor complex component in DNA-DNA renaturation experiments and in 1976 Steinert & Van Assel produced conclusive evidence for the presence of large circular molecules (maxicircles) with a contour length of 11.3 μm in purified kDNA from *Crithidia luciliae*. Maxicircles ranging from 2.7 to 12.6 μm in circumference have been seen in kDNA isolated from several species (Kleisen & Borst 1975, Brack *et al.* 1976) and Kleisen *et al.* (1976b) believe them to be an integral component of kDNA networks, being attached by catenation: they estimate that there are ca. 50 maxicircles per network in *Crithidia*. The edge loops and internal strands of varying length often seen in isolated networks can be selectively digested with certain restriction endonucleases or S$_1$ DNAase, and are believed to be maxicircles *in situ* (Weislogel *et al.* 1977, Fairlamb *et al.* 1978). DNA molecules considerably larger than maxicircles may become associated with kDNA during isolation, causing it to band in cesium chloride gradients at a density intermediate between kDNA and nuclear DNA (Nichols & Cross 1976,

Steinert *et al.* 1976); these molecules are generally believed to be of nuclear origin.

REPLICATION OF KINETOPLAST DNA

During the cell cycle of kinetoplastid flagellates the kDNA disc increases in width and appears to divide by transverse constriction (Brack 1968, Sooksri *et al.* 1972). This process is closely co-ordinated with division of the basal body and, unlike mitochondrial DNA of other cells, synthesis of kDNA, as judged by ^{3}H-thymidine incorporation, appears to be temporarily linked to nuclear DNA synthesis (Cosgrove & Skeen 1970) but how the DNA of this complex structure replicates and segregates is still largely a matter for speculation.

Double-branched circular molecules resembling replicating forms of the type proposed by Cairns (1963) have been observed occasionally in kDNA preparations from *T. cruzi,* and their incidence is increased by treatment of cells with Berenil (Brack *et al.* 1972a, b), a drug which selectively inhibits kDNA synthesis (Newton 1974). While there is no direct evidence that these branched molecules are replicative forms, their presence is consistent with semi-conservative DNA replication and support for such a mechanism is provided by the appearance of a single 'half-heavy' kDNA species after growth for one generation in the presence of 5-bromodeoxyuridine (BUdR) (Newton 1967). However, in other density shift experiments using BUdR (Simpson *et al.* 1974) or D_2O (Manning & Wolstenholme 1976) analysis of minicircles rather than networks has not given such clear results; DNAs with a range of buoyant densities have been observed and it has been suggested that this may be due to extensive recombination. These results make it impossible to conclude that all minicircles replicate, it may be that only a few do so and that the newly synthesized kDNA becomes distributed throughout the network by recombination. Autoradiographs of isolated networks labeled by very short pulses of ^{3}H-thymidine show radioactivity at two sites, 180° apart, on the edge of networks, longer pulses lead to labeling of the entire edge, and after the addition of excess unlabeled thymidine radioactivity appears to move from the periphery to the center of networks (Simpson *et al.* 1974), suggesting that there may be only two replication sites per network, perhaps at points of membrane attachment. If distribution of newly synthesized DNA throughout the network does occur by recombination, this could be facilitated by the presence of multiple nicks in minicircles. Evidence for nicked circles in networks and for ^{3}H-thymidine being predominantly in such open circles after pulse-labeling has now been obtained (Simpson *et al.* 1974, Englund *et al.* 1977) and it has been suggested that a cyclical process of nicking and ligation of minicircles is associated with kDNA replication and network cleavage in *C. fasciculata* (Englund 1978). kDNA networks of this organism can be separated into three forms by centrifugation in cesium chloride/propidium diiodide gradients: form I networks (accounting for ca. 50% of the kDNA of log phase cells) band at high density and contain ca. 5000 covalently closed minicircles; form II networks (ca. 20% of total) band at a lower density and contain about 11,000 minicircles, the majority of which appear to be nicked or gapped; the remaining 30% of the kDNA contains networks of intermediate molecular size and bands in a broad zone between form I and form II peaks: these are believed to be replicating networks. Networks from stationary phase cells are all in form I. Pulse-labeling experiments show that ^{3}H-thymidine is preferentially incorporated into the intermediate band, but after a 30-min cold chase radioactivity is found primarily in form II and after a 60-min chase in form I networks. Centrifugation of pulse-labeled replicating and form II networks in an alkaline sucrose gradient results in virtually all the radioactivity appearing in fragments smaller than minicircles suggesting that these networks contain molecules with multiple nicks or alkali-labile bonds. From these results Englund (1978) concludes that prior to replication networks contain covalently closed circles, then, in S phase, minicircles at the periphery of the network replicate, probably at just two sites 180° apart (Simpson & Simpson 1976) and the progeny remain nicked. As synthesis proceeds replicating networks increase in size and the peripheral zone of nicked minicircles increases until it has doubled in size and all the minicircles are nicked (form II). Later, form II networks constrict transversely and covalent closure of all minicircles and cleavage occurs to give two form I progeny. Intermediates in these final steps have not been detected but it is suggested that ligation and cleavage occur at about the same time. At present there is no information about the replication of maxicircles during this cycle and we know nothing about the way form II networks segregate into two equal-sized progeny.

GENETIC COMPLEXITY AND FUNCTION OF KINETOPLAST DNA

A number of problems are posed by the supposition that kDNA has the same genetic function as mitochondrial DNA of other organisms. If minicircles carry information which can be transcribed and translated, a single molecule (equivalent to $1-3 \times 10^3$ base pairs, depending upon species of origin) could code only for two or three proteins, thus the information content is about one-tenth that of mammalian mitochondrial DNA. A question which must be answered before we can understand the function of kDNA is therefore: Are all minicircles identical? Early experiments suggested that they may be: no variation has been detected in the size of isolated minicircles by electron microscopy and studies of renaturation kinetics and finger print analyses (Wesley & Simpson 1973) led to the conclusion that kDNA from *Leishmania tarentolae* contains only one or possibly two classes of minicircles in terms of base sequence. However, in apparent contradiction of these results, restriction enzyme analysis has provided evidence of sequence heterogeneity in kDNA from recently cloned strains of several species of flagellates (Kleisen & Borst 1975, Riou *et al.* 1975, Brack *et al.* 1976). Enzymes which cut all minicircles of *Crithidia luciliae* networks yield a number of fragments, the combined molecular weights of which far exceed that of a single minicircle; small differences (ca. 4%) in minicircle size have also been detected by prolonged electrophoresis in agarose gels (Kleisen *et al.* 1976a). These results have been taken as evidence for at least 13 different minicircle sequence classes, but an exact correlation between size and complexity remains to be established and the situation is clouded by discrepancies between results of restriction enzyme and renaturation analysis. For example, *T. brucei* kDNA renatures very slowly (Steinert *et al.* 1976) suggesting extensive sequence heterogeneity but endonucleases which cleave all minicircles yield only a small number of fragments (unpublished results: P. Borst, Amsterdam; D. C. Barker, Cambridge). Simpson & Hyman (1976) have suggested three possible interpretations of the restriction enzyme data: (1) there are minor classes of minicircles which differ in base sequence from the majority, (2) all minicircles have identical base sequences but a proportion have blocked or modified restriction sites, (3) all minicircles contain repetitous sequences plus regions of sequence heterogeneity. This third possibility would increase the probability of recombination (Manning & Wolstenholme 1976), sequence diversity perhaps being introduced by unequal crossingover (Kleisen *et al.* 1976a). However our understanding of minicircle complexity will remain unclear until the discrepancies between renaturation and restriction enzyme analysis are explained.

Following the discovery of maxicircles in kDNA preparations, workers in several laboratories have attempted to determine their complexity. Endonuclease Pst I releases linear molecules of maxicircle size from networks and

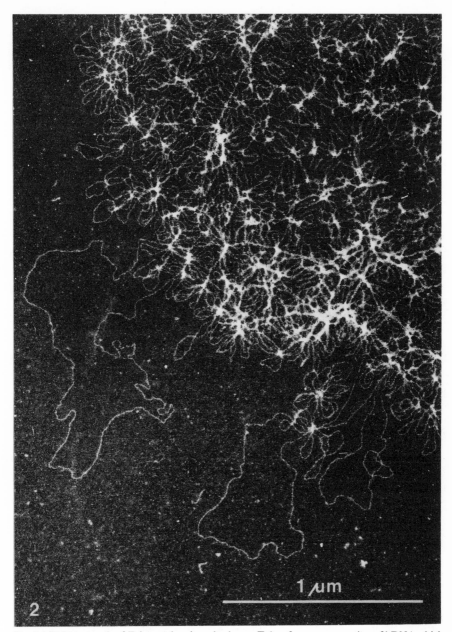

Fig. 2. kDNA network of *T. brucei* showing edge loops. Taken from a preparation of kDNA which did not yield fragments larger than minicircles after restriction enzyme digestion. [Dr. D. C. Barker & Angela Wisby: unpublished observations.]

other endonuclease (Hind II & III, Hap II & Eco RI) give rise to DNA fragments larger than minicircle monomers: it has been concluded that these fragments are derived from maxicircles, that heterogeneity or sequence repetition is absent and that their complexity is commensurate with their size (Fairlamb *et al.* 1978, Borst & Hoeijmakers 1978). On the basis of these findings it has been proposed that maxicircles represent the mitochondrial DNA of kinetoplast flagellates. Clearly this is an attractive hypothesis, the size of maxicircles is in the same range as other mitochondrial DNAs and no other candidate for mitochondrial DNA of these organisms has been found. However, the evidence for this proposal is circumstantial and, in the author's opinion, there is not yet unequivocal proof that large molecular weight fragments separated on gels after endonuclease digestion of networks are derived from DNA which, *in vivo*, forms an integral part of the networks: neither is there proof that the edge loops (Fig. 2) frequently seen in electron micrographs of isolated networks represent maxicircles *in situ*. Unpublished observations (D. C. Barker, Cambridge) suggest the DNA fragments larger than minicircle monomers are released only by endonucleases from preparations of *T. brucei* networks which still contain detectable amounts of a satellite which bands, in cesium chloride gradients, between kinetoplast and nuclear DNA. *T. brucei* networks have been isolated which do not yield fragments larger than minicircles; no additional DNA satellite has been detected in these preparations but electron microscopy clearly shows that they do have edge loops (Fig. 2). These findings make it difficult to accept the conclusion of Fairlamb *et al.* (1978) that edge loops can not be long, tandemly repeated oligomers of minicircles.

If a component of kDNA networks carries information similar to that of other mitochondrial DNAs it should be possible to identify the products of transcription and translation, but progress in this direction has been slow, mainly because intact mitochondria have not yet been isolated from kinetoplastid flagellates. Indirect evidence that kDNA is essential for continued synthesis of mitochondrial respiratory enzymes comes from studies of naturally occurring or drug-induced dyskinetoplastic mutants (reviews: Simpson 1972, Borst & Hoeijmakes 1978). Ribosomes have been visualized in the mitochondrion of *T. brucei* by *in vivo*-labeling of nascent polypeptides in the presence of cycloheximide (Hanas *et al.* 1975) and RNA species believed to represent kinetoplast RNA has been detected (Braly *et al.* 1974, Nichols & Cross 1977). A major advance in this approach has recently been made by Simpson & Simpson (1978); 9S and 12S RNA has been isolated from mitochondrial fractions of

Leishmania tarentolae, in vivo synthesis of both these RNAs (which contain ca. 80% A+U) is inhibited by ethidium bromide and rifampin and both hybridize selectively with restriction fragments from kDNA networks which are larger than minicircle monomers, suggesting that they may have been transcribed from maxicircles.

The gene product, if any, from minicircle DNA remains unknown and minicircle function continues to be a matter for speculation. Borst & Hoeijmakers (1978) argue strongly against a conventional genetic function for this DNA and Steinert *et al.* (1976) have suggested that the minicircle network may have a structural role in cell division. The basal body of the flagellum and the kinetoplast remain closely associated throughout the developmental cycle of kinetoplastid flagellates; Steinert *et al.* (1976) have speculated that the basal body may be involved in segregation of the single mitochondrion in a manner similar to a centriole in chromosome segregation and that the minicircle network may function like a centromere in higher eukaryotes. An argument in favor of minicircles having a function which does not entail transcription stems from hybridization experiments in which complementary RNA, made on kDNA from several species of flagellates' was used to compare kDNA sequences by cytological hybridization (Steinert *et al.* 1973): no cross-hybridization was detected between species of different genera and only partial (ca. 20%) cross-hybridization occurred between closely related species. Hybridization in these experiments would detect only the major component of kDNA (i.e. minicircle DNA) so the results suggest that there is little or no evolutionary conservation of sequences in these molecules, whereas preliminary restriction enzyme (Fairlamb *et al.* 1978) and hybridization (Simpson & Simpson 1978) data implies that sequence evolution in maxicircles may be much slower.

MITOCHONDRIAL FUNCTION AND KINOPLAST DNA
AMPLIFICATION IN *TRYPANOSOMA BRUCEI SSPP*

Unlike the majority of kinetoplastid flagellates *T. brucei* sspp, are characterized by an alternating proliferation and regression of mitochondrial structures during their developmental cycle. In blood forms from the vertebrate host, synthesis of a functional respiratory chain is suppressed but on transfer to the insect vector or *in vitro* culture at 25°, mitochondrial enzymes become fully functional (review: Vickerman & Preston 1976). This unique 'respiratory switch' poses many problems; we have no knowledge of mechanisms involved in its control but dyskinetoplastic mutants, which are unable to develop in the insect vector or in culture, are unable to make functional mitochondria suggesting that kDNA may play some role in the process. Considering this possibility it can be asked whether changes occur in the nature or amount of kDNA in different developmental forms of *T. brucei*. Newton (1976) has obtained evidence that insect mid-gut and 26°culture forms contain four to eight times more kDNA than blood forms. This amplification is a reversible phenomenon in *T. brucei* and does not occur in species of trypanosomes with mitochondria which do not undergo cyclical proliferation and regression. Current work is attempting to establish whether the proportion of maxi- to minicircles changes during the developmental cycle of *T. brucei* and the factors involved in initiation of amplification are being investigated. It has recently been established that transfer of blood forms to a tissue culture system (RPMI 1640+bovine pulmonary cells) which supports their growth at 37° (Hirumi *et al.* 1977) does not induce kDNA amplification whereas growth at 26° in a similar medium (Brun & Jenni 1977) without tissue culture cells does initiate this process (B. A. Newton & E. N. Lupton, unpublished observations).

These findings raise many new questions about kDNA function and perhaps one of the most intriguing concerns the suggested 'mechanical function' of minicircle DNA (Steinert *et al.* 1976): if over 99% of kDNA in both mid-gut and blood forms of *T. brucei* is in the minicircle network which functions like a centromere, why do the developmental stages of this flagellate which grow in the mid-gut of the insect vector require four to eight times more kDNA than forms growing in the mammalian bloodstream?

REFERENCES

Borst, P. (1976) Properties of kinetoplast DNA. In: *Handbook of Biochemistry and Molecular Biology*, vol. 2, 3rd ed., ed. Fasman, G. D., pp. 375–378. CRC Press, Cleveland, Ohio.

Borst, P., Fairlamb, A. H., Fase-Fowler, F., Hoeijmakers, J. H. J. & Weislogel, P. O. (1976) The structure of kinetoplast DNA. In: *The Genetic Function of Mitochondrial DNA*, ed. Saccone, C. & Kroon, A. M., pp. 59–69. North Holland, Amsterdam.

Borst, P. & Hoeijmakers, J. H. H. (1978) Kinetoplast DNA. *Plasmid* 1. In press.

Brack, C. (1968) Elektronenmikroskopische Untersuchungen zum Lebenszyklus von *Trypanosoma cruzi*. *Acta Tropica* (Basel) 25, 289–356.

Brack, C., Bickle, T. A., Yuan, R., Barker, D. C., Foulkes, M., Newton, B. A. & Jenni, L. (1976) The use of restriction endonuclease for the investigation of kinetoplast DNA. In: *Biochemistry of Parasites and Host-Parasite Relationships*, ed. Van den Bossche, H., pp. 211–218. North Holland, Amsterdam.

Brack, C., Delain, E. & Riou, G. (1972a) Replicating covalently close circular DNA from kinetoplasts of *Trypanosoma cruzi. Proc. Natl. Acad. Sci., USA* 69, 1642–1646.

Brack, C., Delain, E., Riou, G. & Festy, B. (1972b) Molecular organization of the kinetoplast DNA of *Trypanosoma cruzi* treated with Berenil, a DNA intercalating drug. *J. Ultrastruct. Res.* 39, 568–579.

Braly, P., Simpson, L. & Kretzer, F. (1974) Isolation of kinetoplast-mitochondrial complexes from *Leishmania tarentolae. J. Protozool.* 21, 782–790.

Bresslau, E. & Scremin, L. (1924) Die Kerne der Trypanosomen und ihr verhalten zur Nuclearreaktion. *Arch. Protistenk.* 48, 509–515.

Brun, R. & Jenni, L. (1977) A new semi-defined medium for *Trypanosoma brucei* sspp. *Acta Tropica* 34, 21–33.

Cairns, J. (1963) The bacterial chromosome and its manner of replication as seen by autoradiography. *J. Mol. Biol.* 6, 208–213.

Cosgrove, W. B. & Anderson, E. (1954) The kinetoplast of *Crithidia fasciculata. Anat. Rec.* 120, 813–814.

Cosgrove, W. B. & Skeen, M. (1970) The cell cycle in *Crithidia fasciculata. J. Protozool.* 17, 172–177.

Delain, E. & Riou, G. (1969) Ultrastructure du DNA du kinetoplaste de *Trypanosoma cruzi* cultivé *in vitro. Comptes Rendus,* Series D 268, 1225–1227.

Du Buy, H. G., Mattern, C. F. T. & Riley, F. L. (1965) Isolation and characterization of DNA from kinetoplasts of *Leishmania eneriettii. Science* 147, 754–756.

Englund, P. T. (1978) The replication of kinetoplast DNA networks in *Crithidia fasciculata. Cell* 14, 157–168.

Englund, P. T., DiMaio, D. C. & Price, S. S. (1977) A nicked form of kinetoplast DNA in *Leishmania tarentolae. J. Biol. Chem.* 252, 6208–6216.

Ephrussi, B., L'Heritier, P. & Hottinguer, H. (1949) Action de l'acriflavine sur les levures. *Annls Inst. Pasteur* Paris 77, 64–77.

Fairlamb, A. H., Weislogel, P. O., Hoiejmakers, J. H. J. & Borst, P. (1978) Isolation and characterization of kinetoplast DNA from bloodstream form of *Trypanosoma brucei. J. Cell. Biol.* 76, 293–309.

Gonder, R. (1912) Experimentelle studien mit Trypanosomen und Spironemen. *Z. Immun. Forsch. Exp. Ther.* 15, 257–268.

Hanas, J., Linden, G. & Stuart, K. (1975) Mitochondrial and cytoplasmic ribosomes and their activity in blood and culture forms of *Trypanosoma brucei. J. Cell Biol.* 65, 103–111.

Hirumi, H., Doyle, J. J. & Hirumi, K. (1977) African trypanosomes: *in vitro* cultivation of animal-infective *Trypanosoma brucei. Science* 196, 992–994.

Horne, R. W. & Newton, B. A. (1958) Intracellular structures in *Strigomonas oncopelti. Exptl. Cell Res.* 15, 103–111.

Kleisen, C. M. & Borst, P. (1975) Sequence heterogeneity of the minicircles of kinetoplast DNA of *Crithidia luciliae* and evidence for the presence of a component more complex than minicircle DNA in the kinetoplast network. *Biochim. Biophys Acta* 407, 473–478.

Kleisen, C. M., Borst, P. & Weijers, ?. (1976a) The structure of kinetoplast DNA. I. The minicircles of *Crithidia luciliae* are heterogeneous in base sequences. *Europ. J. Biochem.* 64, 141–151.

Kleisen, C. M., Weislogel, P. O., Fonk, K. & Borst, P. (1976b) The structure of kinetoplast DNA. II. Characterization of a novel component of high complexity in the kinetoplast network of *Crithidia luciliae. Europ. J. Biochem.* 64, 153–160.

Laurent, M. & Steinert, M. (1970) Electron microscopy of kinetoplast DNA from *Trypanosoma mega. Proc. Natl. Acad. Sci. USA* 66, 419–424.

Laurent, M., Van Assel, S. & Steinert, M. (1971) Kinetoplast DNA, a unique macromolecular structure of considerable size and mechanical resistance. *Biochem. Biophys. Res. Commun.* 43, 278–284.

Manning, J. E. & Wolstenholme, D. R. (1976) Replication of kinetoplast DNA of *Crithidia acanthocephali. J. Cell Biol.* 70, 406–418.

Mattei, D. M., Goldenberg, S., Morel, C., Azêvedo, H. P. & Roitman, I. (1977) Biochemical strain characterization of *Trypanosoma cruzi* by restriction endonuclease cleavage of kinetoplast DNA. *FEBS Letters* 74, 264–268.

Newton, B. A. (1974) Berenil: a trypanocide with selective activity against extranuclear DNA. In: *Antibiotics* III, ed. Corcoran, J. W. & Hahn, F. E., pp. 34–47. Springer Verlag, Berlin.

Newton, B. A. (1967) Interaction of berenil with DNA and some characteristics of the berenil-DNA complex. *Biochem. J.* 105, 50P.

Newton, B. A. (1976) Amplification of kinetoplast DNA in *Trypanosoma brucei.* In: *Biochemistry of Parasites and Host-Parasite Relationships,* ed. Van den Bossche, H., pp. 203–209. North Holland, Amsterdam.

Newton, B. A. & Burnett, J. K. (1972) DNA of kinetoplastidae: a comparative study. In: *Comparative Biochemistry of Parasites,* ed. Van den Bossche, H., pp. 185–198. Academic Press, New York.

Nichols, J. M. & Cross, G. A. M. (1976) Extra components in kinetoplast DNA preparations of *Crithidia fasciculata. Biochem. Biophys. Res. Commun.* 71, 796–802.

Nichols, J. M. & Cross, G. A. M. (1977) Isolation of mitochondria and mitochondrial RNA from *Crithidia fasciculata. J. Gen. Microbiol.* 99, 291–300.

Pitelka, D. R. (1961) Observations on the kinetoplast-mitochondrion and the cytostome of Bodo. *Exptl. Cell. Res.* 25, 87–93.

Renger, H. C. & Wolstenholme, D. R. (1970) Kinetoplast DNA of the hemoflagellate *Trypanosoma lewisi. J. Cell Biol.* 47, 689–702.

Riou, G. & Delain, E. (1969) Electron microscopy of circular kinetoplast DNA from *Trypanosoma cruzi:* Observations on catenated forms. *Proc. Natl. Acad. Sci. USA* 62, 210–217.

Riou, G. & Paoletti, C. (1967) Preparation and properties of nuclear and satellite DNA of *Trypanosoma cruzi. J. Mol. Biol.* 28, 377–382.

Riou, G. & Yot, P. (1977) Heterogeneity of the kinetoplast DNA molecules of *Trypanosoma cruzi. Biochem.* 16, 2390–2396.

Riou, G., Yot, P. & Truhaut, M. R. (1975) Etude de l'ADN kinétoplastique de *Trypanosoma cruzi* à l'aide d'eudonucléases de restriction. *Compt. Rend.* 280, 2701–2704.

Ris, H. (1962) Ultrastructure of certain self-dependent cytoplasmic organelles. *Proc. 5th Int. Congr. Electron Microscopy.* Philadelphia, vol. 2, abs. XXI. Academic Press, New York.

Shipley, P. G. (1916) The vital staining of mitochondria in *Trypanosoma lewisi* with janus green. *Anat. Rec.* 10, 439–445.

Simpson, L. (1972) The kinetoplast of haemoflagellates. *Int. Rev. Cytol.* 32, 139–207.

Simpson, L. & Hyman, B. (1976) Restriction enzyme analysis of *Leishmania tarentolae* kinetoplast DNA. In: *Biochemistry of Parasites and Host-Parasite Relationships,* ed. Van den Bossche, H. pp. 219–224. North Holland, Amsterdam.

Simpson, A. M. & Simpson, L. (1976) Pulse-labeling of kinetoplast DNA: localization of two sites of synthesis within networks and kinetics of labeling of closed minicircles. *J. Protozool.* 23, 582–587.

Simpson, L. & Simpson, A. M. (1978) Kinetoplast RNA from *Leishmania tarentolae. Cell* 14, 169–178.

Simpson, L., Simpson, A. M. & Wesley, R. D. (1974) Replication of kinetoplast DNA of *Leishmania tarentolae* and *Crithidia fasciculata. Biochim. Biophys. Acta* 349, 161–172.

Sooksri, V., Kudo, N., Ozeki, Y. & Inoki, S. (1972) Electron microscopical observations on division of the kinetoplast in *Trypanosoma cruzi. Biken. J.* 15, – .

Steinert, M. (1964) Le chondriome de *Trypanosome mega. J. Cell Biol.* 20, 92–97.

Steinert, M. & Van Assel, S. (1976) Large circular mitochondrial DNA in *Crithidiat fuciliae. Exptl. Cell Res.* 96, 406–409.

Steinert, M., Van Assel, S., Borst, P., Mol, J. N. M., Kleisen, C. M. & Newton, B. A. (1973) Specific direction of kinetoplast DNA in cytological preparations of trypanosomes by hybridization with complementary RNA. *Exptl. Cell Res.* 76, 175–185.

Steinert, M., Van Assel, S. & Steinert, G. (1976) Minicircular and nonminicircular components of kinetoplast DNA. In: *Biochemistry of Parasites and Host-Parasite Relationships,* ed. Van den Bossche, H., pp. 193–202. North Holland, Amsterdam.

Vickerman, K. (1965) Polymorphism and mitochondrial activity in sleeping sickness trypanosomes. *Nature* London 208, 762–766.

Vickerman, K. & Preston, T. M. (1976) Comparative cell biology of the kinetoplastid flagellates. In: *Biology of the Kinetoplastida,* vol. I. ed. Lumsden, W. H. R. & Evans, D. A., pp. 35–130. Academic Press, London.

Weislogel, P. O., Hoijmakers, J. H. H., Fairlamb, A. H., Kleisen, C. M. & Borst, P. (1977) Characterization of kinetoplast DNA networks from the insect trypanosome *Crithidia luciliae. Biochim. Biophys. Acta* 478, 167–179.

Werbitzki, F. (1910) Über blepharoplastlose Trypanosomen. *Zentbl. Bakt. Parasitkde* (Abt. I) 53, 303–315.

Wesley, R. D. & Simpson, L. (1973) Studies on kinetopast DNA. III. Kinetic complexity of kinetoplast and nuclear DNA from *Leishmania tarentolae. Biochim. Biophys. Acta* 319, 267–276.

Wolstenholme, D. R., Renger, H. C., Manning, J. E. & Fouts, D. L. (1974) Kinetoplast DNA of Crithidia. *J. Protozool.* 21, 622–631.

DISCUSSION

PARDUE: Has anybody looked at autoradiograms of labeled uridine incorporation over the networks?

NEWTON: No, I don't think anybody has examined isolated networks in this way. I know of no evidence for the presence of RNA or protein in kDNA networks, however there may be small amounts of material other than DNA but this has not been vigorously established.

BORST: I think that Maurice Steinert did labeled uridine pulses in *Trypanosoma mega* 10 or 15 years ago and found incorporation over the kinetoplast.

PARDUE: Over the whole network?

BORST: Well, this was done *in situ*. When you isolate the DNA and it is purified, we cannot find any RNA or protein associated with networks, but we have intentionally removed it.

NEWTON: I think it is rather difficult to interpret the early experiments of Steinert *et al.* (1969). It is not possible to say from the published autoradiographs whether the uridine was incorporated into the kDNA network, the membranes surrounding it or the cytoplams adjacent to it. Uridine incorporation was also observed in other areas of the cell over other parts of the mitochondrion well removed from the region containing kDNA.

PARDUE: Is it possible to do the kind of an isolation that would leave RNA and protein associated in the spread of the network in the sort of a Miller spread?

BORST: Hoeijmakers in my lab has done Miller spreads of kinetoplast DNA and tried to preserve transcription complexes. Although occasional transcription complexes were seen on long edge loops of kDNA networks, the results were very variable. Good transcription complexes were also rather rare in nuclear DNA from trypanosomes, although they were readily found in *Tetrahymena* DNA spread in parallel.

Steinert, M. *et al.* (1969) *Exp. Cell Res.* 56, 69–74.

DAWID: There is a report about two RNA species in kinetoplasts with the suggestion that these might be ribosomal RNAs of the mitochondria (Simpson & Simpson 1978). Is there any further evidence that you have or know about whether there is a ribosome?

NEWTON: 9s and 12s RNAs have now been isolated by several workers but it must be stressed that they have been isolated from mitochondrial fragments. Zaitseva & Shirshow (1973) have reported the separation of ribosomes (70s) from isolated kinetoplasts of *Crithidia* and shown that protein synthesis by these preparations is inhibited by chloramphenicol.

BORST: To avoid this problem we have looked for transcripts in total unfractionated cell RNA, and we have hybridized these to restriction blots. If the RNA is really clean and free of DNA, we do not find any transcripts of the mini-circles at all under conditions where we can easily find transcripts of the maxi-circles, which are present at a sequence concentration much less than 1/100th of the mini-circles. Secondly, if you use low input RNA or short exposures of your autoradiograms, the predominant segment of the maxi circle which hybridizes is only 2,300–2,400 bp. That fits very nicely the two small RNAs which are the predominant RNAs in the kinetoplast. Our interpretation of these results is that kinetoplast ribosomes indeed contain very small RNAs.

WEISMANN: Maybe Borst would answer this question: If you cleave with *Pst* which I think shows its specificity for the large DNA you then release all small circles or?

Editors Note: Borst's reply replaced by paper p. 294–298.

Simpson, L. & Simpson, A. M. (1978) *Cell* 14, 169–178.
Zaitseva & Shirshov (1973) In: *Progress in Protozoology,* 4th Int. Congress (ed.) de Puytorac Grain, UER Sciences Clermont, p. 452.

Structure and Function of Kinetoplast DNA: A Comment

P. Borst, J. H. J. Hoeijmakers & F. Fase-Fowler

We have previously reported (see Fairlamb *et al.* 1978, Borst *et al.* 1976, Borst & Fairlamb 1976) that intact, pure kinetoplast DNA (kDNA) networks from *Trypanosoma brucei* strains consist of two components:

1. *Catenated mini-circles*, 0.6×10^6 daltons, heterogeneous in sequence and making up about 90% of the network.

2. *Maxi-circles*, 13×10^6 daltons, homogeneous in sequence and making up about 10% of the network. The maxi-circles are catenated into the mini-circle network and they are readily visible as edge loops up to 6 µm long.

In his paper Newton has mentioned an alternative interpretation for our results, i.e. edge loops in kDNA networks are mini-circle oligomers and the non-mini-circle fragments observed by us in restriction enzyme digests of kDNA are not derived from the edge loops (maxi-circles) but from a nuclear satellite component, contaminating the kDNA preparation. We think that this alternative is ruled out by the following experimental results:

1. We have digested the kDNA from *T. brucei* EATRO 427 with restriction endonucleases *Pst*I, *Eco*RI, *Hap*II, *Hha*I (Fairlamb *et al.* 1978), *Bgl*I, *Xba*I, *Sst*I and *Hind*III (unpublished). Each enzyme gives a specific and reproducible set of nonmini-circle fragments and in each case these fragments add up to a mass of 13×10^6 daltons. Double digest analysis shows that these fragments are derived from the same circular DNA molecule (unpublished results) and we have found no evidence for sequence repetition or sequence heterogeneity in this molecule. A recently constructed map of this DNA, which we call the maxi-circle, is presented in Fig. 1.

Section for Medical Enzymology and Molecular Biology, Laboratory of Biochemistry, University of Amsterdam, P.O.Box 60.000, 1005 GA Amsterdam, The Netherlands.

SPECIFIC EUKARYOTIC GENES, Alfred Benzon Symposium 13, Munksgaard 1979

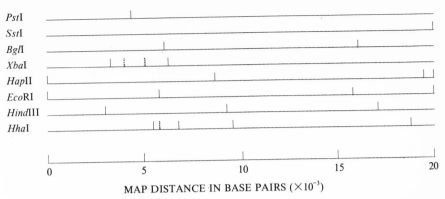

Fig. 1. A physical map of the maxi-circle from kDNA of *T. brucei*, strain EATRO 427. The map is based on (unpublished) overlap analysis by digestion with two restriction enzymes; molecular weights were deduced from co-electrophoresis in agarose gels with marker DNAs of known molecular weights (see Fairlamb *et al.* 1978). The circular map has been linearized to simplify presentation. Broken lines indicate recognition sites not directly identified but inferred from indirect evidence. The bar indicates a segment of DNA which is known to be shorter in the maxi-circles from *T. brucei* strains 1125, 839 and 31.

2. We have found a similar maxi-circle component in kDNA networks from three other *T. brucei* strains, EATRO 31, 839 and 1125. The restriction sites analyzed are conserved in these different maxi-circles, but a single 6.5 kb segment of the DNA is slightly (31,839) or 0.7×10^6 daltons (1125) shorter than in strain 427 kDNA (Fairlamb *et al.* 1978, and unpublished results).

3. Maxi-circles remain associated with networks under a variety of conditions known to remove RNA or protein or to counteract aggregation and they are only released by scission with restriction endonucleases, S_1 nuclease or shear. The fact that S_1 nuclease releases full-length, linearized maxi-circles as the only DNA of high molecular weight, as judged by gel analysis, shows that only one circular component of high molecular weight is present in the network (Fairlamb *et al.* 1978).

Network preparations rarely contain free large circles. We have found 10; they are homogeneous in size and their average contour length is 6.5 μm (unpublished results), in agreement with the mass of 13×10^6 daltons previously found for the maxi-circle of *T. brucei* (Fairlamb *et al.* 1978).

4. Some preparations of kDNA still contain contaminating nuclear DNA and this can readily be detected. It is visible in electron micrographs as heterogeneous linear DNA or as an aggregated mass attached to networks

(Steinert *et al.* 1976). In gels of kDNA digested with restriction endonucleases, it shows up as a general increase in background and after digestion with S_1 nuclease it is liberated as a slow-moving band with a higher apparent molecular weight than the maxi-circle (see Fairlamb *et al.* 1978). Whereas nuclear contamination varies strongly in different preparations, the relative amount of maxi-circle sequences has remained constant in our hands over a period of 4 years, in which at least 30 preparations were made.

5. To establish the relation between edge loops and maxi-circles, the kDNA was digested with endonuclease *Pst*I, which cuts the maxi-circle only once (see Fig. 1) and which liberates less than 10% of the mini-circles from the network. *Pst*I-treated networks looked unaltered in electron micrographs but for the complete loss of all edge loops and long internal DNA. The longer DNA cut from the network consisted of a homogeneous class of linear molecules of maxi-circle size (Fairlamb *et al.* 1978). The only plausible interpretation of these results is that the edge loops are maxi-circles that extend to varying degrees from the network.

Electron microscopy of networks after digestion with endonuclease *Hap*II of *Hha*I also showed a complete removal of all edge loops, without appearance of any free circles longer than mini-circles (unpublished experiments).

6. We have analyzed the kDNA from various *Trypanosoma* strains that are unable to make functional mitochondria. In a *T. equiperdum* and a *T. evansi* strain we have found networks that are very similar to those of *T. brucei*, but these lack any trace of maxi-circles as judged by electron microscopy, by gel analysis of restriction digests or by hybridization with nick-translated maxi-circle DNA from *T. brucei*. In two dyskinetoplastic *Trypanosoma* strains, a *T. evansi* strain and *T. brucei* LUMP 1027, we have been unable to find any trace of maxi-circles or minicircles by gel analysis of total DNA or restriction digests (unpublished results). These results confirm the association of maxi-circles with functional kDNA and provide additional evidence against their derivation from nuclear DNA.

In our opinion, the sum total of the evidence is rather compelling and it is puzzling that the basic observations are difficult to reproduce in Cambridge. We shall exchange kDNA preparations with Newton to straighten this out. In the meantime the following speculative interpretation for the discrepancy can be offered: If the density of maxi-circles and mini-circles in CsCl would differ, broken maxi-circles might show up as a 'shoulder' on the mini-circle network peak and, with damaged networks, the further purification of the network would remove both the 'shoulder' and the maxi-circle bands found in restriction digests of kDNA. This interpretation is based on the observation that there is a large density difference in CsCl between maxi-circles and mini-circles in *Leishmania* (Simpson & Hyman 1976) and on our experience that damage of networks by shear or endonucleases leads to a preferential loss of maxi-circles.

After returning from the Benzon meeting we have done a few experiments to see if this speculative interpretation holds any water. Indeed, we have found that isolated networks band in analytical CsCl gradients as a single peak at 1.689 g/cm^3, whereas the DNA released from this network with endonuclease *Pst*I (about half of which is maxi-circle DNA) contains two bands; about 60% of the DNA bands at 1.682 g/cm^3, about 40% at 1.692 g/cm^3. We think that the 1.682 band is the maxi-circle band, but more experiments are required to prove this. Although this result is interesting it cannot account for Newton's finding of a satellite DNA on the heavy side of the kDNA peak in CsCl. This discrepancy remains to be resolved.

Finally, one comment on the function of kDNA. We have isolated total RNA from the insect trypanosome *Crithidia luciliae*, labeled this *in vitro* with polynucleotide kinase and hybridized this to Southern blots of restriction digests of kDNA from this organism. No mini-circle transcripts were detected, whereas maxi-circle transcripts were readily found (Hoeijmakers & Borst 1978). This agrees with the idea that maxi-circles are the 'true' mtDNA of trypanosomes and that mini-circles do not code for proteins or stable RNAs.

ACKNOWLEDGMENTS

We thank Miss J. Van den Burg for her help in making the maxi-circle map in Fig. 1 and Mr. J. Hoffschlag for running the analytical ultracentrifuge. This work was supported in part by a grant from the Foundation for Fundamental Biological Research (BION), which is subsidized by The Netherlands Organization for the Advancement of Pure Research (ZWO).

NEWTON: Professor Borst's comments add some interesting new information, however, his remarks on my interpretation of restriction enzyme data suggest that he may have misinterpreted my comment on page 286. I do not wish to suggest that kDNA networks do not contain maxi-circles, but merely emphasize that there is as yet no firm evidence that the large restriction fragments are derived from maxi-circles or that all edge loops represent maxi-circles in situ; the possibility that some edge loops may be tandemly repeated oligomers of mini-circles has not, in my opinion, been ruled out.

REFERENCES

Borst, P. & Fairlamb, A. H. (1976) DNA of parasites, with special reference to kinetoplast DNA. In: *Biochemistry of Parasites and Host-Parasite Relationships* (Van den Bossche, H., Ed.), North-Holland, Amsterdam, pp. 169–191.

Borst, P., Fairlamb, A. H., Fase-Fowler, F., Hoeijmakers, J. H. J. & Weislogel, P. O. (1976) The structure of kinetoplast DNA. In: *The Genetic Function of Mitochondrial DNA* (Saccone C. & Kroon, A. M., Eds), North-Holand, Amsterdam, pp. 59–69.

Fairlamb, A. H., Weislogel, P. O., Hoeijmakers, J. H. J. & Borst, P. (1978) Isolation and characterization of kinetoplast DNA from bloodstream form of *Trypanosoma brucei. J. Cell Biol.* 76, 293–309.

Hoeijmakers, J. H. J. & Borst, P. (1978) RNA from the insect trypanosome *Crithidia luciliae* contains transcripts of the maxi-circle and not of the mini-circle component of kinetoplast DNA. *Biochim. Biophys. Acta* 521, 407–411.

Simpson, L. & Hyman, B. (1976) Restriction enzyme analysis of *Leishmania tarentolae* kinetoplast DNA. In: *Biochemistry of Parasites and Host-Parasite Relationships* (Van den Bossche, H., Ed.), North-Holland, Amsterdam, pp. 219–224.

Steinert, M., Van Assel, S. & Steinert, G. (1976) Mini-circular and nonmini-circular components of kinetoplast DNA. In: *Biochemistry of Parasites and Host-Parasite Relationships* (Van den Bossche, H., Ed.), North-Holland, Amsterdam, pp. 193–202.

The Extrachromosomal Ribosomal DNA of *Tetrahymena* and *Paramecium*

*Joseph G. Gall, Meng-Chao Yao, Elizabeth Blackburn, R. Craig Findly &
Martha Wild*

In the macronucleus of the ciliated protozoan *Tetrahymena,* the genes coding for rRNA occur as extrachromosomal molecules (Gall 1974, Engberg *et al.* 1974, Karrer & Gall 1976, Engberg *et al.* 1976). These molecules are about 20 kb in length, varying slightly among species, and each contains two regions coding for the 17S, 5.8S and 25S ribosomal RNAs in reverse repeat orientation. In the macronucleus there are approximately 600 rDNA copies per haploid genome as determined by saturation hybridization experiments (Pearlman *et al.* 1979); since the vegetative macronucleus contains about 45 genome equivalents of DNA (C=0.22 pg; Woodard *et al.* 1972) there are altogether some 14,000 of these palindromic molecules. In sharp contrast to the situation in the macronucleus, the micronucleus contains very little rDNA. Earlier hybridization experiments detected fewer than 10–20 copies per genome, most of which could be accounted for by the known contamination of the micronuclear preparations with macronuclear DNA (Yao *et al.* 1974). Restriction enzyme analysis has recently shown that only a single copy of rDNA is integrated into the micronuclear chromosomal DNA (Yao & Gall 1977). This integrated copy contains only one coding region for the rRNAs and hence is only half as long as the extrachromosomal copies from the macronucleus. Integrated copies of rDNA were looked for in macronuclear DNA, using the same restriction enzyme tests which easily detected the single copy in the micronuclear DNA. These experiments were negative, and from their known sensitivity permit us to conclude that fewer than 10 integrated copies might exist in the macronucleus

Department of Biology, Yale University, New Haven, Connecticut 06520 U.S.A.

SPECIFIC EUKARYOTIC GENES, Alfred Benzon Symposium 13, Munksgaard 1979

(there would be 45 integrated copies if there were only one copy per genome equivalent).

During the sexual cycle (conjugation) the macronucleus is destroyed and replaced with a new macronucleus derived by polyploidization of a division product of the micronucleus. It thus seems probable that the extrachromosomal rDNA of the macronucleus is derived by some type of amplification process from the single integrated copy of the micronucleus. Although the details of amplification remain to be worked out, the absence of integrated rDNA in the macronucleus suggests that the first step might be excision of the integrated copy. In this respect amplification in *Tetrahymena* would resemble the excision of λ phage from the *E. coli* chromosome, or possibly the excision of integrated virus genomes from the DNA of higher eukaryotes.

In order to examine this possibility in more detail we have studied sequences at the termini of the extrachromosomal rDNA molecules. We first looked for the existence of "sticky ends," partly by analogy to λ phage and partly because we knew from electron microscopy that the rDNA occurred occasionally as circular or multimeric molecules. Using *E. coli* DNA polymerase I on rDNA as template, we found very strong incorporation of nucleoside triphosphates, and restriction endonuclease digestion showed that the incorporation was in the termini of the molecules. Further analysis demonstrated that the incorporation was due not to filling in of sticky ends, but was instead a nick-translation reaction extending over several hundred nucleotides at or near the ends of the molecules (Blackburn & Gall 1978). This region was shown to be composed of somes 20–70 repeats of the hexanucleotide 5' C-C-C-C-A-A 3' interrupted at intervals by single-strand discontinuities, probably one-nucleotide gaps.

Since it was not immediately clear what role the repeated C_4A_2 sequence might play in amplification, we looked to see if similar or identical sequences were found elsewhere in the genome. This we did by using as a hybridization probe the terminal restriction fragment of rDNA labeled by nick-translation (or a cRNA synthesized from the same fragment as template). This C_4A_2 probe was hybridized to total *Tetrahymena* DNA which had been cleaved by various restriction enzymes, separated by gel electrophoresis and transferred to nitrocellulose filters (Southern 1975). The probe hybridized to at least several dozen discrete fragments. Because of the strength of hybridization we believe that most of the detected fragments contain runs of C_4A_2 as in the probe. The most interesting feature of this hybridization experiment came from a comparison of macronuclear and micronuclear DNA. Restriction fragments from both

DNAs hybridized with the C_4A_2 probe, but the fragments were smaller on the average in the macronuclear than in the micronuclear DNA. A possible interpretation of this finding is that the C_4A_2 repeat is a specific signal for excision or some other type of molecular reorganization. If, for example, C_4A_2 sequences defined the termini of DNA segments destined to be eliminated, then the restriction fragment(s) containing the C_4A_2 sequences might well be smaller after the excision than before. It is known from a comparison of C_0t curves of macronuclear and micronuclear DNA (Yao & Gorovsky 1974) that middle repetitive sequences found in the micronucleus are reduced or eliminated in the macronucleus, suggesting that some sort of regular genomic reorganization occurs during formation of the macronuleus. We have now obtained several clones containing C_4A_2 repeats (not derived from rDNA). A detailed analysis of the chromosome regions from which these clones were derived in both macronucleus and micronucleus should help to clarify any possible role of the C_4A_2 repeat in sequence rearrangements.

We have recently carried out a detailed analysis of rDNA isolated from *T. pigmentosa* (formerly *T. pyriformis,* syngens 6 and 8; see Nanney & McCoy 1976). We have found an intervening sequence in the region coding for 25S rRNA in some strains but not in others. The rDNA from several strains was purified and analyzed by restriction enzyme digestions and gel electrophoresis. The positions of the 17S and 25S coding regions were determined by transferring restriction fragments to nitrocellulose filters and hybridizing with 17S and 25S rRNA (Southern 1976). Restriction sites within the coding regions were conserved among geographically diverse strains, although some differences were detected in noncoding parts of the molecule. Five strains out of seven contained a restriction fragment within the 25S coding region approximately 400 bp longer than the corresponding fragment in the other two strains, suggesting that an intervening sequence might be present in the strains with the longer coding region. Strain 8(ALP) containing the shorter fragment and strain 6(UM) containing the longer fragment were selected for further study. R-loops between the rDNA and 25S rRNA from both strains were examined by electron microscopy. The rDNA from strain 8(ALP) formed R-loops which each contained a single uninterrupted bubble, whereas rDNA from strain 6(UM) formed R-loops composed of two adjacent bubbles with a short double-stranded DNA loop at their junction. The loop was approximately 350–400 bp in length, and was located in the position predicted by the restriction map. A Hind III fragment from 6(UM), which contains the intervening sequence and a portion of the 25S gene, and the corresponding fragment from 8(ALP), have been cloned in pBR322. A more detailed restriction map of the clones confirmed the presence of the intervening sequence.

Each strain on which these studies have been conducted is homogeneous with respect to the type of rDNA in its macronucleus; that is, the fragments occur in approximately equimolar quantities (except the central fragment which is present in half-molar yield as expected for a palindrome), and a unique map can be constructed for each strain. This means that in strains such as 6(UM) all macronuclear rDNA copies contain the intervening sequence and the functional 25S rRNA therefore must be transcribed from coding regions which contain the intervening sequence. We do not yet know whether the intervening sequence is transcribed and subsequently removed, although studies on mammalian globin mRNA (Tilghman *et al.* 1978), and yeast tRNA (Knapp *et al.* 1978) show that such processing does occur in some RNAs. In the case of the intervening sequence in the rDNA of *Drosophila melanogaster* evidence has been adduced against transcription (Dawid & Long 1979).

Tetrahymena is one of three organisms whose rDNA is known to be organized as palindromic dimers. Both the cellular slime mold *Dictyostelium* (Cockburn *et al.* 1978, Grainger & Maizels 1979) and the acellular slime mold *Physarum* (Vogt & Braun 1976), organisms that are not closely related to each other or to *Tetrahymena,* have rDNA fundamentally similar to that of *Tetrahymena,* although the molecules are considerably larger (88 kb and 56 kb, respectively). Because we were interested in *Paramecium tetraurelia* as a possible organism for the study of rDNA genetics, we recently examined its rDNA (Findly & Gall 1978). Because *Paramecium* and *Tetrahymena* are so closely related (both are holotrichous ciliates) we fully expected the rDNA of *Paramecium* to exist as extrachromosomal palindromic dimers.

Centrifugation of total *Paramecium* DNA on sucrose gradients, followed by hybridization of the gradient fractions with rRNA, showed that the rDNA had a lower average molecular weight than the bulk macronuclear DNA. Electron microscopy of purified rDNA, however, failed to reveal the expected uniform linear molecules. Instead the rDNA contained both linear and circular molecules of various lengths. Partial denaturation maps showed a serially repeated unit in the linear molecules and established that the circles contained two, three or more of the same repeats. Thus, the extrachromosomal rDNA of *Paramecium* is more like the amplified rDNA of *Xenopus* oocytes, which contains circles of discrete sizes and linear molecules (in neither *Xenopus* nor

Paramecium is it known whether the linears preexist in the nucleus or are produced accidentally during isolation). The repeat length in *Paramecium* is somewhat variable, as shown by restriction enzyme mapping, and electron microscopy demonstrated that variability exists even among repeats on the same molecule. This latter fact suggests that *Paramecium* may have more than one chromosomal rDNA copy from which the extrachromosomal molecules are amplified.

Fairly detailed molecular information is now available for several protists. In *Tetrahymena, Physarum* and *Dictyostelium* the rDNA occurs as palindromic dimers. Serially repeated genes are found in *Paramecium,* and isolated single copies of rDNA occur in *Oxytricha* (Lawn *et al.* 1978). At this time, no firm conclusions can be drawn about the significance of these variations. What is striking is the fact that so many cases of extrachromosomal rDNA have been found among the first protists carefully examined. It would seem that a wider survey may turn up additional interesting cases and possibly give clues about the origin of the multiple integrated rDNA copies common in multicellular eukaryotes.

ACKNOWLEDGMENTS

We especially thank Ellen Simon for supplying stocks of *Tetrahymena* and for advice about their use. Supported by Research Grants VC-238 from the American Cancer Society and GM 12427 from the National Institute of General Medical Sciences.

REFERENCES

Blackburn, E.H. & Gall, J.G. (1978) A tandemly repeated sequence at the termini of the extrachromosomal ribosomal RNA genes in *Tetrahymena. J. Mol. Biol.* 120, 33–53.

Cockburn, A.F., Taylor, W.C. & Firtel, R.A. (1978) *Dictyostelium* rDNA consists of non-chromosomal palindromic dimers containing 5S and 36S coding regions. *Chromosoma.* In press.

Dawid, I. & Long, E. (1979) Ribosomal DNA and related sequences in *Drosophila melanogaster.* This volume.

Engberg, J., Andersson, P., Leick, V. & Collins J. (1976) Free ribosomal DNA molecules from *Tetrahymena pyriformis* GL are giant palindromes. *J. Mol. Biol.* 104, 455–470.

Engberg, J., Christiansen, G. & Leick, V. (1974) Autonomous rDNA molecules containing single copies of the ribosomal RNA genes in the macronucleus of *Tetrahymena pyriformis. Biochem. Biophys. Research Commun.* 59, 1356–1365.

Findly, R.C. & Gall, J.G. (1978) Free ribosomal RNA genes in *Paramecium* are tandemly repeated. *Proc. Natl. Acad. Sci. USA*. 75, 3312–3316.

Gall, J.G. (1974) Free ribosomal RNA genes in the macronucleus of *Tetrahymena*. *Proc. Natl. Acad. Sci. USA* 71, 3078–3081.

Grainger, R. & Maizels, N. Personal communication.

Karrer, K.M. & Gall, J.G. (1976) The macronuclear ribosomal DNA of *Tetrahymena pyriformis* is a palindrome. *J. Mol. Biol.* 104, 421–453.

Knapp, G., Beckmann, J.S., Johnson, P.F., Fuhrman, A. & Abelson, J. (1978) Transcription and processing of intervening sequences in yeast tRNA genes. *Cell* 14, 221–236.

Lawn, R.M., Heumann, J.M., Herrick, G. & Prescott, D.M. (1977) The gene-size DNA molecules in *Oxytricha. Cold Spring Harbor Symp. Quant.Biol.* 42, 483–492.

Nanney, D.L. & McCoy, J.W. (1976) Characterization of the species of the *Tetrahymena pyriformis* complex. *Trans. Amer. Microscop. Soc.* 95, 664–682.

Pearlman, R.E., Andersson, P., Engberg, J. & Nilsson, J.R. (1979) Ribosomal DNA synthesis in conjugating *Tetrahymena*. This volume.

Southern, E.M. (1975) Detection of specific sequences among DNA fragments separated by gel electrophoresis. *J. Mol. Biol.* 98, 503–517.

Tilghman, S.M., Tiemeier, D.C., Seidman, J.G., Peterlin, B.M., Sullivan, M., Maizel, J.V. & Leder, P. (1978) Intervening sequence of DNA identified in the structural portion of a mouse β-globin gene. *Proc. Natl. Acad. Sci. USA* 75, 725–729.

Vogt, V. & Braun, R. (1976) Structure of ribosomal DNA in *Physarum polycephalum. J. Mol. Biol.* 106, 567–587.

Woodard, J., Kaneshiro, E. & Gorovsky, M.A. (1972) Cytochemical studies on the problem of macronuclear subnuclei in *Tetrahymena. Genetics* 70, 251–260.

Yao, M.-C. & Gall, J.G. (1977) A single integrated gene for ribosomal RNA in a eucaryote, *Tetrahymena pyriformis. Cell* 12, 121–132.

Yao, M.-C. & Gorovsky, M.A. (1974) Comparison of the sequences of macro- and micronuclear DNA of *Tetrahymena pyriformis. Chromosoma* 48, 1–18.

Yao, M.-C., Kimmel, A.R. & Gorovsky, M.A. (1974) A small number of cistrons for ribosomal RNA in the germinal nucleus of a eukaryote, *Tetrahymena pyriformis. Proc. Natl. Acad. Sci. USA* 71, 3082–3086.

DISCUSSION

SCHAFFNER: Did you check if the intervening sequence is also present in the micronuclear DNA?

GALL: We have not had time to do that, although it would be interesting.

WEISSMANN: Did you say there are several strains which have intervening sequences or is there just one strain?

GALL: There are several strains which have intervening sequences.

WEISSMANN: Do you know if the intervening sequences are the same or similar in different strains?

GALL: In the different strains which we have examined the intervening sequences are of similar length, but we have not done cross hybridization experiments to determine sequence homology. We have strains whose restriction patterns differ outside the 25S region, but differences within the 25S region are limited to the presence or absence of the 400 bp intervening sequence.

WEISSMANN: In the same place?

GALL: Yes, approximately.

BORST: Did you do S1 mapping to check in the strains that do not appear to have an intervening sequence, whether a small sequence is present?

GALL: No, we have not done that.

WEISSMANN: Do you actually get hexanucleotide fragments coming out when you denature rDNA?

GALL: We get a whole series of fragments differing in length by six nucleotides because the gaps do not occur every repeat. That was part of the original evidence for the existence of gaps.

Ribosomal DNA: Extrachromosomal Genes of *Physarum*

Richard Braun & Thomas Seebeck

The presence of a satellite DNA in nuclei of the myxomycete *Physarum polycephalum* had been noticed many years ago (Braun *et al.* 1965), but it was not until considerably later than this DNA was shown to code for ribosomal RNA (Zellweger *et al.* 1972, Newlon *et al.* 1973). The original interest in this particular DNA fraction arose from studies on biochemical events in the mitotic cycle, for which *Physarum* is an extremely suitable organism due to its naturally synchronous mitoses in macroscopic plasmodia (for reviews see Schiebel 1973, Mohberg 1974, Jockusch 1975, Braun *et al.* 1977). With respect to the satellite DNA (=ribosomal DNA), the rather unexpected observation was made that it did not only replicate in the S-phase, but also in the G2-phase of the mitotic cycle (Braun & Evans 1969, Holt & Gurney 1969).

STRUCTURE

The early finding that rDNA could be extracted by the Hirt procedure (Hirt 1967) suggested that it might not be integrated into large chromosomal DNA (Braun & Evans 1969). Further characterization confirmed this and established the structure of the rDNA as a linear unintegrated molecule of about the size of bacteriophage Lambda DNA, localized in the nucleolus. Each rDNA molecule is a huge palindrome or inverted repeat with two coding sequences for 5.8S, 19S and 26S rRNA. The experimental evidence will be discussed rather briefly since a detailed review is to be published shortly (Molgaard 1978).

The isolation of *Physarum* rDNA depends generally on its nucleolar

Institute of General Microbiology, University of Bern, CH-3013 Bern, Switzerland.

SPECIFIC EUKARYOTIC GENES, Alfred Benzon Symposium 13, Munksgaard 1979

localization as well as on its base composition. In isopycnic CsCl gradients rDNA bands at a density of 1.713 g/ml, while the density of bulk chromosomal DNA is 1.700 g/ml. Several intercalating agents such as netropsin, actinomycin D, Hoechst 33258 increase the density difference between the two DNA species, but the practical usefulness of these procedures is, at least in our hands, rather limited (Matthews *et al.* 1978, Seebeck, unpublished). Size and shape of the isolated molecules were determined both by sedimentation analysis and electron microscopy. This showed clearly that *Physarum* rDNA is a discrete linear molecule of 38×10^6 dalton molecular weight (Vogt & Braun 1976a, Molgaard *et al.* 1976). Both groups of investigators further studied the structure of the rDNA and obtained the restriction enzyme map shown in Fig. 1.

Evidence for a palindromic structure comes from the restriction maps and from studying denatured and renatured rDNA molecules by electron microscopy (Vogt & Braun 1976a). Single strands of rDNA, allowed to renature very briefly, form a double-stranded structure whose length is exactly half that of native double-stranded rDNA. The formation of these snap-backs is of course in agreement with the palindromic nature of the rDNA. Pertinent to the structure of the rDNA, these analyses showed the presence of small internal palindromes within the large palindrome. These blocks of short inverted repetitions are in the central third of the native rDNA (Fig. 1). Measured from the center outwards in either direction, they are located from 0 to 0.7×10^6 dalton and from 1.8×10^6 to 5.5×10^6 dalton. The observed internal palindromes vary in length from about 0.1×10^6 to 10^6 dalton and suggest that a basic unit of less than 0.1×10^6 dalton may be tandemly repeated many times over. The two sequences coding for 19S

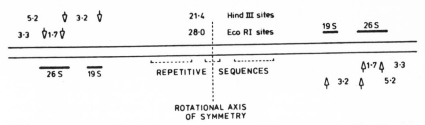

Fig. 1. The structure of *Physarum* rDNA. Each nucleolus of *Physarum* contains 100–200 copies of palindromic rDNA, not integrated into large chromosomal DNA. The structural analysis has been published in detail (Vogt & Braun 1976, Molgaard *et al.* 1976). The transcribed and the nontranscribed sequences have a similar base composition (Matthews *et al.* 1978). Further restriction sites have been mapped (Matthews, personal communication). The sizes of restriction fragments are given in 10^6 dalton. The restriction fragments cleaved from the ends of the rDNA molecule appear to be slightly heterogeneous in length.

and 26S rRNA are located towards the two ends of the native rDNA molecule and distinctly outside the area of small internal palindromes (Molgaard *et al.* 1976).

A different type of experiment supporting the palindromic nature of *Physarum* rDNA was presented by Grainger & Ogle (1978). These authors lysed whole plasmodia and studied nucleoprotein complexes by electron microscopy: occasionally they observed structures looking like two Christmas trees pointing towards each other. The stem had the length expected for a native rDNA molecule and the branches, the putative rRNA molecules, increased in length towards the ends of the presumed rDNA. This would imply that the sequences for 19S rRNA are transcribed before those for 26S rRNA. The difficulty of interpreting these electron micrographs stems from the rarity of the observed structures and also from the fact that whole plasmodia rather than isolated nucleoli were used as the starting material. Since rDNA amounts to only 1–2% of the total DNA, it is difficult to prove conclusively that the observed structures in fact contain rDNA, though this seems very likely.

REPLICATION

In the synchronous plasmodia of *Physarum* mitosis is immediately followed by the S-phase, which, under standard conditions, lasts about 3 h. The largest sector of interphase is taken up by a 6-h G2-phase. Replication of rDNA is out of phase with that of chromosomal DNA: the ribosomal genes replicate throughout interphase with the exception of the first hour of the S-phase (Zellweger *et al.* 1972). The high degree of mitotic synchrony should ideally allow one to selectively label rDNA during the G2-phase. It cannot, however, tacitly be assumed that all thymidine incorporated into nuclear DNA during the G2-phase is in fact in rDNA. Even if only 1% of chromosomal DNA is replicated outside of the S-phase (polyploidization of a few nuclei, repair synthesis, slow termination of normal replication, etc.), this thymidine incorporation could be equal to that expected in rDNA. In all experimental situations it should therefore be carefully analyzed how much G2-phase label is actually in the rDNA.

At the level of the individual rDNA molecule, replication starts close to the center and moves outwards bidirectionally (Vogt & Braun 1977). The eyeloops seen in electron microscopy appeared to initiate at two starting points, the major one very near the center of the molecule and the other one roughly one third off

Fig. 2. Replication of rDNA. Schematic representation of unscheduled replication of rDNA. M=mitosis, S=S-phase. The asterix shows an arbitrarily chosen time point of rDNA replication. The DNA replicated at that time can either replicate a second time in the same interphase (1) or at any other time of the following interphase (2 and 3).

center. The significance of these two replication origins is not clear. As with many other linear DNA molecules, it is not known how the ends of the rDNA molecule are replicated. The length heterogeneity of the restriction fragments bearing the ends of the molecule may be somehow related to the mode of duplication of the rDNA.

The chromosomal DNA of *Physarum* and other eukaryotes is replicated in a scheduled manner (Braun & Wili 1969): each fragment of the genome replicates once per cell cycle and it does this in a definite subfraction of the S-phase. As shown in Fig. 2, this does not hold for rDNA. Density shift and pulse-labeling experiments showed that rDNA replicates in an unscheduled manner although the total amount of rDNA is tightly controlled (Vogt & Braun 1977). The replicative behavior of *Physarum* rDNA is similar to that of stringently controlled bacterial plasmids.

ASSOCIATION WITH PROTEINS

Experiments summarized so far have given a clear picture of rDNA as a free DNA molecule in the sense of not being linked covalently to chromosomal DNA. A graphic illustration of this is shown in Fig. 3. Further work was then devoted to the question of how this free rDNA is organized within the nucleolus. Indirect studies of a possible association of rDNA with proteins has been made by treating nuclei or nucleoli with nucleases and characterizing the DNA breakdown products. A more direct approach involves the isolation of deoxyribonucleoprotein particles containing rDNA (rDNP particles).

Several groups have studied the effect of micrococcal nuclease on nuclei of *Physarum* and concluded that chromosomal DNA is organized in repeating units about 180 base pairs long (Vogt & Braun 1976a, Jerzmanowski *et al.* 1976,

Johnson *et al.* 1976, Staron *et al.* 1977). DNase I analogously gives single-strand fragments of about 10 bases long, as found also in other organisms (Stalder & Braun 1978).

What happens to rDNA during these enzymatic treatments? Several groups have studied the effect of micrococcal nuclease on rDNA, but so far only one study with DNase I is available. For micrococcal nuclease at least one conclusion is clear, namely, that treatment of nuclei with this enzyme does not lead to rapid and preferential degradation of rDNA to acid soluble products. This means that rDNA must in some form and to some extent be protected in the living cell. It is quite possible that the arrangement of protective proteins is different in the coding and in the noncoding regions. In the spacer region of spread chromatin presumed to contain rDNA (Grainger & Ogle 1978) nucleosomelike structures can be seen. The same authors have treated both isolated nucleoli (contaminated with 0.14% nuclei) and nuclei with micrococcal

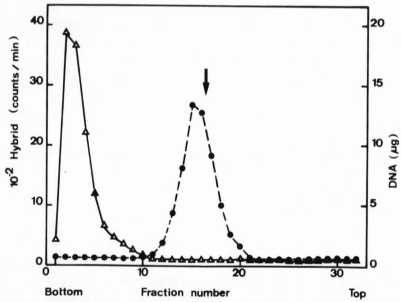

Fig. 3. Size of rDNA. Amoebae of *Physarum* were lysed on top of a sucrose gradient with SDS and proteinase K and the lysate centrifuged in such a manner that phage Lambda DNA (arrow) sedimented about halfway down the gradient. Total DNA (△) was measured colorimetrically and is seen to have sedimented nearly to the bottom. The DNA of each fraction was hybridized with ^{3}H-rRNA and the amount of hybrid assayed (●): rDNA is seen to sediment slightly ahead of Lambda DNA and very little radioactivity is associated with the large chromosomal DNA (Hall & Braun 1977). This shows that most rDNA is not integrated in large chromosomal DNA.

nuclease and after gel electrophoresis in both cases observed nucleosome-size DNA fragments. Though a quantitative analysis of the published data is not possible, it does seem most likely that in the spacer region the rDNA is wound around nucleosomes. Butler *et al.* (1978) also present evidence for the presence of nucleosomes at least in the spacer regions, but since these authors do not show how much of the G2-period-labeled DNA is in fact rDNA in their experiments, such a conclusion from these experiments appears premature. The protection of the coding region was studied using hybridization with rRNA as an assay (Johnson *et al.* 1978, Stalder *et al.* 1978a). Though the experiments performed by the two groups are somewhat different, they can both be interpreted as showing that the coding sequences have some form of protection, but that this protection differs in an undefined way from that offered by standard nucleosomes. Johnson *et al.* treated whole nuclei with enzyme and separated DNA-protein complexes in sucrose gradients. They observed the usual nucleosome fractions and also a slower sedimenting component called peak "A". This interesting peak "A" may be very significant for the study of chromatin in general, since it contains nucleosome-length DNA together with an incomplete set of histones. This points to an extended, perhaps transcriptionally active, modified nucleosome. Peak "A" contains about the same proportion of rDNA to total DNA (0.21%) as does whole DNA (0.18%), but it is enriched in rDNA compared to the mononucleosome (0.11%) and dinucleosome fraction (0.04%). This shows that the coding sequences of rDNA are degraded about double as fast by micrococcal nuclease as bulk nuclear DNA with the accumulation of mononucleosome-size DNA fragment. The nature of the protecting agents, presumably proteins, is not known, since even in peak "A" 99% of the DNA is not rDNA but chromosomal DNA. After treatment of nuclei with micrococcal nuclease, Stalder *et al.* (1978) separated DNA fragments by gel electrophoresis and characterized the fragments by hybridization after their elution from the gels. Clearly rDNA coding sequences did not get degraded preferentially to acid soluble products. The gels showed up nucleosome-sized DNA fragments and multiples thereof from the bulk DNA present in the nuclei. Surprisingly the rDNA coding sequences were not confined to the nucleosome bands and their multiples, but were present in the interband areas in amounts roughly intermediate between those found in the two adjacent bands. The speed of degradation to the mononucleosome-sized DNA is slightly higher for rDNA than for bulk DNA, agreeing in this respect with the experiments of Johnson *et al.* (1978). The data of Stalder *et al.* (1978) can be tentatively interpreted as indicating that the coding sequences of rDNA are being protected by other proteins than nucleosomal histones or by nucleosomes with a structure differing from that of bulk nucleosomes. Taking both sets of data together (Johnson et al. 1978, Stalder et al. 1978), it can be concluded that the coding sequences of rDNA are protected against attack by micrococcal nuclease to a similar extent as in bulk chromatin, but that the protective structures differ substantially from normal nucleosomes.

In another set of experiments nuclei were treated with DNase I and the degradation of the coding sequences of rDNA was compared with the degradation of bulk DNA (Stalder et al. 1978b). At only 30% acid solubility of the bulk DNA, 85–95% of the rDNA coding sequences were degraded. So the coding sequences of rDNA are preferentially degraded in the same way as transcribed genes in other systems (e.g. Flint & Weintraub 1977). It is interesting to note that the same extent of degradation following DNase I treatment is observed irrespective of whether interphase nuclei with a high level of rRNA transcription are used or mitotic nuclei in which rRNA transcription is virtually arrested. This would indicate that mitotic chromatin, though momentarily inactive, still retains a "potentially active configuration".

Recently it has been possible to isolate rDNA in the form of a transcriptionally active deoxyribonucleoprotein (rDNP) complex (Seebeck et al. 1978). The rDNP or minichromosome is obtained by lysing purified nucleoli and fractionating the lysate in a sucrose gradient as shown in Fig. 4. It can be seen that rDNP sediments much faster than deproteinized rDNA: approximately 100S instead of 40S. The figure also shows that the entire RNA polymerase activity is α-amanitin-resistant: the minichromosomes therefore contain only RNA polymerase I and no other active RNA polymerases. The only DNA present in the particles is rDNA. Further experiments using metrizamide gradients showed that the minichromosomes are composed of about equal quantities of nucleic acid and protein, on a weight basis. An inventory of the proteins has not yet been made, though the presence of one particularly interesting protein has been established. This protein of 70,000 dalton substantially stimulates in vitro transcription by the minichromosome, but only if the purified protein is highly phosphorylated (Kuehn, unpublished observations). Polyamines mediate the in vitro phosphorylation of this protein in isolated nucleoli (Atmar & Kuehn 1978). The minichromosomes, when incubated under conditions of RNA synthesis, make mainly ribosomal RNA sequences ranging in size up to about 10S. Intact rRNA precursors (30–40S) have not so far been detected. A detailed study of the structure and function of the rDNP minichromosome may help in elucidating

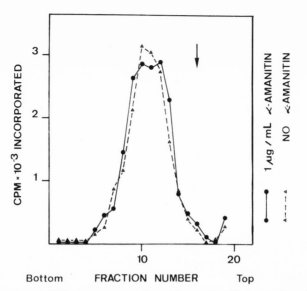

Fig. 4. Sedimentation of rDNP in a sucrose gradient. A lysate of purified nucleoli was layered on top of a sucrose gradient and then centrifuged in such a way that Lambda DNA sedimented about one sixth into the gradient (arrow). Each fraction was assayed for RNA polymerase activity in the presence (●——●) and absence (▲--▲) of *a*-amanitin. The incorporation of ³H-UTP into acid-insoluble product was measured.

the regulation of transcription in eukaryotes, since a considerable amount of information on differential transcription during the mitotic cycle is already available (Hall & Turnock 1976) and moreover, it is one of the few model systems where a specific eukaryotic gene can be isolated together with its structural and regulatory proteins and where both the gene function and gene organization are well understood. Unfortunately it is still not known how much of the rDNA is transcribed under any physiological condition. It seems likely anyhow, that at least late in the G2-period, when the RNA synthesis rate is at its highest, most rDNA molecules are active in transcription. It can be calculated that in late G2 several thousand rRNA molecules are made per rDNA molecule per hour.

CONCLUSIONS

The canonical *Physarum* rDNA is linear, palindromic and behaves in several ways like plasmid DNA in bacteria. In diploid G2-phase nuclei there are approximately 150 rDNA molecules with a total of 300 coding sequences for

5.8S, 19S and 26S rRNA. The 19S and 26S sequences have been mapped, but the exact location of the 5.8S gene on the palindrome has not yet been determined. The 5S rRNA gene and the genes for tRNA are not in the rDNA but in the chromosomal DNA in 700 and 1050 copies, respectively (Hall & Braun 1977). It is not clear whether the huge palindrome carries any other genetic information apart from that used to make rRNA and its precursor. The areas of the rDNA lacking small internal inverted repeats could conceivably code for mRNA or small nuclear RNA species. This would seem economical if the relevant RNA (or protein) were required in similar amounts as rRNA.

Is the free rDNA the product of continually occurring gene amplification? This seems very unlikely for several reasons. All stages of the life cycle of *Physarum* studied so far contain the same amount of rDNA relative to total DNA: plasmodia, amoebae, spherules and even meiotically derived spores (Ryser & Braun 1974, Hall *et al.* 1975, Affolter & Braun 1978). This suggests a high degree of metabolic stability of the rDNA, which in fact has recently been shown directly for plasmodia (Hall *et al.* 1978). In these experiments it was shown that prelabeled rDNA and bulk nuclear DNA were diluted out by growth to the same extent over several subsequent mitotic cycles demonstrating the absence of any rDNA turnover. In addition the replication experiments discussed above involving density shifts with bromodeoxyuridine would have given totally different results if the free palindromic rDNA were not self-replicating. The picture that emerges then is that nucleolar rDNA is stringently controlled in amount, self-replicating and never or only rarely amplified from a master copy. The existence of a master copy in the chromosomal DNA, such as has been found in *Tetrahymena* (Yao & Gall 1977) has not so far been demonstrated in *Physarum*. Conceivably the ratio of rDNA to chromosomal DNA may be increased above the standard ratio when nuclei are maintained in a prolonged G2-phase. Evidence suggesting such a modest degree of amplification has been obtained by autoradiography. However, the technique does not allow an unambiguous distinction between label incorporated into chromosomal DNA and nucleolar rDNA (Guttes 1974) and therefore the question of amplification at certain stages of the life cycle or under specific physiological condition has not yet been satisfactorily answered.

In all organisms studied so far the ribosomal genes occur in multiple copies. In higher eukaryotes they are tandemly repeated in the chromosomal DNA, rarely are they amplified in highly specialized cells such as oocytes (e.g. Wellauer *et al.* 1977). In lower eukaryotes multiple copies of rDNA can also occur in chromosomal DNA, e.g. in yeast (Petes *et al.* 1977), but in this very heterogeneous group of organisms three cases have been detected where multiple copies of free palindromic rDNA are present. In *Tetrahymena* the plasmidlike rDNA is restricted to the macronuclei, while neither *Dictyostelium* nor *Physarum* have such a specialized cell organelle, so that in these two organisms the free rDNA is in the nucleoli of normal somatic nuclei (Taylor *et al.* 1977, Gall 1978). Thus ribosomal genes are an excellent example of how during evolution the increased requirement for multiple gene copies can be fulfilled by different mechanisms leading to very different organizations of the genome.

The extrachromosomal rDNA of *Physarum* presents to the striving molecular biologist a uniquely suitable system for the analysis of structure and regulation of a particular eukaryotic gene with a well-known product. Not only do these ribosomal genes come in a handy size, but they are also fully equipped with an appropriate RNA polymerase and other chromosomal proteins. The investigation of such ribosomal minichromosomes appears to be a sensible approach to a deeper understanding of the organization of chromatin at large.

ACKNOWLEDGMENTS

We wish to thank Glenn Kuehn for communicating unpublished observations and acknowledge critical reading of the manuscript by Ueli Gubler and Dorothy Braun. Supported by grant 3.501.75 of the Swiss National Science Foundation.

REFERENCES

Affolter, H.-U. & Braun, R. (1978) Ribosomal DNA in spores of *Physarum polycephalum. Biochim. Biophys. Acta* 519, 118–124.

Atmar, V. J. & Kuehn, G. D. (1978) Polyamine – stimulation of nonhistone acidic protein phosphorylation in nuclei and nucleoli from *Physarum polycephalum. Eur. J. Biochem.* 30, 29–37.

Braun, R. & Evans, T. E. (1969) Replication of nuclear satellite and mitochondrial DNA in the mitotic cycle of *Physarum. Biochim. Biophys. Acta* 182, 511–522.

Braun, R., Hall, L., Schwärzler, M. & Smith, S. S. (1977) The mitotic cycle of *Physarum polycephalum.* In: *Cell Differentiation in Microorganisms, Plants and Animals,* ed. Nover, L. & Mothes, K., pp. 402–423. VEB Gustav Fischer Verlag, Jena.

Braun, R., Mittermayer, C. & Rusch, H. P. (1965) Sequential temporal replication of DNA in *Physarum polycephalum. Proc. Natl. Acad. Sci. USA* 53, 924–931.

Braun, R. & Wili, H. (1969) Time sequence of DNA replication in *Physarum. Biochim. Biophys. Acta* 174, 246–252.

Butler, M. J., Davies, K. E. & Walker, I. O. (1978) The structure of nucleolar chromatin in *Physarum polycephalum. Nucl. Acids Res.* 5, 667–678.

Flint, S. J. & Weintraub, H. M. (1977) An altered subunit configuration associated with the actively transcribed DNA of integrated adenovirus genes. *Cell* 12, 783–794.

Gall, J. G. This volume, pp. 299–305.

Grainger, R. M. & Ogle, R. C. (1978) Chromatin structure of the ribosomal RNA genes in *Physarum polycephalum. Chromosoma* (Berl.) 65, 115–126.

Guttes, E. (1974) Continuous nucleolar DNA synthesis in late-interphase nuclei of *Physarum polycephalum* after transplantation into postmitotic plasmodia. *J. Cell Sci.* 15, 131–143.

Hall, L. & Braun, R. (1977) The organisation of genes for transfer RNA and ribosomal RNA in amoebae and plasmodia of *Physarum polycephalum. Eur. J. Biochem.* 76, 165–174.

Hall, L. & Turnock, G. (1976) Synthesis of ribosomal RNA during the mitotic cycle in the slime mould *Physarum polycephalum. Eur. J. Biochem.* 62, 471–477.

Hall, L., Gubler, U. & Braun, R. (1978) Metabolic stability of the extrachromosomal ribosomal RNA genes in the slime mould *Physarum polycephalum. Eur. J. Biochem.* 86, 45–50.

Hall, L., Turnock, G. & Cox, B. J. (1975) Ribosomal RNA genes in the amoebal and plasmodial forms of the slime moulds. *Physarum polycephalum. Eur. J. Biochem.* 51, 459–465.

Hirt, B. (1967) Selective extraction of Polyoma DNA from infected mouse cell cultures. *J. Mol. Biol.* 26, 365–369.

Holt, C. E. & Gurney, E. G. (1969) Minor components of the DNA of *Physarum polycephalum. J. Cell Biol.* 40, 484–496.

Jerzmanowski, A., Staron, K., Tyniec, B., Bernhardt-Smigielska, J. & Toczko, K. (1976) Subunit structure of *Physarum polycephalum* chromatin. *FEBS – Lett.* 62, 251–254.

Jockusch, B. M. (1975) Neuere Forschungen über Zellzyklus und Kernteilung am Schleimpilz *Physarum polycephalum. Naturwiss.* 62, 283–289.

Johnson, E. M., Allfrey, V. C., Bradbury, E. M. & Matthews, H. R. (1978) Altered nucleosome structure containing DNA sequences complementary to 19S and 26S ribosomal RNA in *Physarum polycephalum. Proc. Natl. Acad. Sci. USA* 75, 1116–1120.

Johnson, E. M., Littau, V. C., Allfrey, V. G., Bradbury, E. M. & Matthews, H. R. (1976) Subunit structure of chromatin from *Physarum polycephalum. Nucl. Acids Res.* 3, 3313–3329.

Matthews, H. R.,Johnson, E. M., Steer, W. M., Bradbury, E. M. & Allfrey, V. G. (1978) The use of netropsin with CsCl gradients for the analysis of DNA and its application to restriction nuclease fragments of ribosomal DNA from *Physarum polycephalum. Eur. J. Biochem.* 82, 569–576.

Mohberg, J. (1974) The nucleus of the plasmodial slime moulds. In: *The Cell Nucleus,* vol. 1, ed. Busch, H., pp. 187–218. Acad. Press, New York.

Molgaard, H. V. (1978) rDNA organisation in *Physarum polycephalum.* In: *The Cell Nucleus,* vol. 5, ed. Busch, H., Acad. Press, New York.

Molgaard, H. V., Matthews, H. R. & Bradbury, E. M. (1976) Organisation of genes for ribosomal RNA in *Physarum polycephalum. Eur. J. Biochem.* 68, 541–549.

Newlon, C. S., Sonenshein, G. E. & Holt, C. E. (1973) Time of synthesis of gene for ribosomal ribonucleic acid in *Physarum. Biochem.* 12, 2338–2345.

Petes, T. D., Hereford, L. M. & Botstein, D. (1977) Organization of yeast ribosomal DNA. In: *Molecular Approaches to Eucaryotic Genetic Systems,* ed. Wilcox, G., Abelson, J. & Fox, C. F., pp. 239–246. Academic Press, New York.

Ryser, U. & Braun, R. (1974) The amount of DNA coding for rRNA during differentiation (spherulation) in *Physarum polycephalum. Biochim. Biophys. Acta* 361, 33–36.

Schiebel, W. (1973) The cell cycle of *Physarum polycephalum.* In: *Physarum polycephalum,* ed.

Hüttermann, A., pp. 11–38. Gustav Fischer Verlag, Stuttgart.

Seebeck, T., Stalder, J. & Braun, R. (1978) Isolation of a minichromosome containing the ribosomal genes from *Physarum polycephalum. Biochem.* In press.

Stalder, J. & Braun, R. (1978) Chromatin structure of *Physarum polycephalum* plysmodia and amoebae. *FEBS – Lett.* 90, 223–227.

Stalder, J., Seebeck, T. & Braun, R. (1978a) Accessibility of the ribosomal genes to micrococcal nuclease in *Physarum polycephalum. Biochim. Biophys. Acta.* In press.

Stalder, J., Seebeck, T. & Braun, R. (1978b) Degradation of the ribosomal genes by DNase I in *Physarum polycephalum. Eur. J. Biochem.* 90, 391–395.

Staron, K., Jerzmanowski, A., Tyniec, B., Urbanska, A. & Toczko, K. (1977) Nucleoprotein chromatin subunit from *Physarum polycephalum. Biochim. Biophys. Acta* 475, 131–138.

Taylor, W. C., Cockburn, A. F., Frankel, G. A., Newkirk, M. J. & Firtel, R. A. (1977) Organization of ribosomal and 5S RNA coding regions in *Dictyostelium discoideum.* In: *Molecular Approaches to Eucaryotic Genetic Systems,* ed. Wilcox, G., Abelson, J. & Fox, C. F., pp. 309–313. Academic Press, New York.

Vogt, V. M. & Braun, R. (1976a) Structure of ribosomal DNA in *Physarum polycephalum. J. Mol. Biol.* 106, 567–587.

Vogt, V. M. & Braun, R. (1976b) Repeated structure of chromatin in metaphase nuclei of *Physarum polycephalum. FEBS – Lett.* 64, 190–192.

Vogt, V. M. & Braun, R. (1977) The replication of ribosomal DNA in *Physarum polycephalum. Eur. J. Biochem.* 80, 557–566.

Wellauer, P. K., Reeder, R. H., Dawid, I. B. & Brown, D. D. (1976) The arrangement of length heterogeneity in repeating units of amplified and chromosomal ribosomal DNA from *Xenopus laevis. J. Mol. Biol.* 105, 487–505.

Yao, M.-C. & Gall, J. G. (1977) A single integrated gene for ribosomal RNA in a eucaryote, *Tetrahymena pyriformis. Cell* 12, 121–132.

Zellweger, A., Ryser, U. & Braun, R. (1972) Ribosomal genes of *Physarum:* Their isolation and replication in the mitotic cycle. *J. Mol. Biol.* 64, 681–691.

DISCUSSION

WESTERGAARD: May I ask you a question about this 70,000 Daltons protein, which you find is stimulating transcription? Does the protein work on 1) the elongation rates of the RNA polymerase 2) the termination of transcription, or do you know at which level it is working?

BRAUN: All we know is that UTP incorporation is stimulated by a factor of 10 or 20.

BIRNSTIEL: Does this protein bind to ribosomal DNA in any specific way?

BRAUN: Yes, the protein binds more strongly to rDNA than to any other DNA we have studied. In fact, binding occurs only to specific restriction fragments of rDNA.

BIRNSTIEL: Does the secondary site of initiation of DNA synthesis relate closely to the initation of transcription?

BRAUN: No, it is most likely that transcription initiates much farther out on both sides of the rDNA molecule.

GALL: Does the secondary site correspond to the snapback region that is not in the middle of the molecule?

BRAUN: That is right. It corresponds to this repeated sequence region, but it is not known whether there is any causal relation between the presence of small internal snapbacks and initiation of DNA replication.

GALL: Is it possible that the sequences at the center of the molecule are present in three doses?

BRAUN: This would be conceivable. What we would need, of course, is to have a restriction enzyme that cuts in that region and then compare the fragments. But all the restriction enzymes that we have been using up to now do not give small fragments of the central potion of the rDNA. Most restriction cuts are within or close to the coding region of the molecule.

RICH: Have you looked at the histones in the minichromosome and compared them with the other histones?

BRAUN: I should make one comment on this, namely that Grainger & Ogle (1978) have looked at what seems to be rDNA in the process of transcription, and have made Miller pictures of this material. In the nontranscribed area, in the spacer area, they find nucleosomes or structures that look like nucleosomes. So there may well be histones in the nontranscribed spacer. However, in the transcribed region micrococcal nuclease digestion yields fragments which are not identical with the normal nucleosome fragments as regards their size. So there is something different in the protection of the transcribed region from that of bulk chromatin, Johnson *et al.* (1978) have done experiments in the same system. They also find that micrococcal nuclease gives an unexpected result indicating some different spacial organization in the transcribed region from the non-transcribed region. As regards a direct answer to your question, we have done iodinations of proteins, but I cannot comment on the outcome since it has not been clearcut enough.

HOGNESS: Can you isolate minichromosomes during mitosis? Did I get the implication that you were saying, there is no transcription, no synthesis of rRNA at that time, and that at that time this DNA appeared to be sensitive to nuclease as if it were an active form?

BRAUN: To answer your first question: Plasmid-like rDNA has been isolated from interphase as well as from mitosis. To your second question: Although rRNA synthesis virtually stops in mitosis, the sensitivity of r-chromatin to DNase I remains high in mitosis, indicating that the r-chromatin retains some of its features of active chromatin.

HOGNESS: Have you tried to investigate the nucleosome distributions?

BRAUN: We have not done any isolation of whole minichromosomes in mitosis, but the rate of transcription of rRNA is very much reduced in mitosis as it is in other eukaryotic cells. However, what we have looked at is whether the minichromosomes are still present as free, isolatable bits of DNA of standard size. And this is the case, making it unlikely that rDNA is temporarily incorporated into large chromosomes at mitosis.

GALL: Does the nucleolus persist in mitosis?

BRAUN: It is dissolved in mitosis as judged by electron microscopy and light microscopy and then reassembles within an hour after mitosis.

DAWID: Have you looked for one or a few intergrated copies in larger DNA?

BRAUN: This is something that we have been attempting to do for quite a while. The experiments have had certain technical problems. What we can say is that there have to be less than five integrated copies based on experiments involving hybridization across sucrose gradients. Maybe I could point out that in differentiation the same amount of 100 or 150 free copies persist in all stages we looked at. The organism can under adverse condition do all sorts of tricks to protect itself: it can form sclerotia, it can also go through a sexual cycle producing spores and it can make motile amoebae. To our great surprise even in the spores which follow meiosis, we have these 150 free copies. We had thought that the spores might economize on space and only retain few copies of rDNA. But this is not the case. Our findings of course do not eliminate the possibility that rDNA might be temporarily broken down and resynthesized from a master copy during meiosis.

Isolation and Partial Characterization of the Snap-back Form of a Novel Giant Palindromic DNA Molecule from *Tetrahymena*

Hans Klenow

In *Tetrahymena* (Engberg *et al.* 1976, Karrer & Gall 1976) and *Physarum* (Vogt & Braun 1976) the DNA carrying the genes for rRNA is extrachromosomal and has the structure of a giant palindrome, i.e. these DNA molecules have an axis of twofold rotational symmetry with regard to base sequence. The isolation of these molecules is based on their high density relative to that of the bulk of the DNA from the respective organisms.

These findings raise the question of whether other extrachromosomal palindromic molecules with densities close to that of the bulk of the DNA exist in these organisms. To answer this question we have developed a procedure independent of density properties of DNA for the isolation of the snap-back form of free palindromic DNA molecules. The procedure is based on the rapid cooling of a heated solution of isolated total cellular nucleic acids. In the resulting solution the only completely double-stranded DNA present would be free palindromic DNA molecules in their snap-back form. These molecules may be separated from single-stranded DNA by distribution in an aqueous two-phase system containing dextran and polyethylene glycol (Albertsson 1965).

The procedure is as follows: *Tetrahymena* cells were grown at 28° in threefold diluted medium prepared according to Neff *et al.* (1964) to a density of 3×10^5 to 5×10^5 cells per ml. Cells were harvested, lysed and digested with proteinase K

Department of Biochemistry B, Panum Institute, Blegdamsvej 3C, DK-2200 Copenhagen N, Denmark.

SPECIFIC EUKARYOTIC GENES, Alfred Benzon Symposium 13, Munksgaard 1979

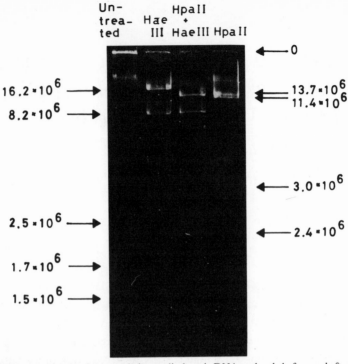

Fig. 1. Gel electrophoresis of the novel giant palindromic DNA molecule before and after treatment with restriction endonucleases Hpa II, Hae III and Hpa II plus Hae III. The molecule was isolated from *Tetrahymena thermophila*. Electrophoresis was performed in 0.7% neutral agarose at 15 mM. The numbers indicate molecular weights.

essentially as described by Karrer & Gall (1976). Total cellular DNA was obtained by gentle treatment of the digest with chloroform: octanol (10:1) followed by addition of 0.8 volume of water and 1.8 volumes of isopropanol to the aqueous phase. The precipitate was collected by centrifugation, thoroughly washed with 50% isopropanol in 10 mM sodium phosphate buffer pH 6.9, redissolved in the same buffer and reprecipitated with 1 volume of isopropanol. The precipitate was dissolved in 15 ml of the phosphate buffer for each 10^9 cells worked up. The solution was heated on a boiling water bath to more than 90° for 4 min and rapidly cooled on ice. To each ml of DNA solution was added 0.63 g phase system (0°) consisting of 9.20 g polyethylene glycol (7000) and 16.80 g dextran (T 500) dissolved in 74.0 ml water. After mixing and centrifugation, the upper phase containing double-stranded DNA was obtained. When the procedure was applied to *Tetrahymena thermophila* about 2% of the DNA was present in this phase. Most of the phase system was removed from the upper phase as follows. The volume was reduced to 30% by evaporation in a stream of air. This resulted in formation of a small, new lower phase containing more than 90% of the DNA. The upper phase was discarded and to each gram of the small lower phase was added 2 ml new upper phase (obtained from a mixture of 1 ml phosphate buffer and 0.63 g phase system) 0.8 ml water and 0.25 ml 0.3 M LiOH. After shaking, more than 90% of the DNA was now present in the upper phase. This phase was collected and the polyethylene glycol present removed by shaking with chloroform. The resulting aqueous solution was subjected to CsCl gradient equilibrium centrifugation. From *Tetrahymena* two density classes of DNA were obtained. The heavier one consisted of the snap-back form of rDNA while the lighter one with a density close to that of bulk DNA consisted of a separate unique molecule.

Analysis by gel electrophoresis of the light DNA component showed the presence of a single-sized class of a molecular weight of about 30×10^6. Treatment with various restriction enzymes gave rise to a number of bands of well-defined sizes. The sum of the molecular weights of the bands obtained by each enzyme was very close to 30×10^6. A physical map of the molecule has been constructed on the basis of treatment with the restriction endonucleases Hpa II and Hae III (Fig. 1). Treatment of ^{3}H-thymidine-labeled molecules with the single-strand specific endonuclease S_1 rendered less than 8% of the radioactivity acid-soluble. Most of the restriction enzyme bands were unaffected by pretreatment with endonuclease S_1.

It is concluded that the isolated molecule is the snap-back form of a novel giant extrachromosomal palindromic DNA molecule. In its native form it would have a molecular weight of about 60×10^6. The cells contain more than 40 of these molecules per haploid genome. A molecule of this type has been isolated from both a micronucleate strain B7 (*thermophila*) and from an amicronucleate strain GL(*pyriformis*) of *Tetrahymena*. The restriction enzyme patterns were different in the two cases.

Hybridization experiments showed the absence in these molecules of genes for 17S rRNA, 25S rRNA, 5S RNA and tRNA (Klenow & Tønnesen 1978).

Experiments on the possible presence in the molecules of genes for mRNA and on their localization in the cell by *in situ* hybridization are in progress.

REFERENCES

Albertsson, P.-Å. (1965) Partition studies of nucleic acids. *Biochim. Biophys. Acta* 103, 1–12.

Engberg, J., Andersson, P., Leick, V. & Collins, J. (1976) Free ribosomal DNA molecules from *Tetrahymena pyriformis* GL are giant palindromes. *J. Mol. Biol.* 104, 455–70.

Karrer, K. M. & Gall, J. G. (1976) The macronuclear ribosomal DNA of *Tetrahymena pyriformis* is a palindrome. *J. Mol. Biol.* 104, 421–455.

Klenow, H. & Tønnesen, T. Unpublished results.

Neff, R. J., Ray, S. A., Benson, W. F. & Wilborn, M. (1964) In: *Methods in Cell Physiology*, vol. 1, ed. Prescott, D. M., pp. 55–83. Academic Press, New York and London.

Vogt, V. M. & Braun, R. (1976) Structure of ribosomal DNA in *Physarum polycephalum. J. Mol. Biol.* 106, 567–589.

DISCUSSION

DAWID: What is the GC content of this palindrome? You have so few *Hae*III and *Hpa*II sites that you might think it very A-T rich.

KLENOW: Yes, it is very A-T rich. Its density in CsCl is a little lower than that of bulk DNA of the same cell. This means that it contains more than 71% A-T.

SCHAFFNER: It could be assumed that the ribosomal palindrome and this new palindrome would replicate in a similar manner. Have you checked by, e.g. cross hybridization, if the ends and/or the center have homologous sequences?

KLENOW: No, we have not made cross-hybridization experiments. But we have evidence that the end groups in the two types of molecules are different. The snapback form of rDNA as isolated by our procedure forms a number of discrete bands after gel electrophoresis, corresponding to mono-, di- and oligomers. The di- and oligomers are converted to monomers by treatment with DNA polymerase I of *E. coli* in the presence of dGTP and dTTP or by treatment with S_1 endonuclease. These observations are in agreement with the findings of Blackburn & Gall (1978) that rDNA molecules near the ends contain repeated hexanucleotide sequences of the type 5' CCCCAA 3'. These sequences are interrupted by a number of gaps or nicks. In the complementary strand the hexanucleotide sequences GGGGTT are probably interrupted by fewer gaps or nicks. After heating and rapid cooling such molecules would contain cohesive ends giving rise to dimers and branched oligomers in agreement with our observations. Since similar structures are not observed for the newly isolated molecule, it may be concluded that the ends of the molecules are different in the two cases.

SCHAFFNER: Do you know if this extrachromosomal element hybridizes to histone sequences?

KLENOW: No, we do not.

Blackburn, E. H. & Gall, J. G. (1978) A tandemly repeated sequence at the termini of the extrachromosomal RNA genes in *Tetrahymena*. *J. Mol. Biol.* 120, 33–53.

BORST: We know that about 1% of the total DNA in *Tetrahymena* is mitochondrial and that this mitochondrial DNA contains inverted duplications. My question is therefore: where in your fractionation does the mitochondrial DNA go? You would expect, because this inverted duplication is only at the ends in most strains, that you would get a partially denatured molecule with one big duplex stretch.

KLENOW: We do not know how mitochondrial DNA after heat treatment would distribute in the two-phase aqueous system. But since it would contain a fairly large proportion of single-stranded DNA I think that it would distribute in favor of the lower phase together with single-stranded DNA. In addition, I believe that both the restriction fragments we have obtained, and the finding that less than 7% of the DNA is made acid-soluble by treatment wit the single-strand specific S_1 endonuclease, talks strongly against the possibility that the molecule we have isolated is the denatured form of mitochondrial DNA.

Extrachromosomal RNA Genes in *Tetrahymena:* Structure and Evolution

Jan Engberg & Nanni Din

INTRODUCTION

In eukaryotes the nuclear genes that code for the common precursor molecules of the cytoplasmic ribosomal RNAs are present in several hundred copies per haploid genome and most, if not all, are either clustered in distinct regions of specific chromosomes, or, in some cell systems, as extrachromosomal amplified nucleolar units (for reviews see, e.g. Gall 1969, 1974, Busch & Smetana 1970, Birnstiel *et al.* 1971, Engberg *et al.* 1974, Tobler 1975). It has been shown by various techniques that these genes are tandemly arranged in repeating units each consisting of alternating transcribed regions and non-transcribed spacer regions. In a given cell system the actual gene sequences are virtually identical while a certain degree of size and sequence heterogeneity may exist in the non-transcribed spacer regions of a gene cluster (Trendelenburg *et al.* 1976, Wellauer *et al.* 1976). Between related species extensive spacer heterogeneity may exist (in transcribed as well as in non-transcribed spacer regions), while the gene regions are still apparently identical (Forsheit *et al.* 1974), but in more distantly related species also the gene regions may be demonstrably different, although they apparently evolve more slowly than the spacer region (Sinclair & Brown 1971).

The ciliated protozoan *Tetrahymena* contains a germinal diploid micro-nucleus which maintains the genetic continuity of the organism, as well as a polyploid macronucleus, which is formed after conjugation from the zygotic nucleus. The macronucleus functions as a somatic nucleus directing most of the cell's transcriptional activity during vegetative growth, but is destroyed at the end of each sexual generation. The two nuclei differ drastically in their content

Biochemical Institute B, Panum Institute, University of Copenhagen, Denmark.

SPECIFIC EUKARYOTIC GENES, Alfred Benzon Symposium 13, Munksgaard 1979

of ribosomal RNA genes. The germinal micronucleus contains a single chromosomally integrated copy per haploid genome (Yao & Gall 1977), while the somatic macronucleus contains about 600 extrachromosomal gene copies per haploid genome (about 1% of the total nuclear DNA, Engberg *et al.* 1976). In the two different species of *Tetrahymena* used in the study of Karrer & Gall (1976) and Engberg *et al.* (1976) the extrachromosomal rDNA was found to be linear DNA molecules, each containing two copies of the rRNA genes arranged as inverted repeats about a central axis of symmetry (so-called palindromes). The size and structure of the rDNA from these two species were clearly different as revealed by restriction enzyme mapping. Each species, however, contained entirely homogeneous rDNA populations.

We have now examined the extrachromosomal rDNA from a large number of different *Tetrahymena* strains to provide insight in the degree of sequence divergence which exists in a specific gene among closely related lower eukaryotes.

METHODS

All *Tetrahymena* strains, with the exception of *T. pyriformis, T. thermophila* BIV and BVII were kindly provided by Ellen Simon of the University of Illinois at Urbana-Champaign. Stock designation and species affiliation for the strains used are given in Table I.

All strains were cultivated in a complex proteose peptone, yeast extract medium as previously described for the strain *T. pyriformis* GL (Engberg & Pearlman 1972). The rDNA was isolated in the form of snap-back molecules by the method of Klenow (this volume) or in its native form by a modification of the hot phenol extraction procedure developed for isolation of mitochondrial DNA (Arnberg *et al.* 1977). The products of restriction enzyme digestion were fractionated by electrophoresis on 0.7, 1.0 or 1.4% agarose slap gels (20 cm × 13 cm × 0.3 cm) in TEAN buffer (50 mM Tris acetate, 2 mM EDTA, 20 mM sodium acetate, 18 mM sodium chloride, pH 8.05). *Eco* RI-generated fragments of phage λ wt, λ d *rif* D18 or λ d *ilv* 5 were used as molecular weight markers. Molecular weights are expressed in daltons (D). The fragments were visualized by fluorography after ethidium bromide staining (Engberg *et al.* 1976) before transfer onto cellulose nitrate filters (Southern 1975). Filters were hybridized to *in vitro*-labeled rRNA as described by Yav & Gall (1977). Unlabeled rRNA was prepared from *T. thermophila* as described by Leick & Plesner (1968)

Table I
Species and mating types of the Tetrahymena complex used in this study

Species	Mating type	Stock designation	Former syngen no.
T. pyriformis	a-sexual	GL	–
T. thermophila	I	A 1873–1a	
	IV	B 1868	1
	VII	B 1868	
T. americanis	II	UI 7101	2
	IV	UM 330	
T. borealis	IV	UM 731	
	VI	UM 779	3
	VII	UM 811	
T. cosmopolitanis	I	UM 913	4
T. pigmentosa	I	UM 1060	
	II	UM 1091	6
	III	UI 7152h	
	I	ALP 6	
	II	IL 12	8
	III	UM 1286	
T. canadensis	I	UM 1215	7
T. tropicalis	III	TC 3	9
T. hyperangularis	I	10 I EN	10
T. australis	II	Au-1-2x	11
T. capricornis	III	AU-F$_1$-1	12

and labeled *in vitro* by a modification (Kay, personal communication) of the procedure of Kimmel & Gorovsky (1978).

RESULTS

Isolation of snap-back rDNA molecules

The demonstration of the palindromic nature of the rDNA molecules from two different species of *Tetrahymena* prompted the development of an isolation procedure for free palindromic DNA molecules. This procedure is based on the isolation of double-stranded DNA after melting of total cellular DNA followed

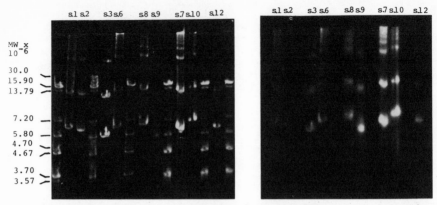

Fig. 1. Agarose gel electrophoretic characterization of snap-back rDNA molecules isolated from different *Tetrahymena* strains.

Isolation of snap-back rDNA and electrophoresis on 0.7% agarose slap gels were performed as described in Methods. *Eco*RI-generated fragments of λ wt and λ d *rif* D18 were used as molecular weight markers. The snap-back rDNA preparations prepared by the method of Klenow (this volume) consisted of monomeric snap-back rDNA molecules as well as dimeric and oligomeric forms. These latter complexes could be converted into the monomeric form by different treatments (Klenow 1977) including digestion with single-strand specific endonuclease. The symbols on top of the different gel slots (S1, S2, etc.) refer to the strain code used in Fig. 2 and Table I.

Fluorograph of the ethidium bromide-stained gel (a). Autoradiograph of the Southern blot of the gel shown in (a) hybridized to ^{32}P-labeled rRNA prepared from *Tetrahymena* S1.

by rapid cooling (Klenow, this volume). When this procedure was applied to *T. pyriformis* and *T. thermophila* snap-back rDNA molecules were isolated which by restriction analysis were shown to be identical to their palindromic counterparts except that the centrally located restriction fragment in the palindromic rDNA now was half of its original size (results not shown). Due to some special sequence arrangements near and at the ends of the free palindromic rDNA molecules (Klenow 1977, Blackburn & Gall 1978), this procedure also yielded snap-back molecules in dimeric and oligomeric complexes. The snap-back DNA isolation procedure was then applied to several different *Tetrahymena* species. In all cases snap-back rDNA molecules could be isolated. The molecules were identified by their strong hybridization to ^{32}P-labeled rRNA and by their restriction enzyme pattern. These results clearly demonstrate that the occurrence of free palindromic rDNA is common to all *Tetrahymena* species. Fig. 1 shows the gel electrophoretic characterization of the rDNA snap-back molecules isolated from representative *Tetrahymena* species together with the autoradiograph of the gel blot hybridized against ^{32}P-rRNA prepared from *T. thermophila.*

Restriction enzyme analysis of rDNA from different species

A structural comparison of the free rDNA molecules from different *Tetra-hymena* species was initiated by digesting purified native rDNA molecules or snap-back molecules with five different restriction enzymes followed by size determination of the restriction fragments produced by gel electrophoresis on agarose gels. The restriction fragments were further characterized by transfer to cellulose nitrate filters followed by hybridization to ^{32}P-labeled rRNA prepared from *T. thermophila.* The molecular weights of the different restriction fragments were established relative to molecular weight markers and varied less than 5% in different experiments. The details of these experiments will be reported elsewhere. From these data it can be seen that the rDNA fragments produced by a given restriction enzyme may or may not be easily distinguished when different species are compared. On the other hand, when additional restriction analyses are performed with rDNA from species which yield similar-sized restriction fragments using one particular restriction enzyme, clear differences in the restriction pattern are now demonstrated. It was therefore concluded that the rDNA molecules from the different *Tetrahymena* species could be unambiguously distinguished from each other by their restriction pattern when a variety of restriction enzymes were used.

Comparison of restriction maps

In order to do a more discriminating comparison of the different rDNA molecules than comparing the size of the different restriction fragments, the individual restriction maps were constructed and compared. Restriction maps could be easily constructed for those enzymes which cut the rDNA molecule relatively infrequently. By comparing the restriction pattern obtained by digesting the snap-back rDNA or the native palindromic rDNA molecules with a given enzyme, the centrally located restriction fragment (from hereon called the central fragment) could immediately be identified as the only fragment being different in the two patterns. In some cases intermediates in the digestion reaction resulting from incomplete digestion could be used to infer a physical linkage between two restriction fragments. In the case of *T. pyriformis* and *T. thermophila* a detailed mapping procedure was performed involving double digestions with different sets of enzymes (this work will be reported elsewhere).

Rotational axis
of symmetry

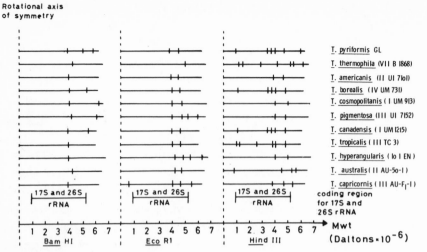

Fig. 2. Restriction maps of the palindromic rDNA molecules from different *Tetrahymena* strains. The dashed vertical lines represent the axis of rotational symmetry. The horizontal lines represent one half of the different rDNA molecules. The recognition sites for the restriction enzymes *Bam* Hl, *Eco* RI and *Hind* III are indicated by small bars. In the case of the *Hind* III maps of S3, S7, S9 and S11, the linear order of some of the smaller-sized fragments has not been definitively proven. The 26S plus 17S rRNA coding region was determined by hybridization of ^{32}P-labeled rRNA to Southern blots of the gels (see Methods). The line indicating the rRNA coding region has been drawn so as to span the region in the rDNA from all the *Tetrahymena* strains.

The *Eco*RI, the *Bam*HI and the *Hind* III maps of the rDNA molecules of members from the different *Tetrahymena* species are shown in Fig. 2. Note that the horizontal lines, which symbolize double-stranded DNA, show only one half of the palindromic molecules. The maps again stress the conclusion made on the basis of the raw restriction data, viz., that rDNA from different *Tetrahymena* species can be identified from each other by the intramolecular location of their restriction sites. More evident, however, is the striking uniformity of the different rDNA molecules in the intramolecular position of some of their restriction sites. Hence, the centrally located *Bam* site gives rise to a central *Bam* fragment of very similar size (about 8×10^6 D) in all the species. With a few exceptions a similar situation exists with respect to the centrally located *Eco*RI site. It can furthermore be noted that the small-size changes of the central *Bam* fragment when different species are compared are paralleled by similar-sized changes of the corresponding *Eco*RI fragment, which suggests that the primary DNA sequence around this position is identical in the different rDNA molecules. These observations taken together with hybridization data showing a high degree of cross hybridization (75–100%) in the rRNA-DNA reaction among the different species (Allen & Gibson 1973) suggest that a very strong conservation of the rRNA sequences has occurred during the estimated 10^6 years since the species diverged (Borden *et al.* 1976).

Comparison of different strains

The structural differences of the rDNA demonstrated so far have been in molecules isolated from different species which, by definition, are noninterbreeding. In interpreting these observations in terms of evolutionary divergence, it would be of great importance to investigate whether sequence differences could be demonstrated in rDNA molecules isolated from different strains within a given species. Restriction analyses similar to the ones described were therefore performed on rDNA isolated from several different strains belonging to different species (Table I). The results for the strains belonging to *T. pigmentosa* (formerly called syngen 6 and 8) will be discussed later. The results for the remaining strains showed that no differences could be detected in the restriction pattern of the rDNA isolated from different strains belonging to the same species (results not shown). Although we have not yet been able to trace the genetic background for all of the different mating types (some may have resulted from the same genetic cross and are therefore not different strains), it is certain that some of the strains used belong to different inbred strain families and/or represent geographically separate single isolates.

rDNA of the T. pigmentosa group

Members of the *T. pigmentosa* group represent a special case in that it consists of what was formerly considered as two noninterbreeding species: syngen 6 and syngen 8. Since conjugation has been observed between members of these two syngens under special conditions, the syngen designation could no longer be withheld (Nanney & McCoy 1976). In view of the conclusion made with respect to the restriction pattern identity of rDNA from different strains within the *T. thermophila, T. americanis* and *T. borealis* species (formerly syngens 1, 2 and 3), it was interesting to note that differences in the restriction patterns of rDNA from the *T. pigmentosa* group were evident. The restriction maps of these rDNA molecules were constructed as previously described and are shown in Fig. 3. The general similarity of the different maps which was observed when the previously shown maps were compared (Fig. 2) is also evident when the maps shown in Fig.

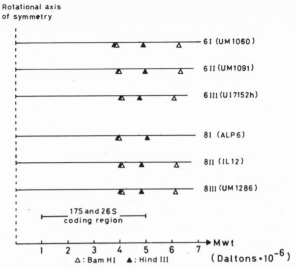

Fig. 3. Restriction maps of the palindromic rDNA molecules from different *Tetrahymena* strains within the *T. pigmentosa* group (formerly syngens 6 and 8). The dashed vertical line represents the axis of rotational symmetry. The horizontal lines represent one half of the different rDNA molecules. The recognition sites for *Bam* HI (△) and *Hind* III (▲) are indicated. The line indicating the 26S and 17S coding region has been drawn as to span this region in all the different strains.

3 are compared. Since the gel electrophoretic technique used for the size determination of the restriction fragments easily resolves molecular weight differences of 0.02×10^6 D in the 0.2 to 1.5×10^6 D range, it is justified to pay attention to even small size differences. It may be noted that the small *Hind*III fragment located distally in the 26S coding region has a size which falls in two distinct classes: 0.75×10^6 D in 6 III, 8 II and 8 III compared with 1.05×10^6 D in 6 I, 6 II and 8 I. If the *Bam* and *Hind* III sites at about 4.0×10^6 D distance from the center is assumed to define an identical strech of DNA sequence in this coding region, the observed difference in distance to the next distally located *Hind* III restriction site when 6 III, 8 II and 8 III is compared with that in 6 I, 6 II and 8 I, may indicate that a small $(0.2–0.3 \times 10^6$ D) insert analogous to what has been demonstrated in the case of the rRNA genes of *Drosophila* (Glover & Hogness 1977) is present in this region of the rDNA from 6 I, 6 II and 8 I. This interesting possibility which was originally suggested by Martha Wild, Yale University, is currently being investigated by R-loop mapping (Wild & Gall, personal communication). Irrespective of the possible presence of an insert in the rDNA of some of the strains of *T. pigmentosa*, it is clear that strain

differences exist with respect to the rDNA restriction pattern. These observations are in contrast with the observations made in *T. thermophila, T. americanis* and *T. borealis* but can be explained simply by suggesting that the strain differences in *T. pigmentosa* unlike the situation in the other species express themselves in the rDNA sequences. The implications of these findings will be pursued later.

DISCUSSION

The following basic observations have been made in the present work: 1) The individual populations of the extrachromosomal rDNA molecules isolated from different *Tetrahymena* strains all consist of palindromic molecules which appear homogeneous with respect to size and base sequence, 2) Basic sequence similarities exist in the rDNA isolated from different species but each species can be unequivocally distinguished from the others by its restriction pattern resulting from the use of several restriction enzymes, and 3) One out of four species examined contained strains which differed in their rDNA sequence.

The absence of size and sequence heterogeneity in spacer as well as in gene region in individual extrachromosomal rDNA populations is most easily explained by assuming that these molecules are derived from a single chromosomally integrated rRNA gene copy. It has been demonstrated that the macronucleus of *T. thermophila* contains no chromosomally integrated rRNA genes (Yao & Gall 1977) and that the extrachromosomal rDNA molecules replicate autonomously during vegetative growth (Truett & Gall 1978). Hence, the formation of extrachromosomal rDNA from an integrated gene copy must occur during the sexual cycle when the zygotic nucleus (which has the genetic constituency of the new micronucleus) develops into a macronucleus. This is in accordance with the fact that the micronucleus in contrast to the macronucleus was shown to contain one chromosomally integrated rRNA copy per haploid genome (Yao & Gall 1977) and that rDNA amplification has been shown to take place at an early stage of the macronuclear development (Pearlman *et al.*, this volume).

However, the amicronucleate species *T. pyriformis* that cannot go through a sexual cycle also contained a homogeneous population of extrachromosomal, palindromic rDNA molecules. Amicronucleate *Tetrahymena* strains are quite common (40% of the *Tetrahymena* found in nature are amicronucleate, Elliott 1973) but it is not known whether these strains are derived from micronuclear species or not. Available data show *T. pyriformis* to be evolutionary very distant from any of the known micronucleate species (Nanney & McCoy 1976). Likewise, it is not possible to invoke a likely micronuclear ancestor for the *T. pyriformis* strain from the present restriction data.

The demonstration of the homogeneity of the individual rDNA populations, together with the uniqueness of the rDNA molecules isolated from different *Tetrahymena* strains, may be helpful for identification purposes. The use of restriction patterns for estimating relatedness may, however, be doubtful in view of the demonstration that strain differences exist within species. The demonstration of these strain differences, on the other hand, is very helpful for other studies involving genetic crosses. The genetic constitution of the micronuclear DNA, with respect to the rRNA genes, of the *T. pigmentosa* strains is not known. The presence of only one type of macronuclear amplified rDNA in each of them may suggest that each of them are homozygous with respect to their micronuclear rRNA genes. If two strains having different rDNA were crossed, one would expect a heterozygous zygotic micronucleus to be produced and subsequently that both types of rDNA would be found as amplified rDNA molecules. However, since macronuclear genes in *Tetrahymena* are subjected to a process called phenotypic assortment which gradually enriches for macronuclear homozygosity during vegetative growth (Nanney 1969), heterozygosity of the micronucleus is not necessarily reflected by the macronucleus. Depending on whether the strains in *T. pigmentosa* are heterozygous or homozygous with respect to their micronuclear rRNA genes, one would expect one of the following results of a given cross: 1) The F1 progeny will contain initially a mixture of the two types of parental rDNA which will gradually assort to homogeneity for one or the other, 2) the F1 progeny will contain parental rDNA as well as nonparental rDNA. The latter situation arises if (at least) one of the parents are heterozygous in its micronuclear rRNA genes or if recombinational events take place. It thus appears that the strains of the *T. pigmentosa* group will be very helpful in investigating these important genetic events at the molecular level.

ACKNOWLEDGMENTS

Dr. Ellen Simon, University of Illinois at Urbana-Champaign, generously provided most of the *Tetrahymena* strains. Restriction enzymes *Eco*RI and *Bam*Hl were gifts from Poul Valentin Jensen and Poul Jørgensen, respectively.

Preparations of phage λ wt, λ d *rif* D18 and λ d *ilv* 5 were gifts from Poul Jørgensen and Dirk Bendiak. Drs. J. Gall, M.-C. Yao, M. Wild, B. Kay (Yale University), A. Arnberg (University of Amsterdam),and R. Pearlman (York University) are all thanked for most helpful communications during this work. Mr. F. Frenzel is thanked for expert technical help. This work was partly supported by the Danish Research Council for Natural Sciences (fellowship to Nanni Din) and by Nato Research Grant 1296.

REFERENCES

Allen, S. L. & Gibson, I. (1973) Genetics of *Tetrahymena*. In: *Biology of Tetrahymena*, ed. Elliott, A. M. p. 363. Dowden, Hutchinson & Ross, Inc., Stroudsburg, Pennsylvania.

Arnberg, A. C., Goldbach, R. W., Van Bruggen, E. F. J. & Borst, P. (1977) The Structure of *Tetrahymena pyriformis* mitochondrial DNA. *Biochim. Biophys. Acta* 477, 51–69.

Birnstiel, M. L., Chipchase, M. & Speirs, I. (1971) The ribosomal RNA cistrons. *Progr. Nucleic Acid Res.* 11, 351–389.

Blackburn, E. & Gall, J. G. (1978) A tandemly repeated sequence at the termini of the extrachromosomal ribosomal RNA genes in *Tetrahymena*. *J. Mol. Biol.* 120, 33–53.

Borden, D., Miller, E. T., Whitt, G. S. & Nanney, D. L. (1976) Electrophoretic analysis of evolutionary relationships in *Tetrahymena*. *Evolution* 31, 91–102.

Busch, H. & Smetana, K. (1970) *The Nucleolus.* Academic Press, New York.

Engberg, J. & Pearlman, R. E. (1972) The amount of ribosomal RNA genes in *Tetrahymena pyriformis* in different physiological states. *Eur. J. Biochem.* 26, 393–400.

Engberg, J., Christiansen, G. & Leick, V. (1974) Autonomous rDNA molecules containing single copies of ribosomal RNA genes in the macronucleus of *Tetrahymena pyriformis. Biochem. Biophys. Res. Commun.* 59, 1356–1365.

Engberg, J., Andersson, P., Leick, V. & Collins, J. (1976) Free ribosomal DNA molecules from *Tetrahymena pyriformis* GL are giant palindromes. *J. Mol. Biol.* 104, 455–470.

Forsheit, A. B., Davidsen, N. & Brown, D. D. (1974) An electron microscope heteroduplex study of the ribosomal DNAs of *Xenopus laevis* and *Xenopus mulleri. J. Mol. Biol.* 90, 301–314.

Gall, J. G. (1969) The genes for ribosomal RNA during oogenesis. *Genetics* (Suppl.) 61, 121–132.

Gall, J. G. (1974) Free ribosomal RNA genes in the macronucleus of *Tetrahymena. Proc. Natl. Acad. Sci. USA* 71, 3078–3081.

Glover, D. M. & Hogness, D. S. (1977) A novel arrangement of the 18S and 28S sequences in a repeating unit of *Drosophila melanogaster* rDNA. *Cell* 10, 167–176.

Karrer, K. M. & Gall, J. G. (1976) The macronuclear ribosomal DNA of *Tetrahymena pyriformis* is a palindrome. *J. Mol. Biol.* 104, 421–453.

Kimmel, A. R. & Gorovsky, M. A. (1978) Organization of the 5S RNA genes in macro- and micronuclei of *Tetrahymena pyriformis. Chromosoma* 67, 1–20.

Klenow, H. (1977) Specific properties of the end groups of rDNA from *Tetrahymena*. Proceedings of the Nato Advanced Study Institute on DNA Synthesis, Italy, 1977.

Leick, V. & Plesner, P. (1968) Formation of ribosomes in *Tetrahymena pyriformis. Biochim. Biophys. Acta* 169, 398–408.

Nanney, D. L. (1969) Macronuclear differentiation and subnuclear assortment in ciliates. In: *The Role of Chromosomes in Development.* ed. Locke, M. pp. 253–273. Academic Press, New York.

Nanney, D. L. & McCoy, I. W. (1976) Characterization of the species of the *Tetrahymena pyriformis* complex. *Trans. Am. Microscop. Soc.* 95, 664–682.

Sinclair, J. H. & Brown, D. D. (1971) Retention of common nucleotide sequences in the ribosomal deoxyribonucleic acid of eukaryotes and some of their physical characteristics. *Biochem.* 10, 2761–2769.

Southern, E. (1975) Detection of specific sequences among DNA fragments separated by gel electrophoresis. *J. Mol. Biol.* 98, 503–517.

Tobler, H. (1975) Occurrence and developmental significance of gene amplification. In: *Biochemistry of Animal Development,* vol. III, ed. Weber, R., pp. 91–143. Academic Press, New York.

Trendelenburg, M. F., Scheer, U., Zentgraf, H. & Franke, W. W. (1976) Heterogeneity of spacer lengths in circles of amplified ribosomal DNA of two insect species, *Dytiscus marginalis* and *Acheta domesticus. J. Mol. Biol.* 108, 453–470.

Truett, M. A. & Gall, J. G. (1978) The replication of ribosomal DNA in the macronucleus of *Tetrahymena. Chromosoma* 64, 295–303.

Wellauer, P. K., Reeder, R. H., Dawid, I. R. & Brown, D. D. (1976) The arrangement of length heterogeneity in repeating unis of amplified and chromosomal DNA from *Xenopus laevis. J. Mol. Biol.* 105, 487–505.

Yao, M.-C. & Gall, J. G. (1977) A single integrated gene for ribosomal RNA in a eukaryote, *Tetrahymena pyriformis. Cell* 12, 121–132.

DISCUSSION

FLAVELL: Is there any knowledge about the molecular nature of the allelic assortment phenomenon; is there a loss of DNA or loss of expression of DNA?

ENGBERG: Apparently it is just a question of statistics. You have an a-mitotic division of the macronucleus – so it is a question of how many generations it takes to obtain a pure population.

GALL: I can make a brief comment on your question, Dick, and then I would like to say something about the breeding experiments. There is no biochemical evidence on the mechanism of allelic assortment that I know of. The geneticists assume that assortment is due to nonuniform distribution of genes during the amitotic division of the macronucleus. One can predict from the known ploidy level how quickly heterozygous genes should become homozygous, and the observed number of generations is approximately correct.

Martha Wild in my laboratory in collaboration with Ellen Simon at the University of Illinois has done some experiments on the inheritance of rDNA which I will summarize briefly. As Jan says, if one takes strains that have been in the laboratory for a number of years and extracts rDNA from the macronucleus, that rDNA is, as far as one can see, absolutely homogeneous. That is, on gels there is one set of restriction fragments that add up to the correct size of the molecule. This is consistent with all extrachromosomal copies having been derived from one integrated copy. Since there are rDNA variants in the *pigmentosa* group, it is obvious that one should be able to get heterozygous strains. We have looked at Fls where the parents differed in restriction enzyme patterns, and in those Fls which have not undergone a large number of divisions the macronuclear rDNA may show restriction fragments which correspond to both parental types. The two parental types are not necessarily equally abundant. What we have not yet done is to carry those Fl strains for a large number of generations and see that their macronuclear rDNA becomes homogeneous. We presume that it will only because none of the laboratory strains are heterogeneous; but there are several possible explanations besides allelic assortment. I should also mention that some of the Fls show restriction fragments different from any in the parents. It is possible that the parents were heterozygous in the micronucleus, although phenotypically homogeneous in the macronucleus, and we are seeing genes which were not amplified in either parent. Although much more needs to be done, what we have observed is consistent with a simple picture of amplification from both genes in heterozygous individuals, but eventual fixation of one type of rDNA as some kind of population phenomenon.

WEISSMANN: I think we should be more precise in discussing relatedness of sequences, because when comparing two strains, a so-called insert in one strain may just reflect a deletion in the other strain and vice-versa. I think that many people will associate insert with something that has been introduced into the sequence. Indel might be a better word to indicate a difference which could have come about by an insertion or a deletion.

BORST: In the yeast strains that we have studied we can see that there are certain blocks of sequences that are present in some strains and not in others. We have always called these insertions/deletions, because we have no way of deciding what they are. One should not call these blocks insertion sequences (as has been done), because there is no evidence that they can move and there is no evidence that a specific indel is present in more than one location in the mtDNA. One of these indels happens to overlap the intervening sequence (or intron) in ribosomal RNA. I do not think that the indel in this case covers the whole intron because this would mean that strains without this indel would have no intron at all in their rRNA. This seems unlikely.

ENGBERG: One may consider a new term, taking into consideration the function of these introns. In the case of ribosomal RNA genes, for example, the inserts may be different from inserts which are put into genes to stop their function.

WEISSMANN: We could designate a sequence that has to be removed from a transcript before it is phenotypically active by the term processon. In principle. a mRNA precursor could give rise to two different mRNAs, depending on the mode of processing, such that a certain sequence could be a processon in the context of messenger I and an expresson in the context of messenger II.

RICH: It is the typical dilemma – whether you name something by its structure or by its function. The classic case is the so-called soluble RNA which was changed to transfer RNA when people knew its function. The problem with the term indel is that somerimes it is there and sometimes not. I would prefer a term which emphasizes its presence rather than its absemce, e.g. extron, because it is extra.

CRICK: I tried to think what the French would do and came up with heterometricon. Semour Benzer might suggest differon because it is different. Both these terms amphasize the difference and not whether it is an addition or a subtraction.

Macronuclear Development:
A Model System to Study Specific Gene
Expression in Nuclear Differentiation

V. Leick[1], B. Bro[2] & P. Bruns[3]

Conjugation in *Tetrahymena thermophila* (formerly *T. pyriformis* syngen 1, see Nanney & McCoy 1976) is both a necessary tool for genetics and a useful model system for studies in development. Conjugation entails an ordered sequence of nuclear events in the two members of a mating pair which first leads to the formation of new recombinant zygote nuclei, and then the development of new germinal (micro) and somatic (macro) nuclei from the zygote nuclei. The whole process takes about 20 h at 30°C and can be performed with large numbers of cells (Bruns & Brussard 1974a). Fig. 1 identifies the nuclear events; at the end of normal conjugation each cell contains a new hybrid micro- and macronucleus.

One aspect of this developmental sequence, the formation of the new macronucleus, may provide useful experimental material for studies in nuclear differentiation; in a 6–8-h period, a transcriptionally silent diploid nucleus is transformed into a transcriptionally active polyploid somatic nucleus (see Gorovsky 1973 for a review of the differences between these two nuclei). Several different methods have been employed to study the specific sequence of events in this process. We shall discuss here three different approaches: cytology, genetics and biochemistry. Each has incorporated into it methods to selectively view only conjugating cells in a mating mixture (mixtures with 100% conjugating cells have not yet been achieved).

Cytological studies allow a direct discrimination between mating and non-mating cells. Although a certain degree of asynchrony is found (the time for a

[1]Biochemical Institute B and [2]Biochemical Institute C, University of Copenhagen, Denmark. [3]Department of Botany, Genetics and Development, Cornell University, U.S.A.

SPECIFIC EUKARYOTIC GENES, Alfred Benzon Symposium 13, Munksgaard 1979

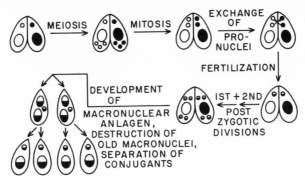

Fig. 1. Conjugation in *Tetrahymena thermophila*. Each conjugant undergoes meiotic reduction of the micronucleus, retains one of the haploid products and mitotically doubles it. Mutual exchange of haploid male pronuclei and following fertilization of female pronuclei produce the diploid zygote nuclei. Two mitotic divisions (post-zygotic divisions) of the zygote nuclei are followed by 1) DNA synthesis in the macronuclear anlagen 2) retention of one new micronucleus, and 3) loss of the second new micronucleus plus the parental macronucleus. The first cellular division (about 20 h after mixing of the cells at 30°c) segregates the new macronuclei, reconstituting the normal makeup of one macronucleus and one micronucleus (from Bruns & Brussard 1974a).

culture to go from 0 to maximum cells in pairs takes several hours), developing macronuclear anlagen are seen 10–18 h following the mixing of prestarved cells of two mating types. Fig. 2 presents several stages in the development of the macronucleus during this time in refed conjugants. The presence or absence of peptone seems to make no difference in the early macronuclear development (prior to 12 h). It is striking that addition of nutrients leads to the development of a macronucleus which cytologically looks rather mature by 18 h (Fig. 2 (3) and Nilsson & Leick 1970).

Manipulation of appropriate genetic markers permits an alternate measure of when the new macronucleus becomes active. Methods for the independent genetic manipulation of the two nuclei have been previously presented (Bruns & Brussard 1974b), as have several dominant drug-resistance mutations (Byrne & Bruns 1974). A strain with a micronucleus homozygous for the mutation *Mpr* which causes resistance to 6-methylpurine (6-mp) when expressed, but with a macronucleus expressing sensitivity, was crossed with a strain identical in all aspects except mating type. Since progeny of this cross develop new micro- and macronuclei containing only the mutant *Mpr* allele, they will become resistant to 6-mp. In order to determine when the cells become resistant, samples of the mating mixture were taken and inoculated into 1 % proteose peptone containing

25 µg/ml 6-mp. All samples taken before 12 h did not grow; all samples taken on
or after 12 h grew in the drug.

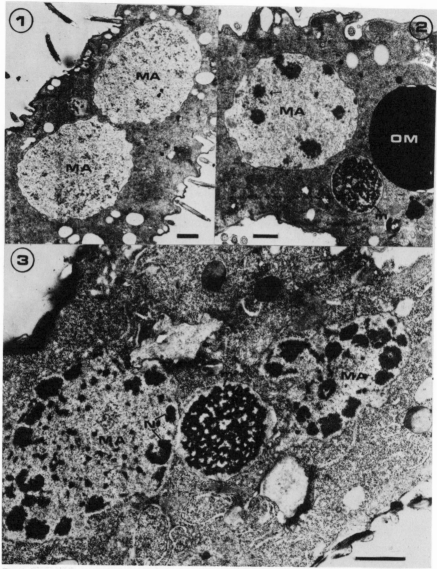

Fig. 2. Electron micrographs of developing macronuclear anlagen in conjugants refed with growth
medium (1% PPY) at 10 h. (1) 9.5 h after mixing of cells; (2) 13.5 h; (3) 18 h. MA: Macronuclear
anlagen. OM: Old macronucleus. N: Nucleoli. Bars indicate 1 µM. Arrow in (2) probably shows
developing nucleolus .

When the same type of experiment was performed with cells homozygous in their micronuclei for *Chx A*, a mutation conferring resistance to cycloheximide (Bleyman & Bruns 1977) but with macronuclei expressing sensitivity-resistance was attained at 15.5 h after mixing the two mating types. Similar results were obtained with a second cycloheximide resistance mutation *Chx B* which is genetically linked to *Chx A* (Ares & Bruns 1978). Both mutations result in ribosomes which have increased cycloheximide resistance *in vitro* (Sutton *et al.* 1978). *Chx A* seems to affect the large ribosomal subunit whereas *Chx B* alters the small subunit.

It should be noted that a somewhat different phenotypic pattern of macronuclear development is observed in cultures of nonfed conjugants, both with respect to cytology and timing of appearance of genetic markers.

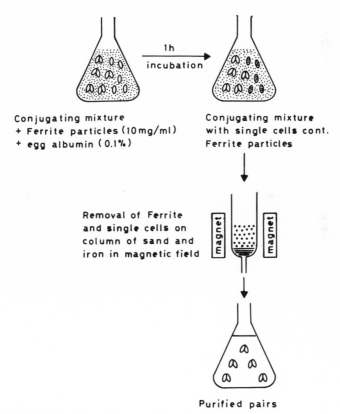

Purified pairs

Fig. 3. Principal scheme for magnetic purification of mating *Tetrahymena*. For further experimental details see Fig. 4 and Bruns *et al.* in prep.

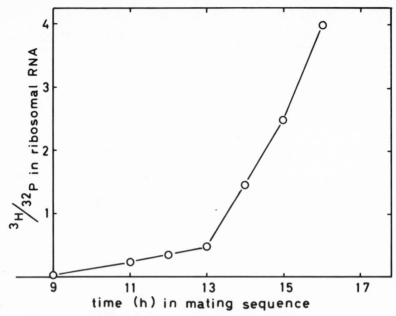

Fig. 4. Ribosomal RNA synthesis during late conjugation. Cells of strains B18684 and *Mpr/Mpr* (6 mpsV) were grown in ^{32}P-phosphate (1 μC/ml) washed into 10 mM tris-HCl pH 7.4 and starved for 15 h. The two mating types were mixed at 0 h. Ferrite (10 mg/ml) and egg albumin (0.1%) was added at 8 h and pairs purified at 9 h. PPY medium + [^{3}H]uridine (0.1 μC/ml) was added at 9 h. RNA was isolated by phenol-SDS at the times indicated and fractionated on 3% polyacrylamide gels and the ^{3}H/^{32}P ratio was determined in the ribosomal RNA fractions (for further details see Leick *et al.* in prep.)

To measure ribosomal RNA synthesis (ribosome synthesis) in refed conjugants, we measured the incorporation of [^{3}H] uridine into purified ribosomal RNA. In contrast to the cytological and genetic approaches mentioned above, such biochemical measurements, in the present case on RNA isolated from random culture samples of conjugating cells, do not necessarily reflect the events occurring in true conjugants. Since the early addition of growth medium would certainly create unacceptable noise by the stimulation of rRNA synthesis in non-mating cells of the mixture (Hallberg & Bruns 1976), we first developed a procedure to purify mating cells (Bruns *et al.* in prep.). The method outlined in Fig. 3 exploits the capacity of single cells but not mating pairs to ingest tiny ferrite particles. The ferrite-laden cells are selectively removed on a column containing a mixture of quartz and iron particles in a magnetic field.

Measurements of [^{3}H] uridine incorporation into rRNA of purified mating cells were made at various time points following refeeding 9 h after that prestarved cells of the two mating types were mixed. Fig. 4 shows that rRNA transcription occurs at a low rate until a point between 13 and 14 h, when the rate increases dramatically. Moreover, measurements of total RNA accumulation in such refed purified conjugants show more than a doubling of the total RNA content in the period 13 to 18 h (Leick *et al.* in prep.).

Thus, these biochemical data on rRNA synthesis are consistent with the notion that rRNA transcription (ribosome production) does not return to vegetative levels until the latter part of macronuclear development, even if growth medium has been present for many hours.

CONCLUSION

In this paper we have discussed different approaches to the study of the development of the new macronucleus during conjugation; all the methods have included the means to look only at the conjugating cells in mating mixtures.

The cytological picture shows that nucleoli develop after the new macronuclei have enlarged, and that nucleolar development can be stimulated by added growth medium. The genetic approach allows a timing of the most advanced cells. Here again the onset of phenotypes determining resistance to 6-methyl purine and cycloheximide occurs in early or middle macronuclear development in refed conjugants. Finally, the biochemical analysis of rRNA transcription in conjugants refed with nutrients confirms the cytological and genetic data, suggesting that the genetic apparatus of developing macronuclei matures in the latter part of macronuclear development.

Since the genetic approach allows a timing of the most advanced cells, it is at present questionable whether resistance to 6-methylpurine (*Mpr*) is attained in the average cell at 12 h or whether this occurs a few hours later. It can be stated, however, that resistance to cycloheximide (*Chx A* or *Chx B*) is attained at a later time than the onset of ribosome synthesis and that new ribosome production perhaps is a prerequisite for attaining resistance to cycloheximide.

Since the isolation of many new mutants with a variety of selectable phenotypes is now possible in *Tetrahymena* (Orias & Bruns 1976, Bruns *et al.* 1976, Bruns & Sanford 1978), we are currently exploring the timing of expression in the new macronucleus of other genes, especially those with phenotypes other than drug resistance. In particular, we are interested in finding new ribosome-associated mutations during conjugation.

ACKNOWLEDGMENTS

This work was supported by N. S. F. grant PCM 77-07056 and the John Simon Guggenheim Memorial Foundation as well as NATO Science Foundation. The skillful technical assistance by Mrs. Marianne Martens is gratefully acknowledged.

REFERENCES

Ares, M., Jr. & Bruns, P. J. (1978) *Genetics*. In press.

Bruns, P. J. & Brussard, T. B. (1974a) Pair formation in *Tetrahymena pyriformis* – an inducible developmental system. *J. Exp. Zool.* 188, 337–344.

Bruns, P. J. & Brussard, T. B. (1974b) Positive selection for mating with functional heterokaryons in *Tetrahymena pyriformis*. *Genetics*. 78, 831–841.

Bruns, P. J., Brussard, T. B. & Kavka, A. M. (1976) Isolation of homozygous mutants after induced self-fertilization in *Tetrahymena*. *Proc. Natl. Acad. Sci. USA* 73, 3243–3247.

Bruns, P. J., Møller, K. M. & Leick, V. (1978) Magnetic purification of mating *Tetrahymena*. In preparation.

Bruns, P. J. & Sanford, Y. S. (1978) Mass isolation and fertility testing of temperature-sensitive mutants in *Tetrahymena*. *Proc. Natl. Acad. Sci. USA* 75, 3355–3358.

Bleyman, L. K. & Bruns, P. J. (1977) Genetics of Cycloheximide Resistance in *Tetrahymena*. *Genetics* 87, 275–284.

Byrne, B. C. & Bruns, P. J. (1974) Selection of somatic and germ line drug resistance mutations in *Tetrahymena*. *Genetics* 77.

Gorovsky, M. A. (1973) Macro- and micronuclei of *Tetrahymena pyriformis:* A model system for studying the structure and function of eukaryotic nuclei. *J. Protozool.* 20, 19–25.

Hallberg, R. L. & Bruns, P. J. (1976) Ribosome biosynthesis in *Tetrahymena pyriformis*, regulation in response to nutritional changes. *J. Cell Biol.* 71, 383–394.

Leick, V., Bro, B. & Bruns, P. J. (1978) Ribosomal RNA transcription during macronuclear development of *Tetrahymena thermophila*. In preparation.

Nanney, D. L. & McCoy, J. W. (1976) Characterization of the species of the *Tetrahymena pyriformis* complex. *Trans. Amer. Micros. Soc.* 95, 664–682.

Nilsson, J. R. & Leick, V. (1971) Nucleolar organization and ribosome formation in *Tetrahymena pyriformis*. *Exp. Cell Res.* 60, 361.

Orias, E. & Bruns, P J. (1976) Induction and isolation of mutants in *Tetrahymena*. *Methods Cell Biol.* 13, 247–282.

Sutton, C. A., Ares, M., Jr. & Hallberg, R. L. (1978) Cycloheximide resistance can be mediated through either ribosomal sub-unit. *Proc. Natl. Acad. Sci. USA* 75, 3158–3162.

DISCUSSION

PEARLMAN: Have you ever looked at incorporation into total RNA rather than into just ribosomal RNA? I am wondering if the genes that you are expressing are phenotypically expressed as protein. Do you know anything either about poly-A-containing RNA or total RNA that may be made earlier to give you an idea of the life time of messengers?

LEICK: No, I guess this research is at a very early stage. We have had so many technical problems just in setting up the system to get pure pairs and so on. That kind of experiments has not been done.

PARDUE: Do these things break down the ribosome after conjugation?

LEICK: I don't think it is known.

PLESNER: We are often very worried about the phasing of our synchronized systems both in lower eukaryotes and also in mammalian cells, especially when you look at cell divisions you see changes in morphology occur very fast. You might imagine also that chemical reactions occur fast. I wonder, in this system, where you are going quite a long time, how good is your phasing, how many cells are in the same phase?

LEICK: I guess this is one of the major problems of the system at the moment, because as you go along the course of conjugation you loose synchrony. When you get to late conjugation, you probably have a spread of several hours. That is the reason why genetics will be quite useful, because you can perhaps stop the cells by a heat-sensitive genetic block at a certain stage in macronuclear development, and thereby restore synchrony in the population.

PLESNER: You had for example a figure of 15.5 h when you attained resistance to cycloheximide. How many cells would you judge were in that stage of development?

LEICK: You are scoring for the first cells getting drug resistant. The way you do this assay is by taking cells out of the conjugating mixture as function of time and put them into the drug-containing medium. And if one cell has become resistant at a particular time of development. It will grow up, and you will score this as drug resistant. Eventually more than 90% of the conjugants are getting resistant at the end of conjugation.

Ribosomal DNA Synthesis in Conjugating *Tetrahymena*

Ronald E. Pearlman[1], Poul Andersson[2], Jan Engberg[2] & Jytte R. Nilsson[3]

INTRODUCTION

In exponentially growing *Tetrahymena thermophila* (formerly *T. pyriformis* syngen I (Nanney & McCoy 1976)), the genes coding for ribosomal RNA (rDNA) constitute approximately 1–2% of total cellular DNA. Macronuclei contain approximately 600 rRNA genes per haploid genome and these comprise >99.9% of cellular rDNA. Macronuclear rDNA is extrachromosomal, localized in nucleoli and is organized as palindromic molecules of 13.2×10^6 daltons, each molecule containing two genes coding for rRNA (Engberg *et al.* 1974a,b, Gall 1974, Engberg *et al.* 1976, Karrer & Gall 1976). In contrast to the macronuclear organization, micronuclei contain a single rRNA gene (6.6×10^6 daltons) per haploid genome which is integrated into chromosomal DNA (Yao & Gall 1977).

The highly polyploid macronuclei are derived from diploid micronuclei during the sexual cycle of *T. thermophila* (Nanney 1953, Ray 1956, Elliot 1973). Generation of a full macronuclear set of rRNA genes during this period requires: 1) an amplification increasing the number of rRNA genes per haploid genome from one to approximately 600, and 2) polyploidization to reach a final ploidy of approximately 45 in the new macronucleus. Amplification and polyploidization of rRNA genes may or may not be separated in time.

We have used RNA/DNA hybridization to ask when rDNA is synthesized preferentially during the sexual cycle. Preferential synthesis is the percentage of

[1] Dept. of Biology, York University, Toronto, Ontario, Canada M3J 1P3
[2] Biochemical Institute B, Panum Institute, University of Copenhagen, Denmark
[3] Institute of General Zoology, University of Copenhagen, Denmark

SPECIFIC EUKARYOTIC GENES, Alfred Benzon Symposium 13, Munksgaard 1979

rDNA in newly synthesized DNA being greater than its percentage in DNA synthesized during exponential growth. Preferential synthesis of rDNA is a necessary condition of rDNA amplification but may also occur in other situations such as during nutritional shift-up or synchronous growth in *Tetrahymena* (Engberg *et al.* 1972, Andersen & Engberg 1975).

MATERIALS AND METHODS

Conjugation

Inbred family B strains of mating types II, IV and VII of *T. thermophila* were used in all experiments. The strain of mating type VII (BVII) is designated as "wild type". The other two strains Mpr-1/Mpr-1 (6mp s, IV) and Chx-2/Chx-2(cy s, II) are functional heterokaryons (Bruns & Brussard 1974). All strains were obtained from Dr. Peter Bruns, Cornell University, Ithaca, New York. Cells were kept in exponential growth in 5 ml of medium composed of proteose peptone, yeast extract and salts (Leick *et al.* 1970). For experiments, cells of complementary mating type were grown separately to exponential growth in either the above complex medium or in a defined medium (Rasmussen & Modeweg-Hansen 1973). Cells were harvested by centrifugation at $40 \times g$ and washed twice in sterile 10 mM Tris-HCl pH 7.6 (Orias & Bruns 1976). Cells were resuspended in sterile 10 mM Tris-HCl pH 7.6 to a concentration of $1-1.5 \times 10^5$ cells/ml and starved separately. After 18–24 h of starvation, equal numbers of cells of the two mating types were mixed. Time of mixing is designated as 0 in all experiments. Growth, starvation and conjugation were all carried out at 28°C. Pairing was followed by fixing cells at various times following mixing (Wolfe 1973) and observing under the light microscope. Percent pairing is defined as number of cells in pairs $\times 100$/total number of cells. Progress through the sexual cycle was determined by fixing and staining cells as described by Pallis & Gorovsky (personal communication). Viability of pairs was monitored by isolating individual pairs into drops of complex medium and monitoring growth.

Autoradiography

Cells labeled with ^{3}H-TdR were concentrated by a brief centrifugation and smeared on slides freshly coated with 2% proteose peptone. After drying, the slides were immersed in fixative (85 ml methanol, 10 ml formalin, 5 ml acetic acid (Böhm *et al.* 1968) for 1 h. The washed slides were stored until emulsion was applied using the dipping method. When test slides showed sufficiently heavy labeling, experimental slides were developed for 5 min in Microdol-x. For microscopic examination, the smears were stained with an aged solution of Giemsa in Tris-HCl pH 7.2.

Preparation of DNA

Cells were cooled to 4°C, harvested by centrifugation at 40×g for 7 min and washed once by centrifugation in 10 mM Tris-HCl pH 7.2, 1 mM $MgCl_2$, 3 mM $CaCl_2$, 100 mM sucrose. The washed cell pellet was either stored at −80°C or lysed immediately. Lysis was accomplished at 55°C by addition of 5% SDS in NET (0.5 M NaCl, 0.05M EDTA, 0.05M Tris-HCl pH 8.5) followed by dilution with NET to a final SDS concentration of 1%. Proteinase K (E. Merck & Co.) from a stock solution 10 mg/ml in 10 mM Tris-HCl pH 7.4 which had been incubated for 2 h at 37° was added to a final concentration of 200 μg/ml. Incubation was continued at 55° until the lysate became clear, generally 2–5 h. The lysate was cooled, diluted with 2 volumes of water and extracted with an equal volume of chloroform/octanol, 9/1. After centrifugation at ≃1000 x g for 20 min, the upper aqueous phase was isolated and centrifuged at 30,000 x g for 20 min to pellet high molecular weight glycogen. The supernatant was hybridized directly by the method of continuous hybridization (Shih & Martin 1973, Engberg et al. 1976) or diluted to 6.0 ml with H_2O, 7.4 g CsCl added and centrifuged at 36,000 rpm for 40–60 h in a type 40 or Ti 50 angle rotor in a Beckman ultracentrifuge. Following centrifugation, fractions were collected from the bottom of the gradient. Aliquots were applied to Whatman 3 MM filter paper discs, precipitated and washed with cold N HCl, rinsed in 95% ethanol, dried and counted in a toluene based scintillation solution. Appropriate fractions were pooled, diluted to the equivalent of 2×SSC and analyzed by continuous hybridization or pooled fractions were denatured in 0.5 N NaOH, neutralized and loaded onto 2.5 cm discs of 0.45 μm nitrocellulose filters (Engberg et al. 1972). Hybridization was carried out in 2×SSC 50% formamide at 37°C by the method of Gillespie & Spiegelman (1965) as described by Engberg & Pearlman (1972) using [32]P rRNA as probe. In some experiments, pooled fractions were analyzed by agarose gel electrophoresis either directly from CsCl or following dialysis and cleavage with restriction endonucleases.

Incorporation of label into DNA of whole cells

Samples of cells, usually 50 μl, labeled with ^{3}H-TdR were lysed by pipetting into an equal volume of 1% SDS in NET. The suspension was made 200 μg/ml in digested proteinase K and incubated at 37°C for 4–12 h; 90 μl of the lysed cell suspension was applied to Whatman 3 MM filter paper discs, precipitated, washed and counted as described above. Proteinase treatment was essential to eliminate acid precipitable radioactivity which was not incorporated into DNA.

Preparation of ^{32}P-rRNA

Unlabeled 17S and 25S rRNA were prepared from whole cells as described by Engberg *et al.* (1972). This was labeled with γ ^{32}P-ATP using T4 polynucleotide 5'-OH kinase (B. Kay, personal communication). Specific activities of probes prepared in this manner ranged from 10^5 to 10^7 cpm/μg of input RNA.

RESULTS

Microspectrophotometric measurements of feulgen-stained conjugating *Tetrahymena* have demonstrated the absence of DNA synthesis in parental macronuclei (Doerder & De Bault 1975). Sugai & Hiwatashi (1974) as well as ourselves have confirmed these observations using light microscope autoradiography. Conjugating cells were labeled with 5 μCi/ml ^{3}H-TdR from 80 min to 7 h after mixing and then prepared for autoradiography. Of 114 pairs (228 cells) scored, only one cell had a labeled macronucleus and 105 pairs had labeled micronuclei. At 7 h after mixing, new anlagen were not yet developing and no pair had progressed past the second post zygotic division, but micronuclei had progressed through mitotic S phase. Varying amounts of cytoplasmic labeling was observed in all cells and no unpaired cells in the population had labeled macronuclei. We were thus able to study DNA synthesis during early conjugation in the absence of a background of macronuclear DNA replication.

The method of continuous hybridization (Shih & Martin 1973, Engberg *et al.* 1976) was chosen to study rDNA synthesis in the presence of a large amount of pre-existing rDNA. Samples of total DNA from cells conjugating in the presence of ^{3}H-TdR were hybridized to a vast excess of unlabeled rRNA covalently attached to phosphocellulose filter discs. A ratio of rRNA to rDNA of 1000 was used to saturate the unlabeled macronuclear rDNA present in the DNA samples. The percentage of ^{3}H-TdR incorporated into DNA being rDNA was calculated from the percentage of input acid precipitable radioactivity recovered as filter-bound DNA-RNA hybrids. This method allows detection of preferential synthesis of rDNA, irrespective of the number of genes synthesized per

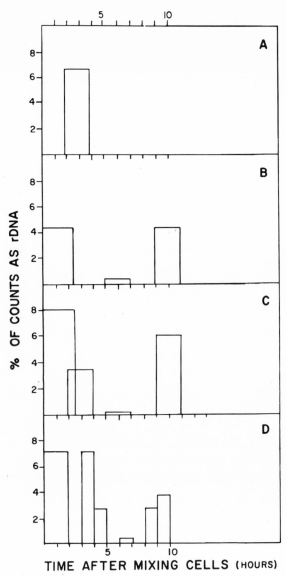

Fig. 1. Pulse labeling of DNA in conjugating *Tetrahymena*. Starved cells of complementary mating type were mixed at 0 time to give a culture containing equal numbers of cells of the two mating types; 5 ml aliquots of this culture were labeled with 30 μCi/ml ³H-TdR (S.A∼60 Ci/mmole) at times indicated by the beginning of each bar. Cells were harvested at a time represented by the end of each bar and DNA was isolated as described under Materials and Methods. The percentage of radioactivity being rDNA was determined for each sample by continuous hybridization. Experiments represented in panels A, B and D are independent experiments. Data in panels B and C were obtained from the same culture except in C, labeling was with 50 μg/ml BUdR as well as ³H-TdR.

23*

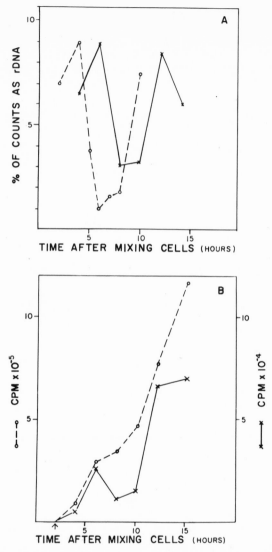

Fig. 2. Continuous labeling of DNA in conjugating *Tetrahymena*. Starved cells of complementary mating type were mixed at 0 time to give a culture containing equal numbers of cells of the two mating types. ^{3}H-TdR (S.A.~60 Ci/mmole) was added to 30 μCi/ml at the times indicated; 5 ml samples were harvested as indicated, DNA was isolated as described under Materials and Methods and the percentage of radioactivity being rDNA was determined by continuous hybridization. At each time point, cumulative accumulation of radioactivity into acid precipitable material was determined on 50 μl aliquots of the culture as described under Materials and Methods.

A ×——×^{3}H-TdR added at 2 h

O""""O^{3}H-TdR added at 0 h

haploid genome and irrespective of the specific activity of the labeled DNA, as an increase in the percentage of rDNA in newly synthesized DNA compared with the percentage expected for exponentially growing cells. Pure rDNA hybridizes 33% by this method (Engberg *et al.* 1976).

Pulse Labeling

To establish the timing of rDNA synthesis during the sexual cycle of *Tetrahymena*, cells were pulse labeled for varying periods at different times after cell mixing. The percentage of ^{3}H-TdR incorporated being rDNA was determined by continuous hybridization (Fig. 1). In cells labeled between 5 and 7 h after mixing < 0.5% of the DNA labeling was rDNA. High percentages of rDNA were however found in DNA pulse labeled during early (0 to 5 h) and late (8 to 11 h) periods of the sexual cycle. Peak values were 8 and 6% of DNA label in rDNA at early and late stages compared to 2% and < 0.01% rDNA in macronuclear and micronuclear DNA, respectively. This suggests two periods of preferential rDNA synthesis surrounding a period of very little rDNA synthesis.

Continuous Labeling

The time course of rDNA synthesis in conjugating *Tetrahymena* was further investigated using continuous labeling of cells and continuous hybridization. Fig. 2A shows the proportion of total ^{3}H-TdR incorporation being rDNA at various times after addition of radioactivity. A peak of preferential rDNA synthesis was observed at 4–6 h followed by a sharp drop in the proportion of rDNA followed by an increase in the proportion of rDNA in newly synthesized DNA. The pattern is consistent with results from pulse labeling experiments. The displacement of the two curves in Fig. 2A probably reflects small variations from experiment to experiment in progression of cells through the sexual cycle. The low proportion of rDNA observed from 6–10 h after mixing cells results from a combination of the low percentage of rDNA being synthesized during this period (Fig. 1) and degradation of labeled rDNA synthesized in the first 4 h after mixing the cells. That degradation of rDNA is occurring can be seen from and into rDNA. Cumulative incorporation of radioactivity into rDNA was Fig. 2B. This shows the time course of incorporation of ^{3}H-TdR into total DNA

B O---O   total acid precipitable radioactivity
X——X radioactivity in rDNA
The arrow represents the time of addition of ^{3}H-TdR.

calculated from the percentage of total radioactivity being rDNA at the times of sampling (Fig. 2A, label added 2 h after mixing cells). The decrease in the cumulative incorporation of ^{3}H-TdR into rDNA from 6–8 h is most readily explained by degradation of previously synthesized rDNA. If no degradation were occurring, cumulative incorporation of radioactivity into rDNA would remain constant in the absence of rDNA synthesis.

Isolation and Characterization of rDNA Synthesized During the Sexual Cycle
In order to characterize the material which hybridized with rRNA and which

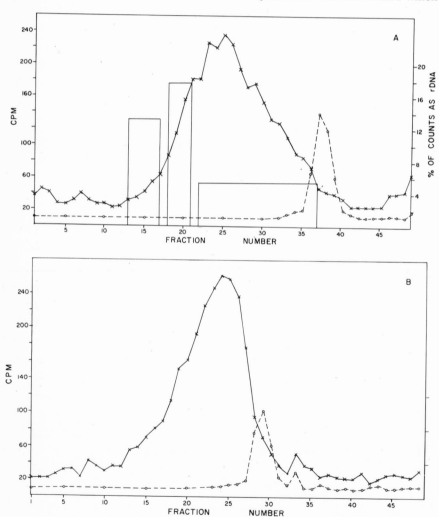

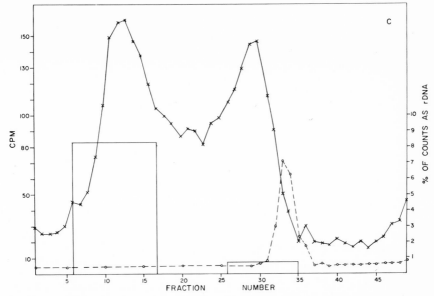

Fig. 3. CsCl density gradient analysis of DNA synthesized during conjugation. Starved cells of complementary mating type were mixed at 0 time to give a culture of approximately 10^5 cells/ml containing equal numbers of cells of the two mating types. Cells were pulse labeled as indicated, harvested, DNA extracted and gradients prepared and analyzed as described under Materials and Methods. In A and C, the bar graph represents the percentage of radioactivity in the pooled fractions being rDNA as determined by continuous hybridization.

   A 9 ml culture labeled from 0–2.5 h with 50 μCi/ml ^{3}H-TdR (S.A. ~60 Ci/mmole) and 50 μg/ml BUdR

   B 4.5 ml culture labeled from 5–7 h with 30 μCi/ml ^{3}H-TdR (S.A. ~60 Ci/mmole) and 50 μg/ml BUdR

   C 4.5 ml culture labeled from 9–11 h with 30 μCi/ml ^{3}H-TdR (S.A. ~60 Ci/mmole) and 50 μg/ml BUdR

   ×—× ^{3}H radioactivity

   O---O ^{14}C radioactivity from DNA from strain B VII added as marker indicating the buoyant density of unsubstituted DNA.

was labeled from 0 to 4 h after mixing cells, we determined its buoyant density in CsCl, its approximate molecular weight by neutral sucrose density gradient analysis and the pattern of digestion with restriction endonuclease Eco RI. Palindromic rDNA from macronuclei of *T. thermophila* has a buoyant density in CsCl greater than that of bulk macronuclear DNA, a molecular weight of 13.2×10^6 daltons and Eco RI restriction fragments of 10.0×10^6 and 1.6×10^6 daltons (Karrer & Gall 1976). Results (data not shown) suggest that palindromic rDNA is synthesized during the first 4 h following mixing of the cells.

We then wished to isolate DNA synthesized in conjugating cells free from contamination with pre-existing DNA. This was accomplished by labeling cells with ^{3}H-TdR in the presence of 50 μg/ml BUdR, isolating the DNA and centrifuging in an isopycnic CsCl gradient. Newly synthesized DNA containing BUdR has a buoyant density greater than pre-existing DNA. In a series of experiments where conjugating cells were pulse labeled with ^{3}H-TdR and BUdR at various times (Fig. 3), the following observations were made. The amount of the density shift relative to unsubstituted bulk DNA from *T. thermophila* is dependent on the time when the pulse was administered. This probably reflects alterations in nucleotide pools and/or uptake of BUdR during the sexual cycle. It is thus impossible to determine whether newly synthesized DNA has undergone one or more than one round of replication in the presence of BUdR. It is of interest however that in all experiments we have carried out of the type described in Fig. 3, the highest proportion of rDNA is always found in the heaviest fractions. In fact individual fractions (e.g. fraction 15 in Fig. 3A) can be shown by continuous hybridization to contain approximately 90% rDNA. The skewing of rDNA to the heavy side of the density-labeled material is consistent with rDNA amplification which may require many rounds of replication. An alternate explanation however which cannot be ruled out is that rDNA and bulk DNA are synthesized from separate thymidine pools and density differences between these DNAs reflect differing rates of BUdR equilibration in the pools. In cells pulse labeled from 5–7 h no rDNA is detectable in newly synthesized DNA by the continuous hybridization method (Fig. 3B). This is consistent with data presented previously(Fig. 1).

In an attempt to obtain a qualitative estimate of the number of rRNA genes synthesized during the sexual cycle, conjugating cells were again pulse labeled with ^{3}H-TdR and BUdR. DNA was extracted and centrifuged in isopycnic CsCl gradients. After analysis of aliquots of the gradient fractions for radioactivity, fractions were pooled in groups of four, DNA was loaded onto nitrocellulose filters and hybridized with ^{32}P-rRNA (Engberg *et al.* 1972). Data from a representative experiment with labeling from 0 to 2.5 h after mixing of the cells are shown in Fig. 4. The peak of hybridization in pooled fractions 22–25 and hybridization in fractions 26–29 represent pre-existing unsubstituted rDNA. If the level of hybridization in fractions 2–5 and 6–9 is assumed to be background, significant hybridization is observed in fractions 10–13 and 14–17. This confirms continuous hybridization data demonstrating that the majority of BUdR substituted rDNA is found skewed to the heavy fractions of newly synthesized

DNA. rDNA in fractions 18–21 is probably mainly unsubstituted although some contribution from BUdR containing DNA may exist. Quantitative estimates of the number of rRNA genes present in the pooled fractions cannot be obtained because hybridization was not carried out with saturating amounts of rRNA. We estimate however that the amount of hybridization in BUdR containing DNA is approximately one-third of that in unsubstituted DNA. Exponentially growing cells contain approximately 600 rRNA genes per haploid genome and these cells (macronuclei) are approximately 45 ploid (Engberg & Pearlman 1972, Yao *et al.* 1974). The number of rRNA genes per cell is thus approximately 27,000. It can be estimated that if all cells in the population contain newly synthesized rDNA, there are approximately 9000 new genes/cell.

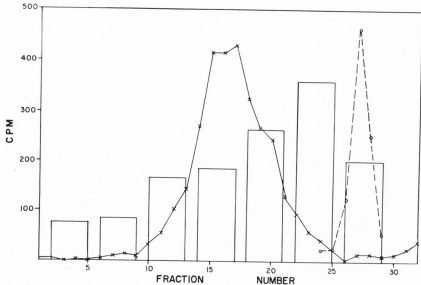

Fig. 4. CsCl density gradient analysis of DNA synthesized during conjugation. Starved cells of complementary mating type were mixed at 0 time to give 20 ml of a culture of approximately 2×10^5 cells/ml containing equal numbers of cells of the two mating types. The culture was labeled from 0–2.5 h with 15 μCi/ml ^{3}H-TdR (S.A.~60 Ci/mmole) and 50 μg/ml BUdR, harvested, DNA extracted and gradients prepared and analyzed as described under Materials and Methods. 0.1 ml aliquots of fractions pooled as indicated were denatured, neutralized, loaded onto cellulose nitrate membrane filters and hybridized with ^{32}P-rRNA for 16 h at 37°C.

×—× ^{3}H radioactivity

O---O ^{14}C radioactivity from DNA from strain B VII added as marker indicating the buoyant density of unsubstituted DNA

The bar graph represents the ^{32}P-radioactivity hybridized to DNA from pooled gradient fractions.

In this experiment, 83% of cells were in pairs at the time of harvest and if we assume rDNA synthesis occurs only in paired cells (see following section), each conjugating cell would contain approximately 10,800 newly synthesized rRNA genes. Pre-meiotic S occurs during starvation prior to mixing cells (Wolfe 1973, Sugai & Hiwatashi 1974, Doerder & De Bault 1975). Amplification of rDNA in these 4C cells (micronuclei) to the level found in macronuclei would give rise to approximately 2,400 new rRNA genes per cell. Thus, even in the first 2.5 h after mixing cells, an approximately 4.5-fold excess number of rRNA genes are apparently synthesized. This is consistent with the observation of degradation of rDNA occurring at later times. Some rDNA is synthesized in all pulse labeling experiments up to 5–6 h after mixing cells although the largest amount of synthesis occurs in the first 2.5–3 h. Whether rDNA synthesis from 3–6 h reflects asynchrony of the system is not known.

A second method of estimating the number of rRNA genes synthesized was also used. A culture of conjugating cells was labeled with ^{3}H-TdR and 50 μg/ml BUdR, from 0–5 h after mixing. The percentage of ^{3}H-TdR incorporated being rDNA was 7.7% as determined by the continuous hybridization procedure. The total amount of radioactivity in rDNA was calculated as described previously (Fig. 2B). Following extraction of DNA and CsCl density gradient ultracentrifugation, a fraction of BUdR containing DNA was obtained which by continuous hybridization was 89% rDNA. From the specific activity of rDNA (4.75 cpm/ng), the total counts incorporated into rDNA (1410 cpm), the molecular weight of an rRNA gene (6.6×10^6 daltons) and the total number of cells in the culture (1.9×10^6) we calculated that approximately 1.4×10^4 newly synthesized rRNA genes were present per cell following the 5-h labeling period. In this experiment, only 55% of the cells were present as pairs so that each conjugating cell would contain 2.6×10^4 newly synthesized rRNA genes. This value agrees well with the estimate obtained using filter hybridization data. The 2.5-fold difference between the two estimates may reflect the longer labeling period in the second experiment as well as differences between the continuous and filter hybridization methods (Engberg et al. 1976).

Is rDNA Synthesized only in Paired Cells?

Because all cells do not form pairs in any given experiment, this is a very difficult question to answer but we have made some observations which relate to this point. Accumulation of ^{3}H-TdR into DNA as a function of time after mixing cells in very dependent on the number of cells pairing; the greater the percentage of paired cells in a population, the greater the accumulation of label. Since the percentage of total radioactivity being rDNA is high under these conditions (Fig. 2), the amount of rDNA synthesis appears to be a function of the number of cells paired. It cannot be ruled out however that these differences in accumulation of label are due to differences in equilibration of DNA precursor pools between single and paired cells.

We have used starved cells as a model for unpaired cells in a conjugating population. Because cells are mixed under non-nutrient conditions (see Materials and Methods) following a 20–24-h starvation period, the metabolism of starved cells should reflect the metabolism of unpaired cells in a conjugating population. Starved cells do accumulate ^{3}H-TdR when label is present from 20 to 25 h of starvation. Total label accumulated per cell in this 5-h period is four-to tenfold less than accumulation per cell in a 0–2-h labeling period of conjugating cells. There does however seem to be preferential rDNA synthesis in starved cells as the percentage of total label being rDNA in a 5-h labeling period varies from a usual 5% to a high of 20% in one experiment. The rDNA synthesized in starved cells appears to be palindromic as evidenced by Eco RI restriction endonuclease analysis.

How many rRNA genes are synthesized in starved cells? Fig. 5 describes an experiment where cells starved for 20 h were labeled for 5 h in the presence of 50 μg/ml BUdR and ^{3}H-TdR. DNA was isolated and analyzed by CsCl density gradient centrifugation. Pooled gradient fractions were applied to nitrocellulose filters and hybridized with ^{32}P-rRNA. Hybridization occurs in the positions expected for pre-existing unsubstituted rDNA although small amounts of hybridization in fractions 25–32 could possibly be accounted for by hybridization with BUdR containing DNA. It is clear, however, that little hybridization to substituted DNA occurs and, in contrast to conjugating cells, no hybridization occurs to the peak fractions of BUdR containing DNA. Calculation by the method described previously of the number of rRNA genes synthesized in a 5-h labeling period in starved cells gives a value of approximately 400 per cell. This is significantly less than the number of rRNA genes synthesized in a conjugating population and strongly suggests that the major contribution to rDNA synthesis in a conjugating population is from paired cells or from cells preparing for conjugation.

If preferential rDNA synthesis at the levels we have described were occurring in unpaired cells after addition of ^{3}H-TdR, it might be due to a shift-up response (Engberg et al. 1972). If this were the case, newly synthesized rDNA would be

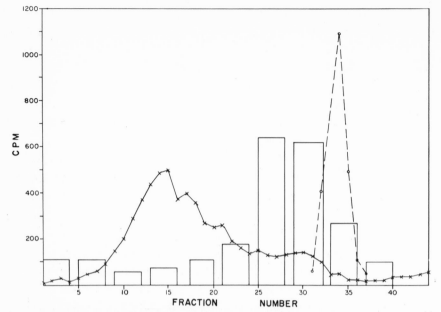

Fig. 5. CsCl density gradient analysis of DNA synthesized during starvation. A 20 ml culture of strain B Vii was starved for 20 h. It was then labeled for 5 h with 15 μCi/ml ^{3}H-TdR (S.A.~60 Ci/mmole) and 50 μg/ml BUdR. Cells were harvested, DNA extracted and gradients prepared and analyzed as described under Materials and Methods. 0.1 ml aliquots of fractions pooled as indicated were denatured, neutralized, loaded onto cellulose nitrate membrane filters and hybridized with ^{32}P-rRNA for 16 h at 37°C.

    ✕—✕ ^{3}H radioactivity

    O---O ^{14}C radioactivity from DNA from strain B VII added as marker indicating the buoyant density of unsubstituted DNA

    The bar graph represents the ^{32}P-radioactivity hybridized to DNA from pooled gradient fractions.

expected to be localized to the peripheral nucleoli in macronuclei and should be resolvable by light microscope autoradiography. Cells labeled with 50 μCi/ml ^{3}H-TdR for 1, 2 or 3 h after mixing show no label in macronuclei. A very few cells show micronuclear labeling in this experiment but this can be explained as being those cells which divided after mixing and before pairing and thus went through a micronuclear S period during the time of labeling. Division occurred because cells must be in the Gl phase of the cell cycle for pairing to occur (Wolfe 1973, Doerder & De Bault 1975, Pearlman, unpublished observations) and a small percentage of cells are in G2 following a long starvation period (Salamone & Pearlman 1977). Between 350 and 450 cells were observed at each of 1, 2 and 3 h after mixing cells. No label was seen in macronuclear nucleoli in starved cells labeled with ^{3}H-TdR from 24–30 h of starvation. In this starved cell population, 0.45% of cells (four of 887) showed heavy macronuclear labeling and the same number showed heavy micronuclear labeling. This can be explained as these few cells progressing slowly through the cell cycle during starvation. We have no explanation at present for the observation that the extensive rDNA synthesis between 0 and 4 h after mixing cells is not seen to be localized to any intracellular structure by light microscope autoradiography. Perhaps micronuclei in the crescent stage are too large to resolve extrachromosomal genes or perhaps spread rather than smear or squash preparations are required to obtain optimum resolution in these experiments (Sugai & Hiwatashi 1974). These possibilities are being investigated.

DISCUSSION

Two periods of preferential rDNA synthesis have been demonstrated during the sexual cycle in *T. thermophila*. rDNA synthesis during the first 5 h after mixing cells is extensive and the number of genes synthesized during this period is sufficient to account for amplification of rRNA genes. In fact, an over-production and subsequent degradation of rDNA apparently takes place. Most of the rDNA synthesis occurs during the first 3 h after mixing. This is after the pre-meiotic S phase and very early in meiosis, before or during crescent formation. Sugai & Hiwatashi (1974) have described this period as correspond-ing to zygotene and pachytene of meiotic prophase. Wolfe *et al.* (1976) however, question whether micronuclear elongation and crescent formation should be considered as meiotic prophase because synaptinemal complexes are not observed. Low levels of DNA synthesis have been observed previously in micronuclei undergoing meiosis (Sugai & Hiwatashi 1974) but this occurred later than the synthesis we have observed. Whether the rDNA synthesis we observe represents gene amplification is not certain. It is unlikely that the extensive synthesis observed is in response to a nutritional shift-up due to the tracer amounts of ^{3}H-TdR. The synthesis does seem to be in response to mixing cells of complementary mating type. The presence of BUdR might induce abnormal DNA synthesis but this seems unlikely because preferential replica-tion of rDNA is observed when labeling with only ^{3}H-TdR. Also, in the presence of BUdR, cells remain viable and the sexual cycle appears normal when analyzed cytologically. Furthermore, if rDNA synthesis were primarily a response to the presence of BUdR, it is difficult to explain why the number of rRNA genes synthesized in conjugating cells in the presence of BUdR is approximately 25 times more than the number synthesized in starved cells prior to mixing different mating types.

If this "early" rDNA synthesis represents gene amplification, the mechanism of DNA synthesis will be of interest. As micronuclear rDNA is chromosomally integrated and macronuclear rDNA is extrachromosomal (Yao & Gall 1977), an excision event is likely to occur during the amplification process. We are presently attempting to isolate rDNA molecules of other than palindromic structure which may be early intermediates in gene amplification. This is being done by analyzing DNA from cells pulse labeled with ^{3}H-TdR and BUdR on CsCl density gradients as described in Fig. 4. DNA from gradient fractions will then be analyzed by agarose gel electrophoresis, transferred to nitrocellulose filters and hybridized with ^{32}P-rRNA probes. Any DNA which hybridizes with rRNA but which does not appear to be mature rDNA molecules (i.e. 13.2×10^6 daltons) will be analyzed further by electron microscopy and other techniques.

A second phase of preferential rDNA synthesis which begins approximately 8 h after mixing cells has not as yet been analyzed in detail. This synthesis begins when new macronuclear anlagen are beginning to develop from the postzygotic division products. It is possible that this rDNA synthesis represents the polyploidization of the already amplified rDNA which must occur in the development of the vegetative macronucleus. If this is the case, polyploidization of rRNA genes may begin before that of the majority of the genome, somewhat analogous to the preferential rDNA replication observed on nutritional shift-up (Engberg et al. 1972).

* Abbr.: rRNA=17S and 26S RNA isolated from ribosomes. These RNA species are derived from an approximately 39S precursor molecule after a number of processing steps
  SDS=sodium dodecyl sulfate
  BUdR=5 bromodeoxyuridine
  TdR=thymidine
  SSC=0.15 m NaCl, 0.015 M Na citrate pH 7

ACKNOWLEDGMENTS
This work was supported by grants from the National Research Council of Canada, the National Cancer Institute of Canada, the Danish Natural Science Foundation, NATO and EMBO. We thank J. Sheehy and E. Høyer for typing the manuscript.

REFERENCES

Andersen, H.A. & Engberg, J. (1975) Timing of the ribosomal gene replication in *Tetrahymena pyriformis*. *Exptl. Cell Res.* 92, 159–163.

Böhm, N., Sprenger, E., Schlüter, G. & Sandritter, W. (1968) Proportionalitätsfehlen bei der Feulgen-Hydrolyse. *Histochemie* 15, 194–203.

Bruns, P.J. & Brussard, T.B. (1974) Positive selection for mating with functional heterokaryons in *Tetrahymena pyriformis*. *Genetics* 78, 831–841.

Doerder, F.P. & De Bault, L.E. (1975) Cytofluorimetric analysis of nuclear DNA during meiosis, fertilization and macronuclear development in the ciliate *Tetrahymena pyriformis* syngen I. *J. Cell. Sci.* 17, 471–493.

Elliott, A. M., ed. (1973) Biology of *Tetrahymena*. Dowden, Hutchinson & Ross, Stroudsburg, Pennsylvania.

Engberg, J. & Pearlman, R.E. (1972) The amount of ribosomal RNA genes in *Tetrahymena pyriformis* in different physiological states. *Eur. J. Biochem.* 26, 393–400.

Engberg, J., Mowat, D. & Pearlman, R. E. (1972) Preferential replication of the ribosomal RNA genes during a nutritional shift-up in *Tetrahymena pyriformis*. *Biochim. Biophys. Acta* 272, 312–320.

Engberg, J., Christiansen, G. & Leick, V. (1974a) Autonomous rDNA molecules containing single copies of ribosomal RNA genes in the macronucleus of *Tetrahymena pyriformis*. *Biochim. Biophys. Res. Commun.* 59, 1356–1365.

Engberg, J., Nilsson, J.R., Pearlman, R.E. & Leick, V. (1974b) Induction of nucleolar and mitochondrial DNA replication in *Tetrahymena pyriformis*. *Proc. Nat. Acad. Sci. U.S.A.* 71, 894–898.

Engberg, J., Andersson, P., Leick, V. & Collins, J. (1976) Free ribosomal DNA molecules from *Tetrahymena pyriformis* GL are giant palindromes. *J. Mol. Biol.* 104, 455–470.

Gall, J.G. (1974) Free ribosomal RNA genes in the macronucleus of *Tetrahymena*. *Proc. Nat. Acad. Sci. U.S.A.* 71, 3078–3081.

Gillespie, D. & Spiegelman, S. (1965) A quantitative assay for DNA-RNA hybrids with DNA immobilized on a membrane. *J. Mol. Biol.* 12, 829–842.

Karrer, K. & Gall, J.G. (1976) The macronuclear ribosomal DNA of *Tetrahymena pyriformis* is a palindrome. *J. Mol. Biol.* 104, 421–453.

Leick, V., Engberg, J. & Emmersen, J. (1970) Nascent subribosomal particles in *Tetrahymena pyriformis*. *Eur. J. Biochem.* 13, 238–246.

Nanney, D.L. (1953) Nucleo-cytoplasmic interaction during conjugation in *Tetrahymena*. *Biol. Bull* 105, 133–148.

Nanney, D.L. & McCoy, J.W. (1976) Characterization of the species of the *Tetrahymena pyriformis* complex. *Trans. Am. Micro. Soc.* 95, 664–682.

Orias, E. & Bruns, P.J. (1976) Induction and isolation of mutants in *Tetrahymena*. In: *Methods in Cell Biology*, vol. 13, ed. Prescott, D.M. pp. 247–282. Academic Press, N.Y.

Rasmussen, L. & Modeweg-Hansen, L. (1973) Cell multiplication in *Tetrahymena* cultures after addition of particulate material. *J. Cell Sci.* 12, 275–286.

Ray, C., Jr. (1956) Meiosis and nuclear behavior in *Tetrahymena pyriformis*. *J. Protozool.* 3, 88–96.

Salamone, M.F. & Pearlman, R.E. (1977) Sizes of G1 and G2 populations in starved *Tetrahymena*. *Exptl. Cell Res.* 110, 323–330.

Shih, T.Y. & Martin, M.A. (1973) A general method of gene isolation. *Proc. Nat. Acad. Sci. U.S.A.* 70, 1697–1700.

Sugai, T. & Hiwatashi, K. (1974) Cytologic and autoradiographic studies of the micronucleus at meiotic prophase in *Tetrahymena pyriformis. J. Protozool.* 21, 542–548.

Wolfe, J. (1973) Conjugation in *Tetrahymena*:The relationship between the division cycle and cell pairing. *Develop. Biol.* 35, 221–231.

Wolfe, J., Hunter, B. & Adair, W.S. (1976) A cytological study of micronuclear elongation during conjugation in *Tetrahymena. Chromosoma* 55, 289–308.

Yao, M.-C., Kimmel, A.R. & Gorovsky, M.A. (1974) A small number of cistrons for ribosomal RNA in the germinal nucleus of a eukaryote, *Tetrahymena pyriformis. Proc. Nat. Acad. Sci. U.S.A.* 71, 3082–3086.

Yao, M.-C. & Gall, J.G. (1977) A single integrated gene for ribosomal RNA in a eucaryote, *Tetrahymena pyriformis. Cell* 12, 121–132.

DISCUSSION

GALL: I will mention briefly some experiments that Meng-Chao Yao did in my lab (Yao 1979) because they give a somewhat different answer. He hybridized ^{3}H-cRNA *in situ* to the rDNA of conjugating cells. He saw no hybridization until the stage of macronuclear anlagen, and then there was a fairly rapid increase in the amount of detectable hybridization. In a normal micronucleus, as in a vegative cell, there is not enough rDNA to get a signal. Thus, positive nuclei are presumably those with amplified rDNA.

Since you find so much synthesis, what do you see in autoradiographs?

PEARLMAN: At present we don't know where it is localized. The experiments that we have done – autoradiographic experiments – have not been done in such a way, really, to ask that kind of question. One has to do I think fairly careful spreads rather than squashes or just smears of the slides, and the only autoradiographic experiments we have done are really to ask the question, is there macronuclear label. From the experiments that we have done, we don't see any localization, which is certainly disconcerting and puzzling.

WEISSMANN: Probably this question is unanswerable at present. Does one know that the triphosphate pool from which overall nuclear DNA is made is the same as that of the ribosomal DNA; I mean, could there be compartmentation?

PEARLMAN: There certainly could be, but there is no evidence for this.

DAWID: I wonder, can you look in the EM and see anything if there is a fairly narrow time in which replication happens? Can one see a replicating form?

PEARLMAN: We have not as yet. That is what we want to do by looking at individual fractions across these BUdR gradients.

Yao, M.-C., Blackburn, E. & Gall, J. G. (1979) Amplification of the rRNA genes in *Tetrahymena*. *Cold Spring Harbor Symp. Quant. Biol.* 42 (in press).

Transcriptional Properties of Isolated Nucleoli from *Tetrahymena*

J. C. Leer, E. Gocke, O. F. Nielsen, & O. Westergaard

INTRODUCTION

Major progress in the understanding of regulation of gene expression can be expected from studies of purified specific genes in their chromatin state. This is at present possible only in special cases, one of which is the extra-chromosomal r-chromatin* from *Tetrahymena*. The rDNA in this organism is organized in about 1000 nucleoli each containing 5–10 rDNA molecules.

The *Tetrahymena* nucleolus is a very attractive system for studies of transcription and its relation to structure since the rDNA molecule itself is a relatively small molecule with a molecular weight of 13×10^6 daltons (Gall 1974, Engberg *et al.* 1974) containing about 75% coding sequences (Engberg *et al.* 1976a, Karrer & Gall 1976, Eckert *et al.* 1978). In the following we describe a procedure for the isolation of free and nucleolus associated r-chromatin. The transcriptional properties of isolated nucleoli mimic the *in vivo* process with respect to 1) strand selection, 2) elongation rate, and 3) termination. Similar properties are observed with free r-chromatin with the interesting exception that the termination signal is deleted.

METHODS

Preparation of nucleoli

Macronuclei of exponentially growing cultures of *Tetrahymena pyriformis*,

---

* Abbr.: rRNA=ribosomal 17S and 25S RNA
　　　rDNA=the DNA coding for rRNA
　　　r-chromatin=rDNA associated with chromosomal proteins
　　　free or soluble r-chromatin=r-chromatin released from the nucleoli
Department of Molecular Biology, University of Aarhus, DK-8000 Århus C, Denmark

SPECIFIC EUKARYOTIC GENES, Alfred Benzon Symposium 13, Munksgaard 1979

harvested at about 80,000 cells/ml, were prepared as described earlier (Leer *et al.* 1976). Nucleoli were released by suspending the nuclei in 10 volumes of "extraction buffer" (10 mM Tris pH 7.2, 140 mM NaCl, 1 mM $MgCl_2$, 10% glycerol, and 1 mM 2-mercaptoethanol) using gentle homogenization. The extracted nuclei were removed by a 500 xg spin and the nucleoli in the supernatant purified by centrifugation into a sucrose cushion (1.5 ml 80% sucrose and 3.0 ml 50% sucrose in "cushion buffer" which is 10 mM Tris pH 7.2, 140 mM NaCl, 1 mM EDTA, and 1 mM 2-mercaptoethanol) in a SW27 centrifugation tube. After centrifugation at 15,000 xg for 30 min, the nucleoli were collected from the interphase between 50% and 80% sucrose solutions.

RNA-polymerase activity and elongation rates

One unit of RNA polymerase is defined as the amount of enzyme which incorporates one pmole UMP into RNA in 10 min at 25°C. The endogenous RNA-polymerase activity was assayed in a mixture containing 30 mM Tris pH 8.0, 5 mM $(NH_4)_2SO_4$, 8 mM $MgCl_2$, 4 mM 2-mercaptoethanol, 0.5 mM EDTA, 2 mM KCl, 50 mM NaCl, 100 μM ATP, GTP, and CTP, 7.5 μM UTP (2 Ci/mmole 5,6-^{3}H-UTP). For elongation-rate studies the same incubation conditions were used except that 30 μM unlabeled UTP and 30 μM a-^{32}P-labeled ATP (2 Ci/mmole) were used.

RNA-gel studies

RNA-size measurements were done on 1.9% agarose gels containing 5M urea (Dudov *et al.* 1976). The gels were calibrated with RNA molecular weight markers from EMC virus ($M_w=2.5\times10^6$ daltons), TMV ($M_w=2.0\times10^6$ daltons) and ribosomal RNA from rat liver and *E. coli.*

Preparation of cDNA

cDNA was synthesized from purified 17S and 25S rRNA after polyadenylation according to the methods of Hell *et al.* (1976). Back titrations with rRNA have shown that all sequences in the 17S and 25S rRNA are equally represented in the cDNA (data not shown); 1.5% cross contamination was found in the 17S rRNA and 6% in the 25S rRNA.

Hybridizations

Nucleolar transcript was synthesized *in vitro* under standard assay conditions except that the ATP concentration was 15 μM (a-^{32}P-ATP), UTP was 20 μM, and

CTP and Hg CTP were 10 μM each. The transcript was purified on a thiol sepharose 4B column (Pharmacia) and fixed amounts of transcript were titrated with 17S cDNA and 17S+25S cDNA. The samples were incubated to a Rot of 0.7 mol · liter^{-1} · sec^{-1} and assayed for S_1-nuclease-resistant hybrid according to Hell *et al.* (1976). The specific activities of transcript and cDNA were 4000 cpm/ng (^{32}P) and 4500 cpm/ng (^{3}H), respectively.

In order to determine the maximal level of hybridization *in vivo* ^{32}P-labeled rRNA (300 cpm/ng) was isolated and hybridized to 17S+25S cDNA under the same conditions.

RESULTS AND DISCUSSION
Preparation of nucleoli
Nucleoli can be extracted from *Tetrahymena* macronuclei in physiological ionic strength buffers and isolated in a sucrose cushion as outlined in Fig. 1, details are given under Methods. The yields of DNA, protein, and RNA polymerase activity are presented for a typical experiment in Table I. Macronuclei contain about 2% rDNA (Engberg *et al.* 1976b, Yao & Gorovsky, 1974) and 1% of the total DNA can be isolated as rDNA in the sucrose cushion, that is in a yield of about 50%. At this stage the protein to DNA ratio is 30:1. In different preparations the specific activity of the RNA polymerase in the sucrose cushion

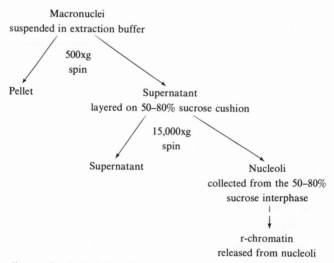

Macronuclei
suspended in extraction buffer

500xg
spin

Pellet

Supernatant
layered on 50–80% sucrose cushion

15,000xg
spin

Supernatant

Nucleoli
collected from the 50–80%
sucrose interphase

r-chromatin
released from nucleoli

Fig. 1. Flow diagram for the isolation of nucleoli from *Tetrahymena.* From the nucleoli, free r-chromatin can be prepared as described in the text.

Table I
Purification table for an 18-liter culture (~10^9 cells)

Fraction	Protein (mg)	DNA (mg)	RNA polymerase activity (units/mg protein)	(units/mg DNA)
Cells	1050	10.9		
Macronuclei	56	10.1	6,000	34,000
Nucleoli[a]	3.6	0.11	22,000	740,000

[a] sucrose cushion purified

varies between 10,000–60,000 units/mg protein. Also the final yield of r-chromatin in the sucrose cushion varies somewhat from preparation to preparation (30–60%). Analysis of the DNA component of nucleoli (sucrose-cushion material) on agarose gels showed that at least 90% was rDNA. The identity of the rDNA has been determined by its density in CsCl, size, EcoRl digestion pattern, and hybridization properties. The nucleoli can be purified further by banding in metrizamide density gradients. Fig. 2a shows symmetrical

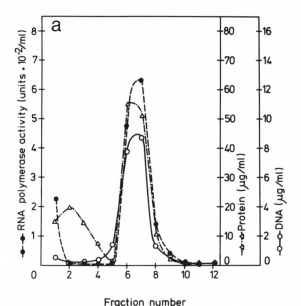

Fraction number

Fig. 2. (a) Metrizamide banding of nucleoli.
Nucleoli from 12 ml of the sucrose cushion were collected by centrifugation, resuspended in 1/4 volume of 45% metrizamide in cushion buffer and applied to the bottom of a preformed 15–40% metrizamide gradient in the same buffer. The gradients were centrifuged at 24 krpm for 2 h in the SW27 rotor. The fractions were assayed for ^{3}H-labeled DNA, protein, and RNA polymerase activity.

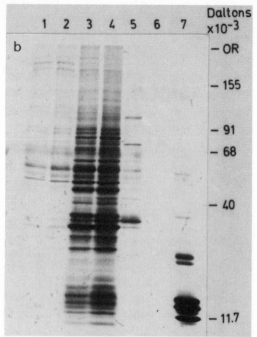

(b) SDS acrylamide gel electrophoresis of proteins in the fractions of the metrizamide gradient. Fractions were pooled two by two and the proteins associated with high molecular weight structures collected by centrifugation. The pellets were dissolved and run on 8–18% acrylamide gels according to the procedure of Laemmli (1970) in lanes 1–6. Acid extracted histones from *Tetrahymena* were run in lane 7.

coinciding peaks of rDNA, protein, and RNA polymerase activity indicating that the isolated nucleoli have a defined composition. The protein to rDNA ratio at this stage is 8:1, which is very similar to the results of Jones (1978a). The protein composition of the nucleoli in metrizamide gradient fractions was analyzed on one-dimensional SDS-acrylamide gels. Fig. 2b shows that the peak fractions contain a complex mixture of proteins. Studies of the nucleolar proteins from *Xenopuls laevis* (Higashinakagawa *et. al* 1977) and Novikof hepatoma cells (Matsui & Busch 1977) have revealed patterns of similar complexity. The samples from the peak fractions contain proteins with molecular weights indistinguishable from those of histones. From the data it is not definitively clear whether these proteins are histones and in what ratio to DNA they are present, but studies of Jones (1978b) indicate that r-chromatin contain histones in a ratio to DNA which is 40% of that in bulk chromatin.

Electron microscopic studies of the isolated nucleoli reveal a membrane-

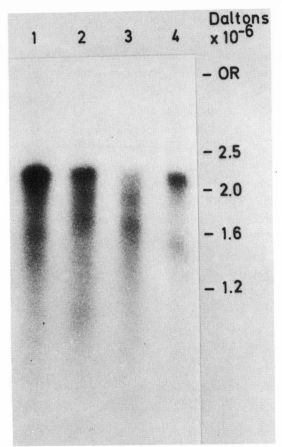

Fig. 3. Size studies of *in vivo* and *in vitro* synthesized nucleolar RNA.
In vivo labeled RNA (lane 4) was extracted from nucleoli of cells grown in presence of 2 μCi/ml ^{32}P-orthophosfate. Samples 1–3 represent *in vitro* transcripts from nucleoli incubated in ^{32}P-ATP assay mixture for $1^1/_2$ min followed by a chase with 250 μM cold ATP for 10 min (1), 3 min (2), and 2 min (3). The samples were analyzed on agarose-urea gels with RNA markers run in parallel.

associated structure similar to that of nucleoli in sections of whole cells. After banding in metrizamide gradients, however, the nucleoli appear swollen or partially disintegrated (results not shown).

Transcriptional properties of the isolated nucleoli
The endogenous RNA polymerase activity has an absolute requirement for all four ribonucleoside triphosphates and for divalent ions, with a slight preference for Mg^{2+}. The activity is not inhibited by a-amanitin but it is inhibited more than

97% at 20 μg/ml actinomycin D. The rate of RNA synthesis is reduced after about 10 min of incubation, in parallel with the polymerases reaching the termination point. Based on results presented below, the time required for a polymerase to synthesize a full-length rRNA precursor *in vitro* can be estimated to be 12–15 min. The incorporation of UMP into RNA continues for a total of 20–60 min depending on the preparation.

The largest stable *in vivo* synthesized precursor rRNA, the 35S rRNA has a molecular weight of 2.3×10^6 daltons (Eckert *et al.* 1978). As shown in Fig. 3 the precursor rRNA can be extracted from isolated nucleoli, labeled with ^{32}P-orthophosphate *in vivo*. The *in vitro* transcript has the same maximal size, indicating that the termination signal is operating *in vitro* (Fig. 3).

The *in vitro* transcript was analyzed by hybridization to excess of 17S cDNA and 17S+25S cDNA (Table II). The saturation level was 26% and 70%, respectively, of transcript resistant to S_1-nuclease. The background level obtained in the absence of cDNA was 15%. This leaves a minimum of 55% hybridized to the cDNA. Hybridization of *in vivo* ^{32}P-labeled rRNA with an excess of 17S+25S cDNA gives a saturation level of 85% with a background of 12%. Using 85% as the maximal level of hybridization obtainable under the experimental condition and subtracting a background of 15%, we find that 79% of the transcript is represented in the 17S+25S cDNA. Since we observe less than 3% transcription in the presence of actinomycin and since the self-annealing of both rRNA and transcript is 12–15%, the remaining 21% of the transcript which is not complementary to the cDNA represents transcribed spacers and not RNA directed or nonsense DNA transcription.

From calculations similar to those mentioned above, the following composition of the *in vitro* transcript can be estimated: 17S RNA : 25S RNA : transcribed

Table II

Hybridization of in vitro transcript and rRNA with excess of 17S cDNA and 17S+25S cDNA

RNA	17S cDNA	17S+25S cDNA
in vitro transcript	26% (15%)	70% (15%)
in vivo synthesized rRNA		85% (12%)

The table gives the percentage of RNA resistant to S_1-nuclease after hybridization with saturating amounts of cDNA. Numbers in parenthesis give background levels of hybrid formed in the absence of cDNA.

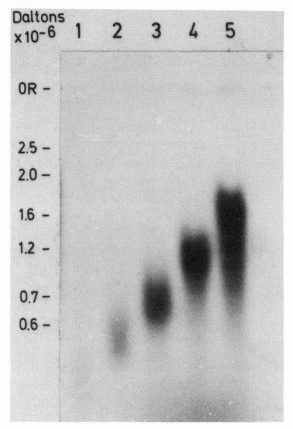

Fig. 4. Elongation rate of the RNA polymerase in isolated nucleoli.
RNA-stripped nucleoli were incubated with ^{32}P-ATP assay mixture. The size of the transcript was estimated on agarose-urea gels in samples stopped after 1, 3, 6, 12 and 25 min (lanes 1–5). RNA marker samples were run in parallel.

spacer ratios are 16% : 63% : 21%. Using the molecular weights of the rRNAs determined from our gel studies (17S : 0.6×10^6 daltons, 25S : 1.2×10^6 daltons, 35 S : 2.3×10^6 daltons) the composition of the precursor rRNA can be calculated to 25% : 52% : 22%. The theoretical compositon of the *in vitro* transcript can be calculated applying the following model: 1) the transcribed spacers are evenly divided between the 5'-end of the molecule and the regions between the 17S and 25S sequences, 2) the RNA polymerases are randomly distributed throughout the transcription unit, 3) no reinitiation occurs during the 15 min used for synthesizing the transcript. Based on these assumptions the ratios are 13% : 75%

: 12% in the same order as above. More detailed investigations will be required in order to explain the discrepancy between this model and the observed composition.

The elongation rate of the endogenous RNA polymerase was measured after stripping the r-chromatin for *in vivo* synthesized RNA-chains by a 5-min incubation at 25°C with pancreatic RN'ase (2.5 ng/ml) followed by an additional sucrose cushion centrifugation. Gel studies with labeled RNA have demonstrated that no residual RN'ase could be detected after the sucrose cushion purification. The time course of the elongation of RNA chains was followed by incubation of the stripped nucleoli in assay mixture. At different time points the reaction was stopped and the size of the transcript estimated on agarose-urea gels (Fig. 4). The elongation rates calculated from the gel studies are summarized in Table III. The initial elongation rate is 12 nucleotides per sec. This is much faster than elongation rates found in other chromatin systems and about half the rate estimated for eukaryotic RNA polymerase *in vivo* (Kafatos 1972). The reason for the reduction in the elongation rate after 6 min of incubation is at the present not clear.

From the amount of transcript synthesized in a standard assay (Table I) and from the elongation rate (Table III) it can be estimated that each gene of the sucrose cusion purified nucleoli contains an average of three active RNA polymerases. However, the number of RNA polymerases can vary between two to eight in different preparations. Calculations based on *in vivo* studies (Leick & Andersen 1970) show that in exponentially growing cultures there must be a minimum of 50 active RNA polymerase molecules per gene. The difference between *in vivo* and *in vitro* might be explained by a loss of RNA polymerase molecules during isolation of nucleoli or by an inactivation of a low percentage of polymerases which would arrest the transcription of polymerases sitting promotor proximal to the inactive molecule.

Table III

Elongation rate of the endogenous RNA polymerase

Incubation period (min)	Elongation rate (nucleotides/sec)
1–3	12
3–6	9
6–12	3
12–25	1

Preparation of soluble r-chromatin from nucleoli

In a previous publication we reported that soluble r-chromatin could be isolated after limited digestion with proteolytic enzymes (Leer *et al.* 1976). We have now developed methods for releasing r-chromatin from the nucleolar matrix using either ammonium sulfate or low concentrations of detergent. Sucrose cushion purified nucleoli (Fig. 1) were diluted with 2 volumes of cushion buffer and added either 175 mM $(NH_4)_2SO_4$ or 0.006% SDS plus 0.012% Triton X-100. After 10 min on ice, insoluble material was removed by centrifugation at 15,000xg for 15 min. The soluble r-chromatin was collected by centrifugation at 150,000xg for 2 h either in a 25–60% sucrose cushion or as pellet which was resuspended in cushion buffer. Using the detergent method the yield of both rDNA and RNA polymerase activity was about 50% of the content in nucleoli. In the case of the ammonium sulfate method the yields of rDNA was about 50% and of RNA polymerase activity about 30%.

Transcription properties of nucleoli treated with detergent, ammonium sulfate or DNA intercalating dyes

Treatment of nucleoli with detergents or ammonium sulfate affects the transcriptional properties in a very specific way, viz., to remove the termination signal. Fig. 5 shows agarose-urea gel electrophoresis of the *in vitro* transcript synthesized from nucleoli in the presence of varying concentrations of either SDS+Triton or ammonium sulfate, gels A and B. Clearly the maximal molecular weight of the transcript has increased from 2.3×10^6 to at least 3.0×10^6 daltons, indicating that the RNA polymerases read through the normal termination signal. These results are supported by hybridization experiments.

The processes of releasing the r-chromatin from the nucleoli and eliminating the termination signal are not linked as shown in experiments with low concentrations of SDS+Triton or ammonium sulfate, which removes the termination signal without solubilizing the r-chromatin from the nucleoli.

Correct termination can also be prevented by certain DNA intercalating dyes. Fig. 5c shows the effect of lucanthone. Similar results have been obtained with proflavine, which prevents termination at concentrations of about 30 μg/ml. The elongation rate of the RNA polymerase was reduced less than 15% in the presence of the dyes (100 μg/ml lucanthone or 30 μg/ml proflavine). The perturbation of the termination process by these two DNA intercalating dyes involves some specific interaction with the r-chromatin, since we have not observed similar effects with other DNA intercalating dyes.

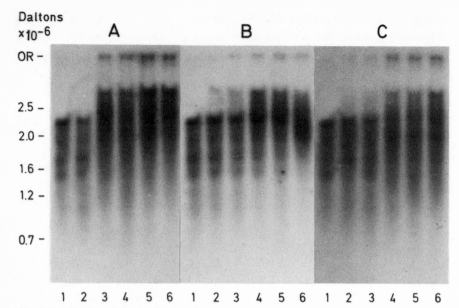

Fig. 5. Inactivation of the termination signal.

Nucleoli were incubated in ^{32}P-ATP mixture for 30 min in presence of either SDS+Triton X-100 (A), ammonium sulfate (B), or lucanthone (C). The transcription products were analyzed on agarose-urea gels.

(A) Nucleoli were incubated in the presence of the following SDS+Triton X-100 concentrations: 0, 0.0006%+0.0012%, 0.0014%+0.0028%, 0.0018%+0.0036%, 0.0028%+0.0056%, 0.0045%+0.0090% (lanes 1–6).

(B) The incubation mixture contained ammonium sulfate in the following concentrations: 0, 25, 50, 100, 125, 150 mM (lanes 1–6).

(C) Lucanthone was present during incubation in these concentrations: 0, 15, 30, 60, 120, 180 μg/ml (lanes 1–6).

It is not possible from the presented results to deduce the actual mechanism of the termination process. Further experiments are required to elucidate the details of the termination process and to establish whether there are any similarities to the Rho-dependent termination in *E. coli*.

ACKNOWLEDGMENTS

This study was supported by grant No. 511–7131 from the Danish Natural Science Research Council and contract No. 204-76-1 BioDK with EURATOM, CEC, Brussels. E.G. was the recipient of a long-term EMBO Fellowship. We want to thank Dr. G.C. Birnie for help with the synthesis of cDNA and Drs. J.R.

Nilsson and K.A. Marcker for helpful discussion. Ms. Kirsten Andersen, Ms. Susanne F. Pedersen, Ms. Else Ørnbøl, and Mr. Ole Nymann are acknowledged for skillful technical assistance.

REFERENCES

Dudov, K. P., Dabeva, M. D. & Hadjiolov, A. A. (1976) Simple agar-urea-gel electrophoretic fractionation of high molecular weight RNA. *Anal. Biochem.* 76, 250–258.

Eckert, W.A., Kaffenberger, W., Krohne, G., & Franke, W.W. (1978) Introduction of hidden breaks during rRNA maturation in *Tetrahymena pyriformis. Eur. J. Biochem.* 87, 607–616.

Engberg, J., Nilsson, J.R., Pearlman, R.E., & Leick, V. (1974) Induction of nucleolar and mitochondrial DNA replication in *Tetrahymena pyriformis. Proc. Nat. Acad. Sci. USA* 71, 894–898.

Engberg, J., Andersson, P., Leick, V., & Collins, J. (1976a) Free ribosomal DNA molecules from *Tetrahymena pyriformis* GL are giant palindromes. *J. Mol. Biol.* 104, 455–470.

Engberg, J., Collins, J., & Leick, V (1976b) Isolation and some characteristics of nucleolar DNA from *Tetrahymena pyriformis* GL. In: *Proceedings of the 9th Congress of The Nordic Society for Cell Biology,* ed. Bierring, F. pp. 213–217. Odense University Press.

Gall, J.G. (1974) Free ribosomal RNA genes in the macronucleus of *Tetrahymena. Proc. Nat. Acad. Sci. USA* 71, 3078–3081.

Hell, A., Young, B.D., & Birnie, G.D. (1976) Synthesis of DNAs complementary to human ribosomal RNAs polyadenylated *in vitro. Biochim. Biophys. Acta* 442, 37–49.

Higashinakagawa, T., Wahn, H., & Reeder, R.H. (1977) Isolation of ribosomal gene chromatin. *Dev. Biol.* 55, 375–386.

Jones, R.W. (1978a) Preparation of chromatin containing ribosomal deoxyribonucleic acid from the macronucleus of *Tetrahymena pyriformis. Biochem. J.* 173, 145–153.

Jones, R.W. (1978b) Histone composition of a chromatin fraction containing ribosomal deoxyribonucleic acid isolated from the macronucleus of *Tetrahymena pyriformis.Biochem. J.* 173, 155–164.

Kafatos, F.C. (1972) The cocoonase zymogen cells of silk moths: A model of terminal differentiation for specific protein synthesis. *Curr. Topics Devel. Biol.* 7, 125–191.

Karrer, K.M. & Gall, J.G. (1976) The macronuclear ribosomal DNA of *Tetrahymena pyriformis* is a palindrome. *J. Mol. Biol.* 104, 421–453.

Laemmli, U. K. (1970) Cleavage of structural proteins during the assembly of the head of bacteriophage T4. *Nature* 227, 680–685.

Leer, J. C., Nielsen, O. F., Piper, P. W. & Westergaard, O. (1976) Isolation of the ribosomal RNA gene from *Tetrahymena* in the state of transcriptionally active chromatin. *Biochem. Biophys. Res. Commun.* 72, 720–731.

Leick, V. & Andersen, S.B. (1970) Polls and turnover rates of ribosomal RNA in *Tetrahymena pyriformis. Eur. J. Biochem.* 14, 460–464.

Matsui, S. & Busch, H. (1977) Isolation and characterization of r-DNA-containing chromatin from nucleoli. *Exptl. Cell Res.* 109, 151–161.

Yao, M.-C. & Gorovsky, M.A. (1974) Comparison of the sequences of macro- and micronuclear DNA of *Tetrahymena pyriformis. Chromosoma* 48, 1–18.

DISCUSSION

PAUL: Have you done any experiments with added polymerase?

WESTERGAARD: No, up till now we have just been working with the endogenous RNA polymerases on the gene. We find 3–8 active RNA polymerase molecules per gene, while *in vivo* there must be a minimum of 50.

KLENOW: I may add that in our laboratory Anne Lykkesfeldt has isolated an RNA polymerase that can use isolated *Tetrahymena* chromatin as a template.

PLESNER: This system seems to be ideal to try *in vitro* effect of other nucleotides than those that are normally used. Have you tried any other nucleotides?

WESTERGAARD: No, so far we have not.

DAWID: Can you spread these nucleoli á la Miller; and have you checked that it really is polymerase I, as we might think; and are the terminated chains released or are they still stuck to the DNA?

WESTERGAARD: It is something we very much would like to do the EM. To the question whether it is RNA polymerase I, we can just say that it is alfa-amanitin resistant at least up to about 400 µg/ml.

RICH: Did you try different substrates for the polymerase, i.e. either naked DNA or the metrizamide-banded material?

WESTERGAARD: We have tried to run the RNA polymerases off the gene in isolated nucleoli, as we thought this would be the simplest way to get the active holo-enzyme. So far we have only seen slight activity (between 2–10%) in these preparations, which might indicate that the enzyme is not leaving the gene at the terminator or that it becomes inactivated.

RICH: Can you use the metrizamide-banded material?

WESTERGAARD: The transcriptional activity of the metrizamide-banded nucleoli is reduced with a factor four to five.

Diadenosine Tetraphosphate (Ap₄A), an Activator of Gene Function

Paul Plesner[1,2] *Mary L. Stephenson*[3], *Paul C. Zamecnik*[3] *& Nancy L. R. Bucher*[3]

Diadenosine tetraphosphate, Ap₄A, has in all probability a regulatory effect on cellular metabolism, possibly as a regulator of transcription or replication. This was suggested at the first of these symposia, 10 years ago (Zamecnik & Stephenson 1969). Descriptions of the *in vitro* biosynthesis, optical properties and occurrence in biological systems have appeared in a series of papers of which the following are representative: Zamecnik *et al.* (1966), Randerath *et al.* (1966), Zamecnik & Stephenson (1968), Scott & Zamecnik (1969) and Rapaport & Zamecnik (1976).

The argument for assuming that Ap₄A was an activator of gene function gained momentum from the finding by Grummt (1978) that Ap₄A triggers initiation of DNA replication in permeabilized baby hamster kidney cells.

In biological systems Ap₄A, at the highest concentration, reaches only about one thousandth of the level of ATP. The early assay was very cumbersome and consisted of three steps of TLC chromatography of a phosphatase-treated extract; the Ap₄A thus isolated was measured using the luciferase method for the ATP which was liberated following phosphodiesterase treatment of the eluted Ap₄A (Stephenson & Zamecnik, unpublished data). More recent isolation involves two-step column chromatography (Rapaport & Zamecnik 1976).

---

[1] Department of Chemistry, Carlsberg Laboratory, Gamle Carlsbrgvej 10, DK-2500 Copenhagen, Valby
[2] Department of Molecular Biology, University of Odense, Denmark
[3] The John Collins Warren Laboratories of the Collis P. Huntington Memorial Hospital of Harvard University at the Massachusetts General Hospital, Boston, Massachusetts, U.S.A.

* Abbr.: Ap₄A = diadenosine 5',5'''-P¹,P⁴-tetraphosphate

      ATCC = American Type Culture Collection

        OD = optical density

       TCA = Trichloroacetic acid

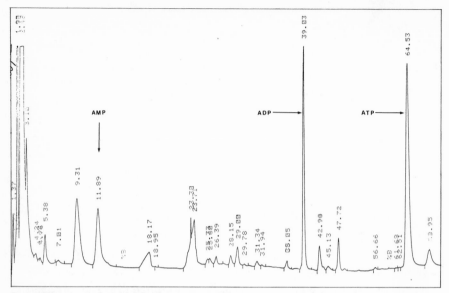

Fig. 1. High pressure liquid chromatogram (HPLC) of nucleotides from *Tetrahymena.* Abscissa: retention time in minutes; ordinate: absorbancy at 254 nm. Instrument: Hewlett Packard 1084A, fitted with a Whatman 25 cm Partisil-SAX strong anion exchanger column. Cells from 10 ml of *Tetrahymena* culture (150×10^3 cells/ml) in proteose-peptone-yeast extract medium were collected by centrifugation and nucleotides were extracted with 1 ml of 10% TCA. The extract was treated five times with 2 ml of ether, then lyophilized. The lyophilized extract was dissolved in 200 μl of water; 100 μl of the solution was chromatographed using a KH_2PO_4-KCl gradient as described by Hartwick & Brown (1975), the integrator attenuation was 5, the temperature of column and solvents 40°C. The adenylate energy charge is 0.73 and the ATP/ADP ratio 1.98 as calculated from the integrator data.

In this paper we describe two simple, rapid methods based on high pressure liquid chromatography (HPLC). We have confirmed and extended earlier findings of the presence of Ap_4A in several pro- and eukaryotic biological systems. We also present additional evidence to support the suggestion that Ap_4A functions as a (positive) metabolic activator.

METHODS AND RESULTS
The pool of free nucleotides
The basis for the analysis of $A_{p4}A$ is the separation and quantitative measurement of free cellular nucleotides by ion exchange chromatography as described by Hartwick & Brown (1975). Fig. 1 shows a typical separation of the free nucleotides in *Tetrahymena pyriformis*, strain GL. The extraction of the

nucleotides by the Khym method as adapted by Chen *et al.* (1977) proved to be essential for obtaining reproducible results. The principle of the chromato-graphic method is a gradient elution of the nucleotides from a strong anion exchange column with an increasing concentration of KH_2PO_4, KCl and an increase in pH.

From the chromatogram in Fig. 1, the adenylate energy charge (Atkinson 1969) is calculated to be 0.73 and the ATP/ADP 1.98, viz. values that are unlikely to occur in cells growing at optimal growth condition. Therefore we omitted the centrifugation step when *Tetrahymena* cells were harvested, and obtained the result shown in Fig. 2B. The nucleosides and nucleotides in the medium dominate the early part of the chromatogram but an estimate of the ATP/ADP ratio is possible, and is found to be 10-fold higher than that from centrifuged cells. The adenylate energy charge can not be determined using these conditions but is most likely quite high. That this is true appears from analyses of *Tetrahymena* cells synchronized for cell divisions and then transferred to inorganic medium (Hamburger & Zeuthen 1957); chromatograms show that prior to the first synchronous division the energy charge is 0.98 and the

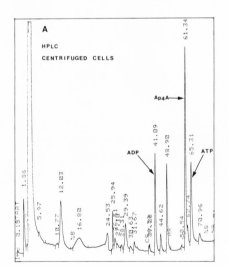
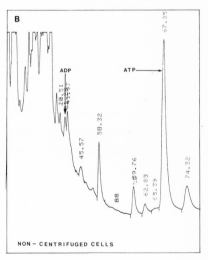

Fig. 2. HPLC of nucleotides from *Tetrahymena.* Abscissae, ordinates and chromatographic technique as described for Fig. 1A: Cells from proteose peptone-yeast extract medium were treated as described in Fig. 1 and chromatographed with $A_{p4}A$ (10 μl of a 1 mg/ml solution). The adenylate energy charge is 0.70 and the ATP/ADP ratio is 1.23. B: One ml of cell culture (150,000 cells per ml) was pipetted into 1 ml of 20% TCA and extracted for 30 min, then centrifuged. The TCA was removed with trioctylamine according to Khym as described by Chen *et al.* (1977). The ATP/ADP ratio is 22. No $A_{p4}A$ was added.

ATP/ADP ratio 28. For this reason we are not reporting any results obtained from centrifuged cells if they are used for quantitation.

Direct determination of $A_{p4}A$

Fig. 2A shows that $A_{p4}A$ can be separated from ATP in the Hartwick & Brown system. By this direct method $A_{p4}A$ could be demonstrated in noncentrifuged cells but not in centrifuged cells. When tritiated $A_{p4}A$ was added, the radioactivity was found to co-chromatograph with the peak we assumed to be $A_{p4}A$.

These findings are in accordance with the fact that in chromatograms of standards, $A_{p4}A$ can be separated from UTP, TTP, and CTP (which are the closest neighbors) provided that these compounds do not exceed nanomolar amounts. This holds for *Tetrahymena,* but not for rat liver cells and all the mammalian cell lines that have hitherto been analyzed, among them hepatocytes, 3T6 cells, BHK cells, spleen cells and chicken embryo fibroblasts.

Differential sensitivity to phosphatase

The difficulty of separating $A_{p4}A$ from UTP could be overcome by performing a preliminary reversed phase separation of UTP from $A_{p4}A$. This method has, however, not yet proved reproducible and the stability of $A_{p4}A$ to alkaline phosphatase was therefore used instead.

A solution of the free nucleotides that had been extracted from the cellular material was treated with phosphodiesterase-free alkaline phosphatase, acidified and then subjected to ion exchange chromatography. The chromatography was simplified so that only an isocratic elution system was needed. The separation obtained with standards is shown in Fig. 3A and the differential sensitivity is demonstrated in Fig. 3B, which shows that only $A_{p4}A$ is left undigested, while the other nucleotides are found as adenosine. The stability of $A_{p4}A$ at a basic pH is made use of in this procedure.

Acidification of the sample to pH 2 after digestion and mixing of the sample with eluting buffer was found to be essential for the chromatography.

Demonstration of $A_{p4}A$ in cellular material

Figs. 4 and 5 demonstrate that $A_{p4}A$ is present in *E. coli,* rat liver and spleen cells on basis of the following criteria: stability to alkaline phophatase and co-chromatography with an added internal $A_{p4}A$ standard. $A_{p4}A$ was also found in *Tetrahymena* by the phosphatase method.

The analyses in Fig. 4A were extended to encompass several points in the growth cycle of *E. coli.* (strain K12, lysine requiring). The results are shown in Table I. Since the curve represents a single experiment we do not attempt any fine dissection of the results in Table I, but note that the highest content of $A_{p4}A$ is found just at the point where the growth curve changes from positive acceleration to logarithmic growth. These results are in complete agreement with earlier findings with *E. coli* using a TLC-phosphodiesterase-luciferase method (Stephenson & Zamecnik 1970, unpublished).

A similar result was obtained from an experiment with starved-refed *Tetrahymena*, a system which has been used by several workers (see e.g. Engberg *et al.* 1974, Hallberg & Bruns 1976). In this system, stages of preferential

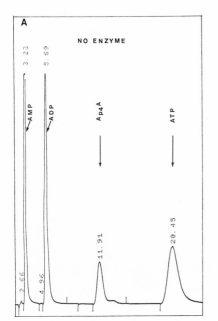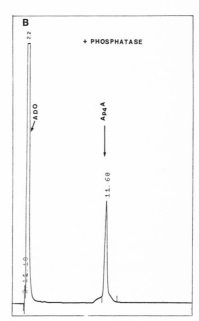

Fig. 3. HPLC of nucleotide standards before and after treatment with alkaline phosphatase. Abscissae and ordinates as in Fig. 1. The chromatograms were eluted isocratically with 0.25 M KH_2PO_4, 0.5 M KCl, pH 4.50 (the high concentration buffer of the Hartwick & Brown system). A Waters chromatograph equipped with a model 6000 A solvent delivery system, a model 440 absorbance detector, and a Hewlett Packard 3380 integrator, were used. A: chromatogram of 5 nanomoles of each AMP, ADP, and ATP, and 1.25 nanomoles of $A_{p4}A$ B: The same amounts of nucleotides in 100 μl 0.1 M Tris pH 8.75 were incubated for 12 h at room temperature with 1 μl of alkaline phosphatase (Wortington *E. coli*).

Further 0.2 μl of phosphatase were then added and the mixture incubated for additional 4–6 h; it was then acidified with 10 μl of 8.5% H_3PO_4, mixed with an equal volume of eluting buffer and chromatographed.

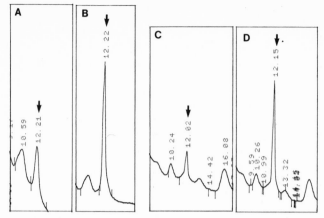

Fig. 4. Demonstration of A$_{p4}$A in *E. coli* and rat liver. A: *E. coli* cells of a lysine requiring mutant ATCC No. 12408 growing on a synthetic medium enriched with lysine (ATCC medium No. 57 without agar), were collected on Millipore filters in less than 15 sec. The filters were quickly transferred to 10% TCA at 4° and extracted for 30 min. The TCA was removed by the Khym method (Chen *et al.* 1977) and the extracts lyophilized. The lyophilized extract, which contained the nucleotides from 1.2 OD$_{450nm}$ units of culture, was dissolved in Tris and treated with alkaline phosphatase as described in Fig. 3, and then chromatographed as in Fig. 3. B: Same as A but with 26 picomoles of A$_{p4}$A added to the mixture prior to injection into the column. C: Rat liver was freeze-clamped between aluminum plates precooled in liquid nitrogen and extracted with 9 volumes of 10% TCA. The extract was treated as described above and an amount corresponding to 10 mg of liver chromatographed. D: same as C but with 26 picomoles A$_{p4}$A added prior to injection. The peaks that are assummed to be A$_{p4}$A are marked with arrows.

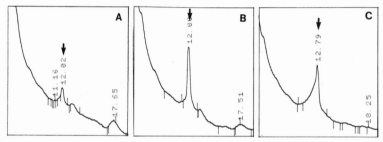

Fig. 5. Demonstration of A$_{p4}$A in human spleen cells. Spleen cells from a patient with Hodgkin's disease were grown as described by Zamecnik & Long (1977). A: Cells from one petri dish (a total of 17×10⁶ cells, grown at 37°) were extracted with 10% TCA as described in Fig. 4. The lyophilized extract was dissolved in 500 µl of Tris and treated with alkaline phosphatase as described in Fig. 3. 200 µl of the digest was acidified and chromatographed. B: Same as A, but with 26 picomoles of A$_{p4}$A added prior to chromatography. C: Cells were grown as described in A, but transferred to 14° for 2 h prior to the extraction with TCA. The total amount of cells in C was 22×10⁶, No addition of A$_{p4}$A prior to chromatography. The integrator data showed that the peak area in C is 6.7 times larger than in A. the peaks that are assumed to be A$_{p4}$A, are marked with arrows.

Table I

Content of A$_{p4}$A in the growth cycle of E. coli

10 ml of a culture of *E. coli,* American Type Culture Collection (ATCC) No. 12408 growing in ATCC medium No. 57 without agar at an optical density of 0.6 at 450 nm per ml, were transferred to 200 ml of the same medium at time 0. Temperature: 37°, A$_{p4}$A was determined by the phosphatase method.

Time after transfer in minutes	Optical density at 450 nm per ml culture	Picomoles A$_{p4}$A per mg protein
140	0.05	+
270	0.10	112
330	0.19	343
375	0.32	148
465	0.52	99
555	0.63	58
650	0.80	47

+ below detection limit

ribosome biosynthesis, replication of ribosomal DNA, and bulk DNA are claimed to occur in a temporal sequence. We starved *Tetrahymena*, strain GL (a gift from Dr. John Moner, Amherst) for 12 h and then refed the cells. The results are shown in Table II and indicate that although no spectacular changes in A$_{p4}$A occur, it is noteworthy that a peak content in A$_{p4}$A is found early after macromolecular synthesis has been turned on. The content of A$_{p4}$A is given per initial 10^6 cells.

Cell divisions occur 3–4 h after the addition of growth medium, but protein

Table II

Content of A$_{p4}$A in Tetrahymena *after refeeding*

Tetrahymena cells were starved for 12 h and refed as described by Engberg *et al.* (1974). 2 ml samples were removed at the times indicated and pipetted into 1 ml of 30% TCA. The amounts of A$_{p4}$A were determined by the phosphatase digestion method

Minutes after addition growth medium	Picomoles A$_{p4}$A per 10^6 cells
90	950
120	1750
150	900
180	1350
210	1100
330	1100
360	1300

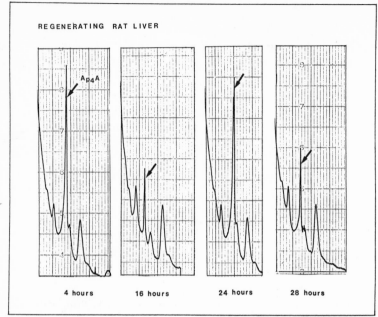

Fig. 6. HPLC of alkaline phosphatase digests of TCA extracts from rat liver. The extracts were prepared and digested as described in Fig. 4C. The arrow indicates the $A_{p4}A$ peak in each panel.

synthesis increases to the same rate as in exponentially growing cells in about 2 h. The data in Table II, therefore, indicate that the $A_{p4}A$ content decreases per unit protein after the time when the peak content has been reached.

Regenerating rat liver also represents a system where stages of macromolecular synthesis occur sequentially (for a comprehensive review, see Bucher & Malt 1971). We determined the content of $A_{p4}A$ at various stages after partial hepatectomy, and found an apparent elevation at 4 h, when RNA synthesis is active and ribosome production is increased, and again at 24 h when the rate of DNA synthesis is near maximal (Fig. 6).

DISCUSSION

High pressure liquid chromatography has in our opinion proven to be very useful for the study of $A_{p4}A$ in biological systems. It is sufficiently sensitive: our results show that 1 or 2 ml of microbial culture or one petri dish of tissue culture provides enough material for both a complete nucleotide analysis by the Hartwick & Brown gradient method as well as material for determination of

$A_{p4}A$ by the phosphatase method. This means that the proliferative rate of the cells, as judged by the energy charge or ATP/ADP ratio, can be evaluated in all samples that are assayed for $A_{p4}A$.

By employing these methods, we have confirmed earlier findings, partly unpublished, that the $A_{p4}A$ content is a very sensitive indicator for the metabolic status of the cells. We do not find $A_{p4}A$ in cells with a low ATP/ADP ratio, whether the low value is caused by adverse physiological conditions or by a traumatic treatment when cells are prepared for extraction.

$A_{p4}A$ has been found in vigorously proliferating cells from all species of cells hitherto examined, pro- and eukaryotic, provided that proper care is taken to preserve the initial ATP content. This fact is noteworthy, because it is what would be expected if $A_{p4}A$ is indeed formed at the aminoacylation step of protein synthesis, which is ubiquitous. That $A_{p4}A$ formation is catalyzed by the ligase *in vivo* has been taken for granted, but never proved. Theoretically $A_{p4}A$ could be formed by a separate specific enzyme; as suggested by S. E. Godtfredsen (unpublished) $A_{p4}A$ might readily be made from ATP and cAMP; the latter does not react in the ligase back reaction *in vitro* (Zamecnik & Stephenson 1968).

The results in Fig. 5A & C indicate that a regulatory mechanism, working through the $A_{p4}A$ system, may respond to changes in the rate of the elongation processes on the ribosomes. The work of Aspen & Hoagland (1978) shows that a selective inhibition of the elongation reactions in protein synthesis may be effected by lowering the temperature to 15°. They suggest that when protein synthesis is blocked and aminoacylation of t-RNA still is progressing at a high rate, amino acids are being hydrolyzed off tRNA by amino-acyl t-RNA hydrolase.

We find from the experiment shown in Fig. 5C (which was designed to elucidate this possibility) that another mechanism may exist: when elongation is preferentially blocked, the acylated amino acids may instead be diverted into formation of $A_{p4}A$ as suggested by Zamecnik & Stephenson (1969). This is an interesting "idling" reaction, as it, contrary to the formation of ppGpp, may occur when ample supplies of amino acid are available.

So far, the discussion has concerned the analysis of $A_{p4}A$ and possible mechanisms of its formation. If we consider the possible effector sites for $A_{p4}A$, the strongest evidence comes from *in vitro* studies. Our data from *E. coli*, *Tetrahymena*, and liver cannot support any fine dissection bearing on the effect. Nonetheless, taken all together, the three sets of data (Tables I, II, Fig. 6), may point to a causal relation between an elevated content of $A_{p4}A$ and an enhanced expression of ribosomal genes. No conclusive evidence can be claimed. However, it has been shown that an elevated content of $A_{p4}A$ is found only when increased rates of macromolecular synthesis are also found. This, together with the *in vitro* results, justify a pursuit of research on the role of $A_{p4}A$ in gene expression.

ACKNOWLEDGMENTS

We thank Professor Martin Ottesen for stimulating and helpful discussions. We are grateful to Dr. Eliezer Rapaport for generous supplies of $A_{p4}A$ and for advice. We thank Maryann Magner, Babette Radner, and Anna Krüger for growing the cells and preparing them for analysis. This work was supported by a grant from the Danish Cancer Society, by grants BC-278 from the American Cancer Society, RO1CA22904-1 from the US Public Health Service and by Contract EY-76-S-02-2404-1 from the Department of Energy. This is publication No. 1551 of the Harvard Cancer Commision.

REFERENCES

Aspen, A.J. & Hoagland, M.B. (1978) Uncoupling of amino acid turnover on transfer RNA from protein synthesis in HeLa cells. *Biochem. Biophys. Acta* 518, 482–496.

Atkinson, D.E. (1969) Regulation of enzyme function. *Ann. Rev. Microbiol.* 23, 47–68.

Bucher, N. L. R. & Malt, R. A. (1971) *Regeneration of Liver and Kidney*, pp. 55–115. Little, Brown and Co., Boston.

Chen, s., Brown, P. R. & Rosie, D. M. (1977) Extraction procedures for use prior to HPLC nucleotide analysis using microparticle chemically bonded packings. *J. Chrom. Sci.* 15, 218–221.

Engberg, J., Nilsson, J.R., Pearlman, R.E. & Leick, V. (1974) Induction of nucleolar and mitochondrial DNA replication in *Tetrahymena pyriformis. Proc. Natl. Acad. Sci. U.S.A.* 71, 894–898.

Grummt, F. (1978) Diadenosine 5',5'''-P',P^4-tetraphosphate triggers initiation of *in vitro* DNA replication in baby hamster kidney cells. *Proc. Natl. Acad. Sci. U.S.A.* 75, 371–375.

Hallberg, R.L. & Bruns, P.J. (1976) Ribosome biosynthesis in *Tetrahymena pyriformis*: regulation in response to nutritional changes. *J. Cell. Biol.* 71, 383–394.

Hamburger, K. & Zeuthen, E. (1957) Synchronous divisions in *Tetrahymene pyriformis* as studied in an inorganic medium. *Exp. Cell. Res.* 13, 443–453.

Hartwick, R.A. & Brown, P.R. (1975) The performance of microparticle chemically-bonded anion-exchange resins in the analysis of nucleotides. *J. Chrom.* 112, 651–662.

Randerath, K., Janeway, C.M., Stephenson, M.L. & Zamecnik, P.C. (1966) Isolation and characterization of dinucleoside tetra- and triphosphates formed in the presence of lysyl-sRNA synthetase. *Biochem. Biophys. Res. Comm.* 24, 98–105.

Rapaport, E. & Zamecnik, P.C. (1976) Presence of diadenosine 5'5'''-P^1,P^4-tetraphosphate ($A_{p4}A$) in mammalian cells in levels varying widely with proliferative activity of the tissue: A possible "pleiotypic activator". *Proc. Natl. Acad. Sci. U.S.A.* 73, 3984–3988.

Scott, J.F. & Zamecnik, P.C. (1969) Some optical properties of diadenosine-5'-phosphates. *Proc. Natl. Acad. Sci. U.S.A.* 64, 1308–1314.

Zamecnik, P.C., Stephenson, M.L., Janeway, C.M. & Randerath, K. (1966) Enzymatic synthesis of diadenosine tetraphosphate and diadenosine triphosphate with a purified lysyl-sRNA synthetase. *Biochem. Biophys. Res. Comm.* 24, 91–97.

Zamecnik, P.C. & Stephenson, M.L. (1968) A possible regulatory site located at the gateway to protein synthesis. In: *Regulatory Mechanisms for Protein Synthesis in Mammalian Cells,* ed. Pietro, A.S. *et al.* pp. 3–16. Academic Press Inc. New York.

Zamecnik, P.C. & Stephenson, M.L. (1969) Nucleoside pyrophosphate compounds related to the first step in protein synthesis. *Alfred Benzon Symposium I, The Role of Nucleotides for the Function and Conformation of Enzymes,* ed. Kalckar, H. *et al.,* pp. 276–289.

Zamecnik, P.C. & Long, J.C. (1977) Growth of cultured cells from patients with Hodgkin's disease and transplantation into nude mice. *Proc. Natl. Acad. Sci. U.S.A.* 74, 754–758.

DISCUSSION

LEICK: How is the variation of Ap$_4$A during the division cycle? I am referring to the fluctuations of ATP during the division cycle.

PLESNER: It is tricky to get the phosphatase method to work on extracts from noncentrifuged cell suspensions in rich medium, that is 2% proteose peptone. The cells described in Table II were refed with only 0.5%. We have obtained data from only one experiment with cells in 2% proteose peptone that were synchronized by the repetitive heat shock regimen. The extracted nuclotides were digested for 3 days with phosphatase. Ap$_4$A could only be detected in one sample, taken immediately before cell division, which coincides with the start of DNA synthesis. We conclude from this that the direct method (Fig. 2) gives too high values for Ap$_4$A. As for the ATP fluctuations you mention, we have in a series of experiments confirmed the finding of considerable variations in the ATP content of cell division synchronized centrifuged cells (Plesner 1961). We have also confirmed that these variations are less pronounced in noncentrifuged cells in agreement with the findings of Andersen Nexø (1975), only the ATP level was higher (30–50 nanomoles per mg protein). The adenosine triphosphate data taken together uncover that a substantial fraction of the ATP that is generated immediately prior to cell division is insensitive to the anaerobiosis induced by centrifugation, as compared with ATP generated in other cellular phases.

KLENOW: Do you know if protein inhibitors have any effect on accumulation of A$_{p4}$A?

PLESNER: Yes, that was one of the findings which prompted us to hope for great variations because you get a drop in the content of Ap$_4$A of 50–100fold, if you add cycloheximide to a cell culture.

Plesner, P. (1961) Changes in ribosome structure and function during synchronized cell division. *Cold Spring Harbor Symp. Quant. Biol.* XXVI, 159–161.

Nexø, B. A. (1975) Ribo- and deoxyribonucleotide triphosphate pools in synchronized populations of *Tetrahymena pyriformis. Biochim. Biophys. Acta* 378, 12–17.

IV. Structural Genes and Their Products

Complexity of Nuclear and Cytoplasmic RNA

John Paul

Now that there are excellent prospects of having detailed structural information about many individual genes within the next few years, it is appropriate to raise again in this context some questions about the determination of the phenotype of differentiated cells. While structural information about genes may give us tools to tackle questions about their expression, it does not necessarily solve them. If we had the entire sequences of a mammalian genome this would run to some 500 volumes, each of a thousand pages, but by itself it would provide little more than a starting point for the analysis of gene function. Moreover, it certainly cannot be assumed that gene expression in eukaryotic cells will be modeled closely after gene expression in prokaryotes, as recent information about the structure of chromatin and the inserts in structural genes in eukaryotes has emphasized. We still have a long way to go before we are likely to understand genetic regulation in eukaryotes in any detail. It will be necessary to make exhaustive studies of several special genes before this goal is approached but some general indications of the problems and the possible nature of some of the answers have been obtained as a result of studies on RNA complexity.

HOW MANY GENES ARE REQUIRED FOR
A COMPLEX EUKARYOTIC ORGANISM?

Long standing genetic arguments have suggested that the maximum number of genes likely to be tolerated in any organism would be of the order of 5×10^4. Detailed analyses in *Drosophila* have led to establishment of close correlation

Beatson Institute for Cancer Research, Wolfson Laboratory for Molecular Pathology, Garscube Estate, Glasgow, Scotland.

SPECIFIC EUKARYOTIC GENES, Alfred Benzon Symposium 13, Munksgaard 1979

between the number of complementation groups and the number of bands in giant chromosomes as analyzed by lethal mutations, i.e. about 5000 (Beerman 1972, Judd *et al.* 1972, Lefevre 1973). However, there is no good information about the ratio of "nonessential" to "essential" genes (O'Brien 1973) and this is probably a lower estimate.

As an alternative approach, direct measurements have been made of the complexity of the polysomal messenger RNA populations in a number of eukaryotic cells. Complexity is defined as the number of nucleotides in unique RNA sequences in an RNA population. It can be converted into an approximate estimate of the number of different messenger RNAs if the number of nucleotides in an average RNA molecule is known and this can be measured quite readily by determining the molecular weight average of messenger RNAs separated on a polyacrylamide gel.

Complexity of RNA has been determined in two ways, both depending on nucleic acid hybridization. One, introduced by Davidson & Hough (1972), depends on first removing all repetitive sequences from a sample of genomic DNA and then determining the fraction of that DNA which is complementary to all the sequences in an RNA sample by saturating it with a very large excess of the RNA. The complexity of the single copy DNA having been determined by measuring the kinetics of renaturation (Britten & Kohne 1968), the complexity of the RNA can then be obtained since it is equivalent to the fraction of DNA saturated by hybridization. Using this approach Davidson and his colleagues have estimated that the messenger RNA of sea urchins has a complexity of between 15 and 22×10^6 nucleotides, depending on developmental stage (Anderson *et al.* 1976, Hough-Evans *et al.* 1977). This is roughly equivalent to 10,000 to 15,000 messenger RNAs.

The second technique requires the isolation of polysomal messenger RNA and its transcription with reverse transcriptase to obtain cDNA which is representative of the messenger RNA population. By following the kinetics of hybrid formation, a direct estimate of complexity can be obtained and information can also be obtained about the abundance of different classes of RNA (Bishop *et al.* 1974, Birnie *et al.* 1974). The figures for complexity obtained by this method are usually rather lower than those for the saturation method, probably because this technique does not give such a precise estimate of the most complex classes of RNA (Kleiman *et al.* 1977). However, in a variety of mammalian cells, numbers of messenger RNA molecules of the same order as found with saturation experiments have been obtained (Birnie *et al.* 1974, Ryffel & McCarthy 1975,

Young *et al.* 1976, Hastie & Bishop 1976). Mammalian brain consistently gives a higher figure than other tissues (Hahn & Laird 1971, Ryffel & McCarthy 1975, Bantle & Hahn 1976), but taking all the data together they indicate that in eukaryotic organisms the number of structural genes which can be shown to give rise to messenger RNAs is on the order of 20,000. From these studies it appears that the great majority of messenger RNA sequences are present as a very small number of copies (perhaps about 10 per cell) while a rather small number of messengers (perhaps about 10) are present in high concentration (some thousands of copies per cell).

ARE DIFFERENT SETS OF GENES USED BY DIFFERENT CELLS?

It has long been a popular idea that differentiation may be caused by "gene switching" and, although it is obvious that certain "housekeeping genes" must be expressed in most tissues, it is suggested that the major differences between one tissue and another are likely to be due to some genes being transcribed in some tissues and not in others. This view is still widely held although the evidence for it is now much less strong than appeared to be the case a few years ago. Some of the evidence is in fact conflicting. In the studies of sea urchin development, Hough-Evans *et al.* (1977) have obtained evidence that maximum gene expression, equivalent to about 14,000 genes, occurs in the mature oocyte and there is then a steady diminution of the number of messenger molecules in the embryo until, at the pluteus stage, only around 10,000 messengers are represented. These findings appear to argue for a very substantial switching off of genes during embryonic development. In experiments in which RNA populations in different mammalian tissues or cell types have been compared, different conclusions have been reached. With the exception of brain, which has already been referred to, evidence has been obtained that essentially the same sequences are present in polysomal messenger RNA in different cell types (Young *et al.* 1976, Hastie & Bishop 1976). The major differences observed between RNA from different tissues in fact seem to be in the abundance of relatively small number of messengers. For example the RNAs extracted from liver and kidney seem to contain the same sequences but these vary in abundance in that a few messengers which exist in a very small number of copies in liver are present in high concentration in kidney and vice versa. Two things should be said about the apparent discrepancy between these two kinds of experiments. In the first place the changes which occur in embryogenesis may be of a different nature from the differences which are seen in mature tissues. Secondly, the kinetic analyses used in the comparisons of adult tissues might not reveal fairly substantial differences in the overall complexity of the RNA.

Some of the results of comparing different tissues and different cells are challenging to the idea that regulation of differentiation is entirely by switching genes on and off. Rather they indicate that some of the major differences between tissues may be due to quantitative differences in the amounts of certain messenger RNAs.

This conclusion may be supported by some observations on the number of copies of globin messenger RNA in erythroid and nonerythroid tissues. In the mature mammalian reticulocyte there are about 150,000 copies of globin messenger RNA. In the polysomes of nonerythroid tissues there are either no copies of globin messenger RNA or a very small number. It would be important to distinguish between the two latter possibilities and indeed some experiments indicate that, in certain nonerythroid cells, a small number of globin messenger RNA molecules may be present (Humphries *et al.* 1975).

IS MOST REGULATION POST-TRANSCRIPTIONAL?

When the same kinds of techniques are used to compare nuclear and cytoplasmic RNA it has invariably been found that nuclear RNA is five to ten times more complex then cytoplasmic RNA (Getz *et al.* 1975, Hough *et al.* 1975, Kleiman *et al.* 1977). This raises other questions. Are some sequences always confined to the nucleus? Are sequences which are confined to the nucleus in one tissue expressed in the cytoplasm in another? Is there, indeed, any evidence of differences in transcription between one tissue and another? The answer to none of these questions is as yet clear because the complexity of nuclear RNA is so high that there are technical difficulties in measuring its precise complexity.

That some kind of regulation occurs at the level of transcription is, however, strongly suggested by experiments on isolated nuclei and chromatin which indicate that specific genes, such as the globin and ovalbumin genes, are in a different conformational state in tissues in which these genes are highly expressed, in that they are more accessible to exogenous polymerases (Gilmour & Paul 1973, Towle *et al.* 1977) and nucleases (Weintraub & Groudine 1976). At least in the case of ribosomal genes the different states of active and inactive chromatin have been demonstrated by the electron microscope (Franke *et al.* 1976).

Thus we are faced with the paradox that there is evidence that most genes are transcribed in most tissues but some genes are apparently subject to control of transcription.

SOME POSSIBLE IMPLICATIONS OF LOW ABUNDANCE MESSENGER RNAs

When one compares the 150,000 copies of one messenger RNA in a highly specialized cell like a mammalian reticulocyte with the five to ten copies of many other messenger RNAs, it raises the question: Are these low abundance mRNAs present in functionally significant amounts? The answer to that question is unequivocally, yes, because it is clear that some functional messengers are indeed present in these small numbers. Indeed it requires only a small number of messenger RNAs to produce a significant number of protein molecules (Galau *et al.* 1977). From the rates of polypeptide chain elongation, which average about 8.5 codons per ribosome per second, and ribosome spacing, which is of the order of about 32 codons in most mammalian cells (Kafatos & Gelinas 1975), it can be calculated that approximately 1,000 polypeptide chains are completed per messenger per hour. In cases where the protein is relatively unstable, say with a half life of 1 h, only 10 molecules of a given mRNA would permit accumulation of a peptide at the rate of about 5,000 copies an hour. Even in a rapidly growing cell this would permit the maintenance of about 100,000 copies of this protein.

If important informational molecules are present in such low concentrations, some speculations may be made about their fate during cell division. If polysomes are randomly segregated during cell division, then, where specific polysomes are present in a small number, some of the cell progeny will have a good chance of having no polysomes of this particular kind. One can easily envisage situations in which this could have profound effects on the subsequent development of the cell. For example if we were dealing with an unstable regulatory protein which had, directly or indirectly, a positive feedback effect on the transcription of its own gene, this could result in the complete cessation of the transcription of that gene, with possible widespread ramifications. It is thought that, in mosaic eggs, differentiation is determined by the spatial localization of polysomes within the cytoplasm. Segregation of polysomes in the manner suggested here could give rise to a very similar result in the development of regulative embryos. Although this notion is entirely speculative, it is worth noting that, if the above assumptions proved to be valid, then the results of such a segregation are mathematically predictable.

REFERENCES

Anderson, D.M., Galau, G.A., Britten, R.J. & Davidson, E.H. (1976) Sequence complexity of the RNA accumulated in oocytes of arbacia punctulata. *Devel. Biol.* 51, 138–145.

Bantle, J.A. & Hahn, W.E. (1976) Complexity and characterization of polyadenylated RNA in mouse brain. *Cell* 8, 139–150.

Beerman, W. (1972) Chromosomes and genes. In: *Results and Problems in Cell Differentiation* Vol. 4, pp. 1–33, ed. Beerman, W. Springer-Verlag, Heidelberg and New York.

Birnie, G.D., Macphail, E., Young, B.D., Getz, M.J. & Paul, J. (1974) The diversity of the messenger RNA population in growing Friend cells. *Cell Diff.* 3, 221–232.

Bishop, J.O., Morton, J.G., Rosbash, M. & Richardson, M. (1974) Three abundant classes in HeLa cells messenger RNA. *Nature* 250, 199–204.

Britten, R.J. & Kohne, D.E. (1968) Repeated sequences in DNA. *Science* 161, 529–540.

Davidson, E.H. & Hough B. (1971) Genetic information in oocyte RNA. *J. Mol. Biol.* 56, 491–506.

Franke, W.W., Scheer, U., Trendelenburg, M.F., Spring, H.& Zentgraf, H. (1976) Absence of nucleosomes in transcriptionally active chromatin. *Cytobiologie* 13, 401–434.

Galau, G.A., Britten, R.J. & Davidson, E.H. (1974) A measurement of the sequence complexity of polysomal messenger RNA in sea urchin embryos. *Cell* 2, 9–20.

Galau, G.A., Klein, W.H., Davis, M.M., Wold, B.J., Britten, R.J. & Davidson, E.H. (1976) Structural gene sets active in embryos and adult tissues of the sea urchin. *Cell* 7, 487–505.

Galau, G.A., Klein, W.H., Britten, R.J. & Davidson, E.H. (1977) Significance of rare mRNA sequences in liver. *Arch. Biochem. Biophys.* 179, 584–599.

Getz, M.J., Birnie, G.D., Young, B.D., Macphail, E. & Paul, J. (1975) A kinetic estimation of base sequence complexity of nuclear poly(A)-containing RNA in mouse Friend cells. *Cell* 4, 121–129.

Gilmour, R.S. & Paul, J. (1973) Tissue-specific transcription of the globin gene in isolated chromatin. *Proc. Natl. Acad. Sci. U.S.A.* 70, 3440–3442.

Hahn, W.E. & Laird, C.D. (1971) Transcription of nonrepeated DNA in mouse brain. *Science* 173, 158–161.

Hastie, N.D. & Bishop, J.O. (1976) The expression of three abundance classes of messenger RNA in mouse tissue. *Cell* 9, 761–774.

Hough-Evans, B. R., Wold, B. J., Ernst, S. G., Britten, R. J. & Davidson, E. H. (1977) Appearance and persistence of maternal RNA sequences in sea urchin development. *Devel. Biol.* 60, 258–277.

Hough, B.R., Smith, M.J., Britten, R.J. & Davidson, E.H. (1975) Sequence complexity of heterogeneous nuclear RNA in sea urchin embryos. *Cell* 5, 291–299.

Humphries, S., Windass, J. & Williamson, R. (1976) Mouse globin gene expression in erythroid and nonerythroid tissues. *Cell* 7, 267–277.

Judd, B.H., Shen, M.W. & Kaufman, Z.C. (1972) The anatomy and functions of a segment of the X chromosome of *Drosophila melanogaster. Genetics* 71, 139–152.

Kafatos, F.C. & Gelinas, R. (1975) mRNA stability and the control of specific protein synthesis in highly differentiated cells. *Biochem. Cell Diff.* 9, 223–264.

Kleiman, L., Birnie, G.D., Young, B.D. & Paul, J. (1977) Comparison of the base-sequence complexities of polysomal and nuclear RNAs in growing Friend erythroleukemia cells. *Biochem.* 16, 1218–1223.

Lefevre, G. (1973) The one band-one gene hypothesis: evidence from cytogenetic analysis of mutant and non-mutant rearrangement breakpoints in *Drosophila melanogaster. Cold Spring Harbor Symp. Quant. Biol.* 38, 591–599.

O'Brien, S.J. (1973) On estimating functional gene number in eukaryotes. *Nature New Biol.* 242, 52–54.

Ryffel, G.U. & McCarthy, B.J. (1975) Complexity of cytoplasmic RNA in different mouse tissues measured by hybridization of polyadenylated RNA to complementary DNA. *Biochem.* 14, 1379–1385.

Towle, H.C., Tsai, M.J., Tsai, S.Y. & O'Malley, B.W. (1977) Effect of estrogen on gene expression in chick oviduct. Preferential initiation and symmetrical transcription of specific chromatin gene. *J. Biol. Chem.* 252, 2396.

Weintraub, H. & Groudine, M. (1976) Chromosomal subunits in active genes have an altered conformation. *Science* 193, 848–856.

Young, B.D., Birnie, G.D. & Paul, J. (1976) Complexity and specificity of polysomal poly(A$^+$)RNA in mouse tissues. *Biochem.* 15, 2823–2829.

DISCUSSION

RICH: How much greater are the number of sequences expressed in brain?

PAUL: About double the complexity in most other tissues.

RICH: And have there been any experiments to measure the extent to which that is a function of sleeping or waking or things like that?

PAUL: No, but we have data which suggest that there is quite a big difference between embryonic brain and the adult brain.

WEISSMANN: But brain is at least two different tissues.

PAUL: Brain is much more than two different tissues. But in liver, too, there are actually something like 15 different cell types, whereas in a pure cell line you are dealing with one cell type. The interesting thing is that one finds that the complexity of cultured cell RNA is very similar to that of whole tissues. It is not absolutely clear what this means, because with cultured cells you are often dealing with rather abnormal organisms, and it may be that they express a very much larger fraction of the total genome. Some studies which have been done at the Pasteur Institute recently with muscle tissue suggest that in relatively normal muscle tissue, which can de-differentiate and re-differentiate in culture, you do apparently see a much bigger shut-off of genes though there is an amplification, of course, of the myosin messenger there is a bigger shut-off of genes than you see with ordinary cultured cells which are presumably transformed.

HOGNESS: Has anyone done these kinetic analyses in *E. coli* or yeast?

PRESCOTT: Hahn *et al.* (1977) did saturation experiments with *E. coli* and within the limits of the experiments found 100% of the DNA to be transcribed. I know also that it has been done with yeast, but I don't remember the percentage of DNA transcribed.

FLAVELL: You mentioned this potentially very interestingly point about

---

Hahn, W. E., Pettijohn, D. E. & Van Ness, J. (1977) *Science* 197, 582–585.

whether there are large, complex RNAs which are nucleus restricted. Is there any experimental evidence for such an RNA? You could imagine a couple of ways you could do such an experiment, the best way would be to have a cloned DNA segment which is complementary to an RNA which is only found in the nucleus.

PAUL: I don't know the answer to that question at present but Dr. Berrice in our laboratory is investigating the question.

MAALØE: I want to say one thing for *E. coli*. By a careful O'Farrel two-dimensional gel analysis of total *E. coli* sap you can identify at least 1,000, maybe 2,000 protein spots. And sum that up, and you know that at least during the growth of this cell better than half the genome was expressed. These analyses are good to the point of making it possible to identify proteins that are present in the cell in a very small number of copies. So you would include that which is so difficult to get out of the Cot-analysis, namely an estimate of message present in very small amounts. In a eukaryote, where the actual message may be a very small segment of the transcript, I'm afraid this approach would not get you very far.

BORST: You mentioned in passing that there is a low degree of expression of globin genes in nonerythroid cells. Could you summarize the evidence for that?

PAUL: There are two instances in which globin messenger RNA is certainly present in cells which are not recognized as erythroid cells. One is that, in our own experience, we have found quite significant amounts – i.e. 20 copies per cell – of globin messenger in a mouse lymphoma cell, the L5178Y cell, which is known to be a thymus-derived tumor. The other instance, which Weintraub has reported, is that he found no evidence for globin messenger in chick fibroblasts, unless these cells were transformed with RSV; then he found undoubted evidence for the presence of globin messenger. These are nonerythroid cells in which globin messenger is undoubtedly produced. But these, of course, are in both instances transformed cells. There is just the possibility that in some normal cells this happens too, but I am not so certain about that.

Inverted Repeats in the Genomes of Mammalian Cells

Warren Jelinek

INTRODUCTION AND SUMMARY

The DNA from virtually every organism examined contains inverted repeated sequences (ir-DNA) of the type abc xyz c'b'a', where a and a', b and b' and c and c' represent intramolecular complementary sequences and xyz, which can vary in length, represents the 'turnaround' or nonbase paired sequences between the two elements of complementary DNA (Davidson *et al.* 1973, Wilson & Thomas 1974, Schmid *et al.* 1975, Deininger & Schmid 1976, Jelinek 1977, 1978, Bukhari *et al.* 1977). The human and Chinese hamster haploid genomes each contain approximately $10^5 - 4 \times 10^5$ such ir-DNA structures that can be isolated by S1 nuclease treatment of denatured DNA (Wilson & Thomas, 1974, Deininger & Schmid 1976, Jelinek 1977). Likewise, the heterogeneous nuclear RNA (hnRNA) contains sequences that can form intramolecular base paired regions (double-stranded hnRNA, ds-hnRNA) that can be isolated by treating the hnRNA with single strand-specific RNAses (Jelinek & Darnell 1972, Jelinek *et al.* 1974, Robertson *et al.* 1977, Jelinek 1978, Jelinek *et al.* 1978). Furthermore, prolonged self-annealing of the hnRNA from human cells effects an increase in the yield of the ds-hnRNA from ca. 5% to ca. 25–30% of the total hnRNA, presumably due to the formation of intermolecular as well as intramolecular double-stranded RNA structures (Federoff *et al* 1977, Jelinek *et al.* 1978). The RNAse T1 fingerprints of the 5% 'snap-back' fraction and the 25–30% self-annealed fraction of RNAse resistant hnRNA are virtually identical to one another and thus contain sequences that appear to be extremely abundant within the hnRNA molecules (Jelinek *et al.* 1978). T1 fingerprints of the *in vitro* RNA transcription products from the isolated ir-DNA from human cells are

The Rockefeller University, New York, New York 10021 U.S.A.

SPECIFIC EUKARYOTIC GENES, Alfred Benzon Symposium 13, Munksgaard 1979

almost indistinguishable from those of the 5% or the 25–30% RNAse-resistant hnRNA (Jelinek 1977), and thus, the entire sequence complement of the ir-DNA appears to be represented in the hnRNA as self-complementary sequences.

The average calculated periodicity of the elements of ir-DNA in the genomes of humans and Chinese hamsters is one element per 3–4.5 kilobasepairs (Deininger & Schmid 1976, Jelinek 1977, Jelinek 1978) throughout the entire DNA, consistent with the notion that these sequences may represent the vast majority, if not all of the so-called 'interspersed' repeated DNA sequences (Davidson *et al.* 1975).

EXPERIMENTAL RESULTS

ds-hnRNA is a descrete sequence subset of hnRNA

The initial observation that isolated ds-hnRNA from HeLa cells was enriched in, if not composed exclusively of, sequences that could hybridize 'rapidly' (i.e. at low Cot values) to human DNA suggested that these structures contained a small subset of the total sequences found in the hnRNA and that they were represented many thousands, if not hundreds of thousands, of times per haploid human genome (Jelinek & Darnell 1972). Subsequent studies showed the RNAse T1 fingerprint of the ds-hnRNA to be comparatively simple relative to the T1 fingerprint of the total hnRNA with an estimated sequence complexity of only ca. 5000 nucleotides (Fig. 1a; Robertson *et al.* 1977, Jelinek 1977, Jelinek *et al.* 1978). More recently similar observations were made for the ds-hnRNA from both Chinese hamster cells (Fig. 2; Jelinek 1978) and mouse L cells (Fig. 2; Jelinek, unpublished).

Sequences characteristic of ds-hnRNA constitute ca. 25–30% of the total hnRNA

Once it was established that a small portion (ca. 3–5%) of hnRNA could be reproducibly isolated because it was resistant to single strand-specific RNAses if the hnRNA was denatured and allowed to 'snap-back' for a minute or less before RNAse treatment, it became of interest to determine if a larger fraction of hnRNA could be rendered RNAse-resistant by prolonged self-annealing. Accordingly, RNAse A- and T2-resistant hnRNA was prepared following extensive self-annealing of the hnRNA. Various proportions of the hnRNA became RNAse-resistant depending upon the conditions used in the self-annealing and digestion steps. Figs. 1a, b, d and e show the RNAse T1 fingerprints of four such samples that represented 3, 5.8, 10.1 and 27% of the

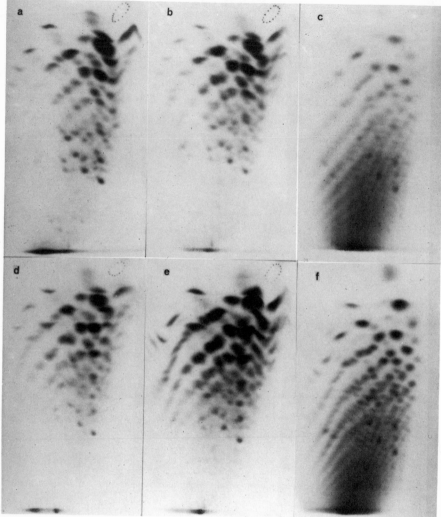

Fig. 1. T1 fingerprints of oligonucleotides in ds-hnRNA from self-annealed HeLa cell hnRNA.

^{32}P-hnRNA was prepared from 4×10^8 cells and either boiled in H$_2$O, quenched and digested with RNAse as indicated below, or self-annealed overnight (RNA from 0.7×10^8 cells in 0.05 ml. 2X SSC, 65°) before digestion and subsequent T1 fingerprint analysis. The percent of each sample remaining acid insoluble after digestion is given. a, boiled, digested with RNAses A & T2 in 0.3M NaCl (3.0% RNAse-resistant); b, boiled, digested with RNAses A & T2 in 0.5M NaCl (5.8% RNAse-resistant); c, boiled, digested with RNAse T1 in 0.3M NaCl (12.0% RNAse-resistant); d, self-annealed and digested with RNAses A & T2 in 0.3M NaCl (10.1% RNAse-resistant); e, self-annealed and digested with RNAses A & T2 in 0.5M NaCl (27% RNAse-resistant); f, self-annealed and digested with RNAse T1 in 0.5M NaCl (43.7% RNAse-resistant). Samples c and f were digested with T1 RNAse instead of RNAses A & T2 as control experiments, the consideration of which is not pertinent to the

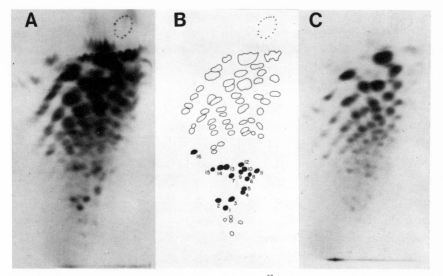

Fig. 2. T1 fingerprints of ds-hnRNA from CHO and L cells. ^{32}P-labeled CHO or L cell hnRNA was boiled, quenched and digested with a combination of RNAse A & T2 in 0.3M NaCl. The RNAse-resistant fraction was then digested with RNAse T1 in 0.01M Tris-HCl, pH 7.4, 0.01M EDTA and the digestion products separated in two dimensions as described for the fingerprinting of HeLa cell ds-hnRNA in Fig. 1.

   A. T1 fingerprint of CHO cell ds-hnRNA

   B. Diagram of A giving the numbering scheme of some of the larger T1 products discussed in the text.

   C. T1 fingerprint of L cell ds-hnRNA.

hnRNA that had been self-annealed or digested immediately at two different NaCl concentrations following denaturation. (Conditions of self-annealing and RNAse digestion are given in the legend to the figure.) The four fingerprints are virtually identical to one another even though there was almost a 10-fold increment in the proportion of the hnRNA that resisted digestion after prolonged self-annealing at the higher NaCl concentration, compared to the sample that was digested at the lower NaCl concentration and not self-annealed. Apparently one quarter to one third of HeLa cell hnRNA is composed of self-

---

discussions presented here. The fingerprinting of samples a, b, d and e was performed simulta-neously, but radioautography for a was three times longer than for b, d and e. The RNAse-resistant RNA from each sample was digested with RNAse T1 in 0.01M Tris-HCl, pH 7.4, 0.01M EDTA, conditions that allow complete digestion of ds-RNA by this nuclease. Separation in the first dimension was by electrophoresis at pH 3.5 and in the second by homochromatography according to the method described by Barrell (1971).

complementary sequences with an estimated sequence complexity of only ca. 5000 nucleotides; these sequences can exist either as intramolecular double strands, or, upon prolonged self-annealing of the hnRNA, as intermolecular double strands (Federoff *et al.* 1977, Jelinek *et al.* 1978).

These results predict that the vast majority of all transcripts from repeated DNA sequences in hnRNA should be the ds-hnRNA sequences. To confirm this prediction, hnRNA was hybridized to DNA immobilized on nitrocellulose filters (low Cot hybridization), the hybrids were treated extensively with RNAses A and T2, and the resulting RNAse-resistant RNA was eluted from the nitrocellulose-bound DNA and its T1 fingerprint prepared. The fingerprint was qualitatively indistinguishable from those shown in Figs. 1a, b, d or e. Furthermore, when this RNA was self-annealed it formed RNAse-resistant double-stranded RNA structures with the same kinetics and to the same extent as did denatured ds-hnRNA that had been prepared by RNAse treatment of hnRNA without any previous hybridization step (i.e. the 'snap-back' ds-hnRNA) (data not shown here, but see Jelinek *et al.* 1978).

Both poly(A)-terminated nuclear and cytoplasmic RNA contain sequences characteristic of the ds-hnRNA, but the smaller nuclear molecules and the cytoplasmic molecules contain ca. 10-fold less of these sequences than do the larger nuclear molecules

A considerable effort over the past 10–15 years has been devoted to the demonstration that hnRNA is the material precursor to mRNA (Darnell 1975). Without the ability to kinetically follow any particular mRNA sequence this has been a difficult task and many studies have resorted to showing sequence homology between the hnRNA and the cytoplasmic mRNA populations. Two kinds of sequences have been shown to be present in these two different RNA classes, those encoding single proteins, e.g. ovalbumin (Dugaiczyk *et al.* 1978, Garapin *et al.* 1978, Mandel *et al.* 1978), hemoglobin (references in Chambon 1977), immunoglobulin (Gilmore-Hebert & Wall 1978), viral proteins from viruses that replicate in the cell nucleus (Bachenheimer & Darnell 1975, Weber *et al.* 1977, Goldberg *et al.* 1977), and repeated sequences, or sequences common to many hnRNAs or mRNAs, e.g. poly(A) (Jelinek *et al.* 1974 and references therein), 'cap' sequences (Shatkin 1976). HnRNA molecules were known to contain transcripts from both 'unique' and 'repeated' DNA sequences and these two types of sequences were known to be present within the same RNA molecules (Darnell & Balint 1970, Davidson & Britten 1973). Furthermore, our

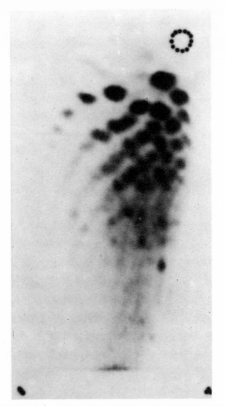

Fig. 3. Tl fingerprint of ds RNA produced from HeLa cell mRNA by self-annealing.

[32]P-labeled, polyribosomal associated, poly(A)-terminated RNA was self-annealed overnight in 0.5M NaCl at 65° and digested with a combination of RNAse A & T2. The RNAse-resistant fraction (ca. 2% of the initial RNA) was then digested with RNAse T1 in 0.01M Tris-HCl, pH 7.4, 0.01M EDTA and the digestion products separated in two dimensions as described in the legend to Fig. 1.

previous experiments showed that almost one third of hnRNA was composed of repeated sequences that could self-anneal or hybridize at low Cots to DNA to become RNAse-resistant and the resistant RNA gave the diagnostic ds-hnRNA T1 fingerprint. We therefore tested mRNA in the same way for the presence of the ds-hnRNA sequences.

Polyribosomal associated, poly(A)-terminated cytoplasmic RNA (mRNA) and poly(A)-terminated nuclear RNA of various sizes were either self-annealed or hybridized to DNA at low Cots. The RNAse-resistant RNA was prepared and its T1 fingerprint obtained. Fig. 3 shows the T1 fingerprint of the RNAse-resistant fraction obtained after the mRNA was hybridized to DNA and the

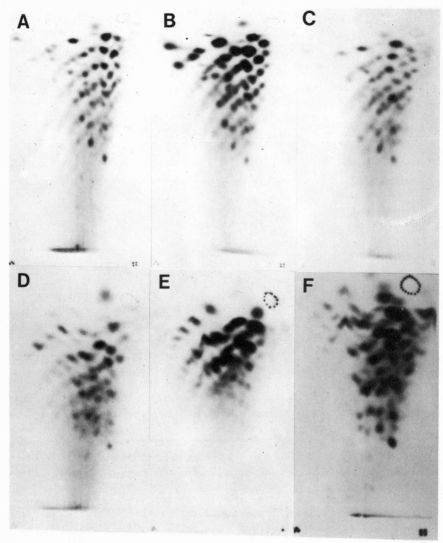

Fig. 4. T1 fingerprints of ds-hnRNA and the *in vitro* transcripts of inverted repeated DNA and total DNA from HeLa cells.

A-D, Inverted repeated DNA was isolated from HeLa cells by treatment of the total denatured nuclear DNA with S1 nuclease and subsequently used in four separate *in vitro* transcription reactions with *E. coli* RNA polymerase, each of the four reactions containing a different alpha-^{32}P nucleoside triphosphate and three unlabeled nucleoside triphosphates. The RNA products were separated from unincorporated nucleoside triphosphates by two precipitations in ethanol and the resulting RNA was digested with T1 ribonuclease and the products separated into two dimensions as described in the legend to Fig. 1. A) alpha-^{32}P ATP, B) alpha-^{32}P GTP, C) alpha-^{32}P CTP, D) alpha-^{32}P UTP. E) As a control, the total HeLa cell DNA was sheared to fragments ca. 400 nucleotides long and used in

RNAse-resistant fraction recovered; it shows the same pattern of diagnostic T1 oligonucleotides that are characteristic of the ds-hnRNA. A similar fingerprint was obtained from the RNAse-resistant mRNA resulting from the self-annealing of poly(A)-terminated cytoplasmic RNA (fingerprint not shown). A quantitative determination showed that per molecule the cytoplasmic poly(A)-terminated molecules contained approximately 10-fold less of the ds-hnRNA characteristic sequences as did the nuclear poly(A)-terminated molecules. Per molecule, the largest poly(A)-terminated nuclear molecules contained ca. 14 times more ds-hnRNA as did the shortest poly(A)-terminated molecules with the medium sized molecules containing an intermediate amount. Thus, the larger the poly(A)-terminated RNA, the greater the molar content of ds-hnRNA (Jelinek *et al.* 1978).

IR-DNA encodes the ds-hnRNA
It has been shown that the DNA from a variety of organisms contains inverted repeated DNA sequences (ir-DNA). Of particular interest to the considerations here was the finding that ir-DNA could be isolated from the human genome by treatment of denatured HeLa cell DNA with S1 nuclease (Wilson & Thomas 1974, Jelinek 1978). Approximately 2–5% of the total nuclear DNA remained resistant to the S1 nuclease and when the *in vitro* RNA transcripts from this DNA were fingerprinted, the fingerprints showed the same pattern of T1 oligonucleotides previously displayed by the ds-hnRNA and the self-annealed poly(A)-terminated hnRNA or mRNA (Fig. 4; Jelinek 1977).

Electron microscopic examination of denatured human placental DNA showed that the base paired regions of the ir-DNA were rather uniform in size with a number average length of ca. 300 base pairs, while the 'loops' or 'turnaround' regions between the complementary sequences varied in length from nondetectable to larger than 20 kilobases (Deininger & Schmid 1976). Since 2–5% of the total human DNA resisted S1 nuclease digestion and its transcripts gave a T1 fingerprint characteristic of the ds-hnRNA, the assumption is that these sequences are ca. 300 base pairs long. Therefore, the calculated frequency of the ir-DNA, or the ds-hnRNA coding sequences in the human genome is ca. $2-4\times10^5$ copies per single strand of haploid genome. (The size of the human genome was taken to be 3×10^9 base pairs.)

---

an *in vitro* transcription reaction identical to that used in D. F) For comparison, [32]P-*in vivo*-labeled ds-hnRNA was prepared from growing HeLa cells and its T1 fingerprint was prepared.

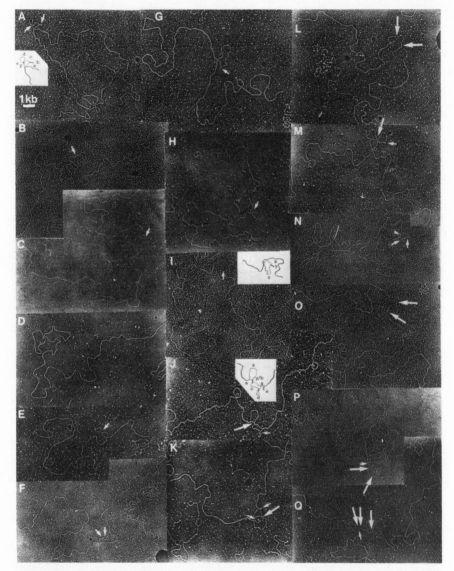

Fig. 5. Heteroduplex analysis of the nine CHO DNA clones described in the text. (A-I) Heteroduplexes formed between Charon 16 A lambda DNA (Chl6A) and the recombinant DNA from each of the nine clones described in the text: (A) Ch16ACHOG49; (B) Ch16ACHOG235; (C) Ch16ACHOG73; (D) Ch16ACHOG25; (E) Ch16AcHOG63; (F) Ch16ACHOG2;
(G) Ch16ACHOH104; (H) Ch16ACHOG200; (I) Ch16ACHOG95; (J-Q) The DNA from clone Ch16AcHOG49 was hybridized with that from each of the eight other clones and examined. (J) Ch16ACHOG95; (K) Ch16ACHOG200; (L) Ch16ACHOG63; (M) Ch16ACHOG73;
(N) Ch16ACHOG235; (O) Ch16ACHOG25; (P) Ch16ACHOG2; (Q) Ch16ACHOG104. Hetero-

Observations similar to those made on the human genome concerning the inverted repeats were also made for the genome of cultured Chinese hamster ovary cells (CHO cells). Fragments from the DNA of CHO cells produced by the restriction endonuclease Eco RI were cloned in Charon 16A lambda bacteriophage and the phage plaques were examined for the ability to hybridize with ^{32}P-labeled ds-hnRNA from the heterogeneous nuclear RNA of these cells. Of 235 clones tested in this way, 87 (37%) contained sequences that could hybridize with the double-stranded hnRNA. Nine of these were chosen for further study. Heteroduplexes were formed by hybridizing the DNA from each of the nine clones with that of the vector and examined by electron microscopy. Fig. 5 shows representative molecules of each of the nine heteroduplexes, each of which contained an insertion loop that was predominantly single stranded, but with one or more ir-DNA structures (indicated by arrows in Figs. 5A–5I). To determine whether the nucleotide sequences in the ir-DNAs of the nine clones would cross-hybridize with one another in the regions of the ir-DNA, clone 49 (Fig. 5A) was hybridized with the DNA from each of the other eight clones and the resulting heteroduplex molecules examined in the electron microscope. Figs. 5J–5Q show representative molecules for each of these heteroduplexes. Each heteroduplex showed cross-strand hybridization in the regions previously identified as inverted repeat sequences in Figs. 5A–5I. (Note that the heteroduplex formed from the DNAs of clone 49 and clone 235, are not shown cross-hybridized in Fig. 5N. Whenever clone 235 showed a cross-strand hybridization with clone 49 DNA, the molecules appeared as tangles and could not be interpreted, presumably because the relative positions of the two elements of ir-DNA in these two clones are reversed with respect to one another in the 5' to 3' direction.)

The cross-strand hybridizations between clone 49 and each of the other clones suggested that the ir-DNA in the nine clones contained common nucleotide sequences, probably in the regions of the ir-DNA. If the ir-DNA gave rise to the ds-hnRNA then each clone should hybridize the common oligonucleotides. Accordingly, ^{32}P-labeled ds-hnRNA was hybridized to filter-bound DNA from

---

duplex formation was as described by Davis *et al.* (1971) and the heteroduplexes were spread from a hyperphase of 50% formamide, 0.1M Tris-HCl, pH 8.5, 0.01M EDTA onto a hypophase of 20% formamide, 0.01 M ammonium acetate, 0.01M Tris-HCl, pH 8.5 and picked up on to Parlodion-coated grids. The bar in A represents 1 kilobase pair of double-stranded NDA. Small arrows, regions of intramolecular double-stranded DNA (ir-DNA); large arrows, in J-Q, regions of cross-strand DNA-DNA hybridization.

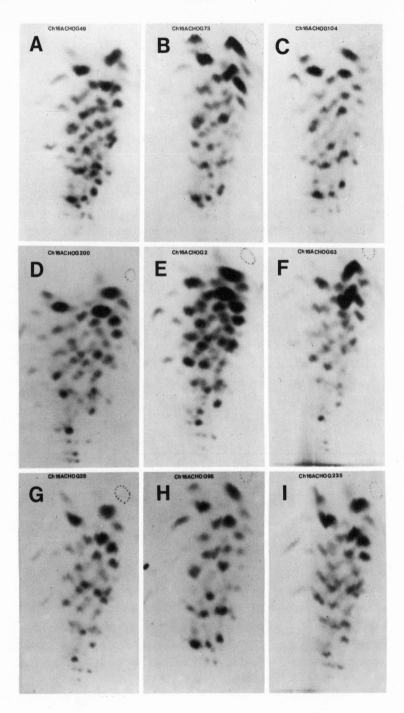

INVERTED REPEATS IN THE GENOMES OF MAMMALIAN CELLS

each of the nine clones and the RNAse-resistant hybrid RNA was eluted, digested with RNAse T1 and subjected to fingerprint analysis. The nine fingerprints are shown in Fig. 6. A number of similarities can be detected among the nine fingerprints and the total ds-hnRNA fingerprint shown in Fig. 2A. Seven of the nine (those of the hybrids to clones 49, 73, 200, 2, 63, 25 and 235) had T1 product number 1 (see Fig. 2B for the numbering scheme used to denote the T1 oligonucleotides), four (clones 49, 73, 104 and 95) had products 2 and 3, and all had products 4 or 5 (clone 73 had both). The identity of products 1, 2 and 3 was confirmed by RNAse U2 digestion and subsequent electrophoresis of the digestion products.

In addition to these T1 products, various other similarities in spot pattern could be detected in the nine fingerprints. For instance, compare the fingerprint of the hybrids to clones 73, 95, 63 and 235, all of which had a single ir-DNA structure detected by electron microscopy (Fig. 5). It should be emphasized that in comparisons of fingerprints, similarities in spot patterns suggest similarities in nucleotide sequence, but differences do not necessarily mean great divergence in sequence. A single changed residue could cause a change in spot pattern, particularly if it involves a G residue. Perfect sequence conservation of some of the larger T1 products (i.e. numbers 1–5) in the various clones strongly suggests significant sequence similarity (but not necessarily exact sequence identity) in the ir-DNAs at various sites in the CHO genome. The calculated frequency for the elements of ir-DNA in the CHO genome is one element every 4.5 kilobase of DNA over the entire genome (Jelinek 1978).

DISCUSSION

The major issue raised by these experiments concerns the nature of the 'interspersed repeat' DNA that has previously been detected by reassociation kinetics of denatured DNA (Britten & Kohne 1968, Davidson *et al.* 1975). These

---

Fig. 6. T1 fingerprints of ds-hnRNA hybridized to DNA from each of the nine clones described. ds-^{32}P-hnRNA was melted by boiling in distilled water and hybridized to DNA immobilized on nitrocellulose filters from each of the nine Ch16ACHOG-clones described (six filters each containing 50 micrograms of DNA). The filters were treated with T1 RNAse in 0.3M NaCl and the nuclease was inactivated with sodium iodoacetate before the RNA was eluted by boiling the filters in distilled water. The eluted RNA was digested with T1 RNAse and fingerprinted Clones: (A) Ch16ACHOG49; (B) Ch16ACHOG73; (C) Ch16ACHOG104; (D) Ch16ACHOG200; (E) Ch16ACHOG2; (F) Ch16ACHOG63; (G) Ch16ACHOG25; (H) Ch16ACHOG95; (I) Ch16ACHOG235.

sequences have been proposed to be organized into 'families' whose individual members were represented in the genome from about 10 to 10,000 times (Davidson & Britten 1973). The data presented here suggest that the vast majority of the interspersed repeated sequences are all closely related to one another and that there may be only a single family (or a very few families) in this type of DNA with slight sequence variation from site to site in the genome. These sequences can be isolated by virtue of their ability to form intrastrand hybrids, however interstrand hybrids between these sequences are also possible. If the complementary segments of the inverted repeats were immediately contiguous they would then appear in the 'snap-back' fraction; if the two elements of an inverted repeat were separated by a long 'turnaround' region, then after the DNA or RNA was broken the two elements would no longer 'snap back' but would appear in the intermolecular hybrid, repeated DNA or RNA fraction. Such sequences could be responsible for the increased recovery of apparent ds-hnRNA in hnRNA that was self-annealed prior to RNAse digestion (Federoff *et al.* 1977, Jelinek *et al.* 1978; Fig. 1).

The calculated frequency for the ir-DNA in the human genome is ca. 10^5–4×10^5 ir-DNAs per haploid genome based on the frequency observed in the electron microscope (Deininger & Schmid 1976) or by the proportion of denatured DNA that resisted S1 nuclease digestion (Jelinek 1977). The frequency in the CHO genome was estimated as follows. The total length of the inserted DNA fragments in the nine clones described here is ca. 40 kilobases. Twenty-four elements of ir-DNA were identified in the nine clones so that, on the average, there is one element of an inverted repeat for every 1.7 kilobases of DNA in these cloned fragments (40 kilobases per 24 ir-DNA elements). If the clones obtained were a random representation of all *Eco* RI fragments cut from the CHO genome, then the average distance between elements of ir-DNA in the total CHO DNA is ca. 4.5 kilobases (37% of all clones hybridized with ds-hnRNA, the average number of ir-DNA elements per cloned DNA fragment was 2.7, the average size of the cloned *Eco* RI fragments was 4.5 kilobases). Thus, there are ca. 6×10^5 elements or 3×10^5 complete ir-DNA structures in one DNA strand of the CHO cell haploid genome (3×10^9 base pairs per genome). If, as determined for many organisms (Davidson *et al.* 1975), only 70% of the genome is organized with alternating unique and interspersed repeated sequences, then the frequency of ir-DNA elements in that portion of the genome that contains them (i.e. 70%) is one element per 3150 base pairs, remarkably similar to that estimated for the rat (another rodent) of one repeat per 3200 base pairs (references in Davidson *et al.* 1975). The frequencies of ir-DNAs in the human and CHO genome are very similar to one another.

The function of the ir-DNA or the ds-hnRNA in eukaryotic genomes is currently unknown. In fact it is even unknown whether these sequences have any function as inverted repeats. When a repeated sequence happens to be in close proximity to a sequence like it and also inverted, it will 'snap back'. However, its biological significance may lie only in the fact that it is repeated, not because it is also inverted. It is not known whether every time one element of an ir-DNA sequence appears in the genome its complement exists as the closest repeated sequence in the same DNA strand, i.e. possibly there are places in the DNA where only one element of a potential ir-DNA appears (unpaired ir-DNA elements). If the cloned DNA fragments described here are a representative example of all such fragments cut from the CHO genome then the frequency of both elements existing in close proximity in the DNA must be high (see Fig. 5 and Jelinek 1978) but not necessarily 1.0. Various proposals have been made for the function of the ir-DNA or the ds-hnRNA. In the DNA, they may be origins of replication (see Tamm *et al.*, this volume), or elements involved in the movement of DNA (see Bukhari *et al.* 1977 for a review of movable elements in bacteria). In the hnRNA they may serve to bring together those noncontiguously transcribed regions of the genome that become 'spliced' to produce mRNAs. Currently it is unknown whether these sequences function in the DNA or the RNA or, perhaps both, or perhaps neither (although this is a formal possibility it is disfavored on the notion that if they had no function they would not be there).

REFERENCES

Bachenheimer, S. & Darnell, J. (1975) Adenovirus-2 mRNA is transcribed as part of a high molecular weight precursor. *Proc. Natl. Acad. Sci. U.S.A.* 72, 4445–4449.

Barell, B. G. (1971) Fractionation and sequence analysis of radioactive nucleotides. In: *Procedures in Nucleic Acid Research* ed. Cantoni, G. L. & Davis, D. R. pp. 751–795. Harper and Row New York.

Britten, R. J. & Kohne, D. E. (1968) Repeated sequences of DNA. *Science* 161, 529–540.

Bukhari, A. L., Shapiro, J. A. & Adhya, S. L. (1977) DNA insertion elements, plasmids, and episomes. *Cold Spring Harbor Laboratory.*

Chambon, P. (1977) Molecular biology of eukaryotic genome is coming of age. *Cold Spring Harbor Symp. Quant. Biol.* 42, 1211–1235.

Darnell, J. E. (1975) The origin of mRNA and the structure of the mammalian chromosome. In: *The Harvey Lectures,* Series 69, Academic Press, N.Y.

Darnell, J. E. & Balint, R. (1970) The distribution of rapidly hybridizing RNA sequences in heterogeneous nuclear RNA and mRNA from HeLa cells. *J. Cell Physiol.* 76, 349–356.

Davidson, E. & Britten R. J. (1973) Organization, transcription and regulation in the animal genome. *Quart. Rev. Biol.* 48, 565–613.

Davidson, E., Hough, B., Amenson, C. & Britten, R. J. (1973) General interspersion of repetitive and non-repetitive sequences in the DNA of Xenopus. *J. Mol. Biol.* 77, 1–23.

Davidson, E. H., Galau, G. A., Angerer, R. C. & Britten, R. J. (1975) Comparative aspects of DNA organization in metazoa. *Chromosoma* 51, 253–259.

Deininger, P. L. & Schmid, C. W. (1976) An electron microscopic study of the DNA sequence organization of the human genome. *J. Mol. Biol.* 106, 773–790.

Dugaiczk, A., Woo, S. L. C., Lai, E. C., Mace, M. L., Jr., McReynolds, L. & O'Malley, B. W. O. (1978) The natural ovalbumin gene contains seven intervening sequences. *Nature* 274, 328–333.

Federoff, N., Wellauer, P. & Wall, R. (1977) Intermolecular duplexes in heterogeneous nuclear RNA from HeLa cells. *Cell* 10, 597–610.

Garapin, A. C., Cami, B., Roskam, W., Kourilsky, P., LePennec, J. P. Perrin, F., Gerlinger, P., Cochet, M. & Chambon, P. (1978) Electron microscopy and restriction enzyme mapping reveal additional intervening sequences in the chicken ovalbumin split gene. *Cell* 14, 629–639.

Gilmore-Hebert, M. & Wall, R. (1978) Immunoglobulin light chain mRNA is processed from large nuclear RNA. *Proc. Natl. Acad. Sci. U.S.A.* 75, 342–345.

Goldberg, S., Weber, J. & Darnell, J. E., Jr. (1977) The definition of a large late transcription unit late in Ad2 infection of HeLa cells: mapping by effects of ultraviolet irradiation. *Cell* 10, 617–621.

Jelinek, W. (1977) Specific nucleotide sequences in HeLa cell inverted repeated DNA: Enrichment for sequences found in double-stranded heterogeneous nuclear RNA. *J. Mol. Biol.* 115, 591–601.

Jelinek, W. (1978) Inverted repeated DNA from Chinese hamster ovary cells studied with cloned DNA fragments. *Proc. Natl. Acad. Sci. U.S.A.* 75, 2679–2683.

Jelinek, W. & Darnell, J. E. (1972) Double-stranded regions in heterogeneous nuclear RNA from HeLa cells. *Proc. Natl. Acad. Sci. U.S.A.* 69, 2537–2541.

Jelinek, W., Adesnik, M., Salditt, M., Sheiness, D., Wall, R., Molloy, G., Philipson, L. & Darnell, J. E. (1974a) Further evidence on the nuclear origin and transfer to the cytoplasm of polyadenylic acid sequences in mammalian cell RNA. *J. Mol. Biol.* 75, 515–532.

Jelinek, W., Molloy, G., Fernandez-Munoz, R., Salditt, M. & Darnell, J. E. (1974b) Secondary structure in heterogeneous nuclear RNA: Involvement of regions from repeated DNA sites. *J. Mol. Biol.* 82, 361–370.

Jelinek, W., Evans, R., Wilson, M., Salditt-Georgieff, M. & Darnell, J. E. (1978) Oligonucleotides in hnRNA: Similarity of inverted repeats and RNA from repetitious DNA sites. *Biochemistry* 17, 2776–2783.

Mandell, J. L., Breathnach, R., Gerlinger, P., LeMeur, M., Gannon, F. & Chambon, P. (1978) Organization of coding and intervenining sequences in the chicken ovalbumin split gene. *Cell* 14, 641–653.

Robertson, H. D., Dickson, E. & Jelinek, W. (1977) Determination of nucleotide sequences from double-stranded regions of HeLa cell nuclear RNA. *J. Mol. Biol.* 115, 571–589.

Schmid, C. W., Manning, J. & Davidson, N. (1975) Inverted repeat sequences in the *Drosophila* genome. *Cell* 5, 159–172.

Shatkin, A. (1976) Capping of eukaryotic mRNAs. *Cell* 9, 645–653.

Weber, J., Jelinek, W. & Darnell, J. E., Jr. (1977) The definition of a large viral transcription unit late in Ad2 infection of HeLa cells: Mapping of nascent RNA molecules labeled in isolated nuclei. *Cell* 10, 611–616.

Wilson, D. A. & Thomas, C. A. (1974) Palindromes in chromosomes. *J. Mol. Biol.* 84, 115–144.

DISCUSSION

SCHAFFNER: Harris Busch and colleagues have described small nuclear RNAs (Busch *et al.* 1976). Do you see a relation to your data?

JELINEK: Well, we think Harris Busch has described a number of RNAs in the nucleus. He has UI and UII which are very uracil-rich, and those things were about 8S. He has also sequences that he calls 4.5 S_I. If you look a t the small nuclear RNAs on a gel,you find a number of peaks, and one of them, which I think Sheldon Penman originally called his species H, is about 4.5S, and is probably Harris Busch's thing. That RNA, when subsequently analyzed onto two-dimensional gels, gives three major bands, and Harris Busch has sequenced one of them. Our RNA – at least in size – is the closest to the 4.5S than it is to other small RNA that has been analyzed by gel electrophoresis or by sequencing. We do not know enough sequence in our stuff to know whether it in fact is the same as Harris Busch has. We think ours is not capped. We think we have multiple species.

WEISSMANN: We found a sequence on cloned beta-globin chromosomal DNA homologous to a 90-nucleotide, uncapped RNA. It is about 2,000 nucleotides downstream from the globin gene.

JELINEK: And that small RNA came from a cytoplasmic extract?

WEISSMANN: Well, I would not want to be too firm on that. In one fractionation we did between nuclear and cytoplasmic RNA, it appeared to be present in both fractions. But it is a minor species of the total small RNA.

PAUL: When you hybridize your messenger RNA to this 4.5S material, how much of the 4.5S is protected?

JELINEK: About 25–30%.

Busch, H., Hirsch, F., Gupta, K. K., Rao, M., Spohn, W. & Wu, B. C. (1976) Structural and functional studies on the "5'-Cap": A survey method for mRNA. In: *Progress in nucleic acid research and molecular biology* (Cohn, W. E. & Volkin, E., ed.) Academic Press, New York and London.

PAUL: What part of the messenger is it associated with?

JELINEK: I don't know. We had such bad luck trying to localize things in messenger RNA by the kind of experiment where you take the messenger RNA and you do a cleavage with alkali and hang it back up on polyU-sepharose.

PAUL: I am unaware of homology among many messengers to this extent.

JELINEK: We do find a small amount of rather specific homology between poly-A-terminated polyribosomal RNAs.

DAWID: I wonder about the hnRNA, you said there was snapback RNA in this material, but when you then anneal it you could drive a very large portion into resistance. I assume that is then for the intermolecular hybrids. Can you estimate quantitatively, how much snapback there is?

JELINEK: No, I don't know, and I think it may be a difficult answer to get. If one looks in the electron microscope at snapback elements that are quite far apart, then they would not necessarily appear as snapbacks within a molecule, but in fact they might appear as bimoleculars. Another way of expressing these numbers is, if one just divides the total genome size by the number of inverted repeat elements, one comes out to one element of inverted repeat per 3–4 kb, and that is a well-known number to those who know it, because it is the interdispersion distance of middle repetitive DNA.

RICH: Do you have any guesses about the relationship of this 4.5S to RNA Heywood's small RNA?

JELINEK: Well, we actually don't know.

SCHAFFNER: With regard to mRNA splicing, there was a rumor that a small adenovirus RNA (VA-RNA) could bring together the junctions at both sides of the intron by hybridizing across. Do you know about the development of that story?

JELINEK: We do not yet, but certainly that is in the back of our minds. That is one of the first things we would like to do.

PARDUE: Did you say that this small RNA was associated with the polysomes?

JELINEK: I did not say that, but it is not. We have done two experiments trying to find it on polyribosomes and although we find the two polyA terminated RNAs on polyribosomes, we have not been able to find the little RNA in the ribosomes. That is actually interesting because – I don't know if the number means anything – if one prepares polyribosomes and then just looks at the distribution of polyA, one finds that approximately one-fifth or one-sixth of the polyA is not in polyribosomes.

New Evidence for Regulated Transcription of hnRNA and for Regulated Translation of Interferon mRNA in Human Cells

Igor Tamm & Pravinkumar B. Sehgal

Recent studies in mammalian cells of the action of 5,6-dichloro-1-β-D-ribofuranosylbenzimidazole (DRB) on transcription catalyzed by cellular RNA polymerase II have provided new insights into the synthesis of nuclear heterogeneous RNA (hnRNA) and of early and late adenovirus RNA (Tamm & Sehgal 1978, Sehgal & Tamm 1978a). DRB has also proven to be a useful tool in the analysis of the regulated production of interferon after induction of cells with poly(I) · poly(C) (Sehgal et al. 1978b).

EFFECTS OF DRB ON CELLULAR AND VIRAL RNA SYNTHESIS
General aspects
DRB selectively and reversibly inhibits the synthesis of approximately two-thirds of hnRNA in human and mouse cells in culture (Sehgal et al. 1975a, Tamm et al. 1976, Sehgal et al. 1976a, Sehgal & Tamm 1976). DRB causes detectable inhibition of RNA synthesis at a concentration of 5 μM and essentially maximal inhibition at 75 μM (Tamm et al.1976, Sehgal et al. 1976a, c). A DRB-resistant fraction of hnRNA, distributed over the entire size range of hnRNA, continues to be synthesized even after treatment of cells with DRB at 150 μM. In contrast, 75 μM DRB blocks the appearance of mRNA in the cytoplasm of HeLa cells by >95% (Sehgal et al. 1976a). DRB does not interfere with post-transcriptional events such as polyadenylation, methylation and capping (Sehgal et al. 1976a).

The Rockefeller University, New York, New York 10021 U.S.A.

SPECIFIC EUKARYOTIC GENES, Alfred Benzon Symposium 13, Munksgaard 1979

Action on the synthesis of hnRNA precursor chains

DRB does not block the initiation of new chains of hnRNA, but blocks growth of approximately two-thirds of the chains beyond a size of about 100–300 nucleotides. The synthesis by RNA polymerase II of short DRB-resistant RNA chains was first detected by a combined *in vivo-in vitro* procedure (Tamm 1977). After treatment of HeLa cells with DRB *in vivo,* nuclei were isolated and incubated in a reaction mix for RNA synthesis *in vitro.* Such nuclei are able to synthesize hnRNA molecules over most of the size range of HeLa cell hnRNA (Tamm 1977). The enzyme that catalyzes this reaction is sensitive to inhibition by a-amanitin at a concentration of 1 μg/ml, and is therefore thought to be RNA polymerase II. There is some chain initiation by RNA polymerase II in isolated nuclei or in homogenates of isolated nuclei *in vitro* (Tamm 1977, Groner *et al.* 1978). Pretreatment of cells with DRB for varying periods results in a time-dependent reduction in hnRNA synthesis by isolated nuclei, as is shown in Fig. 1. In the *in vitro* as well as *in vivo* labeling experiments the maximal inhibition is equivalent to two-thirds reduction in hnRNA synthesis. The key finding is that pretreatment of cells with DRB *in vivo* does not reduce the extent of labeling *in vitro* of those putative hnRNA precursor chains which were initiated *in vivo* immediately prior to isolation of nuclei and which reach the size of 300–700 nucleotides after 15-min incubation of the isolated nuclei *in vitro* (Tamm 1977).

It should be noted that Fig. 1 also shows a discernible shoulder of *in vitro* labeled molecules in the 300–700-nucleotide range in the RNA preparation from nuclei isolated from control cells which had not been treated with DRB. This suggests that even in the absence of DRB some of the putative hnRNA precursor molecules are blocked or delayed in their growth after reaching a certain critical size, which results in a molar excess of short chains. For reasons which are not clear, chains that are blocked or delayed in their growth *in vivo* can apparently elongate *in vitro* after isolation of nuclei, regardless of whether DRB was or was not present *in vivo.* Addition of DRB to isolated nuclei has no effect on the *in vitro* synthesis of RNA. Thus, the DRB-sensitive step, responsible for premature termination of two-thirds of the hnRNA chains *in vivo,* does not occur in isolated nuclei.

What is the critical size of nascent molecules at which chain growth may be prematurely terminated or delayed *in vivo*? Two kinds of experiments have provided independent evidence that hnRNA precursor molecules can be blocked in their growth in the 100–300-nucleotide size range. To be able to carry out kinetic studies of the *in vitro* elongation by RNA polymerase II of those molecules which were initiated *in vivo* immediately prior to nuclear isolation, we have used heparin to block RNA chain initiation *in vitro* (Tamm 1977). Heparin

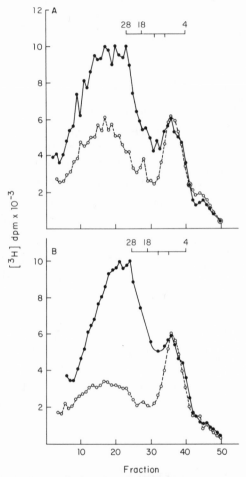

Fig. 1. Effects of pretreatment of HeLa cells with DRB on the synthesis of nucleoplasmic RNA species in isolated nuclei. Cultures were treated with actinomycin D (0.04 μg/ml) for 25 min and exposed to DRB (60 μM) for 10 or 40 min at 37°C. Nuclei were isolated by swelling the cells in hypotonic buffer, rupturing with a Dounce homogenizer, and centrifugation. The isolated nuclei were incubated for 15 min at 26°C in a reaction mix for RNA synthesis containing ³H-UTP. The nucleoplasmic and nucleolar fractions were separated by zonal centrifugation. The RNA was extracted from the nucleoplasmic fractions by phenol-chloroform and analyzed on 1.1% polyacrylamide/1% agarose gels. (A) ●——●, Control; O---O, 60 μM DRB, 10 min (*in vivo*). (B) ●——●, Control; O---O, 60 μM DRB, 40 min (*in vivo*). The two marks below each bar are interpolated positions for RNA of 250,000 daltons (740 nucleotides) and 110,000 daltons (330 nucleotides). From Tamm (1977).

blocks initiation not only by RNA polymerase II, but also the repeated reinitiation *in vitro* of chains of 4.5 S pre-tRNA and 5 S RNA by RNA polymerase III. Heparin has a complex action, which includes stimulation of the synthesis of already initiated chains. In our system, the enhancing effect of heparin is most marked on those molecules whose synthesis was initiated immediately prior to nuclear isolation (Tamm 1977 & in preparation). This facilitates kinetic analysis. Fig. 2A shows that pretreatment of cells with 75 μM DRB does not diminish the population of the most abundant short nascent chains growing *in vitro* in the range from 100 to 800 nucleotides (Tamm, in preparation). Extrapolation of the chain elongation curve for the broad band of the most abundant molecules to 0 time for the *in vitro* reaction indicates that there was, *in vivo,* a block in the synthesis of a fraction of putative hnRNA precursor molecules a short distance (some 100–300 nucleotides) from the origins of the transcripts (Fig. 2B). It can be seen that in the preparation from DRB-treated cells there is little labeling of molecules larger than those in the band. The low level labeling of the larger molecules represents the elongation of that one-third of hnRNA which is resistant to inhibition by DRB. In the preparation from control cells there is considerable incorporation of label into larger molecules which is better visualized in the original gel. It is clear by comparison with Fig. 1 that heparin treatment has preferentially enhanced labeling of the most recently initiated chains.

Confirmatory evidence that DRB blocks a step in transcription of putative hnRNA precursor molecules 100–300 nucleotides from initiation sites was obtained by *in vivo* pulse-labeling of HeLa cells with ^{3}H-uridine for 45 sec after treatment of the cells with DRB for 15 or 40 min. There was a striking shift in the size distribution profile of labeled molecules from DRB-treated cells with a marked decrease in the >150–200 nucleotide range (Tamm, in preparation).

Action on adenovirus RNA synthesis
DRB acts on transcription of specific regions of the adenovirus type 2 genome and causes premature termination of RNA chains (Fraser *et al.* 1978, Sehgal *et al.* 1978a). Its action was first defined on the synthesis of the large (>25 kilobases) RNA molecule which represents close to 85% of the genome and which is transcribed rightward late in infection (Fraser *et al.* 1978). ^{3}H-incorporation into RNA complementary to the restriction fragment containing the origin of the large transcript (SmaI f, *11.6–18.2* map units) was not inhibited as strongly by DRB as that into RNA transcribed from the adjacent rightward

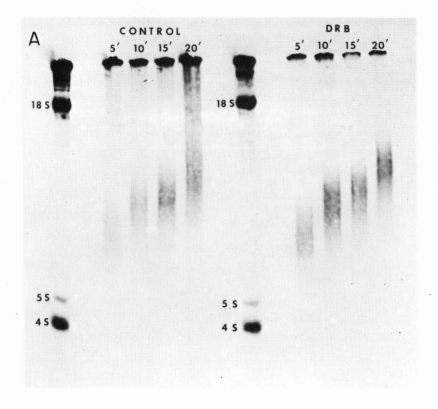

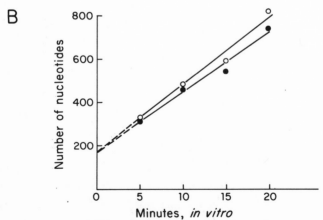

Fig. 2. Effects of pretreatment of HeLa cells with DRB on the abundance of chains growing in the 100–800 nucleotide range *in vitro*. Cultures were treated with glucosamine (20 mM) for 1 h and with actinomycin D (0.04 μg/ml) for 25 min. They were exposed to DRB for 40 min. Nuclei were isolated, pulse-labeled at 26°C for 5 min with ^{3}H-UTP (2 μM; 25 μCi/50 μl) in the presence of heparin (2

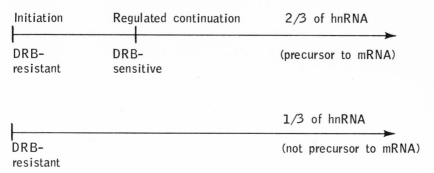

Fig. 3. A model for the action of 5,6-dichloro-1-β-D-ribofuranosylbenzimidazole (DRB) on the transcription of nuclear heterogeneous RNA by RNA polymerase II.

reading fragment. This was due to continued transcription of short pieces of RNA from the promoter-containing region in the presence of DRB. DRB did cause graded inhibition of incorporation across the remainder of the large transcript, consistent with action close to the site of RNA chain initiation. A DRB-resistant short RNA fragment was also found in the other, smaller late transcription unit located in SmaI e *(3.0–11.1)*. Recently similar evidence has been obtained in studies of several transcription units which operate early in adenovirus infection (Sehgal *et al.* 1978a). The results obtained by the DRB technique for locating adenovirus promoters agree with and extend those obtained earlier by ultraviolet irradiation mapping and by pulse-labeling of small RNA. With the DRB technique longer labeling periods can be used which provide more promotor-proximal labeled RNA for hybridization to viral RNA restriction fragments.

It is of great interest that in the tryptophan operon of *E. coli* and in *λ* bacteriophage there exist chain termination signals (attenuators, Yanofsky 1976) within 100–200 nucleotides of the chain initiation site. Transcriptional regulation in these cases is effected by permitting or preventing synthesis past the site of "premature" termination. When synthesis past such a site is prevented, short promoter-proximal RNA molecules are made. Our evidence is compatible

---

mg/ml), and chased with glucosamine (20 mM) and cold UTP (250 μM) for 5, 10 or 15 min. Samples were treated with protease-free and ribonuclease-free pancreatic deoxyribonuclease (Wang & Moore 1978). The RNA was extracted, denatured with 50% v/v formamide at 65°C for 3 min, and analyzed on 3.5% polyacrylamide gels. (A) Gel patterns at 5, 10, 15 and 20 min of *in vitro* incubation. (B) The mean length of the most abundant molecules as a function of incubation time *in vitro*. From Tamm, in preparation.

with the view that attenuator sites may exist in the DNA of mammalian cells and viruses.

Comment

DRB appears to block transcription of two-thirds of hnRNA at what may be attenuator sites or regions a short distance downstream from promoters in a manner similar to its action on adenovirus transcription. DNA from which the one-third of DRB-resistant hnRNA is transcribed may lack such attenuators. It is possible that polymerase II funtions in two forms of which the form that initiates transcription is resistant to DRB, while the DRB-sensitive form carries out a specific step in transcription at regulatory sites downstream. It is suggested that the two-thirds of hnRNA that is sensitive to DRB gives rise to mRNA molecules, but that the one-third that is resistant to DRB is not a precursor to mRNA, or provides only a very small fraction, not yet detected, of the total mRNA. The model proposed for the action of DRB on the transcription of hnRNA is schematically summarized in Fig. 3.

REGULATION OF THE PRODUCTION OF HUMAN FIBROBLAST INTERFERON
We have obtained evidence with the aid of DRB that human fibroblast interferon mRNA is subject to post-transcriptional repression in accordance with the McAuslan-Tomkins hypothesis (McAuslan 1963, Garren *et al.* 1964, Tomkins *et al.* 1972), and that the initial appearance of interferon mRNA after induction is also subject to a negative control mechanism.

Superinduction of interferon production

Confluent cultures of diploid human fibroblasts (FS-4 cells), exposed to poly(I) · poly(C) for 1 h secrete detectable amounts of interferon into the culture medium by 1–2 h after the beginning of induction. The rate of secretion reaches a peak by 2.5–3.5 h and secretion is shut off by 6–8 h (the control curves in Figs. 4 and 5). The rapid shutoff which takes place between 3 and 8 h after induction can be prevented by appropriate exposure of induced cultures to any one of a wide range of inhibitors of RNA or protein synthesis (Vilček *et al.* 1976, Tamm & Sehgal 1978, Sehgal & Tamm 1978a). Fig. 4 illustrates the effect of DRB on interferon production (Sehgal *et al.* 1975a). Cultures induced and maintained in DRB at intermediate concentrations (30–40 μM) show an initial lag in the rate of interferon secretion, compared to DRB-free controls, but reach a peak rate of

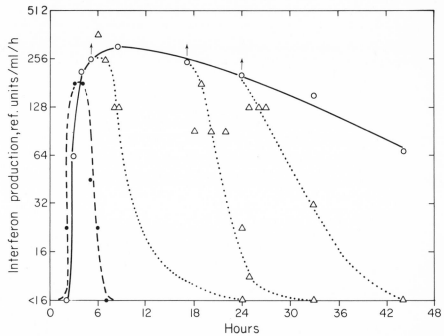

Fig. 4. Rate of interferon production during prolonged treatment with 30 μM DRB and effect of termination of treatment. Four 11-day-old cultures (60 mm dishes) were induced with poly(I) · poly(C) in the presence (○), and one in the absence (●), of DRB and the rate of interferon production was followed by repeated medium replacement (2 ml, with or without DRB) and interferon titration. At 5, 17, and 24 h, one dish, which had contained DRB, was washed four times with warm PBS and the rate of interferon production was from then on monitored in the absence of DRB (△). From Sehgal *et al.* (1975a).

secretion which, on the average, is two- to threefold higher than the peak rate of secretion in DRB-free controls. Interferon production in DRB-treated cultures continues for an extended period of time (up to 4 days, Sehgal *et al.* 1976b). Removal of DRB at any time during the experiment results in a subsequent shutoff of interferon production. Prevention of the rapid shutoff of interferon production by DRB leads to an approximately 10-fold increase in the cumulative interferon yield over the first 24 h of induction (Sehgal *et al.* 1976b). With appropriate use of a combination of cycloheximide (0–6 h) and DRB (3–24 h) a 50-fold increase in 24-h cumulative yield can be achieved (Sehgal *et al.* 1976b). Furthermore, since the inhibitory effect of both of these compounds is reversible, high interferon yields can be obtained from the same culture of diploid FS-4 cells at least four times in succession at intervals of 1 week

(Wiranowska-Stewart *et al.* 1977). This paradoxical increase in interferon production is termed "superinduction" (Vilček *et al.* 1969, 1976, Tan *et al.* 1970, Tamm & Sehgal 1978, Sehgal & Tamm 1978a).

We have attempted to determine the biochemical basis for interferon superinduction using the experiment described in Fig. 4 as a prototype. Interferon mRNA was quantitated by translation of polyadenylated mRNA preparations from FS-4 cells after microinjection into oocytes of *Xenopus laevis* (Reynolds *et al.* 1975, Cavalieri *et al.* 1977, Sehgal *et al.* 1977, 1978b, c). Synthesis of human fibroblast interferon by oocytes was assayed biologically using a cell-protection assay with vesicular stomatitis virus as the challenge virus and FS-4 cells as the substrate.

Correlation between cellular interferon mRNA content and rate of interferon secretion

Transcription of interferon mRNA in poly(I) · poly(C)-induced FS-4 cells is largely complete by 3 h after the beginning of induction both in DRB-free and in DRB-containing cultures (Sehgal *et al.* 1976b, 1978b). Fig. 5 demonstrates that there is a good correlation between the rates of interferon secretion and cellular interferon mRNA levels during normal induction, shutoff and superinduction (Sehgal *et al.* 1977). The rate of interferon secretion during normal induction in the absence of any inhibitor declines with a half-life of 0.5–0.7 h during the shutoff phase. The content of translatable cytoplasmic interferon mRNA during the shutoff phase also declines with a half-life of 0.5–1.0 h (Table I; Sehgal *et al.* 1978b). In contrast, the rate of interferon secretion and the content of translatable interferon mRNA decline with a half-life of 6–8 h during superinduction with DRB (Table I; Sehgal *et al.* 1978b). Thus interferon mRNA is approximately 14-fold more stable in DRB-treated cells. Clearly, increased mRNA stability is a major factor in interferon superinduction by DRB.

Does DRB inhibit the synthesis of interferon mRNA?

In a preceding section we have indicated that DRB (60–75 μM) inhibits cellular mRNA synthesis by >95%. We are therefore led to ask, is interferon mRNA synthesis resistant to inhibition by DRB (40 μM)?

Figs. 4 and 5 show that the rate of secretion of interferon in the presence of DRB lags behind that in its absence for the first 2–3 h after induction. Furthermore, if FS-4 cultures are treated with cycloheximide (0–6 h) and actinomycin D (2.5–3.5 h) such that interferon production measured between 6

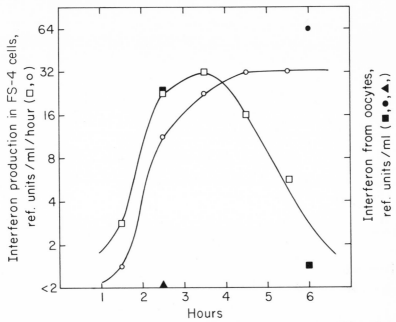

Fig. 5. Correlation between interferon production and interferon mRNA content of FS-4 cells during induction, shutoff, and superinduction. Ten 150-mm Falcon petri dish cultures of confluent FS-4 cells were used for each analysis. The cultures were induced with poly(I) · poly(C) (20 μg/ml) in 10 ml Eagle's minimum essential medium for 1 h starting at "0 hour". One batch of cultures did not receive poly(I) · poly(C) whereas another batch received poly(I) · poly(C) together with 40 μM DRB. The DRB-treated batch was maintained in DRB throughout the experiment. Two of the induced cultures were used to monitor the rate of interferon production by hourly medium (10 ml) change; one culture was from the DRB-free batch (□) and the other was treated with DRB (○). DRB-containing samples were dialyzed prior to the assay for interferon. At 2.5 h, a batch of induced (■) and a batch of uninduced (▲) cultures were harvested, and total cellular RNA was fractionated into polyadenylated RNA and flow-through RNA by using a poly(U)-Sepharose column. Another batch of induced cultures (■) and the DRB-treated cultures (●) were similarly harvested at 6 h after induction. The polyadenylated RNA and the flow-through RNA were ethanol precipitated and dissolved in 20 and 100 μl, respectively, of injection buffer. Approximately 2 μl of each polyadenylated RNA preparation was injected into 13–15 oocytes (30 ng of RNA per oocyte) and interferon synthesis was monitored. From Sehgal *et al.* (1977).

and 24 h is *maximally* enhanced through the combined action of these drugs, then addition of DRB between 0 and 2.5 h after the beginning of induction inhibits interferon yield in a dose-dependent manner (Sehgal *et al.* 1976c). The dose-response relationship describing the inhibitory effect of DRB on interferon yield in this type of experiment is closely similar to that for its inhibitory effect on RNA synthesis (Sehgal *et al.* 1976c). Under these conditions DRB at 40 μM

Table I
Half-life of human fibroblast interferon mRNA

Measurement carried out during	Estimate based on	
	Rate of secretion in culture	mRNA concentration assayed in oocytes
Normal shutoff	0.5–0.7 h	0.5–1.0 h
DRB (40 μM) superinduction	6–8 h	6–8 h

From Sehgal *et al.* (1978b).

inhibits interferon yield by approximately 80%. Thus under appropriate conditions the synthesis of interferon mRNA appears to be as sensitive to inhibition by DRB as that of other cellular mRNA species.

The apparent rate of synthesis of interferon mRNA in the absence or presence of either DRB or cycloheximide alone
In view of the above findings the question arises as to what the rate of appearance of interferon mRNA is in induced cultures treated with DRB or cycloheximide alone. We have attempted to compare the apparent rate of synthesis of interferon mRNA in the presence of DRB alone (40 μM) or cycloheximide alone (50 μg/ml) with that in the absence of these inhibitors by measuring the accumulation of translatable interferon mRNA during the first 3 h of induction (Sehgal & Tamm 1978b). The results of such comparisons are presented in Table II. The "expected" values were calculated by taking into account a 14-fold increase in mRNA stability in the presence of DRB or of cycloheximide (see the next section); and by assuming that DRB at 40 μM inhibits interferon mRNA synthesis by 80% and that cycloheximide has no effect on mRNA synthesis. The data in Table II indicate that a three- to fourfold higher level of interferon mRNA is observed in the presence of DRB alone or cycloheximide alone than would be expected, which, in formal terms, is equivalent to a three- to fourfold higher apparent rate of synthesis of interferon mRNA.

A theoretical analysis of interferon superinduction
Do the 14-fold increase in interferon mRNA stability and the three- to fourfold increase in the apparent rate of synthesis of interferon mRNA in the presence of DRB or cycloheximide completely account for the observed increase in

Table II

Mean content of translatable polyadenylated interferon mRNA in drug-treated cells relative to control cells

	Observed		Expected*		Observed** Expected	
	2 h	3 h	2 h	3 h	2 h	3 h
DRB	1.0	4.8	0.5	0.7	2.0	6.5
Cycloheximide (CHX)	7.2	8.4	2.7	3.7	2.7	2.3

* Based on equation 2a with $S_m^{DRB}=0.2\,S_m^{Control}$, and $S_m^{CHX}=S_m^{Control}$; and $k_m^{DRB}=k_m^{CHX}=\dfrac{\ln 2}{t_{1/2}}=$

$\dfrac{0.693}{7\,h}=0.1\,h^{-1}$, and $k_m^{Control}=\dfrac{0.693}{0.5\,h}=1.4\,h^{-1}$.

** Mean af all four values in this colum is 3.4.
From Sehgal & Tamm (1978b).

interferon production in induced cultures of FS-4 cells? We have constructed a simple mathematical model for the induction of interferon which permits us to evaluate this question (Sehgal *et al.* 1978b, Sehgal & Tamm 1978b). We assumed that interferon mRNA is synthesized at a constant apparent rate, S_m, for a specified length of time after induction ($t'=3$ h) subsequent to which its synthesis is terminated, and that interferon mRNA is subject to a decay process which follows the form of a first order reaction with a rate constant, k_m, which is constant at all times after induction. The rate of change in interferon mRNA concentration, M, is then given by

$$\frac{dM}{dT}=S_m-k_m M \qquad\qquad\text{Equation 1}$$

Solving this equation for M as a function of time, t, gives

$$M=\frac{S_m}{k_m}(1-e^{-k_m t}),\text{ for } t\le t' \qquad\qquad\text{Equation 2a}$$

and

$$M=M_{t'}e^{-k_m(t-t')},\text{ for } t>t' \qquad\qquad\text{Equation 2b}$$

where M_t is the level of mRNA at the time when synthesis is stopped (t') and reflects the maximum level obtained. Equations 1 and 2 summarize the essential features of this simple model. It is anticipated that future refinements will take into account variations in S_m and k_m that may occur during the period of interferon production.

This model can be used to derive expressions for various key parameters of interferon superinduction (Sehgal *et al.* 1978b, Sehgal & Tamm 1978b). Table III presents a comparison between the observed and the calculated values of these parameters. Within the framework of the model interferon superinduction by DRB is adequately explained by two effects: a 14-fold increase in stability of interferon mRNA and a three- to fourfold increase in the apparent rate of interferon mRNA synthesis.

Biochemical basis for increased functional stability of interferon mRNA

There is evidence that the increase in functional stability of interferon mRNA in the presence of inhibitors of RNA or protein synthesis does involve an inhibition of the synthesis of RNA and protein species (Sehgal *et al.* 1975a, b, Sehgal *et al.* 1977, Tamm & Sehgal 1978). This conclusion is essentially based on an evaluation of the dose-response relationships of the effects observed with a wide range of inhibitors. Molecules responsible for the shutoff of interferon synthesis are turned over rapidly with a lifetime of 3–4 h at 37°C (Sehgal & Tamm 1976). Our current working hypothesis is that the mechanism which regulates interferon mRNA stability falls within the framework of the repressor hypothesis proposed by McAuslan (1963) and by Tomkins and his colleagues (Garren *et al.* 1964, Tomkins *et al.* 1972) for translational regulation in mammalian cells. Available techniques permit the development of cell-free systems to investigate the biochemical basis for the increased stability of interferon mRNA in "superinduced" cells.

Inhibition of poly(A) shortening is one possible mechanism by which stability of interferon mRNA might be increased in the continued presence of DRB.

Table III

Interferon superinduction

| | Fold increase | |
	Observed*	Calculated**
Peak rate of secretion (DRB alone from 0 h)	2–3	2.6
24-h cumulative yield		
DRB alone (0–24 h)	10	8.7
CHX (0–6 h) and DRB (3–24 h)	50	41

* Sehgal *et al.* (1975a, 1976a, 1978b).

** See Sehgal *et al.* (1978b) for detailed derivations. $S_m^{DRB} = 0.7\ S_m^{Control}$ and $S_m^{CHX} = 3.4\ S_m^{Control}$. From Sehgal & Tamm (1978b).

However, marked shortening of the poly(A) of interferon mRNA occurs in the presence of DRB (Sehgal *et al.* 1978b). We have also compared the functional stability of interferon mRNA which was deadenylated using polynucleotide phosphorylase (EC 2.7.7.8) with that of native polyadenylated interferon mRNA. The two preparations of interferon mRNA were functionally indistinguishable after injection into oocytes of *X. laevis* (Sehgal *et al.* 1978c). Our results suggest that the poly(A) sequence in interferon mRNA does not contribute to the functional stability of this mRNA.

Biochemical basis for increased apparent rate of interferon mRNA synthesis
At present we do not know whether the increase in the apparent rate of synthesis (S_m) of interferon mRNA in the presence of DRB or cycloheximide is a true increase in the rate of transcription of interferon mRNA or reflects an effect on post-transcriptional processing of mRNA. If it is a true transcriptional effect it may be evidence of the lifting of a transcriptional repressor mechanism in the expression of the human fibroblast interferon gene (Sehgal & Tamm 1978b). An SV40-transformant of human WI-38 cells (line 108) is known which produces human fibroblast interferon when exposed to DRB alone or to cycloheximide alone (Tan *et al.* 1977). Future investigations of the activation of interferon mRNA synthesis using recombinant DNA technology may provide further insight into the regulation of a specific gene in human cells at the transcriptional level.

ACKNOWLEDGMENTS
We thank Doctors James E. Darnell, Jr. and Nigel W. Fraser for helpful discussions and Miss Toyoko Kikuchi for excellent assistance. We are grateful to Doctors D. Wang and S. Moore for protease-free and ribonuclease-free pancreatic deoxyribonuclease and to Dr. Arthur F. Wagner, Merck Sharp & Dohme Research Laboratories for DRB used in these studies. Investigations carried out in the authors' laboratory were supported by Research Grant CA-18608 and Program Project Grant CA-18213 awarded by the National Cancer Institute. P.B.S. is a postdoctoral fellow of the National Cancer Institute.

REFERENCES
Cavalieri, R. L., Havell, E. A., Pestka, S. & Vilček, J. (1977) Synthesis of human interferon

by *Xenopus laevis* oocytes: two structural genes for interferons in human cells. *Proc. Natl. Acad. Sci. U.S.A.* 74, 3287–3291.

Fraser, N. W., Sehgal, P. B. & Darnell, J. E. (1978) DRB-induced premature termination of late adenovirus transcription. *Nature* 272, 590–593.

Garren, L. D., Howell, R. R., Tomkins, G. M. & Crocco, R. M (1964) A paradoxical effect of actinomycin D: the mechanism of regulation of enzyme synthesis by hydrocortisone. *Proc. Natl. Acad. Sci. U.S.A.* 52, 1121–1129.

Groner, Y., Gilboa, E. & Aviv, H. (1978) Methylation and capping of RNA polymerase II primary transcripts by HeLa nuclear homogenates. *Biochem.* 17, 977–982.

McAuslan, B. R. (1963) The induction and repression of thymidine kinase in the pox virus-infected HeLa cell. *Virology* 21, 383–389.

Reynolds, F. H., Premkumar, E. & Pitha, P. M. (1975) Interferon activity produced by translation of human interferon messenger RNA in cell-free ribosomal systems and in *Xenopus* oocytes. Proc. Natl. Acad. Sci. U.S.A. 72, 4881–4885.

Sehgal, P. B. & Tamm, I. (1976) An evaluation of messenger RNA competition in the shutoff of human interferon production. *Proc. Natl. Acad. Sci. U.S.A.* 73, 1621–1625.

Sehgal, P. B. & Tamm, I. (1978a) Halogenated benzimidazole ribosides: Novel inhibitors of RNA synthesis. *Biochem. Pharmacol.* 27, 2475–2485.

Sehgal, P. B. & Tamm, I. (1978b) Two mechanisms contribute to the superinduction of poly(I) · poly(C)-induced human fibroblast interferon production. *Virology,.* in press.

Sehgal, P. B., Tamm, I. & Vilček, J. (1975a) Human interferon production: superinduction by 5,6-dichloro-1-β-D-ribofuranosylbenzimidazole. *Science* 190, 282–284.

Sehgal, P. B., Tamm, I. & Vilček, J. (1975b) Enhancement of human interferon production by neutral red and chloroquine: Analysis of inhibition of protein degradation and macromolecular synthesis. *J. Exp. Med.* 142, 1283–1300.

Sehgal, P. B., Darnell, J. E., Jr. & Tamm, I. (1976a) The inhibition by DRB (5,6-dichloro-1-β-D-ribofuranosylbenzimidazole) of hnRNA and mRNA production in HeLa cells. *Cell* 9, 473–480.

Sehgal, P. B., Tamm I. & Vilček, J. (1976b) Regulation of human interferon production. I. Superinduction by 5,6-dichloro-1-β-D-ribofuranosylbenzimidazole. *Virology* 70, 532–541.

Sehgal, P. B., Tamm, I. & Vilček, J. (1976c) Regulation of human interferon production. II. Inhibition of interferon messenger RNA synthesis by 5,6-dichloro-1-β-D-ribofuranosylbenzimidazole. *Virology* 70, 542–544.

Sehgal, P. B., Dobberstein, B. & Tamm, I. (1977) Interferon messenger RNA content of human fibroblasts during induction, shutoff, and superinduction of interferon production. *Proc. Natl. Acad. Sci. U.S.A.* 74, 3409–3413.

Sehgal, P. B., Fraser, N. W. & Darnell, J. E. (1978a) Early Ad-2 transcription units: only promoter-proximal RNA continues to be made in the presence of DRB. *Virology*, in press.

Sehgal, P. B., Lyles, D. S. & Tamm, I. (1978b) Superinduction of human fibroblast interferon production: Further evidence for increased stability of interferon mRNA. *Virology.* 89, 186–198.

Sehgal, P. B., Soreq, H. & Tamm, I. (1978c) Does 3′ terminal poly(A) stabilize human fibroblast interferon mRNA in oocytes of *Xenopus laevis? Proc. Natl. Acad. Sci. U.S.A.* 75, 5030–5033.

Tamm, I. (1977) Definition of subclasses of nucleoplasmic RNA. *Proc. Natl. Acad. Sci. U.S.A.* 74, 5011–5015.

Tamm, I. (1978) In preparation.

Tamm, I. & Sehgal, P. B. (1978) Halobenzimidazole ribosides and RNA synthesis of cells and viruses. *Adv. Virus Res.* 22, 187–258.

Tamm, I., Hand, R. & Caliguiri, L. A. (1976) Action of dichlorobenzimidazole riboside on RNA synthesis in L-929 and HeLa cells. *J. Cell Biol.* 69, 229–240.

Tan, Y. H. & Berthold, W. (1977) A mechanism for the induction and regulation of human fibroblastoid interferon genetic expression. *J. Gen. Virol.* 34, 401–411.

Tan, Y. H., Armstrong, J. A., Ke, Y. H. & Ho, M. (1970) Regulation of cellular interferon production: enhancement by antimetabolites. *Proc. Natl. Acad. Sci. U.S.A.* 67, 464–471.

Tomkins, G. M., Levinson, B. B., Baxter, J. D. & Dethlefsen, L. (1972) Further evidence for post-transcriptional control of inducible tyrosine aminotransferase synthesis in cultured hepatoma cells. *Nature New Biol.* (London) 239, 9–14.

Vilček, J., Rossman, T. G. & Varacalli, F. (1969) Differential effects of actinomycin D and puromycin on the release of interferon induced by double stranded RNA. *Nature* 222, 682–683.

Vilček, J., Havell, E. A. & Kohase, M. (1976) Superinduction of interferon with metabolic inhibitors: possible mechanisms and practical applications. *J. Infect. Dis.* 133, A22–A29.

Wang, D. & Moore, S. (1978) Preparation of protease-free and ribonuclease-free pancreatic deoxyribonuclease. *J. Biol. Chem.* 253, 7216–7219.

Wiranowska-Stewart, M., Chudzio, T. & Stewart, W. E., II (1977) Repeated "superinduction" of interferon in human diploid fibroblast cultures. *J. Gen. Virol.* 37, 221–223.

Yanofsky, C. (1976) Control sites in the tryptophan operon. In: *Alfred Benzon Symposium IX Control of Ribosome Synthesis,* ed. Kjeldgaard, N. & Maaløe, O. pp. 149–163. Munksgaard, Copenhagen.

DISCUSSION

WEISSMANN: Is the statement that messenger RNA is inhibited over 90% based on polysomal poly-A RNA or do you also look at one specific messenger in any of these instances?

TAMM: It is based first of all on the polysomal poly-A-containing RNA, and also on mRNP associated with polysomes (Sehgal *et al.* 1976). As to looking at any specific mRNA, we have not yet done that except for interferon mRNA. I think it would be very interesting if the synthesis, e.g. of histone message were carefully looked at in DRB-treated cells to determine whether it is inhibited or whether there are messages which escape. The essential point is that the appearance of the bulk of mRNA in the cytoplasm is blocked.

RICH: Do you have any idea about what DRB does? Is it incorporated into the RNA chain?

TAMM: Indirect evidence suggests that DRB may not be incorporated in the RNA chain. The inhibitory effects of DRB on cellular biosynthesis are readily reversible. Inhibition of proliferation of human fibroblasts in culture is also reversible by removal of the compound from the medium (Tamm & Sehgal 1977).

RICH: But it sounds like it might get phosphorylated and then just stick on the enzyme.

TAMM: It has been reported recently that Ehrlich ascites cells do not phosphorylate DRB (Dreyer & Hausen 1978). This finding is of considerable interest because it suggests that DRB does not act as a metabolic antagonist at the nucleoside triphosphate level.

RICH: The only odd thing is that it has this funny partitioning, that it stops some RNAs and not others?

Sehgal, P. B., Darnell, J. E. & Tamm, I. (1976) *Cell* 9, 473–480.
Tamm. I. & Sehgal, P. B. (1977) *J. Exp. Med.* 145, 344–356.
Dreyer, C. & Hausen, P. (1978) *Nucleic Acid Res.* 5, 3325–3335.

TAMM: That is right.

RICH: Unless that is telling us that there are two enzymes, and it knocks out one and does not knock out the other?

TAMM: That is of course the question we have raised, i.e. whether there is more than one RNA polymerase II involved in hnRNA synthesis, or whether RNA polymerase II may function in two forms (Tamm *et al.* 1976, Tamm 1977).

SCHAFFNER: In this context it may be worth repeating what Max Birnstiel has already mentioned, namely that in sea urchin embryos after DRB treatment you get actually more, very large molecular weight histone transcripts made.

TAMM: I would like to ask whether there is an actual increase in the amount of the large transcripts made, or whether there is only a change in the size distribution profile of the RNA labeled.

SCHAFFNER: I don't know. By the way, do you know if the DRB-resistant transcripts differ in their snapback sequences from the DRB-sensitive fraction?

TAMM: Not yet. Quite obviously what would be interesting to do is for example to look for the content of mRNA coding sequences in the one-third of hnRNA that is DRB-resistant, as well as having other properties, but this work has not yet been carried out.

Tamm, I., Hand, R. & Caliguiri, L. A. (1976) *J. Cell Biol.* 69, 229–240.
Tamm, I. (1977) *Proc. Nat. Acad. Sci. USA,* 74, 5011–5015.

Approaches to the Isolation of Tubulin Messenger RNA from Tetrahymena

M.M. Portier, L. Marcaud, M. Milet & D.H. Hayes

Analysis of the mechanism and regulation of mRNA formation in eucaryotic cells was begun in our laboratory in 1974 using *Tetrahymena pyriformis* as a model system. Initially work was confined to the characterization of polysomal and nuclear poly A-containing RNAs, i.e. functional messenger RNAs and their nuclear precursors (Pousada & Hayes 1976); further studies with these materials are planned, e.g. comparison of their kinetic complexities. However, access to specific mRNA species is a prerequisite for many aspects of studies of this type, and more recently an evaluation of the feasibility of isolating specific mRNAs from *T. pyriformis* has been undertaken. Tubulin mRNA was chosen for this study for two reasons:

1. *T. pyriformis* contains large amounts of tubulins in its cilia and cortex, and they can be prepared in a pure state from isolated cilia by published methods (Renaud *et al.* 1968) for use as carriers and markers in the analysis of the products of *in vitro* protein synthesis and for antibody production.

2. Continuous and rapid formation of cilia and cortical material takes place during exponential gowth of *T. pyriformis* which suggests that exponentially growing cells may contain relatively large quantities of tubulin mRNAs.

The results described here were obtained in a series of preliminary experiments directed towards the characterization of tubulin mRNAs and the search for physiological conditions which increase their concentration in total mRNA of *T. pyriformis*. Where comparisons can be made they are in agreement with the results of studies of tubulin mRNA of rat brain (Gozes *et al.* 1975) and *Chlamydomonas reinhardii* (Weeks & Collis 1976).

Laboratoire de Chimie Cellulaire, Institut de Biologie Physico Chimique 13 rue Pierre et Marie Curie, 75005 Paris, France.

SPECIFIC EUKARYOTIC GENES, Alfred Benzon Symposium 13, Munksgaard 1979

MATERIAL AND METHODS

Cells and culture conditions

The amicronucleate GL strain of *T. pyriformis* was used in all experiments. Cells used for RNA preparation were grown in gently shaken cultures in PPY medium (Leick & Plesner 1968) at 28°C (generation time 3–5 h), harvested in early log phase (1.5×10^5 cells/ml) and used immediately. For tubulin isolation, cells were grown in shallow layers of the same medium in Fernbach flasks without shaking and were harvested in stationary phase ($7–10 \times 10^5$ cells per ml). For starvation prior to deciliation cells were harvested from mid-log phase cultures in PPY medium (4×10^5 cells/ml), washed under sterile conditions in 10 mM Tris-HCl pH 7.3, resuspended in the same medium at a concentration of 2×10^5 cells per ml and incubated at 28°C for 20 h with gentle shaking.

Deciliation of T. pyriformis

Two procedures were used. For tubulin isolation, cilia were amputated by the ethanol-calcium procedure (Watson & Hopkins 1962) and viable deciliated cells were prepared by controlled shearing of suspensions of EDTA-calcium-treated cells (Rosenbaum & Carlson 1969).

Regeneration of cilia

Suspensions of starved cells in 10 mM Tris-HCl pH 7.3 after deciliation by EDTA-calcium treatment and shearing contained 5×10^5 cells per ml in 2.5 mM Tris-HCl, 5 mM $CaCl_2$, 25 mM Na acetate, 5 mM EDTA Na_2 pH6. They were diluted with 20 volumes of 10 mM K phosphate buffer pH 7, at 25°C and incubated at 25°C with gentle shaking. Regeneration of cilia was monitored by following recovery of motility by light microscope observation.

Preparation of tubulins

Tubulins were isolated from an acetone powder of cilia as described by Renaud *et al.* 1968. ^{35}S-labeled tubulins were prepared by the same method from cells grown in PPY medium supplemented with (^{35}S)-L-methionine. Electrophoresis of the products in polyacrylamide-SDS gels showed the presence of only two bands corresponding in mobility to a and β tubulins.

Preparation of poly A containing RNA

(All operations at 0–4°C, unless otherwise stated.)
After collection by centrifugation, cells were washed with extraction buffer (0.1

M Tris-HCl, 0.1 M NaCl, 1 mM EDTA, pH 9.0 containing 20 μg/ml of potassium polyvinyl sulfate) suspended in the same buffer at a concentration of about 2×10^6 cells/ml, and lysed by addition of sodium dodecyl sulfate (20 mg/ml). The lysate was deproteinized by two successive treatments with an equal volume of water-saturated phenol containing 0.1% 8-hydroxyquinoline, followed by one extraction with two volumes of chloroform-isoamyl alcohol (24:1 v/v). Nucleic acids were then precipitated (-20°C, 2 h) by addition of NaCl to a final concentration of 0.2 M and two volumes of cold ethanol. The precipitate dissolved in 10 mM Tris-HCl, 5 mM $MgCl_2$, pH 7.5 was treated with RNase-free DNase (60 μg/ml) to remove DNA, the solution was deproteinized by a single treatment with phenol-8-hydroxyquinoline as before, and RNA was recovered by precipitation at $-20°C$ with ethanol (2 volumes) in the presence of 0.2 M NaCl. The product was stored under ethanol at $-20°C$. Poly A and non-poly A-containing fractions were separated from total RNA by affinity chromatography on poly U-sepharose (Gray & Cashmore 1976) concentrated from column eluates by ethanol precipitation and stored under ethanol at $-20°C$.

Sucrose gradient fractionation of poly A-RNA
Poly A-RNA was dissolved in 0.05 M NaCl 0.01 M EDTA pH 7 at a concentration of 40–50 A_{260nm} units per ml and 1-ml samples of the solution were centrifuged for 22 h at 20 000 rpm, 4°C, on 25-ml 5–20% linear sucrose gradients prepared in the same buffer. Centrifuged gradients were collected manually, the A_{260nm} of fractions was measured and RNA was recovered from pooled fractions by ethanol precipitation and stored under ethanol at $-20°C$.

Preparation of polysomes
(All operations at 0–4°C)
Glassware and solutions were sterilized before use. Stock 50% solutions of sucrose were treated with diethylpyrocarbonate before sterilization. Protein synthesis in cell suspensions (samples taken from early exponential phase cultures, cell density 10^5/ml or from suspensions of deciliated cells, 5×10^4/ml) was stopped by addition of cycloheximide (100 μg/ml) followed immediately by 0.25 volumes of crushed frozen suspension medium. Cells were then harvested by centrifugation, washed in lysis buffer (10 mM Pipes, 10 mM NaCl, 5 mM $MgCl_2$, 1 mM $CaCl_2$, 1 mM dithiothreitol, pH 6.5, containing 100 μg/ml spermidine and 250 μg/ml heparin), suspended in the same buffer and lysed by

addition of Nonidet P40 to a final concentration of 0.2%. After lysis (1–2 min) diethylpyrocarbonate (20 μl/ml lysate) was added with shaking, the lysate was centrifuged at 10,000 g for 10 min and the upper two-thirds of the supernatant was recovered and analyzed by centrifugation for 5 h at 24,000 rpm, 4°C on 25-ml 10–50% sucrose gradients prepared in lysis buffer. Gradients were layered on 1-ml cushions of 50% sucrose in lysis buffer and loaded with 20 $A_{260 \text{ nm}}$ units of cell extract. After centrifugation they were collected and their UV absorbtion profiles were determined automatically.

In vitro protein synthesis

Preincubated S30 extract was prepared as described by Roberts & Patterson (1973), from wheat germ supplied by Les Grands Moulins de Paris. Protein synthesis with this preparation was carried out in 50-μl incubation mixtures as described by Gozes et al. (1975). Rabbit reticulocyte lysate was prepared and used (12 μl incubation mixtures) as described by Pelham & Jackson (1976). In preliminary experiments (results presented elsewhere) the optimum values of pH, and of poly A.RNA, Mg^{++}, K^{+}, and spermidine concentrations were determined for each system. Synthesized proteins were labeled by addition of 1–5 μCi of (^{35}S)-L-methionine per reaction mixture and analyzed by electrophoresis in polyacrylamide-SDS gel slabs (Studier 1973) which were stained, dried and autoradiographed (Specific activity of (^{35}S)-L-methionine, 800 ci/mmole).

RESULTS AND DISCUSSION

In vitro translation of T. pyriformis poly A-RNA

In vitro systems containing wheat germ extract (Roberts & Patterson 1973) or reticulocyte lysate (Pelham & Jackson 1976) catalyze efficient translation of eucaryotic messenger RNAs, the latter system being generally considered more efficient than the former, especially for translation of high molecular weight messenger RNAs. Both systems translate T. pyriformis poly A-RNA efficiently and analysis of the reaction products by polyacrylamide gel-SDS electrophoresis reveals the formation in both of a large number of proteins, some with very high molecular weights (Fig. 1A,B,C). Among the more prominent bands in such electropherograms two possess the mobilities of α and β tubulin (Fig. 1). Evidence in support of the identification of these bands as tubulins has been obtained in experiments in which carrier tubulins added to the products of in vitro protein synthesis were reisolated either by precipitation with vinblastine

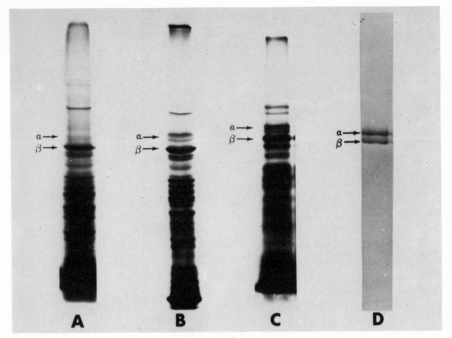

Fig. 1. Polyacrylamide-SDS gel electrophoresis of products of *in vitro* translation of *T. pyriformis* poly A-RNA in the wheat germ extract and reticulocyte lysate systems.

Samples of the same preparation of poly A-RNA of exponentially growing *T. pyriformis* were translated in the following three systems.

A. Wheat germ extract without spermidine (10 μl wheat germ extract, 1.5 μg poly A-RNA, 5 μCi (35S)-L-methionine, 2.4 μg creatine phosphokinase, in a final volume of 50 μl containing (added concentrations, i.e. additional to unknown concentrations in wheat germ extract) 220 μM GTP, 59 mM KCl, 2.16 mM Mg acetate.

B. Wheat germ extract with spermidine. As A but 1 mM Mg acetate, 0.3 mM spermidine.

C. Reticulocyte lysate (5 μl reticulocyte lysate, 0.24 μg poly A-RNA, 4 μCi (^{35}S)-L-methionine, in a final volume of 12 μl containing (added concentrations) 200 μM GTP, 85 mM KCl, 1.2 mM Mg acetate. Reaction mixtures were incubated for 90 min (wheat germ) and 60 min (reticulocyte lysate) at 25°C and those containing wheat germ extract were centrifuged at 100,000 g for 15 min to remove ribosomes.

D. Tubulins purified from cilia prepared from *T. pyriformis* grown in a medium containing (^{35}S)-L-methionine.

In all cases, (^{35}S)-labeled products or *in vivo*-labeled tubulin were prepared for analysis and electrophoresis was carried out as described by Studier (1973). After electrophoresis, gel slabs were stained, dried and autoradiographed.

(Gozes *et al.* 1975) or by one cycle of tubulin polymerization and depolymerization (Shelanski *et al.* 1973, Gozes *et al.* 1975). In both cases a several-fold enrichment of the radioactivity in the two presumed tubulin bands was observed (results not shown) although the reisolated proteins contained small but significant amounts of radioactive components with the electrophoretic mobilities of most of the bands visible in Fig. 1. These results show that poly A-RNA isolated from crude extracts of *T. pyriformis* contains significant quantities of functional tubulin messenger RNAs.

Inspection of the results in Fig. 1 shows that labeling of the α tubulin band is considerably less intense than that of the β tubulin band in both *in vitro* protein synthesis systems. This difference in labeling of α and β tubulins *in vitro* has been observed reproducibly in numerous experiments. In contrast, equal amounts of (^{35}S)-L-methionine are incorporated into the proteins present in the α and β tubulin bands when labeling is carried out *in vivo*, as can be seen in channel D of Fig.1. Since the α and β bands separated by electrophoresis of tubulin preparations in polyacrylamide-SDS gels stain with equal intensity, they probably contain equal amounts of protein. The fact that they are labeled to a similar extent *in vivo* therefore shows that they have the same methionine content and eliminates one possible explanation for their unequal labeling *in vitro*, i.e. the presence of different amounts of methionine in the proteins they contain. Although the cause of the unequal labeling of the α and β tubulins *in vitro* remains unknown, several other possible explanations for this observation have been eliminated. Extensive contamination of the β band by non-tubulin proteins is made unlikely by the observation that partial purification of *in vitro* synthesized tubulins by vinblastine precipitation or microtubule polymerization and depolymerization does not alter the relative intensities of labeling of the α and β bands. The possibility that α tubulin mRNA has a shorter poly A sequence than β tubulin mRNA and therefore is partially lost during isolation of poly A-RNA is eliminated by the absence of α tubulin mRNA activity in the fraction of total RNA which is not retained on poly U-sepharose columns. Lower stability of α than of β tubulin mRNA and consequent differential loss of the former during isolation of poly A-RNA are excluded by the observation of the same unequal labeling of α and β tubulins *in vitro* when total RNA of *T. pyriformis*, its poly A containing component, and sucrose gradient purified size fractions of the latter (see below, Figs. 2, 3) are used as sources of tubulin messenger RNA. Unequal labeling of α and β tubulins *in vitro* could also be accounted for by supposing 1) that *T. pyriformis* contains a smaller amount of α than of β tubulin mRNA and translates the former more efficiently than the latter, whereas both mRNAs are translated with the same efficiency in heterologous systems *in vitro* or 2), that the α and β tubulin mRNAs are present in equal amounts in poly A-

RNA isolated from *T. pyriformis* but are translated with unequal efficiencies in the two *in vitro* systems used in our experiments. An explanation of this type is suggested by the observation (Nudel *et al.* 1973) that translation of globin mRNA *in vitro* in a Krebs ascites cell-free system leads to formation of *a* and *β* globins in a mole ratio of about 1:2 and that the formation of *a* globin can be increased, raising this ratio to about 1:1 by adding a factor extracted from reticulocyte ribosomes to the *in vitro* system. However it has not so far been possible to alter the unequal *in vitro* labeling of *a* and *β* tubulins by supplementing the wheat germ or reticulocyte lysate systems with protein preparations obtained by salt washing of crude *T. pyriformis* ribosomes.

Size of tubulin mRNA

A preliminary estimate of the molecular weight of tubulin mRNA has been obtained by isolating different size classes of poly A-RNA from sucrose gradients made in low ionic strength medium and analyzing their *in vitro* translation products. Fig. 2 shows the sedimentation profile of poly A-RNA in a sucrose gradient made in 0.05 M NaCl, 0.01 M EDTA. The bulk of the poly A-

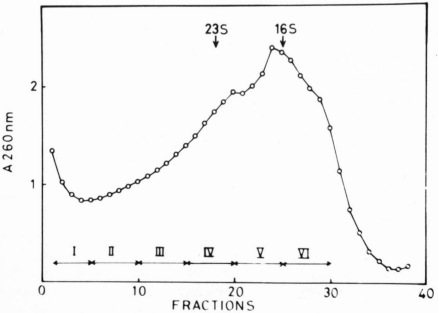

Fig. 2. Sucrose gradient sedimentation of poly A-RNA of exponentially growing *T. pyriformis*. Poly A-RNA was prepared and centrifuged on sucrose gradients in low ionic strength medium as described in Materials and Methods.

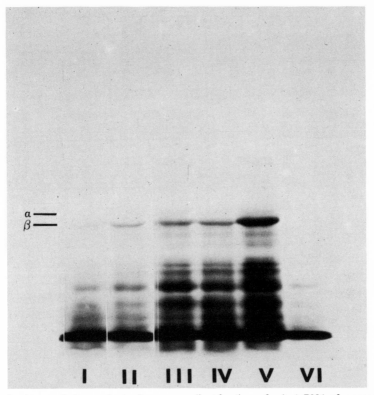

Fig. 3. In vitro translation products of sucrose gradient fractions of poly A-RNA of exponentially growing *T. pyriformis.*
Poly A-RNA fractions isolated from pools I-VI, Fig. 3, were used to direct *in vitro* protein synthesis in a wheat germ system without spermidine (legend to Fig. 1). (^{35}S)-labeled reaction products were analyzed by polyacrylamide-SDS gel electrophoresis (legend to Fig. 1). The positions of a and β tubulins are those occupied by the stained bands of the nonradioactive proteins in parallel tracks in the gel slab whose autoradiograph is shown in Fig. 3.

RNA sediments in a broad peak with a maximum at about 16S, but the presence of considerable amounts of fast-sedimenting material suggests that some aggregation occurred under the conditions of this experiment. Fractions from this gradient were pooled as indicated (I-VI) and RNA recovered from the pools was used to direct protein synthesis in the wheat germ system. Electrophoretic analyses of the synthesized products gave the results shown in Fig. 3. Messenger RNA activity was found mainly in poly A-RNA fractions II-V with a maximum in fraction V. Partial purification of tubulins from the six samples of *in vitro* translation products by vinblastine precipitation showed that tubulin mRNA activity was distributed in the same way as total mRNA activity and was highest in poly A-RNA fraction V. This fraction contains species sedimenting between about 16S and 21S (Mwt $5-8 \times 10^5$). Since the average molecular weight of a and β tubulins is 55,000 (Everhart 1971), this estimate of the molecular weight of their mRNA is in agreement with the expected minimum value.

Tubulin mRNA in starved deciliated T. pyriformis

T. pyriformis can be deciliated without loss of viability and deciliated cells are able to regenerate cilia and recover motility in 60–90 min while in suspension in non-nutrient medium (Rosenbaum & Carlson 1969, Nelsen 1975). Regeneration of cilia under these conditions is inhibited by cycloheximide (Rosenbaum & Carlson 1969) and therefore requires protein synthesis, but the proteins whose formation is necessary are probably not tubulins since most of the tubulins incorporated into newly formed cilia by deciliated cells are derived from a preexisting intracellular pool of these proteins (Nelsen 1975). Examination of RNA synthesis in reciliating cells shows that it remains at a very low level until 60 min after deciliation, i.e. until regeneration of cilia is almost complete, and then increases rapidly reaching a maximum 2–3 h after deciliation (Table I). This

Table I

Suspensions of starved deciliated cells were labeled with (^{3}H)-uridine (EXP 1, 5 μCi/ml, EXP 2, 20 μCi/ml for 1-h periods during reciliation as indicated. Suspensions of control (starved non-deciliated) cells were labeled in the same medium (see Materials and Methods) and under the same conditions as those containing deciliated cells. When actinomycin was present (EXP 2) it was added immediately after deciliation at a concentration of 25 μg/ml. Total RNA was isolated from labeled cells and its specific activity was measured.

Synthesis of RNA in deciliated cells

Duration of Labeling (hours after deciliation)	Specific activity of total RNA (^{3}H cpm/μg)	
	deciliated cells	control cells
EXP 1 0–1	480	400
1–2	6400	160
2–3	9300	160
3–4	4100	80
EXP 2 2–3	45600	600
2–3 + actino	33	–

suggests that RNA synthesis is not required for regeneration of cilia and the observation that reciliation of deciliated cells is not affected by the presence of actinomycin confirms this conclusion (Marcaud, unpublished results). Although actinomycin does not prevent regeneration of cilia, it does inhibit the RNA synthesis observed during the later phases of the reciliation process (Table I). Probably for this reason its presence during reciliation prevents further reformation of cilia after a second deciliation treatment. In contrast, cells which have regenerated cilia under conditions that permit RNA synthesis can do so again after a second deciliation (Marcaud, unpublished results). We interpret

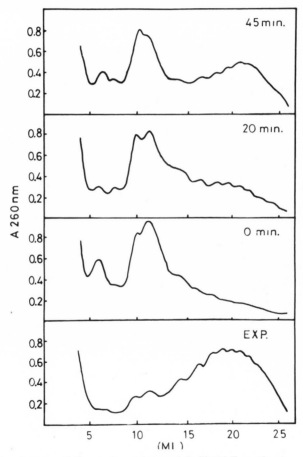

Fig. 4. Polysomes of exponentially growing and starved deciliated *T. pyriformis.*
Polysomes were extracted from exponentially growing cells (EXP) and from samples of starved, deciliated cells taken immediately after deciliation (0 min) and 20 and 45 min later and analyzed on sucrose gradients as described in Materials and Methods.

29*

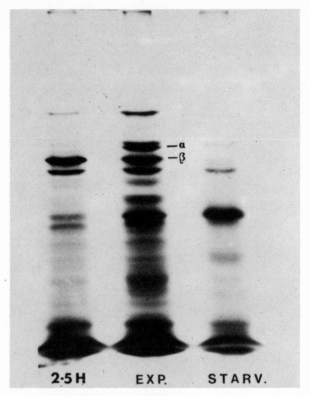

Fig. 5. In vitro translation products of poly A-RNA of starved, and starved deciliated cells.
Poly A-RNAs samples prepared from exponentially growing *T. pyriformis* (EXP), from starved cells
(STARV) and from starved deciliated cells 2.5 h after deciliation (2.5 H) were used to direct *in vitro*
protein synthesis in the reticulocyte lysate system (legend to Fig. 1). (^{35}S)-labeled products were
isolated and analyzed as described in the legend to Fig. 1.

these observations as evidence that the RNA synthesis which takes place at late
times in the reciliation process is induced by the depletion of intracellular pools
of ciliary proteins rather than by deciliation per se and that mRNAs for these
proteins, e.g. tubulin mRNAs, are among the products of this synthesis. A study
of mRNA metabolism during reciliation of deciliated cells was therefore
undertaken. In order to reduce the endogeneous mRNA activity of cells, they
were subjected to prolonged starvation before deciliation since this treatment
leads to almost complete loss of polysomes but does not alter the rate or extent of
cilia regeneration after deciliation. As has been reported by others (Guttman &
Gorovsky 1975) polysomes are reformed slowly in deciliated starved cells. Fig.4
shows sedimentation profiles of polysomes prepared from exponentially

growing cells and from starved deciliated cells immediately after deciliation and 20 and 45 min later. Polysomes of all size classes are formed progressively during reciliation and the fraction of the cell complement of ribosomes which is present in polysomes in starved cells ($\leqslant15\%$) increases considerably reaching $\simeq60\%$ 45 min after deciliation (Fig.4). Thus a significant increase in the cellular content of functioning (polysomal) mRNA takes place during reciliation. This increase could possibly be accounted for by the small amount of RNA synthesis which is detectable during the first 60 min of the deciliation process (Table I) but could also be the result of mobilization of a pool of mRNAs conserved in stable inactive form in starved cells. Further experiments will be necessary to evaluate the contributions of these two possible sources of mRNA to polysome formation in deciliated cells.

Polyacrylamide-SDS gel electrophoresis of the *in vitro* translation products of poly A-RNAs isolated from exponentially growing and starved cells and from starved deciliated cells 2.5 h after deciliation gave the results in Fig. 5. We interpret these results as follows. During prolonged starvation the concentrations of mRNAs corresponding to most of the major protein bands seen in the products of translation of poly A-RNA of exponentially growing cells and in particular those of tubulin mRNAs are greatly reduced. Exceptions to this include the mRNA or mRNAs whose translation products form the very intense band in the lower half of the electrophoresis pattern of products of *in vitro* translation of poly A-RNA of starved cells (compare STARV. and EXP., Fig. 5). Translation products of poly A-RNA extracted from cells 2.5 h after deciliation contain increased amounts of several of the bands which are prominent among proteins synthesized by translation of poly A-RNA of exponentially growing cells. This is particularly notable in the case of the β tubulin band. Thus deciliation of starved *T. pyriformis* seems to lead to selective formation of a group of mRNAs including β tubulin mRNA. Further experiments using poly A-RNAs extracted from deciliated cells at earlier times after deciliation have shown that the amount of β tubulin in their *in vitro* translation products has increased detectably 20 min after deciliation and reaches a maximum at 1–2 h after deciliation (Marcaud, unpublished results).

CONCLUSIONS

The results of the experiments described here lead to the following conclusions:

1. Poly A-RNA extracted from exponentially growing *T. pyriformis* contains functional mRNAs for a and β tubulins.

2. The molecular weights of these RNAs ($5-8\times10^5$) are close to the minimum value expected for mRNAs coding for proteins with molecular weights of about 55,000.

3. Poly A-RNA extracted from starved deciliated *T. pyriformis* during the late phase of the reciliation process probably contains a higher proportion of tubulin mRNA than poly A-RNA of exponentially growing cells.

ACKNOWLEDGMENTS

Financial support for the work described here was provided by grants from the Centre National de la Recherche Scientifique (E.R. 101) and the Delegation à la Recherche Scientifique et Technique (contract no. 77 7 0281). We thank Madame Tichonivtsky for help with the preparation of rabbit reticulocytes.

REFERENCES

Everhart, L.P. (1971) Heterogeneity of microtubule proteins of *Tetrahymena cilia. J. Mol. Biol. 61,* 745–748.

Gozes, I., Schmitt, H. & Littauer, U.Z. (1975) Translation *in vitro* of rat brain messenger RNA coding for actin and tubulin. *Proc. Nat. Acad. Sci. USA 72,* 701–705.

Gray, R.E., & Cashmore, A.R. (1976) RNA synthesis in plant leaf tissue: The characterization of mRNA species lacking and containing poly A. *J. Mol. Biol. 108,* 595–608.

Guttman, S.D., & Gorovsky, M.A. (1975) Cilia regeneration in starved *Tetrahymena. J. Cell Biol. 67,* 149a (15th annual meeting American Society for Cell biology, abstract n° 298).

Leick, V. & Plesner, P. (1968) Formation of ribosomes in *T. pyriformis. Biochim. Biophys. Acta 169,* 398–408.

Nelsen, E.M. (1975) Regulation of tubulin during ciliary regeneration in non-growing *Tetrahymena. Exp. Cell Res. 94,* 152–158.

Pelham, H.R.B. & Jackson, R.J. (1976) An efficient mRNA-dependent translation system from reticulocyte lysates. *Eur. J. Biochem. 67,* 247–256.

Renaud, F.L., Rowe, A.J. & Gibbons, J.R. (1968) Some properties of the protein forming the outer fibers of cilia. *J. Cell Biol. 36,* 79–90.

Roberts, B.E., & Patterson, B.M. (1973) Efficient translation of TMV RNA and rabbit globin 9S RNA in a cell-free system from commercial wheat germ. *Proc. Nat. Acad. Sci. USA 70,* 2330–2334.

Rodrigues-Pousada, C. & Hayes, D.H. (1976) Poly A-containing RNA in *Tetrahymena pyriformis. Eur. J. Biochem. 71,* 117–124.

Rosenbaum, J.L. & Carlson, K. (1969) Cilia regeneration in *Tetrahymena* and its inhibition by colchicine. *J. Cell Biol. 40,* 415–425.

Shelanski, M.L., Gaskin, F., & Cantor, C.R. (1973) Microtubule assembly in the absence of added nucleotides. *Proc. Nat. Acad. Sci. USA 70,* 765–768.

Studier F.W. (1973) Analysis of bacteriophage T7 early RNAs and proteins on slab gels. *J. Mol. Biol. 79,* 237–248.

Watson, L.R. & Hopkins, J.M. (1962) Isolated cilia from *Tetrahymena pyriformis*. *Exp. Cell Res. 28*, 280–295.

Weeks, D.P. & Collis, P.S. (1976) Induction of microtubule protein synthesis in *Chlamydomonas reinhardi* during flagellar regeneration. *Cell 9*, 15–27.

DISCUSSION

RICH: I have seen some reports that there is microheterogeneity in tubulin. Do you see that in *Tetrahymena*?

HAYES: Yes we do. SDS gel electrohoresis resolves *Tetrahymena* tubulin preparations into two components analogous to the alfa and beta fractions observed in numerous other studies with tubulins from many sources. Recent work has shown that the alfa component can be resolved into at least five, and the beta component into three subfractions by electrofocusing (Wetman *et al.* 1972, Piperno & Luck 1976, Kobayashi & Mohri 1977). We find the same microheterogeneity when the alfa and beta components of *Tetrahymena* tubulin are analyzed by electrofocusing.

RICH: In metazoa there is a similar story with the actins. And there it has been shown that there are about five actins; furthermore, you get differences depending upon where in the life cycle you look at the cells. I don't know whether you get differences in terms of the life cycle in protozoa?

HAYES: We have done no experiments bearing on this possibility.

RICH: I don't suppose anyone has studied tubulin synthesis in trypanosomes which possess a very highly developed subpellicular cytoskeleton composed of microtubules?

HAYES: I believe there is some work going on in Brazil in that direction, but I don't know at what state it is.

HOGNESS: Is there anything known in this organism or others about the gene frequency of tubulin?

HAYES: Not that I know of.

Wetman, G. B., Carlson, K. & Rosenbaum, J. L. (1972) *J. Cell Biol.* 54, 540–555.
Piperno, G. & Luck, D. J. (1976) *J. Biol. Chem.* 251, 2161–2167.
Kobayashi, K. & Mohri, H. (1977) *J. Mol. Biol.* 116, 613–617.

Low Molecular Weight RNA Components: Occurrence, Metabolism and Genes

Sune Frederiksen & Per Hellung-Larsen

Low molecular weight RNA components (LMW RNA) with a molecular weight between that of 5S RNA and 18S RNA were found in mammalian cells more than 10 years ago (Galibert *et al.* 1965, Peacock & Dingman 1967, Knight & Darnell 1967, Dingman & Peacock 1968, Prestayko & Busch 1968, Weinberg & Peacock 1968, Prestayko & Busch 1968, Weinberg & Penman 1968, Larsen *et al.* 1969). The components had a chain length from 80 to 300 nucleotides, were metabolically stable and were localized in the nuclei. LMW RNA has recently been reviewed by Naora (1977) and Hellung-Larsen (1977). A profile of LMW RNA components obtained from mammalian cells is shown in Fig. 1. This figure shows the gel-electrophoretic pattern of RNA extracted from Ehrlich ascites nuclei. The three components with a mobility between that of tRNA and 5S RNA are called H_1, H_2 and H_3 and they correspond to the three 4.5S RNA components isolated from Novikoff hepatoma cells, one of which has been sequenced (Ro-Choi *et al.* 1972). The components migrating slower than 5S RNA are called D, C, A and L using the nomenclature of Weinberg & Penman (1968) and they correspond to U_1, U_2, U_3 and 8S RNA (?) respectively, in the nomenclature of Ro-Choi & Busch (1974). U_1, U_2 and U_3 from Novikoff hepatoma cells have a Cap in the 5' end (Reddy *et al.* 1974, Shibata *et al.* 1975, Busch *et al.* 1975). U_1 and U_2 have been completely sequenced (Reddy *et al.* 1974, Shibata *et al.* 1975) and it was shown that the $m_3^{2,2,7}$ guanylic acid initially found in LMW RNA by Saponara & Enger (1969) is actually part of the Cap at the 5'-

Department of Biochemistry B, Panum Institute, University of Copenhagen, Copenhagen, Denmark

SPECIFIC EUKARYOTIC GENES, Alfred Benzon Symposium 13, Munksgaard 1979

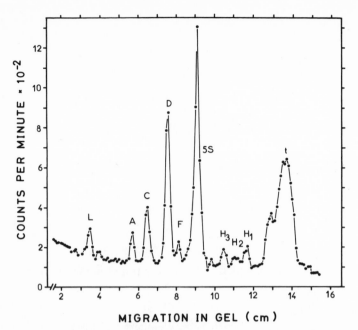

MIGRATION IN GEL (cm)

Fig. 1. Gelelectrophoretic migration of LMW RNA components L, A, C, D, F and H extracted from Ehrlich ascites nuclei. Ehrlich ascites cells were labeled for 2 days *in vivo* with uridine-5-^{3}H. Nuclei were prepared by a freeze-thaw technique and RNA was extracted with phenol-phosphate buffer at 0° and analyzed on a 13% polyacrylamide gel (Hellung-Larsen & Frederiksen 1972).

end with a tripyrophosphate linkage (Cory & Adams 1975) to the neighboring methylated nucleotide. U_1, U_2 and U_3 are methylated and U_2 contain 13 pseudouridylic acids thus being the most modified RNA molecule known so far. Components L, A, C and D from Ehrlich ascites cells each amounts to 0.2% up to 0.7% of the total cellular RNA (Hellung-Larsen & Frederiksen 1972). Separation under denaturing conditions on different types of gels indicates that these four components are homogeneous and that D consists of two components (Hellung-Larsen & Frederiksen 1975).

Subcellular localization

The LMW RNA components were originally found in the cell nuclei and further fractionation of the nuclei demonstrated that components D and C were preferentially localized in the nucleoplasm and A in the nucleolus (Weinberg & Penman 1968, Larsen *et al.* 1969, Prestayko *et al.* 1970, Hellung-Larsen & Frederiksen 1972). When BHK cells were separated into cytoplasmic and nuclear fractions by different aqueous homogenization techniques, we repeatedly found that about 95% of L and 40–60% of A, C and D were in the cytoplasmic fraction (Fig. 2). In order to confirm these results we have performed similar fractionations in nonaqueous media, which will prevent leaking out of nuclear material into the cytoplasm. Rat liver cells were separated into a nuclear and a cytoplasmic fraction by the nonaqueous technique of Siebert (1967a,b). The presence of LMW RNA in the cytoplasm is shown in Fig. 3. In other experiments where the optical density of RNA was recorded, the profile showed also the presence of component A. Calculations show that more than 80% of L is in the

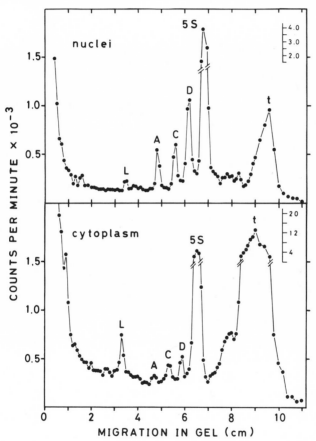

Fig. 2. LMW RNA patterns of the nuclear and the cytoplasmic fractions of BHK cells. The cells were labeled in spinner cultures for 20 h with ^{32}P-orthophosphate and then homogenized in C-buffer with triton-X-100. RNA was extracted with phenol at 0° and analyzed on a 10% gel (Frederiksen *et al.* In preparation).

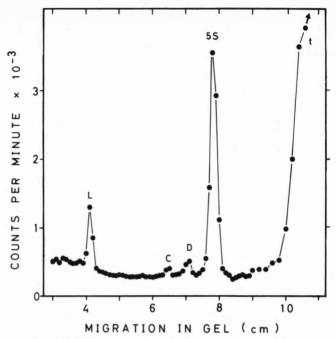

MIGRATION IN GEL (cm)

Fig. 3. Demonstration of LMW RNA components L, C and D in a cytoplasm-preparation from rat liver cells obtained by a nonaqueous technique. Rats were injected i.p. with 2.5 mC$_i$ orotic acid-5-^{3}H 24 h before the liver was removed by a freeze-clamp technique and freeze-dried. The material was homogenized in petrol ether and separated into a nuclear and several cytoplasmic fractions by repeated centrifugations in mixtures of cyclohexane and tetrachloromethane as described by Siebert (1967a,b). The cytoplasmic fraction of highest purity was extracted with phenol-acetate buffer-SDS at 0° and the RNA purified and analyzed on a 10% gel (Frederiksen *et al.* In preparation).

cytoplasm and that 40–60% of the total cellular amounts of C and D is in this fraction. These results do not neccesarily contradict the conclusions made from other investigations that LMW RNA is associated with the chromatin fraction (Prestayko & Busch 1968, Marzluff *et al.* 1975), is found in RNP particles containing the hnRNA (Sekeris & Niessing 1975, Deimel *et al.* 1977) and that LMW RNA is associated with the nuclear skeleton (Zieve & Penman 1976, Miller *et al.* 1978).

Precursors
In mammalian cells mRNA, rRNA and tRNA are formed from larger precursors. It was of interest to know whether the LMW RNAs are also formed from larger unstable precursors. In BHK cells we have demonstrated that components

A and C are formed from precursors which are about 10 nucleotides longer than the mature product and that D is formed from a precursor about five nucleotides longer (Fig. 4). Component L is apparently synthesized in its mature form or processed very fast (Frederiksen & Hellung-Larsen 1975). The presence of precursors for LMW RNA is indicated by the following observations: 1) Pulse-labeling experiments show the presence of components slightly larger than A, C and D. 2) The precursor A and precursor C could be quantitatively chased into mature A and mature C, respectively. 3) More precursor relative to mature LMW RNA was found in cells grown at suboptimal temperatures. Previously it has been shown that the precursor rRNA/rRNA ratio and the precursor tRNA/tRNA ratio are increased in cells grown at suboptimal temperatures (Stevens & Amos 1971, 1972). Two short-lived small RNA components have been demonstrated in the cytoplasm of HeLa cells (Eliceiri 1974, Eliceiri & Gurney 1978) and it is suggested that they are precursors for C and D.

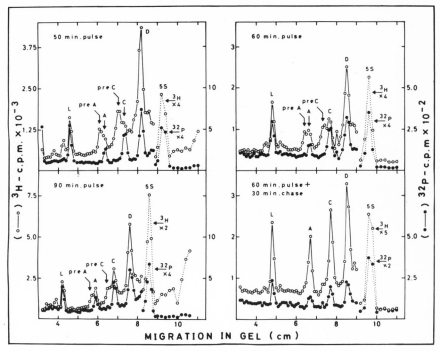

Fig. 4. Demonstration of precursors to LMW RNAs. BHK-21 cells were labeled in spinner cultures for 20 h with ³²P-orthophosphate. Uridine-5-³H was added and incubation continued as indicated in the figures. The actinomycin D treatment was started after 60 min of labeling and continued until 90 min after addition of uridine-5-³H. The cells were extracted with phenol-reticulocyte standard buffer at 0° and RNA analyzed on a 10% gel.

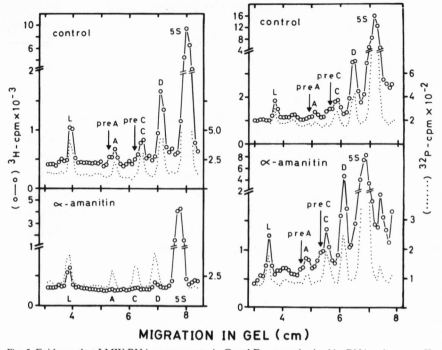

Fig. 5. Evidence that LMW RNA components A, C and D are synthesized by RNA polymerase II.
Left part: Hamster cells were grown for 20 h with ³²P-orthophosphate, *a*-amanitin (5 μg/ml) was
added; and 4 h later uridine-5-³H was added and the incubation was continued for further 90 min.
RNA was extracted and analyzed as described in Fig. 4.

Right part: Mutant hamster cells (Ama-1) (Chan *et al.* 1972, Ingles *et al.* 1976) were used in this
experiment.This mutant cell line has a polymerase II which is 800-fold more resistant to *a*-amanitin
than the wild type. The cells were labeled 4 h with ³²P-orthophosphate and then further incubated
with *a*-amanitin (5 μg/ml) for 19 h. Uridine-5-³H was added and incubation continued for 90 min.
RNA was extracted and analyzed as described in Fig. 4 (Gram Jensen *et al.* In preparation).

Polymerase

Three different polymerases exist in mammalian cells. Polymerase I catalyzes
the synthesis of pre-rRNA, polymerase II catalyzes the synthesis of hnRNA and
polymerase III catalyzes the synthesis of 5S and tRNA (reviewed by Chambon
1975). What enzyme catalyzes the synthesis of LMW RNA? We have approached
this question indirectly by studying the RNA metabolism in cells treated with
different inhibitors of DNA, RNA and protein synthesis such as: cytosine
arabinoside, *a*-amanitin, formycin A, 5-azacytidine, 5-fluorouridine, adriamy-
cin, daunorubicine, 5,6-dichloro-1-*β*-D-ribofuranosylbenzimadazole, 3'-deoxy-
adenosine, actinomycin D, emetine, cycloheximide and puromycin. The drug

having the most characteristic differential inhibitory effect on RNA synthesis is a-amanitin. Under conditions of long preincubation periods as described by Kedinger & Simard (1974) where the synthesis of rRNA, tRNA or 5S RNA is not inhibited, the synthesis of A, C and D is profoundly inhibited and even blocked (Fig. 5, left part and Table I). Under these conditions the synthesis of hnRNA is also inhibited (Frederiksen *et al.* 1978). The results suggest that polymerase II catalyzes the synthesis of A, C and D. This conclusion is supported by the differential inhibitory effect of actinomycin D and 3'-deoxyadenosine on RNA synthesis in BHK cells (Frederiksen *et al.* 1974). Under conditions where the synthesis of rRNA is strongly inhibited, the incorporation of uridine-5-^{3}H into LMW RNA is increased and the synthesis of 5S RNA is only moderately affected. The results are summarized in Table II. The conclusion made on the basis of these inhibitor studies does not agree with the results of Zieve *et al.* (1977). Based on results obtained with camptothecin, toyocamycin, actinomycin D and different alterations in HeLa cell metabolism, these authors conclude that A, C and D are synthesized by polymerase I. Studies with isolated nuclei (Udvardy & Seifart 1976)and nuclei added polymerase III (Sklar & Roeder 1977) suggest that polymerase III is the enzyme responsible for the synthesis of LMW RNA. On the background of this controversy we have approached by a different method the question about what enzyme catalyzes LMW RNA. A mutant cell line of Chinese hamster ovary cells (Chan *et al.* 1972) contains a polymerase II which is 800-fold more resistant to a-amanitin (Ingles *et al.* 1976). When this mutant cell line is treated with a-amanitin in concentrations from 5 μg up to 200

Table I

Effect of a-amanitin on the synthesis of different RNAcomponents

Preincubation (h)	Specific activity in % control							
	28S	18S	L	A	C	D	5S	t-RNA
2	-	-	93	37	31	52	89	80
3	110	89	92	50	47	49	100	110
4	100	95	88	14	10	17	84	93
5	115	101	63	10	12	16	129	81
7	82	56	25	0	0	0	108	121
17	6	7	27	0	0	0	83	43

BHK-21 cells were preincubated with a-amanitin (5 μg/ml for the time indicated. Uridine-5-^{3}H was added and incubation continued for 90 min. RNA was extracted with RSB and phenol and analyzed on polyacrylamide gels. Specific activity was determined from the ^{3}H cpm in the peak divided by the area of the corresponding absorbance peak.

Table II

Effect of actinomycin C and 3'-deoxyadenosine on the incorporation of uridine-5-^3H *into different RNA components*

	Specific activity in % of control						
	28S	18S	L	A	C	D	5S
actinomycin D (µg/ml)							
0.025	2	8	139	288	267	238	55
0.05	0	2	192	59	93	92	58
0.10	0	0	55	0	0	0	53
0.20	0	1	11	0	0	0	40
3'-deoxyadenosine (mM)							
0.02	63	68	150	188	208	227	89
0.05	34	38	119	184	200	181	81
0.10	8	22	39	50	73	80	77
0.20	3	6	7	3	5	10	31

BHK-21 cells were preincubated with actinomycin D for 30 min or 3'-deoxyadenosine for 35 min and uridine-5-^3H then added. After 20 h of incubation RNA was extracted and analyzed as described in Table I.

µg per ml, no effect on the synthesis of LMW RNA is seen (Fig. 5, right part). This evidence, together with the above-mentioned results, allows us to conclude that polymerase II catalyzes the synthesis of LMW RNA components A, C and D. The inhibitor studies indicate that component L may be synthesized by polymerase III but this can not be definitely decided upon at the present stage of knowledge.

Occurrence in different species

LMW RNAs have been studied in different eukaryotic cells (reviewed by Naora 1977). For this reason we found it relevant to study how similar the pattern of LMW RNAs is in different cells. It would however be of interest also to get an insight into the pattern of LMW RNAs in cells from different levels of the taxonomy and to which extent such a pattern might be conserved during evolution. We have compared the gel-electrophoretic mobility of LMW RNAs from different vertebrate cells (Fig. 6, right part). The patterns are strikingly similar in that they all show components L, A, C and D in about the same quantities. Component A shows a different mobility for some species. In several cases different tissues were analyzed from one species but no tissue specificity was observed. The only exception to this rule is the nucleated erythrocytes from

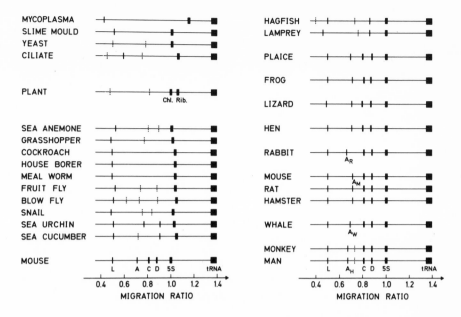

Fig. 6. Occurrence of LMW RNA components in different species.

Schematic presentation of the gel-electrophoretic migrations of the LMW RNA components from different unicellular organisms and invertebrates (left part) and vertebrates (right part). The migration ratios are given relative to Ehrlich ascites 5S RNA which is set to 1.00. Electrophoresis was performed in normal 10% polyacrylamide gels since denaturing conditions (8 M urea) give a poor separation of components A and C (Hellung-Larsen & Frederiksen 1975). Part of this work has been published (Hellung-Larsen & Frederiksen 1977).

Table III

Effect of cycloheximide on the synthesis of different RNA components

Concentration	Incubation	Specific activity in % of control						
μg/ml	hours	28S	18S	L	A	C	D	5S
0.5	3	18	31	42	13	52	50	53
0.2	15	24	18	48	0	36	56	40
0.5	15	25	13	31	0	39	52	34
0.5	21	55	52	60	19	114	92	83

BHK-21 cells were preincubated with cycloheximide for 15 min before addition of uridine-5-^{3}H and incubation then continued for the time indicated. RNA was extracted and analyzed as described in Table I.

hen and frog. These cells have an inactive nucleolus and component A is absent.

The pattern of LMW RNA at lower levels of the taxonomy is remarkably different from the vertebrate pattern (Fig. 6, left part). The pattern of LMW RNAs from invertebrates shows fewer components and each of them accounts for a smaller amount of the total cellular RNA. Component L or its counterpart is, however, present in cells from all taxonomic levels. A series of 10–12 LMW RNAs has been demonstrated in *Drosophila melanogaster* (Rubin & Hogness 1975). Some of the Drosophila LMW RNAs have been compared gel-electrophoretically with mammalian LMW RNA and found to have different mobilities (Zieve *et al.* 1977).

DISCUSSION

Much information has been published about LMW RNAs during the last 10 years. There are however only few biological properties to be agreed about even if one is restricted to the four major LMW RNAs of the 13 previously found in mammalian cell and does not include the new class of small nuclear RNA molecules recently described by Benecke & Penman (1977). What has been demonstrated in two or more laboratories is that LMW RNA components L, A, C and D are present in mammalian cells, they are not degradation products, they are metabolically stable, a large fraction of the cellular amounts of A, C and D and only a small fraction of L is present in the nuclear compartment. The following important questions are still not settled:

Nomenclature? Which one of the seven different nomenclatures used for LMW RNAs in vertebrate cells should be used?

Shuttling RNAs? The vertebrate type of LMW RNAs has been demonstrated in amoeba and these components shown to "shuttle" between nucleus and cytoplasm (Goldstein & Ko 1974). However, the presence of vertebrate LMW RNA in amoeba does not fit into the scheme of LMW RNAs in lower organisms which we have presented.

Polymerase? Polymerase I or III has previously been shown to synthesize LMW RNA and we conclude that polymerase II is the responsible enzyme.

Cellular localization? The distribution of A, C and D between the nucleus and the cytoplasm is still a matter of controversy as is the intranuclear localization.

Number of genes? It was shown that BHK cells have about 2000 gene copies for each of the LMW RNAs (Engberg *et al.* 1974) but the number of copies in myeloma cells varies from 100 to 2000 (Marzluff *et al.* 1975).

Function? The biological function of LMW RNAs is not known. One possible functional connection is seen between nucleolar function – the synthesis of rRNA – and component A. In the nucleated erythrocytes from chicken and frog which have inactive nucleoli, component A is absent from the cells. In cells where nucleolar function is inhibited by cycloheximide (Table III) or toyocamycin (Hamelin *et al.* 1973), the synthesis of component A and rRNA both are more affected than are the synthesis of other cellular RNA components. In sea urchin embryos one LMW RNA component is also connected with nucleolar appearance and functioning (Frederiksen & Hellung-Larsen 1974).

The metabolically stable LMW RNA components A, C and D and the high molecular weight heterodisperse nuclear RNA now seem to have three features in common. They are both capped although with different caps (Fernandez – Munoz *et al.* 1977), they are synthesized by RNA polymerase II and they appear in the same nuclear particles (Deimel *et al.* 1977) or are very closely associated to hnRNA particles in the nuclear skeleton (Miller *et al.* 1978).

REFERENCES

Benecke, B.J. & Penman, S. (1977) A new class of small nuclear RNA molecules synthesized by a type I RNA polymerase in HeLa cells. *Cell* 12, 939–946.

Busch, H., Choi, Y.C., Nazar, R.N. & Ro-Choi, T.S. (1975) In: *Biochemistry of the Cell Nucleus* Vol. 33, pp. 125–138. (Hidvégi, E. J., Sümegi, J. & Venetianer, P.)

Chambon, P. (1975) In: *Ann. Rev. Biochem.* Vol 44, pp. 613–638 eds. (Snell, E.E., Boyer, P.D., Meister, A. & Richardson, C. C.)

Chan, V.L., Whitmore, G.F. & Siminovitch, L. (1972) Mammalian cells with altered forms of RNA polymerase II. *Proc. Natl. Acad. Sci. USA* 69, 3119–3123.

Cory, S. & Adams, J.R. (1975) Modified 5'-termini in small nuclear RNAs of mouse myeloma cells. *Mol. Biol. Reports* 2, 287–294.

Deimel, B., Louis, Ch. & Sekeris, C.E. (1977) The presence of small molecular weight RNAs in nuclear ribonucleoprotein particles carrying HnRNA. *FEBS Letters* 73, 80–84.

Dingman, C.W. & Peacock, A.C. (1968) Analytical studies on nuclear ribonucleic acids using polyacrylamide gel electrophoresis. *Biochem.* 7, 659–668.

Eliceiri, G.L. (1974) Short-lived, small RNAs in the cytoplasm of HeLa cells. *Cell* 3, 11–14.

Eliceiri, G.L. & Gurney Jr., T. (1978) Subcellular location of precursors to small nuclear RNA species C and D and of newly synthesized 5S RNA in HeLa cells. *Biochem. Biophys. Res. Com.* 81, 915–919.

Engberg, J., Hellung-Larsen, P. & Frederiksen, S. (1974) Isolation and DNA-RNA hybridization properties of small molecular weight nuclear RNA components from baby hamster kidney cells. *Eur. J. Biochem.* 41, 321–328.

Fernandez-Munoz, R., Lavi, U. & Darnell, J.E. (1977) 5' Caps in hnRNA: absence of $m_3^{2,2,7}$ G and size distribution of capped molecules. *Nuc. Acid. Res.* 4, 3357–3369.

Frederiksen, S. & Hellung-Larsen, P. (1974) Synthesis of small molecular weight RNA components during the early stages of sea urchin embryo development. *Exp. Cell Res.* 89, 217–227.

Frederiksen, S. & Hellung-Larsen, P. (1975) Precursors to small molecular weight RNA components. *FEBS Letters* 58, 374–378.

Frederiksen, S., Pedersen, I.R., Hellung-Larsen, P. & Engberg, J. (1974) Metabolic studies of small molecular weight nuclear RNA components in BHK-21 cells. *Biochim. Biophys. Acta* 340, 64–76.

Frederiksen, S., Hellung-Larsen, P. & Gram Jensen, E. (1978) The differential inhibitory effect of α-amanitin on the synthesis of low molecular weight RNA components in BHK cells. *FEBS Letters* 87, 227–231.

Galibert, F., Lelong, J.C., Larsen, Ch.J. & Boiron, M. (1965) Position of 5-S RNA among cellular ribonucleic acids. *Biochim. Biophys. Acta* 142, 89–98.

Goldstein, L. & Ko, C. (1974) Electrophoretic characterization of shuttling and nonshuttling small nuclear RNAs *Cell* 2, 259–269.

Hamelin, R., Larsen, C.J. & Tavitian, A. (1973) Effects of actinomycin D, toyocamycin and cycloheximide on the synthesis of low molecular weight nuclear RNAs in HeLa cells. *Eur. J. Biochim.* 35, 350–356.

Hellung-Larsen, P. (1977) Low molecular weight RNA components in eukaryotic cells (Thesis, Copenhagen, FADL's Forlag).

Hellung-Larsen, P. & Frederiksen, S. (1972) Small molecular weight RNA components in Ehrlich ascites tumor cells. *Biochim. Biophys. Acta* 262, 290–307.

Hellung-Larsen, P. & Frederiksen, S. (1975) Studies on the homogeneity and conformational states of small molecular weight nuclear RNA components. *Int. J. biochem.* 6, 361–370.

Hellung-Larsen, P. & Frederiksen, S. (1977) Occurrence and properties of low molecular weight RNA components from cells at different taxonomic levels. *Comp. Biochem. Physiol.* 58B, 273–281.

Ingles, G.J., Guialis, A., Lam, J. & Siminovitch, L. (1976) α-Amanitin resistance of RNA polymerase II in mutant Chinese hamster ovary cell lines. *J. Biol. Chem.* 251, 2729–2734.

Kedinger, C. & Simard, R. (1974) The action of α-amanitin on RNA synthesis in Chinese hamster ovary cells. *J. Cell Biol.* 63, 831–842.

Knight, Jr., E. & Darnell, J.E. (1967) Distribution of 5S RNA in HeLa cells. *J. Mol. Biol.* 28, 491–502.

Larsen, Ch.J., Galibert, F., Hampe, A & Boiron, M. (1968) Fractionnement par electrophorèse sur gel polyacrylamide des RNA de faible poids moléculaire présente dans les noyaux de celluleles KB. *Compt. Rend. Acad. Sci.* Paris 267, 110–113.

Larsen, C.J., Galibert, F., Hampe, A. & Boiron, M. (1969) Etude des RNA nucléaires de faible poids moléculaire de la cellule KB. *Bull. Soc. Chim. Biol.* 51, 649–668.

Marzluff Jr.W.F., White, E.L., Benjamin, R. & Huang, R.C.C. (1975) Low mulecular weight RNA species from chromatin. *Biochem.* 16, 3715–3724.

Miller, T.E., Huang, C.Y. & Pogo, A.O. (1978) Rat liver nuclear skeleton and small molecular weight RNA species. *J. Cell Biol.* 76, 692–704.

Naora, H. (1977) In: *The Ribonucleic Acids* pp. 62–71 eds. (Stewart, P.R. & Letham, D.S. Springer Verlag.

Peacock, A.C. & Dingman, C.W. (1967) Resolution of multiple ribonucleic acid species by polyacrylamide gel electrophoresis. *Biochem.* 6, 1818–1827.

Prestayko, A.W. & Busch, H. (1968) Low molecular weight RNA of the chromatin fraction from Novikoff hepatoma and rat liver nuclei. *Biochim. Biophys. Acta* 169, 327–337.

Prestayko, A.W., Tonato, M. & Busch, H. (1970) Low molecular weight RNA associated with 28S nucleolar RNA *J. Mol. Biol.* 47, 505–515.

Reddy, R., Ro-Choi, T.S., Henning, D. & Busch, H. (1974) Primary sequence of Novikoff hepatoma ascites cells. *J. Biol. Chem.* 249, 6486–6494.

Ro-Choi, T.S., Reddy, R., Henning, D., Takano, T., Taylor, C.W & Busch, H. (1972) Nucleotide sequence of 4.5S ribonucleic acid₁ of Novikoff hepatoma cell nuclei. *J. Biol. Chem.* 247, 3205–3220.

Ro-Choi, T.S. & Busch, H. (1974) In: *The Molecular Biology of Cancer* pp. 241–276. ed. Busch, H.

Rubin, G.M. & Hogness, D.S. (1975) Effect of heat shock on the synthesis of low molecular weight RNAs in Drosophila: Accumulation of a novel form of 5S RNA. *Cell* 6, 207–213.

Saponara, A.G. & Enger, M.D. (1969) Occurrence of N^2, N^2, 7-trimethylguanosine in minor RNA species of mammalian cell line. *Nature* 223, 1365–1366.

Sekeris, C.E. & Niessing, J. (1975) Evidence for the existence of a structural RNA component in the nuclear ribonucleoprotein particles containing heterogeneous RNA. *Biochem. Biophys. Res. Comm.* 62, 642–650.

Shibata, H., Ro-Choi, T.S., Reddy, R., Choi, Y.C., Henning, D. & Busch, H. (1975) The primary nucleotide sequence of nuclear U-2 ribonucleic acid *J. Biol. Chem.* 250, 3909–3920.

Siebert, G. (1967a) In: *Methods in Cancer Res.* ed. Busch H. Vol. 2, pp. 287–301.

Siebert, G. (1967b) In: *Methods in Cancer Res.* ed. Busch H. Vol. 3, pp. 47–59.

Sklar, V.E.F. & Roeder, R.G. (1977) Transcription of specific genes in isolated nuclei by exogenous RNA polymerases. *Cell* 10, 405–414.

Stevens, R.H. & Amos, H. (1971) RNA metabolism in HeLa cells at reduced temperature. I.Modified processing of 45S RNA. *J. Cell Biol.* 50, 818–829.

Stevens, R.H. & Amos, H. (1972) RNA metabolism in HeLa cells at reduced temperature. II. Steps in the processing of transfer RNA. *J. Cell Biol.* 52, 1–7.

Udvardy, A. & Seifart, K.H. (1976) Transcription of specific genes in isolated nuclei from HeLa cells *in vitro. Eur. J. Biochem.* 62, 353–363.

Weinberg, R.A. & Penman, S. (1968) Small molecular weight monodisperse nuclear RNA. *J. Mol. Biol.* 38, 289–304.

Zapisek, W.F., Saponara, A.G. & Enger, M.D. (1969) Low molecular weight methylated ribonucleic acid species from Chinese hamster ovary cell I. Isolation and characterization. *Biochem.* 8, 1170–1181.

Zieve, G. & Penman, S. (1976) Small RNA species of the HeLa cell: Metabolism and subcellular localization. *Cell* 8, 19–31.

Zieve, G., Benecke, B.J. & Penman, S. (1977) Synthesis of two classes of small RNA species *in vivo* and *in vitro. Biochem.* 16, 4520–4525.

DISCUSSION

WEISSMANN: If I understand you correctly, all the inhibition experiments with α-amanitine were done by incubating for a rather long period of time. Is it not possible that you have some cascade mechanism, that in fact the inhibition is not at the level of polymerase II, but due to a more general damage?

FREDERIKSEN: But you see the effect already after 2 h. Then the synthesis of LMW RNA is inhibited and only several hours later is ribosomal RNA inhibited and the synthesis of tRNA and 5S RNA is still not inhibited. There has been a lot of confusion in the literature about the effect of α-amanitin on whole cells, also because tissue culture cells have been compared to liver cells and in liver cells α-amanitin is apparently taken up very quickly and causes a rapid inhibition of RNA synthesis. When you inject α-amanitin into rats you can not see a differential inhibitory effect on RNA synthesis in liver cells. Kedinger & Simard (1974) studied the effect of α-amanitin on Chinese hamster ovary cells in culture. They found that these cells should be incubated for relatively long periods in order to see an effect of α-amanitin. The synthesis of extranucleolar RNA was first inhibited and after 8 h of treatment which caused severe fragmentation of the nucleoli, however, the synthesis of ribosomal RNA was still not inhibited. These results agree well with our data. If there is a kind of cascade reaction the inhibition of LMW RNA must be an early event.

WEISSMANN: I think it is interesting that it is inhibited. The question is whether it is a primary effect or a secondary effect. Have you never experimented with isolated nuclei or with ruptured cells?

FREDERIKSEN: No, we have not used isolated nuclei.

RICH: Do these small RNAs have secondary structures, e.g. are they partially digested by S1 nuclease?

FREDERIKSEN: They have a secondary structure since we can show different conformers by gel electrophoresis. We have not tried S1 nuclease but they are degraded by ribonuclease, although they may be degraded somewhat slower than other RNA species. The 4.5S RNA I can fit into a cloverleaf structure with partially double-stranded regions as shown by Ro-Choi & Busch (1974). This component could possibly be the one described earlier by Dr. Jelinek although this has not been proven.

JELINEK: We find that the little RNA we have is actually completely susceptible to S1.

LEICK: The pattern of occurrence of these RNA components in eukaryotes does not seem to be the same when you go down the evolutionary scale – Can you say anything about the difference in pattern between different groups of eukaryotes?

FREDERIKSEN: The vertebrates show a very similar pattern, but if you go down to lower levels of the taxonomy the pattern of LMW RNA is quite different. You see fewer components and in less amounts than in vertebrate cells. Only component L or its counterpart is conserved.

Structure and Function of a Gene Product: Yeast Phenylalanine Transfer RNA

Alexander Rich

The transfer RNA (tRNA) molecule is an ancient component of biological systems. It is likely that it arose some 4 billion years ago in the early prebiotic period, during which time the increasing development of complex organic molecules led to the creation of polynucleotide chains which had the capacity to contain information as well as carry out molecular self-replication. Although the nucleic acids are effectively selected for these functions, they are unable to express genetic information. The major mode for expressing genetic information is in the synthesis of proteins which provide the large variety of complex chemical environments needed to create catalytic activities and structural features which are the molecular basis of living systems. The tRNA molecule acts at the crossroads between the information-containing polynucleotide chains and the proteins which express genetic information. At one end of the tRNA molecule the three anticodon bases interact with messenger RNA; at the other end the molecule is attached to the growing polypeptide chain during protein synthesis. This molecule is possibly as ancient a component of biological systems as the system of expressing genetic information through the polymerization of amino acids.

The tRNA molecules are active in protein synthesis where they participate in two major activities: aminoacylation which takes place on the surface of the aminoacyl synthetases, and protein synthesis which takes place inside ribosomes. In a sense, there is a paradox in trying to understand this central biochemical function of tRNA. On the one hand, the tRNA molecules must be sufficiently unique to be discriminated by different aminoacyl synthetases. At the same time they must be sufficiently identical so that they can all go through the same

Department of Biology, Massachusetts Institute of Technology, Cambridge, Mass. 02139 USA.

SPECIFIC EUKARYOTIC GENES, Alfred Benzon Symposium 13, Munksgaard 1979

ribosomal apparatus during protein synthesis. We would like to understand the manner in which this twofold chore is carried out in an effective and relatively error-free mode.

In 1965 Holley and co-workers reported the sequence of the first tRNA molecule. They noted that there were segments of the polynucleotide chain which appeared complementary if the chain folded back upon itself. One of these foldings has given rise to the cloverleaf diagram in which sequences are represented as a series of stems and loops, the stems largely composed of complementary bases with Watson-Crick hydrogen bonding similar to those which are found in the DNA double helix. As additional sequences were reported, it became apparent that this cloverleaf folding was expressing something of a fundamental nature concerning the molecule. Up to the present, over 100 different tRNA molecules have been sequenced and Fig. 1 shows the cloverleaf sequence for yeast phenylalanine tRNA (Barrell & Clark 1974, Rich & RajBhandary 1976).

There are a number of invariant and semi-unvariant nucleotides in all tRNA

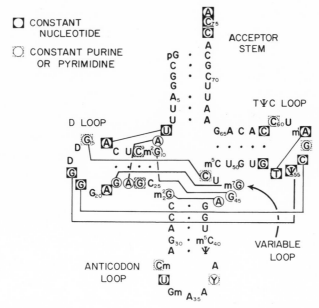

Fig. 1. Cloverleaf diagram of the nucleotide sequence of yeast tRNA[Phe]. Tertiary base-base hydrogen-bonding interactions are shown by solid lines, which indicate one, two, or three hydrogen bonds. The invariant and semivariant positions are indicated by solid and dashed boxes around the bases. Y_{37} is a hypermodified base.

sequences. The reasons behind this large number of conserved residues remained unknown until the elucidation of the three-dimensional structure of yeast phenylalanine tRNA (tRNA^{Phe}).

It is interesting to note that the cloverleaf arrangement plus the large number of invariant positions imply considerable constraints on the three-dimensional form of the molecule. Prior to the elucidation of the three-dimensional structure of yeast tRNA^{Phe}, a number of attempts were made to anticipate the conformation by building various models of tRNA folding. These models usually maintained the stem regions as double helices and additional tertiary base-base interactions were used to stabilize the three-dimensional conformation. None of the proposed models was correct. The principal reason was the fact that the proposed models emphasized Watson-Crick hydrogen bonding in the tertiary interactions between residues which were not in stems. There are nine base-base tertiary hydrogen bonding interactions found in the three-dimensional structure of yeast tRNA^{Phe} shown by the solid lines in Fig. 1; however, only one of them is a Watson-Crick interaction and the other eight involve alternative types of hydrogen bonding. Watson-Crick hydrogen bonds are of great utility in building a regular helical structure, but the hydrogen bonding potential of bases is much more varied and it is utilized in many different ways in building the highly irregular and non-repeating interactions found in the globular coiling of the tRNA polynucleotide chain.

CRYSTALS AND STRUCTURE

Transfer RNA molecules were first crystallized in 1968 independently in several different laboratories. A large number of species were found to form crystals and this gave rise to optimism that the three-dimensional structure would be known in a relatively short time period. At this time, however, it was not generally appreciated that all of the crystal forms had one defect in common: they were all disordered. In protein crystallography it is recognized that one needs to have an X-ray diffraction pattern with a resolution of between 2 and 3Å in order to trace the polypeptide chain. In order to fix the position of the bases, sugars and phosphate groups, a comparable resolution is required.

The origin of the disorder in tRNA crystals is not readily apparent. A large part of it however must be due to the polyelectrolytic nature of the molecule. These molecules have from 75 to 90 negative charges and the exact ordering of the tRNA molecules in the crystal lattice is very sensitive to the nature and

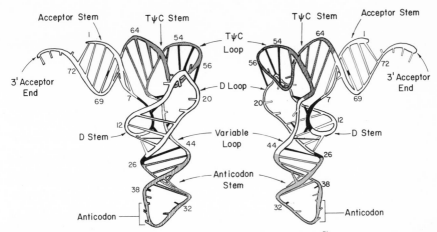

Fig. 2. A schematic diagram showing two side views of yeast tRNA^Phe. The ribose-phosphate backbone is depicted as a coiled tube, and the numbers refer to nucleotide residues in the sequence. Shading is different in different parts of the molecules, with residues 8 and 9 in black. Hydrogen bonding interactions between bases are shown as cross-rungs. Tertiary interactions between bases are shown as solid black rungs, which indicate either one, two, or three hydrogen bonds between them as described in the text. Those bases that are not involved in hydrogen bonding to other bases are shown as shortened rods attached to the coiled backbone.

number of cations found in the crystallizing mixture. It is likely that the polyelectrolytic nature of the molecule gives rise to frequent mistakes in the building of the lattice. After much effort we reported in 1971 that if one added the oligo cation spermine to yeast tRNA^Phe, an orthorhombic crystal could be formed which yielded an X-ray diffraction pattern with a resolution of nearly 2Å (Kim *et al.* 1971).

In early 1973 (Kim *et al.*), the folding of the polynucleotide chain was traced from an electron density map at 4Å resolution. The tracing was made possible at this resolution because the electron-dense phosphate groups could be seen even at this low resolution. The folding of the chain (Fig. 2) was highly unusual and had not been anticipated by any of the model builders. The stem regions which had been assumed to be in the form of RNA double helices from the sequence data were indeed in that form. Furthermore, the stems had an unusual organization. The molecule was L-shaped with the acceptor stem and TψC stem forming one limb of the L while the D stem and anticodon stem formed the other limb. The 3' terminal adenosine to which the amino acid was attached was at one end of the L while the anticodon was at the other end, some 76Å away. The molecule was fairly flat, about 20–25Å thick. Although the coiling of the chain could be seen at 4Å resolution, the details of the tertiary interactions had to await the results of a higher resolution analysis.

In 1974 (Kim *et al.* 1974a) the analysis was extended to 3Å and it revealed a number of tertiary interactions (Figs. 1 and 2). In particular, it showed the detailed manner in which the TψC and D loops interact in order to stabilize the corner of the molecule. In 1974, Robertus *et al.* also presented 3Å results for the same spermine-stabilized yeast tRNA^{Phe} in the monoclinic crystal lattice. This showed a virtually identical folding of the molecule.

It can be seen in Fig. 1 that many of the base-base tertiary hydrogen bonding interactions involve the invariant or semi-invariant nucleotides. This suggests the structure of yeast tRNA^{Phe} may be a generalized model for understanding the structure of all tRNAs.

At the present time the analysis has been extended to 2.5Å resolution and crystallographic refinement calculations have been carried out to the point where many details concerning the tertiary interactions in the molecule can be observed. These results are illustrated diagrammatically in Fig. 2. Fig. 3 shows two views of the entire molecule.

The major structural unit in yeast tRNA^{Phe} is the RNA double helix which comes from the cloverleaf stems. These are very close to an RNA helix with approximately 11 residues per turn. This conformation is maintained due to the presence of the ribose 2' OH group in the backbone. DNA lacks this groups and its double helix is substantially different.

The presence of a 2' hydroxyl group in the ribose phosphate backbone contributes to the stabilization of the standard ribose 3' *endo* conformation which is found generally in RNA molecules. Its absence in the DNA molecule leads to a deoxyribose 2' *endo* conformation. This is responsible for the difference in the overall shape and form of the RNA double helix as compared to the DNA double helix. The RNA double helix differs from the familiar DNA double helix in that the base pairs in the double helix are not perpendicular to the helix axis, but rather are tilted about 15°. Furthermore, they are not found on the axis of the helix, but rather are displaced away from the center. Indeed, there is a hole of approximately 6Å in diameter which goes down the center of the RNA double helix so that the molecule looks more like a band wrapped around an imaginary cylinder rather than a double helical twisted molecule which fills its axis. The hole can be seen in Fig. 3, left side. A consequence of this is the fact that the deep groove of the RNA double helix is extremely deep whereas the narrow groove is extremely shallow.

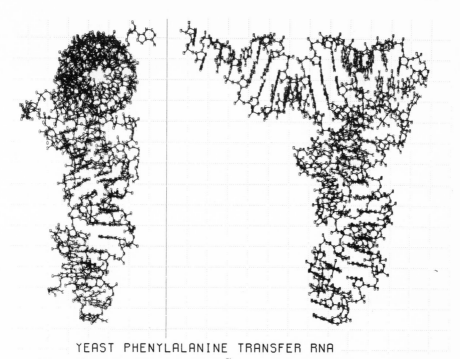

YEAST PHENYLALANINE TRANSFER RNA

Fig. 3. Diagram showing two views of yeast tRNA[Phe]. Left side: This view is looking down the axis of the acceptor and T stems. The hole shown in the upper part is the axis of these stems, and is a normal feature of double-stranded RNA. The protrusion at upper left is due to D16 and D17. The side chain of Y37 protrudes at lower left. Residue A76 extends away from the molecule at top right. Anticodon is at the bottom. Right side: The anticodon is at the bottom.

The helix joining the acceptor stem and TψC stem seems almost uninterrupted. The sequence of yeast tRNA[Phe] (Fig. 1) shows a G-U pair in the acceptor stem. This introduces only a slight pertubation in the helix. Examination of the electron density map at 2.5Å (Fig. 4a) shows these bases are held together by two hydrogen bonds in a typical "wobble" pairing (Crick 1966).

HYDROGEN BONDING AND BASE STACKING

One of the outstanding features of the yeast tRNA[Phe] molecule is the fact that most of the bases are involved in base stacking as well as hydrogen bonding interactions. That this involves the bases in the double helical stem regions was of no great surprise, but it was of considerable interest to find the extent to which these same interactions also involved the bases in the nonhelical loop regions. It can be seen that virtually all of the bases in the molecule are organized into two large base stacking domains along each of the two limbs of the L-shaped molecule (Fig. 3). The horizontal stacking domain in Fig. 3 includes bases of the acceptor and TψC loop and some from the D loop. Most of the remaining bases are involved in the vertical stacking domain which extends down to and includes bases in the anticodon loop. Only five of the 76 bases are not involved in stacking interactions. The two dihydrouracil residues, D16 and 17 and G20 are not stacked nor is U47 from the variable loop. These all come from regions with variable numbers of nucleotides. In addition, the 3' terminal adenosine A76 is unstacked as seen in Fig. 3. It is interesting that there is such a good correlation between bases not involved in stacking interactions and the fact that they are found in the segments of the polynucleotide chain which do not have constant numbers of nucleotides in all tRNA molecules. This suggests a structural explanation for this variability. These bases are found in regions in which there is a bulging out or arching of the polynucleotide chain backbone. This arching makes it possible to accomodate variable numbers of nucleotides in different tRNA molecules; a larger arch is likely to be found for those containing larger numbers of nucleotides. The structure thus provides information relative to the question of whether yeast tRNA^{Phe} can serve as a model for all tRNAs. In this case, something special in the structure is found in regions of nucleotide variability.

THE DOUBLE HELIX TURNS A CORNER

There are two regions in the yeast tRNA^{Phe} molecule in which there is moderate structural complexity. One is at the corner of the molecule where the TψC and D loops interact to stabilize the L-shaped conformation. The other is in the core of the molecule near the D stem in which there is considerable additional hydrogen bonding.

The TψC loop is organized in such a manner as to stabilize its interaction with the D loop and thereby maintain the two limbs of the molecule approximately at right angles to each other. This is accomplished using both detailed hydrogen bonding and base stacking interactions. All of the bases in the TψC loop are stacked parallel to the bases in the TψC stem, with the exception of U59 and C60 which are excluded from the stacking interactions by a number of hydrogen bonds. However, the bases U59 and C60 are oriented at right angles to the rest of the bases in the loop where they serve to nucleate the stacking interactions on which the vertical stacking domain in Fig. 3 is built. Hydrogen bonding in the

TψC loop has many unusual features as seen in the electron density sections of Fig. 4 (Quigley & Rich 1976). It can be seen that T54 forms a hydrogen bonded pair with m^{1}A58. However, this pair does not use the conventional Watson-Crick pairing which is seen in the double helical segments, but rather the pairing involves the imidazole nitrogen N7 of the adenine residue (Fig. 4b). The base plane next to this has a complex interaction in which U55 is hydrogen bonded both to G18 and to the phosphate group P58 (Fig. 4c). O4 of U55 is within hydrogen bonding distances of both nitrogen N1 and the amino group N2 of G18. The hydrogen bonding interaction between U55 and P58 stabilizes the sharp turn of the polynucleotide chain in this corner of the molecule. There is an unusual stacking of three guanine residues with G57 inserted between G18 and G19. G19 forms a tertiary hydrogen bonding interaction with C56. This is the only Watson-Crick hydrogen bonding interaction found among the nine tertiary base-base hydrogen bonding interactions. As shown in Fig. 4c, G57 has several hydrogen bonding interactions with the backbone, two of which involve interactions with the ribose 18 and ribose 19. N7 of G18 receives a hydrogen bond from the 2' hydroxyl group of ribose 55. The major stabilization which accrues from the presence of a purine in position 57 is due to the enhanced stacking interaction when it is intercalated between the two constant guanine residues at positions 18 and 19. This intercalation is accomplished by having the ribose phosphate backbone along 18 and 19 in the unusual 2' *endo* conformation which has the effect of separating the bases from each other, in contrast to the normally occurring 3' *endo* conformation which is found in the bulk of the molecule.

In this corner of the molecule we see many features which have the overall effect of bringing about a rather intricate or detailed fitting together of different components of the molecule which stabilize the unusual conformation. Broadly, the tRNA molecule has the appearance of a molecule in which the double helix has been engineered to make a right angle turn. The corner of the molecule has many features which appear to be designed to stabilize this conformation.

The core of the molecule immediately beneath the TψC stem in Fig. 2 includes some of the most complex hydrogen bonding interactions. As seen in Fig. 5 there are four segments of polynucleotide chains which come into this region, two of the chains are part of the D stem and the others are from the variable loop and the section of chain joining the acceptor stem to the D stem (residues 8 and 9). We can examine the hydrogen bonding from the top down as seen in Fig. 3 by looking at sections which are generally horizontal. Uppermost (Fig. 3) is the pairing between G15 and C48 which stacks immediately beneath the residue U59. As shown in Fig. 5a these bases are hydrogen bonded together through a *trans* pairing rather than the *cis* pairing which is normally found in G–C base pairs. This pairing is imposed by the fact that the polynucleotide chains are oriented in the same direction in this section of the molecule. Immediately below that is the hydrogen bonding of U8 and A14 as shown in Fig. 5b. This is a reversed Hoogsteen hydrogen bonding and residue A21 is located nearby where it interacts with the 2' hydroxyl of ribose 8. Immediately below this is a complex

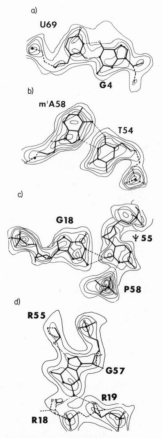

Fig. 4. Electron density sections from the acceptor stem and the corner of yeast tRNA^{Phe}. Curved lines represent contours of electron density; heavier solid lines represent the molecular model as defined by the refined atomic coordinates. Hydrogen bonds between the bases are shown as thin, dashed lines. Heavier dashed lines are used to show segments of the polynucleotide chain which are outside the plane of the section. Oxygen atoms are shown as small open circles, nitrogen atoms as small solid circles. The phosphorus atoms are slightly larger solid circles.

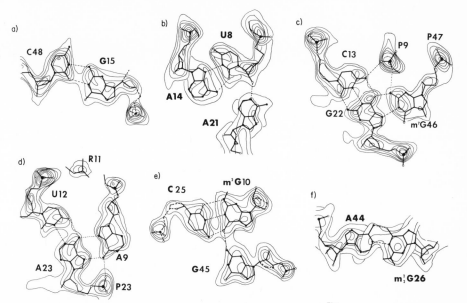

Fig. 5. Electron density sections from the core region of yeast tRNA^{Phe}. See legend of Fig. 4 for description.

system of hydrogen bonding in which the C13–G22 base pair of the D stem has hydrogen bonding interactions with two other elements: one involving m^{7}G46 of the variable loop and the other involving phosphate 9 as shown in Fig. 5c. Four polynucleotide chains are seen in this section and they are all hydrogen bonded together. The molecule is stabilized here by the positive charge which is found on the m^{7}G56 base due to methylation in position 7. This positive charge makes for stronger hydrogen bonding by N1 and N2 of the guanine residue and it also stabilizes the molecule electrostatically because of the close proximity of phosphate 9 and 22.

In the section immediately below (Fig. 5d), the base pair U12–A23 of the D stem has residue A9 hydrogen bonding into its major groove. The hydrogen bonding here is the same as that found between the two adenine residues in double helical polyriboadenylic acid (Rich *et al.* 1961). The similarity even extends to the interaction between the amino groups of A9 and phosphate P23 which is found in the synthetic polynucleotide.

Other base-base tertiary interaction found in this region includes hydrogen bonding between G45 and the C25-m^{2}G10 base pair of the D stem (Fig. 5e). Immediately below this is an unusual hydrogen bonding between A44 and m$_2^2$G26 which are paired as shown in Fig. 5f, with the bases tilted rather sharply in a propeller-like conformation. This has the effect of maximizing the stacking interaction of m$_2^2$G26 with base pair C25m-^{2}G10 immediately above it (in Fig. 2) while the marked tilting of A26 maximizes its stacking with the base pair below it, C27–G43, which is the uppermost base pair of the anticodon stem. In this particular instance, dimethylation of the amino group of guaning contributes to the propeller-like twisting of the two paired bases, each with a structurally different part of the molecule.

The anticodon stem is an RNA double helix with about 11 residues per turn. The conformation of the bases in the anticodon loop is somewhat similar to that suggested by Fuller & Hodgson (1967) in that the three anticodon bases are at the end of a stacked series of bases at the 3' end of the loop. The constant residue U33 plays an interesting role in maintaining the conformation of the loop since it is hydrogen bonded through N3 to the phosphate group of P36. Indeed, there is great similarity between the conformation of the polynucleotide chain in the region of the TψC loop and the conformation in the anticodon loop (Quigley & Rich 1976). In both places, the polynucleotide chain makes a sharp bend and a uridine residue (U33 or U55) plays a key role in stabilizing this sharp turn through the formation of a hydrogen bond to a phosphate residue on the other side of the loop.

The configuration of the anticodon bases is shown in Fig. 6 as viewed from the bottom of the molecule. It can be seen that the three anticodon bases have the form of a right-handed helix with approximately eight residues per turn. They

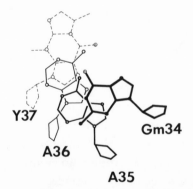

Fig. 6. Diagram illustrating the stacking of anticodon bases 34–36 on the hypermodified Y base as viewed from the exterior of the molecule. Ribose rings are shown as irregular pentagons. Oxygen atoms are stippled circles, nitrogen atoms are unstippled circles. Not all of the side chain of the Y base is included. It can be seen that the anticodon takes the form of a right-handed helix.

are in a conformation such that they can form hydrogen bonding interactions with the codon. At the present time, however, it is not clear whether the anticodon conformation seen in the crystal is maintained when it interacts with messenger RNA.

tRNA IN SOLUTION

The orthorhombic crystal of yeast tRNA^{Phe} contains approximately 75% water. This suggests that the transformation from the crystalline state to completely aqueous solution is not likely to have enormous structural consequences. The available evidence strongly supports this interpretation. A variety of experimental techniques have been used to correlate the structure which is observed in the crystal with that found in solution. All of these studies come to the same general conclusion: the structure appears to be the same in solution as it is in the crystalline state (Rich & RajBhandary 1974).

There is good reason to believe that the molecular structure of yeast tRNA^{Phe} can be used as a model for understanding the molecular structure of all of the tRNAs (Kim *et al.* 1974). Differences in the number of nucleotides in different tRNA sequences can be accommodated by variable-sized arches looping out of the molecule. However, there is uncertainty about the conformation of those tRNAs that have very large variable loops containing 13 to 21 nucleotides. These undoubtedly form a stem and loop structure which is likely to project away from the molecule, but further work will be necessary before the details of this conformation are known.

There are likely to be some altered forms of hydrogen bonding which are found in other sequences. Basically those hydrogen bonds in yeast tRNA^{Phe} which do not involve invariant or semivariant positions are probably altered in other tRNA molecule. In several cases it is possible to guess the detailed nature of these modifications, but many will need to be determined by further experimentation.

tRNA AND PROTEIN SYNTHESIS

Now we return to the paradox described at the beginning of this article. What is the mechanism whereby nature differentiates between different tRNA species during aminoacylation and at the same time allows all of these molecules to pass through the same ribosomal apparatus? In short, where are the components of uniqueness and the components of commonality?

There has been considerable effort to understand the mechanism of aminoacylation and find those regions of the tRNA molecule which may be recognized by synthetase enzymes. Different workers have suggested the acceptor stem, the D stem or the anticodon (Kisseler & Favorova 1974). Much experimental work on synthetase-tRNA interactions is in accord with the suggestion that synthetases recognize varying aspects of the tRNA structure along the diagonal side of the molecule (Rich & Schimmel 1977). It is clear that the synthetases are probably all different and there is not likely to be a common recognition system even if they all approach the same side of the tRNA molecule. It is likely that tRNA-synthetase recognition takes two parts. One is a recognition of the ribose phosphate chain which would be sensitive to the folding of the tRNA molecules. Secondly, there must be a recognition by the protein of specific bases in the double helical stems or among the unpaired segments of the molecule. There are several ways in which proteins can recognize nucleic acid sequences (Seeman *et al.* 1976). It is likely that the basis of specificity resides in this detailed sequence recognition rather than in any conformational differences between tRNA molecules. Furthermore, there is an adequate basis for specificity in these sequences. The number of nucleotides or base pairs recognized by the enzyme need not be very large in order to obtain the requisite specificity.

Far more puzzling is the question of what goes on in the ribosome. Our information in this field is scanty. For example, there are two sites within the ribosome, one which is occupied by the peptidyl-tRNA and the other by the aminoacyl-tRNA. Information is available which suggests that these two sites are physically distinct.

It is likely that both sites are occupied at the same time and for this reason the tRNA molecule may have been designed to have the form of a double helix that turns a corner. The L shape of the molecule may make it possible for two adjacent tRNAs to come close together at one end near their anticodons while they are interacting with adjacent codons of the messenger RNA. At the same time the CCA acceptor ends may also be able to come close together due to the L shape. These two CCA ends must come close together in order to allow the ribosomal peptidyl transferase to transfer the peptide chain from one tRNA molecule to the other. It is not at all clear how this is accomplished although it has been suggested that the two codons become unstacked during the reading process so that in effect the messenger "turns a corner" while it is read (Rich 1974). This remains an exciting area for further research work.

Work by Erdmann and his colleagues (1973) has suggested that the TψC loop may become disengaged from the D loop inside the ribosome so that it can then hydrogen bond with the 5S RNA of the ribosome. This interaction may be an important component in the translocation of tRNA from aminoacyl site to the peptidyl site. If this is true, the tRNA molecule undergoes a conformational change within the ribosome. Determination of the nature of these events remains an important goal of research in this area. It is possible that this conformational change may be triggered by codon-anticodon interactions and this may be a consequence of the fact that the tRNA molecule as a whole exhibits long range order (Rich & RajBhandary 1974). Thus interactions at one end of the molecule may give rise to a change in reactivity or in conformation at a more remote part of the molecule.

tRNA AND THE ORIGIN OF PROTEIN SYNTHESIS

At present we have good models for understanding the early stages in the origin of life including the accumulation of organic chemicals and the formation of nucleotides and polynucleotides. However, we do not have convincing models for the origin of polynucleotide-directed polypeptide formation. It is reasonable to believe that the molecular mechanics of mRNA reading in the ribosome as well as peptide bond formation may provide a clue to its origin. An important issue here is whether or not the anticodon undergoes a significant conformational change in the ribosome. Woese (1970) has suggested that tRNA has two different conformations during protein synthesis: one as is seen in the crystal structure with a 3' stacking, and another with a 5' stacking. Crick *et al.* (1976) have used this conformational change to develop a scheme for the origin of protein synthesis. However, recent results suggest that this change in tRNA conformation may not occur in the ribosome.

An alternative scheme for the origin of protein synthesis can be developed (Rich, to be published). Here we assume the conformation of the anticodon does not have a large change between the two ribosomal sites. We postulate a specific tRNA-tRNA interaction in the ribosome when they are in the aminoacyl and peptidyl sites. This interaction is such that it has a spacing between the two anticodons which is directly responsible for the triplet code. However, we can also use the residues in positions 37 and 38 to form hydrogen bonds with the mRNA in the peptidyl site as is assumed by Crick *et al.* (1976). If these were both guanine residues in the prebiotic system, then our primitive protein synthetic system would have only four amino acids; purines in these positions would allow eight amino acids. It is clear that a family of models can be developed depending upon the assumptions (Rich, to be published).

Continued structural work on tRNA and its interactions with the ribosome will remain an interesting area for a considerable period of time. As we obtain knowledge about the events in the ribosome, we may gain information which will allow us to make reasonable guesses about the origin of protein synthesis.

ACKNOWLEDGMENTS

This work was supported by grants from the National Institutes of Health, National Science Foundation, National Aeronautics and Space Administration and the American Cancer Society.

REFERENCES

Barrell, B.G. & Clark, B.F.C. (1974) *Handbook of Nucleic Acid Sequences,* ed. Joynson-Bruvvers, Oxford.

Crick, F.H.C. (1966) Codon-anticodon pairing: The wobble hypothesis. *J. Mol. Biol.* 19, 548–555.

Crick, F.H.C., Brenner, S., Klug, A., & Pieczenik, G. (1976) A speculation on the origin of protein synthesis. *Origins of Life* 7, 389–397.

Erdmann, V.A., Sprinzl, M. & Pongs, O. (1973) The involvement of 5S RNA in the binding of tRNA to ribosomes. *Biochem. Biophys. Res. Commun.* 54, 942–948.

Fuller, W. & Hodgson, A. (1967) Conformations of the anticodon loop in tRNA. *Nature* 215, 817–821.

Holley, R.W., Apgar, J., Everett, G.A., Madison, J.T., Marquisse, M., Merrill, S.H., Penwick, J.R. & Zamir, A. (1965) Structure of ribonucleic acid. *Science* 147, 1462–1465.

Kim, S.H., Quigley, G.J., Suddath, F.L., & Rich, A. (1971) High resolution X-ray diffractions patterns of tRNA crystals showing helical regions of the molecule. *Proc. Natl. Acad. Sci. U.S.A.* 68, 841–845.

Kim, S.H., Quigley, G.J., Suddath, F.L., McPherson, A., Sneden, D., Kim, J.J., Weinzierl, J. & Rich, A. (1973) Three-dimensional structure of yeast phenylaline transfer RNA: Folding of the polynucleotide chain. *Science* 179, 285–288.

Kim, S.H., Suddath, F.L., Quigley, G.J., McPherson, A., Sussman, J.L., Wang, A., Seeman, N.C., & Rich, A. (1974a) Three-dimensional tertiary structure of yeast phenylalanine transfer RNA. *Science* 185, 435–439.

Kim, S.H., Sussman, J.L., Suddath, F.L., Quigley, G.J., McPherson, A., & Rich, A. (1974b) The general structure of transfer RNA molecules. *Proc. Natl. Acad. Sci. U.S.A.* 71, 4970–4974.

Kisselev, L.L. & Favorova, O.O., (1974) Aminoacyl-tRNA synthetases: Some recent results and achievements. *Advs. Enzmol.* 40, 141–238.

Quigley, G.J. & Rich, A. (1976) Structural domains of transfer RNA molecule. *Science* 194, 796–806.

Rich, A. & RajBhandary, U. (1976) Transfer RNA: Molecular structure, sequence, and properties. *Annu. Rev. Biochem.* 45, 805–860.

Rich, A. & Schimmel, P.R. (1977) Structural organization of complexes of transfer RNAs with aminoacyl transfer RNA. *Nucleic Acids Res.* 4, 1649–1665.

Rich, A., Davies, D.R., Crick, F.H.C., & Watson, J.D. (1961) The molecular structure of polyadenylic acid. *J. Mol. Biol.* 3, 71.

Rich, A., (1974) How transfer RNA may move inside the ribosome. In: *Ribosome*. ed. Nomura, M., Tissieries, A. & Lengyel, P. Cold Spring Harbor Laboratory, New York, 871–884.

Robertus, J. D., Ladner, J. E., Finch, J. T., Rhodes, D., Brown, Clark, B. F. C. & Klug (1974) Structure of yeast phenytalanine tRNA at 3 Å resolution. *Nature* 250, 546–551.

Seeman, N.C., Rosenberg, J.M. & Rich, A. (1976) Sequence-specific recognition of double helical nucleic acids by proteins. *Proc. Nat. Acad. Sci. U.S.A.* 73, 804–808.

Woese, C.R. (1970) Molecular mechanics of translation: a reciprocating ratchet mechanism. *Nature* 226, 817–820.

DISCUSSION

LEICK: How do you visualize in this protein-free system that you form the peptide bond?

RICH: If you have aminoacylated tRNAs, they already have energy for breaking an ester bond and forming an amide bond. What is difficult to imagine is how you get the right spatial organization that would build a protein chain.

LEICK: In the normal ribosome peptide bond, formation is carried out by peptidyl transferase, which probably is a true enzymatic catalysis?

RICH: That is right. You would have to reproduce that in a primitive form which you could make do with a variety of small molecules at a very low level of efficiency. That is a common problem, but we have lots of time in which to carry out this process in terms of the evolutionary time span.

HOGNESS: You do have the time problem with this reaction relevant to the stability of these configurations which you have. It is not a trivial question.

CRICK: I think proximity goes a long way to answer this as far as we know. If you bring them very close together you get a reasonable rate of peptide bond formation. The real problem is how to get the right amount of amino acid on the right tRNA.

WEISSMANN: Well, you have lots of time.

CRICK: It is not enough to have lots of time; you must also not make lots of mistakes. You must have the right amino acid, within a reasonable accuracy.

RICH: You can have a fairly sloppy system, but as long as it has a bias to it, eventually the system can become more effective.

CRICK: I am not sure about that.

RICH: Well, it won't be highly efficient in the beginning as you will have lots of errors. But if it has a strong bias or reactivity in one direction, then by selection you may go further.

WEISSMANN: I would have said that there is a defined relationship between the amount of information and the sloppiness.

CRICK: That is for nucleic acid replication, whereas at the moment we are talking about the accuracy of protein synthesis. With the proteins you can afford to have some false copies which may not work, provided you can produce more good copies.

WEISSMANN: Yes, but if the error becomes too big then the self-reinforcement of the system will disappear.

CRICK: First of all I don't think it was necessarily all that inaccurate at the beginning. If you get anything going, why should it not be reasonably accurate, since the difference of energy needed for increased accuracy is really quite small. You can afford bigger mistakes in protein synthesis than you can in replicating DNA.

RICH: Yes, the errors are not disasterous, because you can overcome them by making more proteins.

SORSA: Do you think that RNA was the first thing to appear and that DNA came later?

RICH: That is what I think because RNA can both contain information, replicate, and carry out protein synthesis. DNA was a specialized molecule which developed later on.

WEISSMANN: There are also what might be evolutionary traces, e.g. the use of RNA in DNA replication, which may be sort of a hangover from the transition from RNA to DNA genomes.

CRICK: You could make a stronger case by asking under what conditions is RNA, particularly single-stranded RNA, found in genetic material. The answer is that it is always for viruses which have a small number of bases.

RICH: If you try to make the tRNA out of a DNA chain it will be considerably less stable, because although the 2' hydroxyl does not do much in the double-stranded regions, it is involved in a great deal of hydrogen bonding in the loops. About more than half of the 2' hydroxyls are involved in hydrogen bonding interactions which hold the molecule together.

WEISSMANN: What are the current ideas as to how correct internucleotide linkages originated nonenzymatically?

RICH: That is what Leslie Orgel is doing. The experiments generally are the following: You take some polynucleotide and some activated monomers and see if you can cook them in such a way that you can replicate the nucleotide. I believe he is able to make oligonucleotides up to 10–15 long.

WEISSMANN: Held together by 3',5'phosphodiester bonds?

RICH: He has been troubled in the past because most of the oligonucleotides have come out 2',5', but recently I believe ha has had more success forming 3',5' linkages. I think this problem of abiogenic nucleotide polymerization is a solvable one. It is not particularly easy, however, because you have to fish around through a large number of conditions. It is entirely possible that certain minerals may form the catalytic surfaces in helping these reactions go. There are lots of different minerals to work with and it is not that obvious what kind of things to look for as catalytic surfaces.

Intervening Sequences in Precursors of *t*RNA: A Comment

Alexander Rich

One of the few cases where we may have some idea about the physical organization of an intervening sequence in eukaryotic RNA is in the precursor transfer RNA molecules. Recently, intervening sequences have been found for both the phenylalanine and tyrosine precursor tRNA molecules in yeast. The results are quite interesting. They indicate that the intervening sequences found in these two different groups of molecules have important similarities. They are small intervening sequences of approximately 15–20 nucleotides and in both cases the intervening sequence is found in the anticodon loop of the molecule. Knapp *et al.* (1978) carried out a calculation of the most probably structure adopted by these two transfer RNA molecules with their small insertion sequences. They found that the molecules tend to make secondary structures in which the two ends of the insertion sequence are physically distant from each other. There are two points worth considering here. The insertion sequences are both at one end of the transfer RNA molecule in the anticodon loop. This strongly suggests that the rest of the molecule will fold up in its stable conformation similar to that which has been found in the three-dimensional structure of yeast phenylalanine transfer RNA. The only difference will be an altered conformation in the anticodon where the additional intervening sequences are found. This raises the question as to whether the splicing enzyme which cuts out the intervening sequence operates by recognizing the remainder of the transfer molecule. This is not an unreasonable possibility since the bulk of the molecule may not be greatly affected by the intervening sequences, and its conformation may be similar to the native molecule. In addition, the most probable secondary structure in these molecules has the ends of the intervening sequence physically removed from each other. This suggests that the splicing enzyme may in fact

Department of Biology, Massachusetts Institute of Technology, Cambridge, Mass. 02139, U.S.A.

SPECIFIC EUKARYOTIC GENES, Alfred Benzon Symposium 13, Munksgaard 1979

bring about a conformational change in its substrate, in order to bring the ends of the molecule together just prior to the splicing operation. This must be regarded as purely speculative at present since it is entirely possible that the splicing operation involves several different steps and only one of these processes may bring the ends together.

REFERENCE

Knapp, G., Beckmann, J. S., Johnsson, P. F., Fuhrman, S. A. & Abelson, J. (1978) *Cell* 14, 221–236.

Concluding Remarks

V. Leick & H. Klenow

These concluding remarks should not be considered as a detailed summing up of all contributions at this symposium, but rather regarded as an attempt to present a few general conclusions and possible outlines of future research on the structure and function of eukaryotic genomes.

Probably for more than one billion years now the typical eukaryotic cell has chosen to organize its nuclear genetic information in very high molecular weight DNA arranged into cytological structures such as chromosomes or other chromatin elements. The molecular weight of chromosomal DNA is generally very high, probably so high, as has been shown in *Drosophila* by Kavenoff *et al.* (1973), that there is just one molecule per chromosome and that such a molecule contains several thousand replication initiation sites, as pointed out by Tamm *et al.* Hence, the genetic information in one chromosome seems to be organized in a linear way in a molecule of DNA which again is physically packed in the chromosome (which is about 10^4 times smaller than the constituent DNA molecule) in a very ordered fashion in nucleosomes in chromatin, at least in the part of the DNA which is inactive, as discussed by Francis Crick. Moreover, structurally and functionally the chromosome itself on the microscopical level appears to be a linear structure where certain functions can be correlated to specific sites in the chromosome structure (chromomeres and puffs) which can be used as tools to study specific gene structure and expression at different levels.

Certain genes seem to have predictable positions on the chromosome as exemplified by the position of the nucleolar organizer in the short arm near the telomere as described by Lima-de-Faria. Moreover, we have obtained more detailed information about some tissue-specific puffs. Isolation and partial

---

References cited without date are to papers included in this volume.

SPECIFIC EUKARYOTIC GENES, Alfred Benzon Symposium 13, Munksgaard 1979

characterization of two DNA restriction sequences which contain structural genes for a specific heat-shock protein in *Drosophila melanogaster* was reported by Artavanis-Tsakonas *et al.*, and detailed electron microscopy in particular of the zeste-white region (revealing up to 20 bands) was reported by Sorsa.

In reference to the chromosomal architecture as such, we would like to comment briefly on the possible relationship between genetic stability and the physical organization of DNA in the eukaryotic genome. It has been proposed by Edström & Lambert (1975) that genetic stability of the eukaryote genome may be intimately coupled with the basic cytological structure of chromosomes, since diploidy which masks recessivitys together with crossing over during meiosis – might be two important factors which ensure genetic stability. However, chromosome structure and thereby gene linkage and genetic stability might be preserved in a physical sense by keeping the DNA in the chromosomal DNA in a state of very high molecular weight. The macronuclear DNA in the cilcated hypotrichs *Stylonichia* and *Oxytricha* – as discussed by Prescott – might be an interesting example of a naturally occurring fragmentation of genomes into relatively small pieces of DNA. This event may be related to genetic instability and senescence since hypotrichs only survive a few hundred generations before they must make a new macronucleus. New macronuclei are formed from micronuclei that contain DNA of very high molecular weight. The macronuclear DNA of *Tetrahymena* has, in contrast to that of the hypotrichs, a very high molecular weight and this organism also has a much higher degree of genetic stability as judged from the high stability of amicronucleate strains which have been maintained in the laboratory for several hundred thousand generations without showing signs of senescence. Moreover, Cummings reported on senescence in *Podospora anserina* which may be related to the occurrence of multimeric circular DNA and to gene diminution in mitochondrial DNA.

One of the major advances in recent years in attempts to dissect the fine structure of eukaryotic high molecular weight DNA has been the possibility of generating artificial but specific DNA fragments using site-specific restriction endonucleases, with possible subsequent cloning of the generated fragments. Using such pieces of specific eukaryotic DNA and with the growing number of techniques for generation of clones, and for identification titration and sequencing of gene specific DNA fragments, the field has indeed opened up, and now an almost unlimited number of possibilities to dissect almost any eukaryotic genome down to the nucleotide level is possible. Maniatis among others told us about one of the newest techniques for gene isolation without prior partial purification of the DNA. With the sequencing of the family of histone genes and determination of their mutual arrangement, it seems now soon possible to understand the function of this gene down to the nucleotide level, as appeared in the presentation of Max Birnstiel. By the surrogate genetics approach he reported that histone genes injected into *Xenopus* oocytes are getting expressed at a reasonable level. Of interest in this context was also Goodman's report on the isolation of DNA sequences complementary to the mRNA of a number of peptide hormones including a portion of the sequence coding for human growth hormone. His group has succeeded in obtaining bacteria that synthesize rat growth hormone. Schaffner reported on the construction of the first recombinant virus DNA in which SV40 DNA was linked to a segment of eukaryotic DNA (sea urchin histone DNA). This molecule may be integrated into the rat genome. After cell fusion the recombinant DNA may be recovered by excission and extrachromosomal replication. Moreover, genes and gene intervening sequences from several sources of chromosomal DNA have been isolated and studied by restriction enzyme mapping and sequencing techniques. In the human β-globin gene Flavell reported on the presence of a 600 base pair deletion at the 3' side of a second β-globin band in patients with β-thallasemia suggesting that physical mapping of globin genes might find an application in the study of human genetic deseases.

The session on extrachromosomal genetic elements dealt with DNA molecules from mitochondria, kinetoplasts and nucleoli. These types of molecules were shown to be very useful for the study of DNA entities containing a limited number of genes. The genes are often arranged in an unusual manner like the genes for rRNA in *Physarum* and *Tetrahymena*, which are palindromic as reported by Braun & Seebeck and Engberg & Din and by Gall. Some types of extrachromosomal DNA molecules have quite specific structures, as for the kinetoplast DNA. In kinetoplast DNA there is suggestive evidence that only the maxicircles which comprise only 10% of the kinetoplast DNA network contain genetic information, whereas the minicircles are heterogeneous in sequence – comprising 90% of the DNA network – and may serve a purely structural purpose (Newton, Borst *et al.*). The studies of these relatively small DNA molecules will probably within a limited time span lead to a detailed description of their structure and function as is the case today with many bacteriophage DNA molecules.

A useful approach to study eukaryote DNA pieces of specific function has been the generation of cDNA copies from RNA molecules of defined origin such as viral RNA or specific mRNAs. In cDNA copies made from specific mRNAs, the so-called intervening sequences are missing. Therefore although the *in vitro* manufacturing of such cDNA molecules is extremely useful for identification and cloning of specific sequences chromosomal DNA, other important genetic elements such as spacer sequences, intervening sequences and certain control elements are not present in cDNA copies made from specific cytoplasmic RNAs.

The striking difference between cDNA sequences and the gene itself with flanking sequences and possible intervening sequences indicates that an elaborate processing of a primary gene product must occur before it reaches its final destination in the ribosome.

It has been known for a number of years that probably 10% or less of eukaryotic DNA is expressed at the protein level, partly because the eukaryotic genome contains special kinds of repeated DNA sequences. Moreover, long DNA stretches of unknown function flank most structural genes, and intervening nontranslated sequences in structural genes are eliminated from messenger RNA probably during processing by a splicing mechanism involving specific RNase cleavage and following RNA ligation. Pre-messenger RNA or HnRNA is, however, also cleaved during processing and in most cases polyadenylation occurs at the 3' end. The resulting messenger RNA is therefore an extensively modified product. This is for example reflected in the degree of sequence complexity which Paul described to be five to ten times lower for mRNA than for HnRNA in mammalian cells. Moreover, it seems to be preferentially sets of inverted repeats which are lost from the HnRNA during processing as pointed out by Jelinek. In the DNA, one inverted repeat was found per 3–5 kb. Another characteristic of higher cell RNA metabolism seems to be the occurrence of a family of metabolically stable RNA components called L, A, C and D which appear to be a general constituent of vertebrates, but which have an unknown function, as reported by Frederiksen & Hellung-Larsen. In this connection it should be noted that a 4.5S RNA component from Chinese hamster ovary cells was found associated with mRNA (reported by Jelinek) which perhaps suggests some metabolic function of low molecular weight RNA.

It is only in recent years we have learned that, due to the presence of intervening sequences in structural genes, many RNA molecules may be spliced products. The possible meaning of such intervening sequences in eukaryotic DNA has been discussed at this meeting and also recently in *Nature* by Gilbert

(1978) and by Blake (1978). On one hand such proposed pre-mRNA excission and splicing must require enzymatic cleavage and ligation of extreme fidelity to ensure that the RNA chains are spliced at exactly the right nucleotide. A number of characteristics of intervening sequences have been described at this meeting. When comparing β-globin genes of mouse and rabbit, Weissman had evidence that there seems to be a selection pressure for constant size and location, but not for constant sequence of the two β-globin gene intervening sequences. Moreover, there seems to be cases where ribosomal DNA inserts are conserved but not transcribed as in *Drosophila embryo* cells (reported by Dawid) raising the possibility that ribosomal RNA gene insertions may have different physiological implications from the intervening sequences. It should however be mentioned here that Gall reported on the presence of an insert in a ribosomal RNA gene in strains of *Tetrahymena*. In this case the insert is apparently being transcribed together with the ribosomal RNA gene. Similarly, in yeast mitochondrial DNA the intervening sequence in the 21S rRNA seems to be transcribed as reported by Borst.

The evidence obtained so far seems to suggest that *intra*molecular splicing – but not *inter*molecular ligation – of RNA chains occurs. It is, however, an attractive hypothesis that intermolecular RNA splicing of mRNA pieces coming from different parts of the genome could be a useful evolutionary supplement to genetic changes which have occurred by mutation. By splicing RNA pieces comming from different parts of the genome, new possibilities of gene products may be tried out during evolution with a much faster rate than could occur by mutation alone by generating novel proteins from parts of old ones. However, at this time we must wait for further experimental evidence to support such hypothesis. The concept of the "fragmented" genome containing exons and introns (intervening sequences/inserts) may lead to considerations of whether this "fragmentation" on the DNA level is in any way reflected on the protein level by the presence of similar domains within individual polypeptide chains. We would like to point out that a number of larger proteins with two or more functions harbored in the same polypeptide chain, indeed, are made up to pieces – so-called domains – which correspond to independently folded globular units with separate functions. The growing number of domain enzymes, or multifunctional enzymes (presently the number is about 40, Bisswanger & Schmincke-Ott, in press) show that we are not simply dealing with a few cases of accidentally fused structural genes, but with a typical organizational scheme for proteins comparable to that of multienzyme complexes. An example of a multifunctional eukaryotic enzyme is the pyruvate kinase from cat muscle, which contains three domains (A, B and C) in its polypeptide chain (Levine *et al.* 1978). Domain A, the largest one, contains 220 amino acid residues and shows a similarity to the structure of triose phosphate isomerase. Another domain, the C-part, contains 120 residues and shows similarity to the mononucleotide-binding part of lactate dehydrogenase (LDH). The B fragment contains 100 residues. It can presently only be stated that any proposed correlation of exonic regions in DNA with folded protein units in multifunctional enzymes is probably testable as soon as the eukaryotic DNA fragment which codes for one of the known multifunctional enzymes has been isolated and sequenced.*

In one case – namely when speaking about processing of intervening sequences in yeast tRNA precursors (Knapp *et al.* 1978) – some possible structure/function consequences of RNA splicing in eukaryotes can be seen. One of the consequences of splicing of precursors of tRNA^{Tyr} and tRNA^{Phe} in yeast is the generation of the single-stranded anticodon loop which of course is a prerequisite for that both normal and primitive protein synthesis can occur as reported by Rich.

ACKNOWLEDGMENTS

On behalf of the organizing committee we would like to thank the participants in this Alfred Benzon Symposium for their contributions to this meeting.

On behalf of the editors we would also like to express our gratitude to the Alfred Benzon Foundation for making this Symposium possible and for their helpfulness in organizing the meeting.

REFERENCES

Bisswanger, H. & Schmincke-Ott, E. (1978) Multifunctional proteins. In: *Multifunctional Proteins* (monograph) ed. Bisswanger & Schmincke-Ott, John Wiley & Sons, in press.

Blake, C. C. F. (1978) Do genes-in-pieces imply proteins-in-pieces? *Nature* 273, 267.

Edström, J.-E. & Lambert, B. (1975) Gene and information diversity in eukaryotes. *Prog. Biophys. Molec. Biol.* 30, 1, 57–82.

Gilbert, W. (1978) Genes in pieces. *Nature* (News and Views) 271, 501.

---

* Note added in proof: It has recently been found that the three protein domains and the hinge region of immunoglobulin heavy chain are encoded in DNA segments separated by insertions of varying lengths (Sakano *et al.* 1979).

Kavenoff, R., Klotz, L. C. & Zimm, B. H. (1973) On the nature of chromosome-sized DNA molecules. *Cold Spring Hab. Symp. Quant. Biol.* 38, 1–8.

Knapp, G., Beckman, J. S., Johnson, P. F., Fuhrman, S. A. & Abelson, J. (1978) Transcription and processing of intervening sequences in yeast tRNA genes. *Cell* 14, 221–36.

Levine, M., Muirhead, H., Stammers, D. & Stuart, D. I. (1978) Structure of pyruvate kinase and similarities with other enzymes: Possible implications for protein taxonomy and evolution. *Nature* 271, 626–630.

Sakano, H., J. H. Rogers, K. Hüppi, C. Brock, A. Traunecker, R. Maki, R. Wall & S. Tonegawa (1979) Domains and the hinge region of an immunoglobulin heavy chain are encoded in separate DNA segments. *Nature* 277, 627–633.

Index of Authors and Discussants

(Numbers in italics refer to invited papers, numbers in plain type to contributions to discussions).